W9-DGV-733

PSA 1994

VOLUME TWO

PSA 1994

PROCEEDINGS OF THE 1994
BIENNIAL MEETING
OF THE
PHILOSOPHY OF SCIENCE
ASSOCIATION

volume two

Symposia and Invited Papers

edited by

DAVID HULL,
MICKY FORBES
&
RICHARD M. BURIAN

1994
Philosophy of Science Association
East Lansing, Michigan

Library of Congress Catalog Card Number 72-624169

Cloth Edition: ISBN 0-917586-37-9

ISSN: 0270-8647

Manufactured in the United States of America

CONTENTS

PREFACE

This is the second of two volumes comprising the proceedings of the 1994 Biennial Meeting of the Philosophy of Science association held in New Orleans, Louisiana. the first volume, consisting of the program and the contributed papers, was published in advance of the meeting in October, 1994. the second volume consists of the presidential address, invited papers and symposia. Northwestern University provides generous support for the preparation of these volumes.

The Program Committee, consisting of Richard M. Burian (chair), David Gooding, Gary Hatfield, don Howard, Helen Longino, Miriam Solomon, and James Woodward, arranged for the symposia and invited papers. Micky Forbes, Assistant Editor of these *Proceedings*, supervised the editing and processing of the papers to produce uniform, camera ready copy. The PSA Business Office saw the copy through to publication.

We wish to thank the Program Committee and the authors. We are grateful to Northwestern University for financial suppport. Special thanks are due Wendy Ward, whose expertise and imagination with graphics and desktop publishing facilities shows up on every page of the volume.

Richard M. Burian
Center for the Study of Science in Society
Virginia Polytechnic Institute and
State University

David Hull and
Micky Forbes
Department of Philosophy
Northwestern University

Synopsis

The following brief summaries, arranged here alphabetically by author, provide an introduction to each of the papers in this volume.

1. *Explanation v. Prediction: Which Carries More Weight?* **Peter Achinstein**. Do predictions of novel facts provide stronger evidence for a theory than explanations of old ones? Sometimes yes, sometimes no. Which obtains has nothing to do with whether the evidence is predicted or explained, but only with the selection procedure used to generate the evidence. This is demonstrated by reference to a series of hypothetical drug cases and to Heinrich Hertz's 1883 cathode ray experiments.

2. *HPS and the Classic Normative Mission.* **Brian S. Baigrie.** The new inter-disciplinary eclecticism championed by many philosophers of science has generated a heterogeneous family of science studies projects. Philosophers who favor an inter-disciplinary approach face many problems if they are to successfully forge a hybrid science studies that does not violate their integrity as philosophers in particular, they must isolate an intellectual space in which traditional agendas, such as the concern for the clarification of concepts, can hold court. In this paper, I outline what I regard as a new brand of HPS, one that is deeply rooted in the history of the exact science. The virtue of this New HPS, I will submit, is that it furnishes philosophers of science with a fresh perspective from which to carry on philosophy's classic normative mission.

3. *Meaning in a Material Medium.* **Davis Baird.** Recently we have learned how experiment can have a life of its own. However, experiment remains epistemologically disadvantaged. Scientific knowledge must have a theoretical/propositional form. To begin to redress this situation, I discuss three ways in which instruments carry meaning: 1. Scientific instruments can carry tremendous loads of meaning through association, analogy and metaphor. 2. Instrumental models of complicated phenomena work representationally in much the same way as theories. 3. Instruments which create new phenomena establish a new field of material possibilities. I suggest that scientists employ a "visual/physical/material logic," analogous to propositional logic, which establishes relations between different material forms.

4. *Deciding on the Data: Epistemological Problems Surrounding Instruments and Research Techniques in Cell Biology.* **William Bechtel.** The question whether research techniques are producing artifacts or data is often a crucial one for scientists. The potential for artifacts results from the fact that generating data often requires numerous procedures that are often brutal, poorly understood, and very sensitive to details of the procedure. Through a case–study of the introduction of electron microscopy as a tool for studying cells, I examine how scientists judge whether new techniques are introducing artifacts. Three factors seem to be most salient in their judgments: determinateness of the results, consilience of different procedures, and ability of the results to fit into emerging theories.

5. *Dynamics of Theory Change: The Role of Predictions.* **Stephen G. Brush.** The thesis that scientists give greater weight to novel predictions than to explanations of known facts is tested against historical cases in physical science. Several theories were accepted after successful novel predictions but there is little evidence that extra credit was given for novelty. Other theories were rejected despite, or accepted without, making successful novel predictions. No examples were found of theories that were accepted primarily because of successful novel predictions and would not have been accepted if those facts had been previously known.

6. *The Metaphysics of the Disunified World.* **Nancy Cartwright**. Pluralism is usually opposed to realism. This paper argues that the two come naturally into conflict only given a third assumption—imperialism, i.e., the doctrine that some one, or some handful, of our favourite theories are universal. This paper attempts to show why that assumption is implausible, even in the case of fundamental theories in physics. It argues first that physics theories are true only in their models: for the most part the successes of a theory are confined to situations that resemble the models. Second it argues specifically for the possibility of peaceful co-existence between quantum and classical physics.

7. *Poincaré, Richard's Paradox and Indefinite Extensibility.* **Peter Clark.** A central theme in the foundational debates in the early Twentieth century in response to the paradoxes was to invoke the notion of the indefinite extensibility of certain concepts e,g. definability (the Richard paradox) and class (the Zermelo-Russell contradiction). Dummett has recently revived the notion, as the real lesson of the paradoxes and the source of Frege's error in basic law five of the Grundgesetze. The paper traces the historical and conceptual evolution of the concept and critices Dummett's argument that the proper lesson of the paradoxes is that set theory is a theory of indefinitely extensible domains.

8. *Reasoning Strategies in Molecular Biology: Abstractions, Scans, and Anomalies.* **Lindley Darden and Michael Cook.** Molecular biologists use different kinds of reasoning strategies for different tasks, such as hypothesis formation, experimental design, and anomaly resolution. More specifically, the reasoning strategies discussed in this paper may be characterized as (1) abstraction-instantiation, in which an abstract skeletal model is instantiated to produce an experimental system; (2) the systematic scan, in which alternative hypotheses are systematically generated; and (3) modular anomaly resolution, in which components of a model are stated explicitly and methodically changed to generate alternative changes to resolve an anomaly. This work grew out of close observation over a period of six months of an actively functioning molecular genetics laboratory.

9. *The Contemporary Interest of an Old Doctrine.* **William Demopoulos.** We call Frege's discovery that, in the context of second-order logic, Hume's principle—viz., The number of Fs = the number of Gs if, and only if, F ª G, where F ª G (the Fs and the Gs are in one-to-one correspondence) has its usual, second-order, explicit definition—implies the infinity of the natural numbers, Frege's theorem. We discuss whether this theorem can be marshalled in support of a possibly revised formulation of Frege's logicism.

10. *Against Scientific Imperialism.* **John Dupré.** Opponents of the unity of science have generally been concerned with horizontal relations between theories, with attempts, that is, to subsume scientific accounts of complex objects under accounts of the behavior of their constituent parts. In this paper I suggest that scientific pluralism should be defended not only against this traditional physicalistic and mechanistic reductionism, but also against the imperialistic expansion of quite specialized scientific perspectives into ever wider domains of application. This tendency is particularly prevalent in scientific approaches to human behavior, and is most clearly illustrated by the imperialist aspirations of economics and evolutionary biology. Here I illustrate the problem primarily with reference to some of the worst excesses of imperialist economics.

11. *Pluralism, Normative Naturalism, and Biological Taxonomy.* **Marc Ereshefsky**. Several authors have argued for taxonomic pluralism in biology –the

position that there is a plurality of equally legitimate classifications of the organic world. Others have objected that such pluralism boils down to a position of anything goes. This paper offers a response to the anything goes objection by showing how one can be a discerning pluralist. In particular, methodological standards for choosing taxonomic projects are derived using Laudan's normative naturalism. This paper also sheds light on why taxonomic pluralism occurs in biology as well as illustrates the usefulness of normative naturalism.

12. *Critical Reasoning in Galileo's Dialogue.* **Maurice A. Finocchiaro.** Galileo's Dialogue (1632) can be read from the viewpoints of methodological judgment and critical reasoning; methodological judgment means the avoidance of one-sidedness and extremes; and critical reasoning means reasoning aimed at the analysis and evaluation of arguments. Classic sources for these readings are Thomas Salusbury (1661) and the Port-Royal logicians (1662). This focus does not deny the book's scientific, historical, rhetorical, and aesthetic dimensions; it is critical of excessively rhetorical readings; and it suggests solutions to the problems of hermeneutical pluralism, interpretation versus evaluation, and theory versus practice. The book's methodological judgment and critical reasoning can be shown to correspond to Galileo's self-reflections.

13. *Poincaré on Mathematics, Intuition and the Foundations of Science.* **Janet Folina.** In his first philosophy book, Science and Hypothesis, Poincaré provides a picture in which the different sciences are arranged in a hierarchy. Arithmetic is the most general of all the sciences because it is presupposed by all the others. Next comes mathematical magnitude, or the analysis of the continuum, which presupposes arithmetic; and so on. Poincaré's basic view was that experiment in science depends on fixing other concepts first. More generally, certain concepts must be fixed before others: hence the hierarchy. This paper attempts to dissolve some potential problems regarding Poincaré's hierarchy. One is an apparent epistemological circularity in the hierarchy. A more serious problem regarding the epistemology of analysis is also addressed.

14. *The Technological Infrastructure of Science: Commentary on the Papers of Davis Baird, Peter Kroes, and Michael Dennis.* **Allan Franklin.** One important point that has emerged from recent work on the history and philosophy of experiment is that technology plays an integral role in experiment, and therefore in science. Technology determines what experimenters can measure and how well it can be measured. The importance of technology, along with several new questions that its use raises, has been made quite clear in the papers presented in this session.

15. *Viewing Science.* **Ronald N. Giere.** This address focuses on those of us engaged in viewing science, particularly philosophers and sociologists of science. I begin with a historical perspective on the philosophy of science, focusing on the historical contingencies which have shaped its development since the 1930s. I then turn my gaze to the more recent history of the sociology of science. For both disciplines I hold up to view the reflexive problem of the status of that discipline's claims from its own perspective. I conclude with a realist vision of science which rejects asymmetric notions, such as rationality, in favor of a naturalistic, perspectival realism.

16. *Psychological, Social, and Epistemic Factors in the Theory of Science.* **Alvin I. Goldman.** This article blends psychological and social factors in the explanation of science, and defends the compatibility of a psychosocial picture with an epistemic picture. It examines three variants of the 'political' approach to interpersonal persuasion advocated by Latour and others. In each case an 'epistemic' or mixed account is more promising and empirically better supported. Psychological research on motivat-

ed reasoning shows the epistemic limits of interest–driven belief. Against social constructivism, the paper defends the viability of a truth–based standard, and reports how truth–possession can be promoted even when scientific work is motivated by political/professional considerations.

17. *Philosophy of Psychology Meets the Semantic View.* **Valerie Gray Hardcastle.** Many philosophers of psychology fail to appreciate the constructivist process of science as well as its pragmatic aspects. A well-developed philosophy of science helps to clear many conceptual confusions. However, ridding ourselves of popular complaints only opens more sophisticated worries regarding how we generalize specific events and how we use those generalizations to build physical systems and abstract models. These questions can still be answered though by realizing that science is largely a social enterprise, and how and what we explain depends a great deal upon who is asking the question of whom and when.

18. *Philosophy of Psychology as Philosophy of Science: Introduction.* **Gary Hatfield**. This paper serves to introduce the papers from the symposium by the same title, by describing the sort of work done in philosophy of psychology conceived as a branch of the philosophy of science, distinguishing it from other discussions of psychology in philosophy, and criticizing the claims to set limits on scientific psychology in the largely psychologically uninformed literatures concerning "folk psychology' and "wide" and "narrow" content. Philosophy of psychology as philosophy of science takes seriously and analyzes the explanatory structures, conceptual problems, and evidentiary practices of extant scientific psychology.

19. *What are Quanta, and Why Does it Matter?* **Nick Huggett.** I criticize a certain view of the 'quanta' of quantum mechanics that sees them as fundamentally non–atomistic and fundamentally significant for our understanding of quantum fields. In particular, I have in mind work by Redhead and Teller (1991, 1992 and Teller 1990). I prove that classical particles do not have the rather strong flavour of identity often associated with them; permuting positions and momenta does not produce distinct states. I show that even the label free excitation formalism is compatible with a mild form of atomism. Finally, I summarise some of the principle objections to an 'oscillator' interpretation of quantum fields.

20. *Who's Afraid of the Human Genome Project?* **Philip Kitcher.** There are a number of controversies surrounding the Human Genome Project (HGP). Some criticisms are based on the contention that the full human sequence will be scientifically worthless; others stem from short-term worries about the social impact of genetic testing and the release of genetic information about individuals. I argue that, properly understood, the HGP is a valuable scientific project with a misleading name, that the moral issues surrounding the short-term difficulties are relatively straightforward but that there are problems of practical politics in implementing the obvious solutions. Finally, I suggest that the HGP serves as the occasion for raising deeper philosophical questions about our commitment to improve the quality of human lives.

21. *Science, Technology and Experiments: the Natural Versus the Artificial.* **Peter Kroes.** Hacking has maintained that in experiments phenomena are created, not discovered, and that scientific entities are tools for doing. These claims undermine the distinction between the natural and the artificial: phenomena and scientific entities become artifacts. Hacking's view raises the question whether the distinction between the natural and the artificial has to be given up. The paper argues 1) that phenomena are created, but in a sense that does not undermine the distinction between the natural

and the artificial, 2) that scientific entities are used as tools instead of being tools, and 3) that Hacking's view on experiments may be reconciled with the traditional view provided the concept of nature be reinterpreted.

22. *Putting Philosophy of Science to the Test: the Case of Aristotle's Biology.* **James G. Lennox.** During the Middle Ages and Rennaissance, it was commonly believed that Aristotle's biological studies reflected his theory of demonstrative science quite well. By contrast, most commentators in the twentieth century have taken it that this is not the case. This is largely the result of preconceptions about what a natural science modelled after the proposals of Aristotle's Posterior Analytics would look like. I argue that these modern preconceptions are incorrect, and that, while the Analytics leaves a variety of issues unanswered that a practicing biology must have answers to (hence Parts of Animals I), Aristotle's biological practice conforms to the Analytics model. It is further argued that establishing this claim requires reading philosophically through entire biological treatises--that is, one will miss the logical structure by following the usual practice of 'sampling' these treatises rather than reading them systematically.

23. *Scientific Classics and Their Fates.* **Ernan McMullin**. If classics of science were to be defined as works that mark scientific revolutions, in the sense of sharp shifts in research tradition, then none of the three works discussed in our symposium quite qualifies. I briefly indicate the fate of each. While impressed by his argument, I express some reservations about Lennox's claim to have dissolved the "problem of demonstration" for Aristotle's De Partibus Animalium. I question Finocchiaro's challenging assertion that in structuring the Dialogo as he did, Galileo "operated within the restrictions" laid on him. Finally, I argue that the legacy of Newton's Opticks was in crucial respects a divided one for the generations that followed.

24. *Unified Theories and Disparate Things.* **Margaret Morrison.** Some very persuasive arguments have been put forward in recent years in support of the disunity of science. Despite this, one is forced to acknowledge that unification, especially the practice of unifying theories, remains a crucial aspect of scientific practice. I explore specific aspects of this tension by examining the nature of theory unification and how it is achieved in the case of the electroweak theory. I claim that because the process of unifying theories is largely dependent on particular kinds of mathematical structures it is possible to have a theory that displays a degree of unity at the level of theoretical structure without an accompanying ontological unity or reduction. As a result, unity and disunity can coexist not only within science but within the same theory.

25. *Feminist Values and Cognitive Virtues.* **Lynn Hankinson Nelson and Jack Nelson.** We consider Helen Longino's proposal that "ontological heterogeneity", "complexity of relationship", and "the non–disappearance of gender" are criteria for good science and cannot be separated into cognitive and social virtues. Using a research program in neuroendocrinology investigating a hormonal basis for sex–differentiated lateralization as a case study, the authors disagree concerning whether the first two criteria can be construed as criteria for good science. Concerning the non–disappearance of gender criterion, we argue that its appropriateness is context specific, and that its cognitive and social formulations are separable and should be construed as such.

26. *Toward a Ralistic Assessment of PKU Screening.* **Diane B. Paul.** Newborn screening for the genetic disease phenylketonuria (PKU) is generally considered the greatest success story of applied human genetics. Even those generally skeptical of the

value of genetic testing often comment enthusiastically on this program. In fact, PKU screening has been plagued with serious problems since its inception in the early 1960s. This essay describes some of these difficulties and asks what lessons they hold for other screening programs. It also argues that realism in our assessment of such programs requires that we pay greater attention to the concrete experience of families. How screening should work in theory is of less importance than how it does work in practice.

27. *After Representation: Science Studies in the Performative Idiom.* **Andy Pickering.** Studies of science are usually addressed in a representational idiom which takes it for granted that the defining characteristic of science is its production of representations of nature. Here I advocate the move to a performative idiom which thematises the agency of machines and human beings. This move leads to a temporally emergent and posthumanist analysis of scientific culture and practice, and promises an antidisciplinary synthesis of the science-studies disciplines, spanning an impure sociology of science, a displacement of the traditional philosophical problematics of realism and incommensurability, and a historiography of science centered on performative intertwinings of science, technology and society.

28.*Methodological Norms in Traditional and Feminist Philosophy of Science.* **Elizabeth Potter.** I argue against the assumption that the influence of non–cognitive values must lead to bad science and against the methodological norm that seems to some philosophers to follow from it, viz. that a good philosophy of science should analyze the morally and politically neutral production of good science. Against these, I argue for the assumption that non–cognitive values are compatible with good science and for the metaphilosophical norm that a good philosophy of science should allow us to see whether and how non–cognitive values influence good science. In pursuit of one of its scandalous goals, viz. determining whether and when gender politics influence good scientific work, feminist philosophy of science is well served by this methodological norm.

29. *The Vacuum in Relativistic Quantum Field Theory.* **Michael Redhead**. The status of the vacuum in relativistic quantum field theory is examined. A sharp distinction arises between the global vacuum and the local vacuum. The concept of local number density is critically assessed. The global vacuum state implies fluctuations for all local observables. Correlations between such fluctuations in space-like separated regions of space-time are discussed and the existence of correlations which are maximal in a certain sense is remarked on, independently of how far apart those regions may be. The analogy with the mirror-image correlations in the singlet state of two spin-1/2 particles is explained. The connection between these maximal correlations and the well-known violation of the Bell inequality in the vacuum state is discussed, together with the way in which the existence of these correlations might be exploited in developing a vacuum version of the Einstein–Podolsky–Rosen argument. The recent relativistic formulation of the Einstein–Podolsky–Rosen argument by Ghirardi and Grassi is critically assessed with particular reference to the vacuum case.

30. *The History and Philosophy of Quantum Field Theory.* **Don Robinson.** This paper is intended to be an introductory survey of subjects related to the problems dealt with in the three other papers in this symposium on quantum field theory. A brief history of quantum electrodynamics is given and some of the objections to it are stated. A brief history of quantum field theories from the 1970's to the present is then provided. Finally, a sketch of some of the philosophical work that has been done on quantum field theories is presented. The object of the paper is to explain why philosophers of physics have tended to neglect quantum field theories and to point out several of the conceptual issues raised by quantum field theories that call out for further analysis.

31. *Methodological Issues in the Construction of Gender as a Meaningful Variable in Scientific Studies of Cognition.* **Phyllis Rooney.** Specific methodological limitations of traditional sex differences research are uncovered by feminist psychologists who argue for a shift toward a theoretical appropriation of gender that reveals its significance as a site of ongoing situated social regulation. I argue that such a shift has important implications for studies on gender and cognition, and that such studies have the potential to significantly expand our understanding of the contextual and situated nature of both social and "non-social" cognition.

32. *Subversive Reflections on the Human Genome Project.* **Alex Rosenberg.** By developing an elaborate allegory, this paper attempts to show that the advertised aim of the Human Genome project, to sequence the entire 3 billion base pair primary sequence of the nucleic acid molecules that constitute the human genome, does not make scientific sense. This raises the questions of what the real aim of the project could be, and why the molecular biological community has chosen to offer the primary sequence as the objective to be funded, when identifying functionally important sub–regions of the genetic material is both far more useful and independently attainable an aim.

33. *Engaging Science Through Cultural Studies.* **Joseph Rouse.** The paper introduces cultural studies of science as an alternative to the "legitimation project" in philosophy and sociology of science. The legitimation project stems from belief that the epistemic standing and cultural authority of the sciences need general justification, and that such justification (or its impossibility) arises from the nature or characteristic aim of the sciences. The paper considers three central themes of cultural studies apart from its rejection of these commitments to the legitimation project: first, focus upon the sciences as ongoing and dynamic practices; second, a deflationary and non-representationalist approach to understanding scientific knowledge; and third, foregrounding questions about the significance of scientific practices, statements, and the objects they engage, and how that significance changes within ongoing practices.

34. *A Dissolution of the Problem of Locality.* **Simon Saunders.** Debates over the significance of the particle concept, and the problem of locality—how do we represent localized phenomena?—appear to presuppose that particles and observed phenomena are things rather than events. Well-known theorems (Hergerfelt, Reeh-Schlieder), and a recent variant of Hergerfelt's theorem due to David Malement, present a problem of locality only given the tacit appeal to the concept of thing, in fact an individual, in a sense contrary to particle indistinguishability. There is no difficulty with the particle concept per se, but it is a global construction more than one step removed from events actually observed, which are represented by local integrals over self-adjoint field densities.

35. *Interactions Among Theory, Experiment, and Technology in Molecular Biology.* **Kenneth F. Schaffner.** This article examines how a molecular "solution" to an important biological problem—how is antibody diversity generated? was obtained in the 1970s. After the primarily biological clonal selection theory (CST) was accepted by 1967, immunologists developed several different contrasting theories to complete the SCST. To choose among these theories, immunology had to turn to the new molecular biology, first to nucleic acid hybridization and then to recombinant DNA technology. The research programs of Tonegawa and Leder that led to the "solution" are discussed, and some of their strategies and heuristics are broadly characterized: (1) to what extent does the new recombinant DNA technology provide what the scientists claim is "direct evidence," what does that term mean, and what are the implications of that claim for biological "realism," and (2) is this episode one of reduction,

partial reduction, or explanatory extension, and what do these terms mean in the context of a successful molecular "solution" to a biological problem.

36. *Newton's Opticks as Classic: On Teaching the Texture of Science.* **Dennis L. Sepper.** Using the example of Newton's Opticks, the author develops the concept of 'classic' as applied to landmark works in the history of the sciences. A discussion of themes drawn from H.-G. Gadamer and T. Kuhn is followed by an introduction of the notions of the texture and contexture of scientific works, conceived as the result of an author's weaving together foreground and background concerns. These notions assist in understanding how certain works can exercise a continuing appeal to both specialists and nonspecialists. The essay concludes with reflections on the pedagogical purpose of using classic scientific texts in university education.

37.*What is Psychophysics?* **Lawrence A. Shapiro.** Since the founding of psychophysics in the latter half of the nineteenth century, controversy has raged over the subject matter of psychophysical laws. Originally, Fechner characterized psycho physics as the science describing the relation between physical magnitudes and the sensations these magnitudes produce in us. Today many psycho–physicists would deny that sensation is or could be a topic of psycho–physical investigation. I consider Savage's (1970) influential objections to the possibility of such an investigation and argue that they depend upon (i) holding psychophysics to higher standards than those to which we hold other sciences; and (ii) misrepresenting Fechner's stated goals for psychophysics.

38. *Empirical and Rational Components in Scientific Confirmation.* **Abner Shimony.** Some desiderata for scientific confirmation are formulated in the light of a tentative scientific world view. Bayesian confirmation theories generically satisfy most of these desiderata, but one of them, "the strategy of ascent," fits best in a tempered personalist version of Bayesianism. There are both empirical and rational components, dialectically combined, in tempered personalism. The question of explanation vs. prediction is treated in a Bayesian manner, and it is found that both operations are susceptible to characteristic systematic errors. If these are eliminated, however, then explanation and prediction provide equally good evidential support for hypotheses.

39. *Convergence in Radical Probabilism.* **Brian Skyrms.** It is shown how martingale convergence theorems apply to coherent belief change in radical probabilist epistemology.

40. *Contextualizing Science: From Science Studies to Cultural Studies.* **Vassiliki Betty Smocovitis.** This paper consists of two parts: the first is a brief historical summary of relevant discussions to date involving members of the panel; the second part is a discussion of the new contextualism within science studies, the consequent move towards the cultural study of scientific knowledge, and what this means for intellectual/cultural historians of science in terms of specific procedures. Thus, my role on this panel—as I understand it-- will be to play the sociologically and philosophically minded historian to the sociologically and historically minded philosophers as all of us attempt to adapt cross-disciplinary procedures to our specific disciplinary needs.

41. *Multivariate Models of Scientific Change.* **Miriam Solomon.** Social scientists regularly make use of multivariate models to describe complex social phenomena. It is argued that this approach is useful for modelling the variety of cognitive and social factors contributing to scientific change, and superior to the integrated models of scientific change currently available. It is also argued that care needs to be taken in drawing normative conclusions: cognitive factors are not instrinsically more "rational"

than social factors, nor is it likely that social factors, by some "invisible hand of reason," generally work to produce scientific success. A multivariate model of the biasing factors within a scientific community at particular times is developed. This model, which is an example of work in social epistemology, yields normative conclusions.

42. *Shifting Frames: From Divided to Distributed Psychologies of Scientific Agents.* **Peter J. Taylor.** I characterize and then complicate Solomon, Thagard and Goldman's framing of the issue of integrating cognitive and social factors in explaining science. I sketch a radically different framing which distributes the mind beyond the brain, embodies it, and has that mind-body-person become, as s/he always is, an agent acting in a society. I also find problems in Solomon's construal of multivariate statistics, Thagard's analogies for multivariate analysis, and Goldman's faith in the capacity of the community of users of scientific method to home in on true beliefs.

43. *Explaining Scientific Change: Integrating the Cognitive and the Social.* **Paul Thagard.** Cognitive and social explanations of science should be complementary rather than competing. Mind, society, and nature interact in complex ways to produce the growth of scientific knowledge. The recent development and wide acceptance of the theory that ulcers are caused by bacteria illustrates the interaction of psychological, sociological, and natural factors. Mind-nature interactions are evident in the use of instruments and experiments. Mind-society interactions are evident in collaborative research and the flow of information among researchers. Finally, nature-society interactions are evident in the role of granting agencies in determining the availability of instruments and the funding of experiments.

44. *Science, Probability, and the Proposition.* **Bas C. van Fraassen.** In a traditional view of science we come to fully believe the main accepted theories (the 'body of scientific knowledge'). Some of the hypotheses "possible for all that science tells us" seem more likely than others: enter probability as grading the possibilities left open. Probabilism contends with this tradition. Richard Jeffrey told us never to resolve doubt but only to quantify it, and to give maximal probability only to tautologies. Despite severe difficulties, I shall argue that the traditional view is reconcilable with (moderate) probabilism. I will propose a single unified account with conditional personal probability as basic, allowing for full belief in empirical theories, with our probabilities grading the possibilities left open.

45. *The Notion of Accuracy in Current Social Perception Research.* **Barbara Von Eckardt.** People often make trait judgments (e.g. John is intelligent) about themselves and others. Social perception researchers have attempted to study the accuracy of such judgments. Such studies raise the philosophical/conceptual question of what it means to say that a person's judgment is accurate. Two attempts have recently been made to taxonomize current research in terms of the notion of accuracy which has been adopted. My aim in this paper is twofold: first, to argue that the proposed philosophical taxonomies are problematic and, hence, should be abandoned, and second, to recommend adoption of an alternative "minimalist" notion of accuracy.

46. *Discourse, Practice, Context: From HPS to Interdisciplinary Science Studies.* **Alison Wylie.** There seems the prospect, at this juncture, of articulating programs of research in science studies that will be genuinely interdisciplinary, integrating philosophical, historical, and sociological/anthropological interests in science. This introduction describes the rationale for the symposium, "Discourse, Practice, Context," to which four contributors were invited whose work across disciplinary boundaries puts them in a position to take stock of these initiatives and their impact on existing disciplinary practice.

Part I

PRESIDENTIAL ADDRESS

Viewing Science

Ronald N. Giere

University of Minnesota

1. Introduction

A presidential address provides a rare opportunity for public, disciplinary self-reflection. This is particularly true in the context of a joint meeting with related disciplines. Accordingly, rather than simply presenting my own view of science, I shall focus on those of us engaged in viewing science, particularly philosophers, psychologists, historians, and sociologists of science. I will, of course, be doing the viewing from the vantage point of the philosophy of science, which thus fills the foreground. The middle distance will be occupied by the sociology of science, while the history of science and cognitive studies of science occupy the background.

2. Philosophy of Science in Historical Perspective

I begin with a historical view of the philosophy of science itself. The most common picture of the recent history of the philosophy of science in North America is that, after a long period of dominance, Logical Empiricism was superseded in the 1960s by an historical approach to the philosophy of science inspired by Kuhn's (1962) *Structure of Scientific Revolutions*. That picture presents a very distorted view of the historical landscape. Nevertheless, there have been some large issues at stake since the 1960s. One large issue is this: How are we to understand the practice of the philosophy of science itself? In particular, how are we to understand relations between the philosophy of science and the history, psychology, and sociology of science? I suspect that part of the reason the contrast between logical and historical approaches to the philosophy of science has seemed so important to so many is that it implicitly raises these reflexive questions.

These questions are not new. They were explicitly debated both in the United States and in Germany in the 1920s and 1930s. John Dewey provides an exemplar of how the debate went in the United States. By 1929, when he turned seventy, Dewey was a philosophical naturalist, and to some extent even an evolutionary naturalist. That is, he rejected all claims to knowledge of the world based on anything but empirical scientific methods. There was, for Dewey, no special philosophical knowledge, particularly none that could provide a foundation or ultimate legitimization for the sciences. Rather, our understanding of evolutionary biology, of psychology, and of culture, provides a basis for an understanding of scientific inquiry itself. What was special to philosophy, for Dewey, was the modernist task of bringing to moral and po-

PSA 1994, Volume 2, pp. 3-16

litical inquiries the conclusions and methods of the sciences. He was far less concerned with the truth of scientific conclusions than with their usefulness for solving current societal problems.[1]

My exemplar of the debate in Germany focuses, of course, on a small community of philosophers and scientists, operating on the fringes of the German philosophical world, advocating a "scientific philosophy". The history of this movement is only now emerging from the realm of disciplinary founder myths into that of historical scholarship. I draw only briefly, and very imperfectly, on this new scholarship.[2]

In retrospect, one could describe the program of scientific philosophy as that of "naturalizing" philosophy, where philosophy is understood as consisting primarily of neo-Kantian metaphysics. More specifically, in scientific philosophy the problem of developing a *philosophical* understanding of arithmetic and geometry, and of space, time, and causality, was eliminated in favor of a *scientific* understanding of these concepts provided by the then new researches into the foundations of arithmetic and geometry, and by the new physics, particularly relativity theory and quantum mechanics. But if philosophical metaphysics is replaced by scientific theory, what role remains for the philosopher of science? Carnap (1937) provided the canonical answer: philosophy of science becomes the logical analysis of the language, concepts, and theories of the sciences, an enterprise that, like modern mathematical logic itself, takes place in the philosophically secure realm of the analytic a priori. It is this view of the philosophy of science that underlay what became Logical Empiricism in post-World War II America.

For Dewey, as noted above, the methods of empirical science were themselves a subject for scientific inquiry drawing heavily on psychology. Prior to 1933, the German scientific philosophers had little interest in empiricist methods as such. They were more concerned with the general possibility of any correspondence between the structure of experience, or of language, and the structure of the world — a typical Kantian concern. As they moved into the Anglo-American context, the logical empiricists had to take a stand on more traditionally empiricist questions about scientific method. They decided that such questions belong in the province of philosophy, and are thus a matter of logic rather than psychology or any other science. This decision was codified in the famous distinction between "the context of discovery" and "the context of justification".

Ironically, most of the later critical literature on this distinction implicitly honors it by considering only its legitimacy and not inquiring into its origins. The recognized source of the distinction is Hans Reichenbach's *Experience and Prediction*, published by the University of Chicago Press in 1938. This book was written, in English, during the years 1933-38 at the University of Istanbul where Reichenbach, along with fifty or so other former German professors, found refuge in Mustafa Kemal's new Republic. He had been dismissed from his post as professor of the epistemology of physics in the physics (not philosophy!) department at the University of Berlin following imposition of Nazi racial laws in early 1933. But versions of the distinction had been common in German philosophy for more than fifty years. The neo-Kantian, Rudolph Hermann Lotze, for example, used a version in the 1870s to distinguish questions regarding the psychological genesis of spatial representations from questions regarding the validity of geometrical knowledge of such representations (Hatfield 1990, 163-64).[3]

Reichenbach introduces his English version of the distinction in the very first section of *Experience and Prediction* where he sets out the task of epistemology as he conceives it. Here he is primarily concerned to distinguish epistemology from psychology. This he does by associating the concerns of epistemology with those of logic, and then drawing on a more recent tradition of distinguishing logic from psychology. The distinction between discovery and justification reappears only once in *Experience and Prediction*, and then only briefly, near the end of the final chapter on probability and induction. Here Reichenbach writes:

> What we wish to point out with our theory of induction is the logical relation of the new theory to the known facts. We do not insist that the discovery of the new theory is performed by a reflection of a kind similar to our expositions; we do not maintain anything about the question of how it is performed—what we maintain is nothing but a relation of a theory to facts, *independent of the man who found the theory* (1938, 382, emphasis added).

He then cites the example of Einstein and the general theory of relativity. The contrast between "the man who found the theory" and a "[logical] relation of a theory to facts" exactly parallels that between the contexts of discovery and justification.

I conjecture that part of the significance of the distinction for Reichenbach at this time was its implicit denial that characteristics of a *person* proposing a scientific hypothesis have anything to do with the scientific validity of the hypothesis proposed. This applies, in particular, to that person being a Jew. My only other textual evidence for this conjecture appears in the final paragraph of a paper on the state of "Logistic Empiricism in Germany" which Reichenbach published from Istanbul in 1936 in The *Journal of Philosophy*. There he wrote (1936, 160): "Science, surely, is not limited to national or racial boundaries; we prefer to stand for this historical truth, in spite of all the pretensions of a certain modern nationalism." In philosophical terms, Reichenbach seems to have made it a precondition on any scientific epistemology that it rule out the possibility of any distinction between, for example, Jewish and Aryan science. But I think there was more to it than this. Separating questions of the origins of ideas from questions of their validity seems to have been for Reichenbach, at that time, a matter as deeply personal as it was philosophical. And this sentiment surely must have been shared by everyone in the movement.[4]

If one is going to insist on so strong a distinction between discovery and justification, one is obliged to produce a theory of justification to back it up. That Reichenbach did. His own theory of induction does satisfy the precondition that the justification of a hypothesis be independent of its origin. His rule of induction operates as a relationship between purely formal aspects of a fixed set of data and a single hypothesis—a relative frequency in a finite sequence of occurrences and a postulated limiting relative frequency, respectively. There is simply no place in such a formal relationship for any aspects of the wider context to enter into the calculation. This is not to say that Reichenbach, as well as contemporaries like Carnap and Popper, did not have other motives for wanting to make empirical justification a purely formal relationship. But I do think the particular historical circumstances at that time strongly reinforced those motives. And the commitment of philosophers of science to seeing the evidential relationship as purely formal has waned as those circumstances have receded into the past.

So how did a dissident European movement advocating the replacement of much established philosophy by Wissenschaftliche Philosophie transform itself into an establishment North American philosophy of science? And how did a naturalistic pragmatism incorporating an empirical theory of inquiry get replaced by a philosophy that reduced the philosophical study of scientific inquiry to the analysis of a formal relationship between evidence and hypothesis? That episode is only beginning to be subjected to historical study.[5] One can only wonder how the philosophy of science in North America would appear today if the Social Democrats rather than the National Socialists had come to power in Germany in 1933.

At this point I can imagine some of my philosophical colleagues objecting that the history of Logical Empiricism, how it came to prominence in North America, and how it changed in the process, is quite irrelevant to the question of its merits as a philosophy of science. The fact that such an objection can still resonate strongly within the community of philosophers of science demonstrates the enduring power of Reichenbach's distinction and the continuing reluctance to see Logical Empiricism as the contingent historical development it surely must have been. But we must learn to see it as such if we are ever to put aside old arguments and devote our undivided energies to developing new views of the nature of science.

The deep commitment to Reichenbach's distinction following World War II helps to explain the initial very negative reaction to Kuhn's work among philosophers of science. For Kuhn's view was that the history of science is a story of major changes in accepted theory driven by historical contingencies: by socialization into a scientific specialty, by psychological crises following the failure of established techniques to solve recognized problems, by sudden gestalt switches, by older opponents dying, and by textbooks being rewritten. Here there is no formal logical relationship between data and theory to tell us which theory is the better justified, and thus no way to separate origins from validation. Indeed, there is no such thing as validation in the older sense. Kuhn was, of course, accused of relativism. Motivating this charge, though seldom even alluded to in print, was, I think, the specter of Jewish science.

Contrary to common historiography, the predominant reaction to Kuhn among analytically trained philosophers of science was to forge closer links not with the history of science, but with contemporary science itself. This was particularly evident in territories already much explored by the logical empiricists, physics, and probability and induction, but also in the newly rediscovered realm of the philosophy of biology.[6] Viewed in retrospect, the form this reaction took now seems to me to have been profoundly mistaken. Abandoning the logical empiricists' clear distinction between a science and the philosophical analysis of that science, many philosophers of science in the 1960s and 1970s came to view their work as *continuous* with that of scientists in the fields they studied — physicists, statisticians, and biologists. To think that people trained in logic and philosophy should actually contribute to the solution of major theoretical problems in the sciences sounds presumptuous. Mainly it was naive. The enterprise assumes, quite mistakenly, that one can extract the theories of a science from their disciplinary culture and analyze them in the abstract. Later analytic philosophers of science were thus victims of an assumption they adopted uncritically from their logical empiricist elders. The typical result has been the creation of relatively isolated sub-disciplines populated by philosophers and a few scientific sympathizers. The sciences in question have continued to develop following their own dynamics.

But those philosophers of science who turned to history did not necessarily choose a better path. To the extent that there has been a "historical school" in the philosophy of science, Kuhn's inclusion in that school has been problematical. Steven Toulmin (1972), Ernan McMullin (1970), Dudley Shapere (1984), Imre Lakatos (1970), and Larry Laudan (1977), to name only a few of the most prominent candidates, have been as united in their opposition to Kuhn as in their opposition to Logical Empiricism. Their joint project, pursued in different ways, has been to show that science exhibits *rational progress*. So the project became one of offering an account of scientific rationality. But what is the status of any such account? Or, what is the conception of the project of philosophy of science in which such an account is offered? For the most part, it seems to me, the project has been one of analytic philosophy in historical robes — providing a conceptual analysis of rationality using historical rather than logical categories. Among those mentioned, only Lakatos (1971) and Laudan squarely faced up to this metamethodological problem, and only Laudan (1987) seems finally to have broken with the analytic tradition to embrace a form of naturalism.

I would now like briefly to explore the extent to which accounts of rational progress offered by members of the historical school succeed in preserving a separation between discovery and justification sufficient to rule out the relativism they perceived in Kuhn. But first let me swing our view around to another direction. Sandra Harding (1986) has popularized "the science question in feminism" for feminists. There are equally serious "feminism questions in science" for philosophers of science. For example: Is it possible that the actual *content* of methodologically acceptable science might reflect the specifically gendered interests of the predominately male scientists who created it? A positive answer to this question follows directly from an assumption which many members of the historical school quite correctly borrowed from Kuhn, namely, that theory choice always involves a comparative evaluation among existing rivals which do not exhaust the range of logically possible rivals. This assumption is clearly built into both Lakatos' and Laudan's accounts of rational progress as arising out of a clash among rival research traditions.

The argument is simple. Suppose there are two rival theoretical programs which together do not exhaust the logically possible programs. Suppose one program ends up more progressive by the stipulated methodological criteria. That it does so depends on which among the possible rivals was in fact the actual rival. Against other logically possible rivals, the current favorite might not have fared so well. So we must consider the process by which possible rivals get into the game. There is nothing in any of the proposed accounts of rational progress to rule out gendered interests, or any other sort of interest, from playing a major role in this process. It is simply a matter of persuading enough investigators to consider a possible rival as a serious alternative. And who can deny that gendered interests are powerful persuaders. Thus any sort of theory exhibiting only moderate success by the stipulated criteria can end up the progressive choice, provided only that its de facto rivals do significantly worse. And what goes for gendered interests goes for religious interests, or any other sort of interest. The possibility of Jewish science is not eliminated in these accounts of rational progress.

I think we will just have to live with the empirical possibility that, at any given time, our best sciences may nevertheless embody all manner of cultural interests and values in their very content. But, like feminist empiricists, I also believe that particular interests embedded in specific theories can be identified, and sometimes eliminated, by creating empirically superior theories. So my view of science differs from those for whom the possibility of cultural interests influencing the content of science must be regarded as unavoidable, and not subject to empirical criticism, namely constructivist sociologists of science.

3. A View of Constructivist Sociology of Science

For those willing to treat spoon-bending on a par with traditional establishment sciences (Collins and Pinch 1982), the possibility that the content of any science might be influenced by interests based on religious tradition or gender could hardly be denied. Nor are there strong motivations to deny it. I have suggested that upholding a strong distinction between origins and validity was emotionally rooted in the personal experiences of the founders of Logical Empiricism during the 1930s. For the founders of constructivist sociology of science, by contrast, the formative experiences were those of the 1960s. In Europe these experiences included not only the Vietnam war, but also Prague Spring and the student revolts. Here science was seen not as a savior, but a villain, part of the established authority to be resisted. The project became one of critique, indeed, of undermining the claims of the sciences to any special cognitive authority. Thus, as I see it, a significant source of the current antagonism between philosophy and sociology of science reflects the different experiences of different generations—roughly the generation of the 1930s versus that of 1960s. That is a difference in viewpoints unlikely to be reconciled by verbal argument. For those for whom neither the 1930s nor the 1960s have been particularly formative, I offer the following pictures for your viewing pleasure.

First, it is worth remembering that there has been generational conflict within the sociology of science as well as between sociologists and philosophers of science. Robert Merton's work, which dominated the sociology of science up to the 1960s, was grounded in the experiences of the 1930s and 1940s. The essay introducing his famous four norms constituting the ethos of science, which now goes under the title "The Normative Structure of Science" (Merton 1973), was originally published in 1942 under the title "A Note on Science and Democracy," and reprinted in 1949 under the title "Science and Democratic Social Structure." The essay seems designed to exhibit a correspondence between the ideals of science and the ideals of liberal democracy. Certainly the specter of Nazi Germany looms large in this early essay.[7] And the methodological autonomy of science is never questioned.

Returning to later developments, there has never been a single view with the title "social constructivism". At the moment there are maybe a half dozen distinct views that could claim the title. In order to avoid too long a show, I will introduce a couple of philosophical filters, as it were, to reduce the multiplicity of views to two. That simplifies the overall picture, of course, but leaves it rich enough for my purposes.

The one view I will label *epistemological* constructivism. This view is explicitly agnostic about the existence of the entities and processes reported by scientists. Such things may or may not be there in the world independent of any social practices. But, as a matter of fact, if one looks carefully enough at the actual historical sequence of events through which scientists come to hold the beliefs they do, one finds the major determinants of their beliefs in the realm of social interests, interactions, and associations. The influence of the supposed entities on actual beliefs, even if these entities were to exist as claimed, turns out to be minimal at best.[8]

The second view I will label *ontological* constructivism. On this view the entities and processes named in theoretical scientific discussions are *constituted* by the social practices, interactions, and associations of scientists. Like positive laws in the Anglo-American system of justice, it makes no sense to abstract from the social context and speak of scientific laws as if they existed antecedently to, or apart from, the social context. This was the view of Latour and Woolgar's *Laboratory Life* (1979), and it remains Woolgar's view (1988a). It is shared by many others.

My philosophical filters remove most of what is exciting about constructivist studies. But the excitement comes mainly from the richness of the cases, not the theoretical colorations. The theoretical views suffer from a major anomaly that has been there from the start, and recognized as such. It just has never been resolved. This anomaly is the problem of reflexivity, and it exists for both epistemological and ontological views of constructivism. The problem arises if we ask: What is the character of constructivist sociology of science itself? The problem becomes a reflexive problem if one answers that the sociology of science is itself a science, subject to the same sorts of investigation constructivists have carried out for other sciences. Epistemological constructivists would have to conclude their own beliefs about the scientists they study were determined more by their own interests and social interactions as sociologists than by whatever might really be going on among their subjects. For ontological constructivists, the results of such an investigation would have to be that the objects of investigation, the beliefs, interests, etc., of their subject scientists, are constituted by their own practices as constructivist sociologists.

The initial responses to this realization were simply to accept it. That is not an inconsistent position. Of course it appears self-defeating from a realist perspective in which scientific investigation is supposed to yield at least a tolerably good picture of what is really going on. But if one's goal is radical critique, what better way to exhibit the total futility of any attempt to establish scientific authority? Thus, as I read him, Steve Woolgar now recommends we celebrate the reflexive irony of total deconstruction, including self-deconstruction (Woolgar 1988b). Another response to reflexivity, which I associate with Harry Collins, is to be a realist about the social world, but a constructivist about the natural world (Collins and Yearley 1992). That position at least avoids self-deconstruction, but it requires a dubiously sharp demarcation between the social and the natural worlds.

Of course there remains the possibility of denying reflexivity. This would remove the sociology of science from the realm of the sciences altogether. That is what the scientific philosophers did for philosophy of science by understanding it as logical analysis rather than as science. Perhaps this is part of the strategy of those who associate constructivism with hermeneutics or ethnomethodology.

Realism, by contrast, is immune to the disease of reflexivity. On a realist view, scientists sometimes succeed in discovering how some antecedently existing bit of the world actually works, and we in science studies, likewise, may sometimes succeed in explaining how they in fact did it. That explanation often involves exhibiting a causal link between the scientists and what they discover. Of course they don't always succeed, and neither do we; but we might sometimes succeed in explaining why they don't when they don't. In either case, our explanations of how we ourselves succeed are of the same type as our explanations of how they succeed.

Nor does realism undermine the project of critique—on the contrary. For illustration, take Andy Pickering's (1984) account of the weak neutral current in *Constructing Quarks*. Read from a realist perspective, which is how most scientists would read it, the book has real punch. A Nobel Prize was awarded for the discovery of the weak neutral current, and it is now part of the "standard model" of high energy physics. But, assuming Pickering was writing as an epistemological constructivist, his conclusion was that the belief that such a phenomenon exists, and the whole practice of high energy physics incorporating that belief, would have been adopted largely as it was *even if nature contains nothing resembling the supposed weak neutral current*. One need not accuse the scientists involved of deliberately engaging in deception, for they could be as deceived as everyone else. Nevertheless, from a realist perspective, if Pickering is right, this should be an international scandal. But such a conclusion depends on there being a workable distinction between cases in which there is a real discovery and cases in which the supposed objects of discovery are mere social constructs. And that distinction is denied by all forms of social constructivism.

In these latter comments I have invoked a realist vision of science, and realism is regarded as problematic not only by most recent sociologists of science, but also by many philosophers of science. So let me add some details to this vision. It will ultimately be a vision not only of the philosophy of science, but of science studies as a whole.

4. A Realist Vision of Science

A lot depends, as we have seen, on how one conceives the goals of one's discipline. Constructivist sociologists of science begin with the assumption that what needs to be accounted for are the commonly held beliefs of members of scientific communities. But how the world might be constituted is thought to have no direct influence on anyone's beliefs. It is only *other beliefs* about the world that matter. There seems, therefore, no way logically to force consideration of anything beyond beliefs. So the social study of science can proceed in complete autonomy from what might be the character of the world beyond anyone's beliefs.

For philosophers, the logical structure of this situation is all too familiar. Classical phenomenalism, for example, begins with the assumption that all we ever really experience are our own sensations. From that assumption flows "the problem of the external world". Similarly, empiricists of less radical persuasions (van Fraassen 1980) begin with the assumption that all evidence consists of what is observable, and then challenge anyone logically to force them to move beyond claims about the observable. These are fools games because it is impossible to meet the challenge as formulated. They present, as John Dewey once said, problems not to be solved, but to be gotten over. So the following views may be regarded as designed to help one get over the problems caused by isolating science studies from the internal content of the sciences it investigates.

What should then be the goals of science studies? They are, of course, numerous. Most generally, we should seek to provide our various cultures with an understanding of how different sciences operate within those cultures. This requires developing a set of concepts in terms of which all of us, including scientists, can understand the development and workings of the various sciences. And this understanding should sometimes provide a basis for criticizing both particular practices in science and specific uses of science. But included in this understanding, I would insist, must be some explanation of how the social practice of science came to produce, and continues to produce, the extraordinary range of knowledge it in fact does produce. In short, one of the goals of science studies should be to explain the successes of modern science.

I hasten to add that by "success" here I mean what most people outside the philosophy or sociology of science mean by success. We have learned that the earth revolves around the sun, not vice versa. We now know that there are not only five planets, but at least nine. We know there are atoms, and that the speed of light is finite. We know the continents move and that DNA has two strands. These things are now known, and not merely socially acceptable to believe. Of course it is logically possible that even such robust claims as these might turn out to be mistaken, and logically possible to question any one of them. But that only means that our knowledge is not logically infallible, not that we don't really know these things. That it seems necessary to highlight such obvious examples of scientific success should be regarded as a scandal in science studies.

"How naive can you be?" I imagine a critic saying. If you were a theologian in 1492, you would be telling us how no one could possibly deny the divinity of Christ or the virgin birth. Of course that is right. But it is beside the point because the situations are not symmetrical. We have a big advantage over our fifteenth century counterparts, namely, five hundred years of hindsight regarding the historical development of science. The inability of anyone to collapse that hindsight into a logically compelling five line argument is no basis for anti-realism, or even for agnosticism. On the other hand, taking a common sense realist position regarding the history of modern science does not commit one to any of the myriad *interpretations* of scientific practice that have accompanied that history.

Take, for example, the notion of a universal law of nature, an idea associated with science at least since the seventeenth century, and still assumed in much of twentieth century philosophy of science. I have looked in vain for a broad-based historical treatment of this notion. From the bits and pieces available, I have concluded that the original view of science as discovering universal laws of nature had little basis in the actual practice of science, but was imported largely from theology. In this theology, God laid down the laws for human conduct and for nature. The task of natural philosophers, then, was to discover God's laws for nature, which are of course universal—except, perhaps, when God himself intervenes. In spite of its theological origins, the idea that there are universal laws of nature provided a powerful resource for Enlightenment philosophers. If the laws of the universe, both moral and natural, are discoverable by human reason alone, what need have we for priests and kings, and ultimately for God as well?

But one need not appeal to history to deconstruct the concept of a law of nature. The concept is theoretically suspect as well. For example, any law of nature refers to only a few physical quantities. Yet nature contains many quantities which often interact one with another, and there are few if any truly isolated systems. So there cannot be many systems in the real world that exactly satisfy any purported law of nature. Consequently, understood as general claims about the world, most purported laws of nature are in fact false. So we need a portrait of science that captures our everyday understanding of success without invoking laws of nature understood as true, universal generalizations.[9]

While we are being iconoclastic, what about the concept of truth itself? I don't mean the everyday concept which one might use to say "Yes, it is true that the continents move." I mean philosophical *theories* of truth such as a correspondence theory of truth. And not only theories of truth, but the whole of formal semantics which incorporates Tarski's version of the correspondence theory of truth. Should this view of truth, originally developed for investigations into the foundations of logic and mathematics, be part of our interpretation of science? I think not.

Though not his original intention, Hilary Putnam (1981) provided a reason for suspicion of this whole semantic apparatus over a decade ago. Suppose that God wrote down for us a complete description of the whole universe in the language of set theory, so that every statement therein was true. That, Putnam proved, in purely logical terms, would not uniquely fix the reference of the terms in those statements. In plain English, we could be given the whole truth about the universe, as expressible in set theory, and still not know what we were talking about. Putnam, who took realism to be the view that we may take the terms of our best confirmed theories as genuinely referring to real objects, concluded that realism is mistaken.

In response, philosophers such as Nancy Cartwright (1983) and Ian Hacking (1983) argued that we can have direct evidence for the objects of scientific inquiry through experimentation, without worrying about having true theories. The linguist George Lakoff (1987) drew the more radical conclusion that the whole logical machinery of truth and reference which frames Putnam's analysis fails to capture the role of language in empirical science—whatever might be its virtues in the realm of logic and mathematics. It is not realism we should abandon, but the semantic framework in which Putnam initially framed it.

But if we abandon standard analyses of truth and reference, along with the notion of a law of nature, what resources remain to express a useful notion of realism? What remains, I think, is a more general notion of *representation.* In place of the usual exemplar of linguistic representation, e.g., "The cat is on the mat," I would suggest beginning with maps, e.g., a standard road map. Maps have many of the representational features we need for understanding how scientists represent the world. There is no such thing as a universal map. Neither does it make sense to question whether a map is true or false. The representational virtues of maps are different. A map may, for example, be more or less accurate, more or less detailed, of smaller or larger scale. Maps require a large background of human convention for their production and use. Without such they are no more than lines on paper. Nevertheless, maps do manage to correspond in various ways with the real world. Their representational powers can be attested by anyone who has used a map when traveling in unfamiliar territory.

Nor is the connection between road maps and representation in science at all far-fetched. Oceanographers map the ocean floors, astronomers map the heavens (star maps are centuries old), geneticists are busy mapping the human genome, and neuroscientists are mapping the mind (or at least the brain). The recent appearance of numerous articles on visual modes of representation in the science studies literature is evidence that historians, philosophers, and sociologists of science are finally becoming aware of how much of science has been done, and increasingly is being done, using pictorial and diagrammatic modes of representation. Of course some of this literature is cited in support of a constructivist picture of science, but it can equally well be viewed as supporting a more liberal notion of realism, something we might call "perspectival realism".

There is a metaphysics (a scientific metaphysics, of course) that goes along with a perspectival realism. Rather than thinking of the world as packaged in sets of objects sharing definite properties, think of it as indefinitely complex, exhibiting many qualities that at least appear to vary continuously. One might then construct maps that depict this world from various perspectives. In such a world even a fairly successful realistic science might well contain individual concepts and relationships inspired by religious or gendered interests. It is possible, therefore, that our currently acceptable scientific theories embody cultural values and nevertheless possess many genuinely representational virtues.

Here we have a way of combining what is valuable in both constructivism and realism, but it requires abandoning the universal applicability of either view. We can agree that scientific representations are socially constructed, but then we must also agree that some socially constructed representations can be discovered to provide a good picture of aspects of the world, while others are mere constructs with little genuine connection to the world. This compromise does not reduce the sociology of science to the sociology of error. Explanations of success and failure remain symmetrical in that both invoke the same sorts of activities on the part of scientists. In particular, there is no presumption that success is the product of rational deliberation while failure results from the intrusion of social factors. There is no need to introduce asymmetric notions such as rationality.

5. Rationality

Although they are often associated, even equated, realism and rationality are two very different things. My picture of science is realistic in the sense that it allows for genuine correspondences between the natural world and the various representational devices deployed by scientists. Yet rationality does not appear in this picture—at least not the sort of rationality one finds in the writings of Aristotle, or in Enlightenment glorifications of science, or in the writings of many historical philosophers of science. That is primarily what makes my picture "naturalistic".

For Aristotle, rationality was an essential characteristic of humanity. Humans were defined as rational animals. In the Christian era, rationality became a property of the soul, thus making it possible later to argue the legitimacy of subjugating African slaves, and women, on the grounds that they lacked a rational soul. Since Darwin, however, the idea that there are essential characteristics of anything but abstract entities has been under constant attack. Humans, we now think, are born with capacities to develop various cognitive and sensory-motor abilities, but there are no genes for rationality over and above the genes that determine natural cognitive potentialities. So what can now be meant by attributing rationality to a scientist?

The only remaining legitimate use for the concept of rationality, I think, is in discussing the effective use of appropriate means to achieve desired goals. Then we can label as "irrational" people who employ manifestly inappropriate means in attempts to attain their goals. But this labeling has little to do with understanding how science is done. What is important are the goals of various scientific inquiries and the appropriateness of the methods used to achieve them.

Take, for example, the goal of determining whether antioxidants, such as Vitamin E, prevent heart attacks. We know that randomized clinical trials are more reliable than prospective studies for this purpose because they are more effective at eliminating alternative causal explanations for observed differences in the incidence of heart attacks in different groups of subjects. In general, the desirable characteristics of scientific methods are things like reliability, discrimination, efficiency, sensitivity, and robustness. Once one has determined the superiority of a given method in these terms, nothing of substance is added by labeling it more rational.

In rationality we have another concept that is long overdue for a sustained historical deconstruction. What historical research will reveal, I suspect, is a social construct that has served various interests in various historical contexts. In this vein, one wonders what interests have been served by the vigorous philosophical defenses of rationality and rational progress developed since the 1960s. My suspicion is that among the interests served has been the autonomy of the philosophy of science itself. Scientists investigate the effectiveness of various experimental techniques; historians record the progress made; but only philosophers get to pronounce these as rational or not. Ironically, many philosophers of science have been attacking social constructivism in the sociology of science in the name of their own social construct: rationality.

6. A Vision of Science Studies

Debates across disciplinary divides bear a discouraging resemblance to debates in politics and other areas of the public arena. Opposing views are reduced to simple stereotypes, and the point of debate is too often not understanding the subject matter, and certainly not understanding the opposing views, but maintaining one's disciplinary integrity. Thus one finds philosophers of science describing social constructivism as the view that "scientists produce the world" (Roth and Barrett 1990, 591). A reverse stereotype is a naive rationalism which portrays "scientific knowledge as the simple result of human rationality's encounter with reality" (MacKenzie 1990, 342). A vision of science studies that overcomes such stereotypes could produce a far richer picture of science than anyone now possesses.

I have already said that one of our goals should be understanding how science succeeds, when it does. This is admittedly contentious, though I have left open many possible different accounts of what constitutes success and how it is achieved. Less contentious is the view of science as a highly complex activity, at least as complex as the reality it investigates. This great complexity implies, I think, that it is impossible to obtain an adequate overall picture of science from any one disciplinary perspective. Different perspectives highlight different aspects while ignoring others. The only adequate overall pictures will be collages of pictures from various perspectives. There can be no uniquely adequate collage, but some may be put together with more skill and sensitivity than others, and may therefore be more enlightening than others—at least for some purposes.

In my picture, science studies cannot be autonomous. Its inquiries must draw on knowledge from many disciplines, including some of the sciences it studies. But is there a special role for the philosopher of science in this enterprise? Yes and no. Current training in the philosophy of science prepares one to be a good synthesizer of scientific knowledge and to use this knowledge in constructing theoretical models of various aspects of science. It also prepares one to raise normative issues, that is, to be critical of specific scientific projects in light of acquired empirical knowledge of how science typically works. And it prepares one to take part in debates over the role of science in the larger society. On the other hand, none of these activities are ones that could not also be carried out by historians or sociologists of science, or even scientists themselves, should they be so inclined. Just as philosophy can no longer claim to be queen of the sciences, neither can philosophy of science claim to be queen of science studies. But so long as we are willing to put aside our pretensions to possessing autonomous forms of knowledge, philosophers of science have much to contribute to the larger enterprise.

Notes

[1]For Dewey's views on these issues, the best single work is probably his Logic: *The Theory of Inquiry* (1938). For a broader view of Dewey's work at that time, see Schilpp and Hahn (1939).

[2]For some recent contributions to this literature, and further references, see Giere and Richardson (1996). My afterword to this volume (Giere 1996) includes an expanded version of the following remarks.

[3]Another version appears in Karl Popper's *Logik der Forschung* (1935), but this version had little influence before publication of the revised English edition in 1959 under the misleading title, *The Logic of Scientific Discovery*.

[4]One must here recall how vicious and personal the attacks on Einstein by Nazi sympathizers were in early 1933 (Clark 1971). Einstein himself was in the United

States when Hitler came to power and shortly thereafter resigned his posts from the safety of his temporary residence in Belgium. He did not return to Germany. Reichenbach, by contrast, remained in Berlin long enough to experience first hand the attacks on his patron.

[5]Gerald Holton for example, has recently written on the influence of Mach in America (1992) and "The Vienna Circle in Exile" (Forthcoming), which was organized by Philip Frank at Harvard from the late 1930s through the 1950s. My question would be why Frank's group had so little influence on the strain of Logical Empiricism that got institutionalized as professional philosophy of science in succeeding years. For a more general cultural history of the period, including specific reference to Reichenbach, see Hollinger (Forthcoming).

[6]Here I must note that philosophers of biology have been among those taking the history of science most seriously. The original leaders in the new philosophy of biology, such as David Hull and Michael Ruse, have also produced genuinely historical studies. This tradition continues.

[7]David Hollinger (1983) has traced the evolution of Merton's paper from its origins as a contribution to anti-fascist movements in the United States during the 1930s and 1940s to its emergence as a founding document for the development of sociology of science as a distinct field within sociology.

[8]Philosophical readers may notice many parallels between epistemological constructivism in sociology of science and van Fraassen's (1980) constructive empiricism in the philosophy of science.

[9]Skepticism regarding the usefulness of the concept of a universal law of nature for understanding science may be found in works of Cartwright (1983) and van Fraassen (1989), as well as my own (Giere 1988, 1995).

References

Carnap. R. (1937), *The Logical Syntax of Language*. London: Routledge & Kegan Paul.

Cartwright, N. (1983), *How the Laws of Physics Lie*. Oxford: Clarendon Press.

Collins, H.M. and Pinch, J.T. (1982), *Frames of Meaning*. London: Routledge & Kegan Paul.

Collins, H. and Yearley, S. (1992), "Epistemological Chicken", in A. Pickering, (ed.), Science as Practice and Culture. Chicago: Univ. of Chicago Press, pp. 283-300.

Dewey, J. (1938), *Logic: The Theory of Inquiry.* New York: Holt.

Giere, R.N. (1988), *Explaining Science: A Cognitive Approach*. Chicago: Univ. of Chicago Press.

_ _ _ _ _ _ _. (1995), "Science Without Laws of Nature", in F. Weinert, (ed.), Laws of Nature. Hawthorne, NY: Walter de Gruyter.

_ _ _ _ _ _ _. (1996), "From Wissenschaftliche Philosophie to Philosophy of Science", in R. N. Giere and A. Richardson, (eds.), The Origins of Logical Empiricism, Minnesota Studies in the Philosophy of Science, Vol. 16. Minneapolis: University of Minnesota Press.

Giere, R.N. and Richardson, A. (eds.) (1996), *Origins of Logical Empiricism,* Minnesota Studies in the Philosophy of Science, Vol. 16. Minneapolis: University of Minnesota Press.

Hacking, I. (1983), *Representing and Intervening*. Cambridge: Cambridge University Press.

Harding, S. (1986), *The Science Question in Feminism*. Ithaca: Cornell University Press.

Hatfield, G. (1990), *The Natural and the Normative: Theories of Perception from Kant to Helmholtz*. Cambridge: MIT Press.

Hollinger, D.A. (1983), "The Defense of Democracy and Robert K. Merton's Formulation of the Scientific Ethos", *Knowledge and Society*, 4:1-15.

_ _ _ _ _ _ _ _ _ . (Forthcoming), "Science as a Weapon in Kulturkämpfe in the United States During and After World War II", *Isis*.

Holton, G. (1992), "Ernst Mach and the Fortunes of Positivism in America", Isis 83:27-60.

Holton, G. (Forthcoming), "On the Vienna Circle in Exile: An Eyewitness Report", in F. Stadler, (ed.), Yearbook: Vienna Circle Lecture Series, Boston: Kluwer.

Kuhn, T.S. (1962), *The Structure of Scientific Revolutions.* Chicago: University of Chicago Press (2nd ed. 1970).

Lakoff, G. (1987), *Women, Fire, and Dangerous Things: What Categories Reveal About the Mind*. Chicago: University of Chicago Press.

Lakatos, I. (1970), "Falsification and the Methodology of Scientific Research Programmes", in I. Lakatos and A. Musgrave, (eds.), *Criticism and the Growth of Knowledge*. Cambridge: Cambridge University Press, pp. 91-195.

_ _ _ _ _ _. (1971), "History of Science and its Rational Reconstructions", in R. C. Buck and R. S. Cohen, (eds.), *Boston Studies in the Philosophy of Science*, Vol. 8. Dordrecht: Reidel.

Latour, B. and Woolgar, S. (1979), *Laboratory Life.* Beverly Hills: Sage.

Laudan, L. (1977), *Progress and Its Problems*. Berkeley: Univ. of California Press.

_ _ _ _ _ _. (1987), "Progress or Rationality? The Prospects for Normative Naturalism", *American Philosophical Quarterly* 24:19-31.

MacKenzie, D. (1990), *Inventing Accuracy: A Historical Sociology of Nuclear Missile Guidance*. Cambridge: MIT Press.

McMullin, E. (1970), "The History and Philosophy of Science: A Taxonomy", in R. Stuewer, (ed.), *Historical and Philosophical Perspectives of Science*, Minnesota Studies in the Philosophy of Science, Vol. 5. Minneapolis: University of Minnesota Press, pp. 12-67.

Merton, R.K. (1973), *The Sociology of Science*, ed. N. Storer. New York: Free Press.

Pickering, A. (1984), *Constructing Quarks: A Sociological History of Particle Physics*. Chicago: University of Chicago Press.

Popper, K.R. (1935), *Logic der Forschung: Zur Erkenntnistheorie der Modernen Naturwissenschaft*. Vienna: Julius Springer.

________. (1959), *The Logic of Scientific Discovery*. London: Hutchinson.

Putnam, H. (1981), *Reason, Truth, and History.* Cambridge: Cambridge University Press.

Reichenbach, H. (1936), "Logistic Empiricism in Germany and the Present State of its Problems", *The Journal of Philosophy*, 33:141-60.

__________. (1938), *Experience and Prediction.* Chicago: University of Chicago Press.

Roth, P. and R. Barrett (1990), "Deconstructing Quarks", *Social Studies of Science* 20:579-632.

Shapere, D. (1984), *Reason and the Search for Knowledge*. Dordrecht: Reidel.

Schilpp, P.A. and Hahn, L.E. (eds.) (1939), *The Philosophy of John Dewey.* La Salle, IL: Open Court.

Toulmin, S. (1972), *Human Knowledge*. Princeton: Princeton University Press.

van Fraassen, B.C. (1980), *The Scientific Image*. Oxford: Oxford University Press.

___________. (1989), *Laws and Symmetry*. Oxford: Oxford University Press.

Woolgar, S. (1988a), *Science: The Very Idea*. London: Tavistock.

______. (ed.) (1988b), *Knowledge and Reflexivity: New Frontiers in the Sociology of Knowledge*. London: Sage Publications.

Part II

PHILOSOPHY OF PSYCHOLOGY AS PHILOSOPHY OF SCIENCE

Philosophy of Psychology as Philosophy of Science

Gary Hatfield

University of Pennsylvania

The spirit of the papers that follow, reflecting the title of the original symposium, is to treat the philosophy of psychology as a branch of the philosophy of science. As such, philosophy of psychology is to be conceived on a parallel with philosophy of physics and philosophy of biology, as an instance of the "philosophy of the special sciences." The philosophy of the special sciences treats each of the sciences as potentially having its own explanatory structures, conceptual problems, and evidentiary relations, which may be more or less similar to those once discussed under "general philosophy of science," with its typical reliance on examples from physics. In this connection, work in the philosophy of psychology over the past two decades has analyzed the structure of psychological explanations (Cummins 1983; Hardcastle 1992; Haugeland 1978), has examined the conceptual issues attending such notions as that of representation (Dretske 1981; Hatfield 1988b; Lloyd 1989; Shapiro 1993) or qualitative experiential content (Dennett 1991; Hardin 1988), and has examined the theoretical structure and explanatory possibilities of the new connectionism (Horgan and Tienson 1991; Ramsey et al. 1991). Such work in philosophy of psychology takes seriously the concepts, theories, and practices of the experimental psychology pursued by working scientific psychologists.

If the truth be told, though, much of what goes under the title of "philosophy of psychology" has only a tenuous relation, if any, to actual scientific psychology. In some cases this arises innocently and understandably from the equivocal use this label permits: some philosophers use the title "philosophy of psychology" as a catch-all for problems in philosophy of mind. In other cases, philosophers have appealed to results in scientific psychology to speak to questions in metaphysics, epistemology, philosophy of mind, and even philosophy of science, without making psychology an object of analysis in its own right: Goldman (1986, 1993) uses psychology in his work on epistemology, Thagard (1988) and Solomon (1992) use psychology to explain scientific cognition, recent work on color marshals psychological findings to support claims about color ontology (Hilbert 1987), and many discussions in the Putnam/Fodor functionalist literature aimed to elucidate the mind-body problem, rather than the concepts, theories, or practices of scientific psychology (Kim 1972; Putnam 1967). These are all legitimate instances of drawing on recent science to advance work on a traditional philosophical problem, much as a philosopher interested in causation might turn to physics or chemistry for instances of causal laws.

PSA 1994, Volume 2, pp. 19-23

Unfortunately, though, a great part of the literature in philosophy of psychology from the past fifteen years falls into another category, that of pretendingÚ to be about "scientific psychology" without actually being so. In the literature I have in mind, philosophers make a pretense of adjudicating the actuality or possibility of a scientific psychology, but without engaging the extant scientific psychology in any serious manner. Perhaps the most striking example of such abuse has been the raging controversy over folk psychology, in which bold claims were made about the possibility, or, more usually, the impossibility, of scientific psychology (Churchland 1986; Stich 1983). These claims have usually pivoted on the question of whether so-called "folk psychology"—the allegedly "everyday" psychology that seeks to explain behavior via attributions of beliefs and desires—can meet the rigorous standards of natural science. Almost never were any actual psychological results discussed or even mentioned, as one was invited to speculate on the capacities of "Mrs. T" (Stich 1983, Chap. 4), or to judge whether folk psychology was such a bad "theory" that the research program of mentalistic psychology was destined to go the way of vitalist biology (Churchland 1986, Chaps. 7, 9). On the same battlefield raged the contest over "wide" and "narrow" content, presented as a question about whether psychology could be "scientific" only if it eschewed genuine distal content and stuck to states defined by their causal role within a system, the classic "functionalist" mental states of Putnam/Fodor functionalism (Fodor 1980). Again, grand claims were made about the possibility or impossibility of theories of representational content, but these claims were based on ethereal, otherworldly twin examples (Fodor 1987), with, at best, citation of extant psychological theory in an appeal to authority (Burge 1986), unaccompanied by philosophical analysis of the cited theory. And yet this literature had the patina of philosophy of science, because it invoked criteria such as explanatory generality or causal explanatory efficacy. It was truly philosophy of science without the science, or what my former and now late colleague David Sachs used to call "philosophy of science fiction."

The conclusions found in this literature regarding the impossibility of scientific psychology are limited in their force because the arguments backing them neglect actual scientific psychology. Thus, the eliminative materialist arguments presented in Churchland (1986) were aimed at the folk psychology of other philosophers, but did not at all engage extant perceptual and cognitive psychology (Hatfield 1988a). More seriously, the entire project of evaluating folk psychology is based on an unexamined assumption about the subject matter and object of explanation of psychology: the assumption, apparently left over from the heyday of behaviorism past, that the aim of psychology is to explain and predict behavior, updated to include attributions of beliefs and desires in the explanans (Davidson 1973). A question worthy of attention now in philosophy of psychology is that of the very subject matter and object of explanation of the science. Does psychology try to explain behavior, or does it rather use behavior as a form of evidence for studying the psychological capacities of organisms and the mechanisms that underlie them? If it were seeking to explain individual behaviors, it would be undertaking a project similar to that of a fictional discipline of physics that sought to predict and explain the behavior of individual physical objects, such as a leaf falling from a tree of anyone's choosing. But even when psychology was considered the science of behavior, the effective aim was to discover behavioral laws, not to explain free-standing individual behavior. In any event, analysis of actual work in contemporary perceptual and cognitive psychology suggests that in these central areas of experimental psychology the aim is to analyze perceptual and cognitive capacities rather than to formulate behavioral laws (Hatfield, 1991; von Eckardt, 1984). Moreover, those laws found in experimental psychology need not be behavioral. Consider Emmert's Law relating perceived size to visual angle and perceived distance (Goldstein 1989, 250-251). It pertains to the phenomenal content of perception, not to behavior; it is an empirical generalization describing lawful relations among percepts. As such, it is a candidate for explanation by appeal to the functional organization of the psychological processes underlying size and distance perception.

The agenda reflected in the papers that follow is not to replace philosophy of mind with philosophy of psychology or to imply criticism of philosophers who apply results from psychology to epistemology or another area. Rather, it is to provide examples of philosophy of psychology treated as a branch of the philosophy of science. This sort of philosophy of psychology attends to questions that arise from scientific practice, engages in the analysis of actual scientific concepts, dissects living scientific theories considered in relation to the data that support them and in relation to genuine (i.e., actually existing or able to exist) theoretical alternatives. Examples of the sorts of topics it might treat are given in the following "table of contents" of an imaginary anthology in philosophy of psychology as philosophy of science.

Table of contents for imaginary anthology in philosophy of psychology

Philosophy of Psychology
(as a branch of the philosophy of science)

I. The subject matter and object of explanation of psychology

1. Is psychology a science of behavior?
2. The study of cognitive capacities and mental mechanisms
3. Developmental and social psychology: Behavior or cognitive structure?

II. Theories and theoretical concepts in psychology

4. Mental images and experiential content
5. Representation and narrative in theories of memory
6. How do the theoretical concepts of psychology relate to those of neuroscience?

III. Explanation in psychology

7. Explanation: Covering law model vs. systematic explanations
8. Are mentalistic concepts ineliminable from psychological explanation?
9. Mental mechanisms as explanations of cognitive capacities

IV. Theory and evidence

10. Behavior: object of explanation or form of evidence?
11. Does neurophysiological data place firmer constraints on psychological theorizing than behavioral observation?
12. Experimental design and the structure of psychological explanation

V. Social and cultural factors in psychology

13. Natural scientific psychology and the mind as a cultural product
14. The cultural background to thought and problem solving
15. Social perception and social knowledge

References

Burge, T. (1986), "Individualism and Psychology", *Philosophical Review* 95:3-45.

Churchland, P.S. (1986), *Neurophilosophy: Toward a Unified Science of the Mind-Brain*. Cambridge: MIT Press.

Cummins, R. (1983), *The Nature of Psychological Explanation*. Cambridge: MIT Press.

Davidson, D. (1973), "The Material Mind", in P. Suppes (ed.), *Logic, Methodology and Philosophy of Science* IV. Amsterdam: North-Holland.

Dennett, D.C. (1991), *Consciousness Explained*. Boston: Little, Brown and Co.

Dretske, F.I. (1981), *Knowledge and the Flow of Information*. Cambridge: MIT Press.

Fodor, J. A. (1980), "Methodological Solipsism Considered as a Research Strategy in Cognitive Psychology", *Behavioral and Brain Sciences* 3:63-109.

_______. (1987), *Psychosemantics: The Problem of Meaning in the Philosophy of Mind*. Cambridge: MIT Press.

Goldman, A.I. (1986), *Epistemology and Cognition*. Cambridge: Harvard University Press.

________. (1993), *Philosophical Applications of Cognitive Science*. Boulder: Westview Press.

Goldstein, E.B. (1989), *Sensation and Perception*, 3d ed. Belmont: Wadsworth.

Hardcastle, V.G. (1992), "Reduction, Explanatory Extension, and the Mind/Brain Sciences", *Philosophy of Science* 59:408-428.

Hardin, C.L. (1988), *Color for Philosophers: Unweaving the Rainbow*. Indianapolis: Hackett Pub. Co.

Hatfield, G. (1988a), "Neuro-Philosophy Meets Psychology: Reduction, Autonomy, and Physiological Constraints", *Cognitive Neuropsychology* 5:723-746.

_______. (1988b), "Representation and Content in Some (Actual) Theories of Perception", *Studies in History and Philosophy of Science* 19:175-214.

_______. (1991), "Representation in Perception and Cognition: Connectionist Affordances", in Ramsey et al. (1991), pp. 163-195.

Haugeland, J. (1978), "The Nature and Plausibility of Cognitivism", *Behavioral and Brain Sciences* 1:215-260.

Hilbert, D.R. (1987), *Color and Color Perception*. Stanford: Center for the Study of Language and Information.

Horgan, T. and Tienson, J. (eds.) (1991), *Connectionism and the Philosophy of Mind*. Dordrecht: Kluwer.

Kim, J. (1972), "Phenomenal Properties, Psychophysical Laws, and the Identity Theory", *Monist* 56:177-192.

Lloyd, D.E. (r1989), *Simple Minds*. Cambridge: MIT Press.

Putnam, H. (1967), "The Mental Life of Machines", in Hector-Neri Castañeda (ed.), *Intentionality, Minds, and Perception*. Detroit: Wayne State University Press, pp. 177-200.

Ramsey, W., Stich, S.P., and Rumelhart, D.E. (eds.) (1991), *Philosophy and Connectionist Theory*. Hillsdale: L. Erlbaum Associates.

Shapiro, L.A. (1993), "Content, Kinds, and Individualism in Marr's Theory of Vision", *Philosophical Review* 102:489-513.

Solomon, M. (1992), "Scientific Rationality and Human Reasoning", *Philosophy of Science* 59:439-455.

Stich. S.P. (1983), *From Folk Psychology to Cognitive Science: The Case against Belief*. Cambridge: MIT Press.

Thagard, P.R. (1988), *Computational Philosophy of Science*. Cambridge: MIT Press.

von Eckardt, B. (1984), "Cognitive Psychology and Principled Skepticism", *Journal of Philosophy* 81:67-88.

Philosophy of Psychology Meets the Semantic View

Valerie Gray Hardcastle

Virginia Polytechnic Institute and State University

Philosophers of science have much to say that could be useful to philosophers of mind, especially naturalistic philosophers of psychology. We should listen. In particular, I believe that if philosophers of mind were clearer on how explanations function in science in general, then many of their present worries would either dissolve or be altered beyond recognition. In what follows, I show you what I mean.

First, though, I shall spend a few moments recapitulating the semantic view of theories and how it applies to psychology. This section will be fairly brief since details have already been presented elsewhere (see esp. Bickle 1993). However, let me emphasize at the outset that I am not adopting the semantic view because I think it is inherently superior to the more traditional models (though I do). Indeed, everything that I claim can be translated into any view of theory you might have with greater or lesser ease. Instead, I chose the semantic view because it highlights certain features of theories that will be important for the discussion to come.

This discussion comprises the bulk of my paper. I have selected two popular positions in philosophy of psychology (or, at least, two positions held by popular philosophers of psychology) that are untenable because they assume an outmoded view of scientific explanation: Searle's (1992) distinction between observer-relative and intrinsic features of the world and Davidson's (1980) defense of anomalous monism. Both of these positions, if correct, would impact how we conceive of psychological theories relative to the rest of science significantly. If Searle is correct, then any computational theory would be purely instrumentalist; if Davidson is correct, then while psychology would not be instrumentalist, it would be discontinuous with the rest of science. If they are incorrect, however, that would be grist for my mill that psychology is just another science, with much of the same power and many of the same difficulties.

1. The Semantic View

Not surprisingly, there are many different versions of the semantic view, distinguishable by the type of mathematical system used to formalize theories. In general, though, the semantic view holds theories to be abstract pictures of relations among variables. A picture with all of its parameters fixed is a model. Each theory has several (maybe indefinitely many) models, and we can think of a model as representing one of the possible worlds allowed by the theory. These models range in the amount of empirical or semantic content, from highly abstract, purely formal models to de-

PSA 1994, Volume 2, pp. 24-34

tailed sets of observed phenomena and their relations. What links the models together as a single theory is their common mathematical structure.[1]

This view of theories highlights the fact that scientists do not apply theoretical laws directly to observed or hypothesized phenomena; instead, they use laws (defined as a theoretical model) to explain the behavior of physical systems abstracted from observations (an empirical model) by correlating the appearance of the world with the empirical and theoretical models via structural isomorphism. A successful correlation leads scientists to identify the attributes of the abstract systems with properties in the real world, thereby explaining them in terms of the posited laws.

It will be important to keep in mind that scientists have no intention of accounting for all the details of their subject matter when they construct their models. For they create even the rich empirical models by abstracting a small number of parameters away from some collection of observed phenomena. Scientists regularly disregard the complexities of the actual world and define artificial domains isomorphic to the world in only a few aspects. Scientists calculate the behavior of these abstract systems, which they then use in explaining interactions in the actual world.

Which parameters are chosen as important in theory-building depends on the sort of explanation required. In particular, model choice turns on various pragmatic considerations because explanations are inherently pragmatic. Explanations answer why-questions of the form 'Why G_k?',[2] which are elliptical for the question 'Why G_k and not G_a, G_b, G_c, ... ?'. These elliptical questions are then asked against a background context K, which contains at least the propositions accepted by the interested scientific community. A question is genuine if K implies G_k or the proposition that (G_k &, for all $i \neq k$, $\sim G_i$). That is, questions of the form "Why G_k?" are appropriate against context K, if the topic of that sentence is true, and if all members of the contrast class are false. (This formulation is a simplification of van Fraassen 1980.)

The essence of this conception of explanation is that explanations form a three-way relation among theories, data, and context. Exactly how to specify the relations involved is beyond the scope and interest of the paper; all we need to note is that whether something counts as an explanation depends at least upon the goals of individual inquiry, the audience for whom the explanation is directed, the history of the study, and so on, for these determine K and thereby the contrast class. Explanations differ as each of the constraining factors differ. Similarly, the models used in the explanations are not immune from pragmatic considerations either. Which model is appropriate in answering a why-question depends upon the choice of contrast class, which again in turn depends upon the actors and their presumed audience as well as the history of the question.

To summarize: theories represent abstract physical systems, pared down and idealized versions of some aspect of the world. As a result, scientists operate two removes from actual appearances, and they focus on building models by correlating sets of data. The corresponding laws in the theoretical models are sensitive only to these correlations, which may or may not correspond to how the world actually functions in all its messy details. In addition, which physical system is abstracted, which model is used, and which explanation is ultimately given turns on local social and historical facts. A correct answer is one that is appropriate for a given community at a certain time with particular needs.

I take it that these two facts about scientific theories—that theories aren't about the world simpliciter and that theoretical models and their concomitant explanations are heavily pragmatic—are well known by now. Psychological theories are no exception either; they fit the mold of the semantic view of theories quite nicely (see also Bickle 1993). To illustrate, let us take the particular example of Anne Treisman's feature-integration hypothesis (Treisman 1986). (In what follows I rely on set-theoretic notation, though what I say can be translated into other formulations.)

The two basic features of her feature-integration hypothesis are:

(FI1) Preattentive processing, a relatively early stage in sensory processing, occurs in parallel, without attention, and automatically. It merely registers which features are present in the sensory field, though it may not register their locations.

(FI2) Focused attention, the next stage in sensory processing, occurs serially, requires attention, and with conscious subject involvement. It selects which features belong together as a unit via a master map of locations.

To simplify my presentation, I only use time and a master map of locations as the defining characteristics for the processes involved in feature integration.

We can define the predicate, "is a model of feature-integration (FI)," as:

x is a model of FI ($x \in M(\text{FI})$) iff
(1) $x = <S, F, O, L, T, \Re, P, A>$
(2) S is a finite, possibly empty set
(3) F is a finite, possibly empty set
(4) O is a finite, possibly empty set
(5) L is a singleton set
(6) T is a finite, ordered, non-empty set $<t_1, t_2, t_3, \ldots >$
(7) P: $\exists (t_1)(t_1$ and $S^* \longrightarrow F^*$ where $S^* \subseteq S$ and $F^* \subseteq F)$
(8) A: $\forall o_i \in O^*$ where $O^* \subseteq O(F^{\#} \times L = o_i$ where $F^{\#} \subseteq F^*$ and $O^* \times T$
$\longrightarrow \Re+)$

On the intended application of FI, S is the set of possible sensory input a subject could receive, F is the set of possible features present to the subject, O is set of the possible representation(s) of the final object (or objects), L is the master map of locations, T is the set of time instances, P is the preattentive processing relation from a proper subset of stimuli input to a set of features, and A is the focused attention processing relation from a proper subset of the set of features to the set of perceived objects.

Notice that this model also fits a version of the Shiffrin-Schneider distinction between controlled and automatic processing (Schneider and Shiffrin 1977, Shiffrin and Schneider 1977). On this application of FI, S is the set of possible sensory input a subject could receive, F is the set of possible object/action memory schemas, O is set of the possible memories of objects, L is the attentional mechanism, T is the set of time instances, P is the automatic detection processing relation from a proper subset of stimuli input to a set of objects or action memory schemas, and A is the controlled search processing relation from a proper subset of the set of object or action schemas to the set of perceived object memories. In my simplified presentation, the same model represents two different hypotheses (that is, the structure of the two hypotheses are the same) and hence the two hypotheses are actually of the same theory.

This model can then be used to answer the following sorts of questions: 'Why did Mick see an orange carrot and a blue lake, and not a blue carrot and an orange lake?' ('Why did o_1 occur at t_1 and o_2 occur at t_2, and not o_3 at t_1 and o_4 at t_2?') 'Why is Keith faster at recognizing the letter E presented among a display of numbers (after learning that as a target letter) than if it is presented among a display of other letters?' ('Why did f_i, where $f_i \in F$, occur at t_i and o_1 occur at $t_j > t_i$?') The answer to the first is that a triangular shape and an orange color occurred at the same place on the master map of locations, while a circle and a blue color occurred at a different location. Hence, attentional processing would bind the triangle with the orange and the circle with the blue.[3] The answer to the second is that recognizing a letter among digits requires only automatic processing, while recognizing a particular letter among letters requires controlled processing. (This answer just falls out of the model itself.)

These two questions and their answers exemplify of the types of problems involved in explaining visual processing; however, they are problems that concern two different psychological communities.[4] The first question contrasts seeing one particular arrangement of features with seeing a very different arrangement of the same features, while the second contrasts the speed of processing information across categories with the speed of processing information within a category. The contrast class of the first question (a different mix of the same features) simply would not arise for Shiffrin and Schneider because (for historical reasons that need not detain us here) their community was more interested in explaining the perceptual categories one uses than how object representations are constructed. Similarly, the contrast class of the second question would not occur in (this version of) Treisman's community because it concerns abstractions beyond the concatenation of features that she is interested in. Let us now put this machinery to use.

2. Searle's Observer-Relative Facts

John Searle has recently argued that information processing models in psychology cannot be part of the natural sciences because:

> The aim of natural science is to discover and characterize features that are intrinsic to the natural world. By its own definitions of computation and cognition, there is no way that computational cognitive science could ever be a natural science because computation is not an intrinsic feature of the world. It is assigned relative to observers. (1992, 212)

This is by now a fairly standard objection to computational models: computation is not a natural kind, so theories that parse the world on the basis of computational notions do not pick out fundamental bits of the universe (see, e.g., Kripke 1981, Stabler 1987). If correct, then psychology would be hampered greatly, for most theories of the mind these days at least have pretenses of being computational. And if assigning mathematical functions to a system is not a legitimate move in science, then computational theories of mind aren't scientific.[5]

It should be immediately obvious though from the discussion of the semantic view above that this simple objection to computationalism can't work. For insofar as all theories are sets of mathematically described structures, then all theories would fall prey to this alleged difficulty. However, we can generalize Searle's complaint to any model. To wit: using the history of the inquiry, the immediate concerns of the community, and other accepted theories, scientists *decide* what to count as the boundaries of any system, which parameters are the relevant ones in the system so bounded, what the tolerable levels of errors are for correlating the empirical models with sets of data, and so on. Indeed, what scientists try to correlate are mathematical structures and *their own observations*. As a result, the application of any model (even those from physics) to observational phenomena hinges fundamentally on the observer.

What Searle et al. miss is that classic (and perhaps intuitively plausible) accounts of theorizing cannot determine which factors are important to preserve in abstractions and which are irrelevant for any particular case. If we observe a subject reporting orange carrots and blue lakes while seated in a room with fluorescent lights, we are not inclined to say that the light causes the subject's responses. Even though we could give some "explanation" of that behavior from the instantiation of definitions (7) and (8) above by this subject seated under a fluorescent light, we would still maintain that neither the light nor the chair are relevant factors in determining that this system "computes" the equations. In an abstraction of the event that includes only the physical facts needed for theorizing about feature integration in subjects, the light and the chair would be absent.

Any good hypothesis should pick out only the pertinent components operating in the event to be explained. The pragmatics of explanation does exactly that. The community in which the question occurs sets the contrast class, which (partially) defines the factors germane for theorizing. Treisman's community of inquiry contrasts one set of features with another, not one lighting environment with another. Hence, explanations that include these sorts of contextual features would be inappropriate. Local social and historical biases determine what psychologists designate as the correct abstractions from the world in order to assign computational models, just as in any science.

What counts as a natural kind and what doesn't turns on the scope of individual theories and not anything more "out there" in the "real world." Theories are interpreted to make universal statements about the set of possible objects which fall under the theory. These sets of possible objects form the classes of natural kinds. Theories involving psychological properties might encompass things like living creatures, or chordate organisms, or mammals, or humans and primates, or just *Homo Sapiens*. Regardless, as long as these sets are describable by proper lists of natural attributes, they can be subsumed by the laws of some theoretical system.

Nevertheless, Searle might still have a point. Intuitively, we want to say that some models represent aspects of the world correctly and others don't. However, if pragmatic considerations govern the choice of models, then there is no principled reason that we could not have chosen differently. Had the history of psychology gone otherwise, perhaps Treisman would care about fluorescent lights after all. In fact, properly gerrymandered and pruned, any set of observations could fit any model. We need a way to distinguish the broader notion of some system merely *satisfying* some mathematical model from *actual* computation, in which the system satisfies the model because it *really* approximates the equations in the model. Searle is trivially wrong about modern cognitive theories, for there is nothing special about computationalism per se. On the other hand, he inadvertently raises a deep issue in the application of models: *How do we decide which function (if any) some system is actually computing?*

Let us agree that there is no principled way of deciding which model best captures the activity of some system but that scientists still assign unique computational structures to the measured relations based on their own understanding of how the abstracted system dovetails with the background K. Let us further agree that these decisions depend on the historical circumstances of the inquiry, the technological limitations in measuring magnitudes, and the types of questions the scientists hope to address. Nevertheless, whether there are pragmatic reasons for the assignments we do make might be beside the point, because in principle we could have made a different assignment. Systems that really fit the hypothesized relations are subsets of systems that merely satisfy some mathematical model.[6] How are we to sort out this difference?

We need to be able to say that psychological subjects satisfy the equations that define the model *and* compute them as well. Following Shagrir (1991), I suggest the following: We assign mathematical models as *an explanatory strategy* in accounting for actual computing systems, while we do not for systems that merely satisfy models. In general, in accounting for the behavior of some psychological system, we answer the question, "Why G_1?" by answering the question, "How did G_1 occur?". That is, we explicate how the interaction of the system's basic components generated G_1 in order to explain why G_1 obtained and not the contrast class (G_2, G_3, G_4, . . .). So, in psychology, we explain why the system behaves the way it does by analyzing the capacities that produce G_1.

Hence, adopting the criterion of explanatory mathematical models in psychology essentially amounts to adopting the well-known and much discussed strategy of functional analysis or functional decomposition. Loosely speaking, *functionalism* is the view that the various states of some system can be understood in terms of their functional or causal role with respect to input to the system, the output from that system, and the other states within the system causally connected to the states to be explained. Correlatively, *functional analysis* is a type of explanation in which some system is decomposed into its component parts and the workings of the system are explained in terms of the capacities of the parts and the way the parts are integrated with one another. The component parts and their interactions are specified entirely in terms of causal relations. That is, the parts are picked out by their causal role in a stream of inputs to outputs, and they display that role in virtue of their causal or "functional" connections to other surrounding component parts.

For philosophy of psychology, the hope is that scientists can use this approach to dissolve many of the mysteries of our mind. Decomposing our mental faculties into primitive components should let us redescribe intentionally defined mental events in non-intentional terms. That way, any psychological explanation of our behavior or thoughts would beg no questions concerning what factors are actually responsible for our mental life, and we should be able to overcome any charges of latent *homunculi* actually performing the explanatory labor.

However, many philosophers mistakenly assume a stronger interpretation of functionalism and functional analysis than is warranted by the explanations. They are concerned to answer more than just, "Why G_1?"; in addition, they want to know, "What are G's?". Some take functionalism to be an ontological thesis, that *all there is* to some mental state are its causal relations to other states, inputs, and outputs (see, for example, Armstrong 1970, 1977; Lewis 1969, 1970, 1972; Smart 1959, 1971). The intuitions that guide these sorts of metaphysical claims are that a mental state's computational or functional role in the mental life of an individual fully determines what kind of mental event that state is, and that an explication of that relation in computational terms would exhaust the meanings of mental terms. A functional individuation of mental events would specify the essence of various mental states.

However, the methodological considerations mentioned above (in particular, the fact that determining which function a physical system is computing turns directly on practical decision-making) should force us to understand functionalism and functional analysis as purely *explanatory* theses: we can know a state only in virtue of its causal/computational relations. Given the centrality of pragmatic factors in building mathematical models, the best we can hope to say about any functionally defined state is that we understand it in virtue of a computational model, not that it and the model are equivalent. It is far better to remain agnostic about the true essence of cognizing and instead focus on how to describe it as fruitfully as possible.

Returning to the feature-integration hypothesis, we can see that it exemplifies an "explanatory" functional analysis in that, loosely speaking, what we need to know for our theories about feature integration is captured in definitions (1) through (8). It turns out that Treisman's hypothesis is a good, but not perfect, predictor of mistakes in feature integration. Her hypothesis suggests that when attention is divided, errors in assigning locations on the master map are likely to occur. To a first approximation, this is true. However, more integration errors occur across categorization or unitization boundaries than within (Prinzmetal 1981). For example, we are less likely to make an error integrating features within a word than we are integrating features across words. Nevertheless, Treisman's hypothesis still serves as a useful approximation for an admittedly more complex interaction, and usually we take it to be enough to capture and explain feature integration in our perceptual system. Even though we know that, strictly speaking, the hypothesis is wrong, we still use it in explaining perception for pragmatic reasons. We could add various bells and whistles to definition (8) to take into account the effect of top-down processing, but to do so might complicate the definition beyond its usefulness. It is preferable to claim that (8) "satisfices" because it gives us useful information in exchange for relatively minor labor. It doesn't capture precisely what we know actually occurs, but it is good enough to get the epistemological job done.

In sum, then, a functional analysis in philosophical psychology refers to a specific type of explanatory strategy in which all we need in order to account for some system is a model of its internal computational/functional relations. Functional analyses in psychology are methodologies; whether a physical system is actually computing turns on whether the description of the computation explains that system. I have argued that whether the assignment of a mathematical model to a physical system counts as an explanation depends upon the contingent interests of the relevant community. Such pragmatic factors cannot ground any further metaphysical claims. Hence, Searle's complaint about the ontological status of computational systems is misguided. "Computational" systems are just like any other system under investigation—their explanations fundamentally turn on observer-relative features.[7]

3. Davidson's Anomalous Monism

Donald Davidson (and others[8]) holds that only strict or basic or exceptionless laws support causal interactions. That is, only things like the laws of particle physics can provide the nomologically sufficient conditions for true causal transactions. Psychological laws, even psychophysical laws, are neither strict, nor basic, nor exceptionless. They are used to relate sets of events only in conjunction with ceteris paribus clauses. Hence, they cannot support true causal interactions. Hence, mental properties qua mental are causally suspect (anomalous). Hence, the science of psychology is discontinuous with the rest of the natural sciences.

In response, Jerry Fodor (1989) had denied that "hedged laws can't ground mental causes" (72). Ceteris paribus laws engage in "serious scientific business" (73) because they hold nomologically whenever the ceteris paribus conditions are satisfied. The real difference between the more basic laws and the laws in psychology is that the latter requires additional mediating mechanisms in order to implement causal transactions, while the former does not.

Earnest LePore and Barry Loewer (1987, 1989) defend Davidson on the grounds that the lower level physical properties have ontological priority for the only way to have mental properties is via physiological properties: "The basic physical properties and laws determine both the causal relations among events and the non-basic [lawlike relations]" (1989, 187). Again, psychology would be discontinuous by being parasitic on the other, "more basic," sciences.

But this debate over ceteris paribus conditions and ontological priority is a red herring in psychology because, in point of fact, all theories rely on ceteris paribus hedges. The real difficulty is that Davidson, Fodor, and others rely upon a deficient notion of scientific explanation. It is simply erroneous to assume that the basic laws of physics (or any laws of any science) are not hedged in important and fundamental ways. As mentioned in section 1, scientists have no intention of accounting for all the intricacies of their subject matter. To take a clear example from "basic science," classical particle mechanics uses point-masses, velocities in frictionless environments, and distances traveled over time to characterize falling bodies. Theoretical physicists want to explain only the general pattern of behavior of moving objects; hence, they can rightly ignore the color of the body, the date of its falling, interference from gravitational attraction, and so on. They predict behavior based only on the position and momenta of extensionless points interacting in a vacuum.

We can see this same picture of how science works in the "softer" sciences as well. Chomskian theories of competence in linguistics, the Nernst equation in neurophysiology, the genetic theory of natural selection, and theories of attention in psychology, including Treisman's feature-integration hypothesis and the Shiffrin-Schneider distinction between automatic and controlled processing, all describe the behavior of abstract mechanisms under ideal conditions which only approximates the behavior of real phenomena in virtue of a few "fundamental" properties under normal conditions.

The description of what we actually observe must be altered such that we can talk about what we would have observed had only the few relevant parameters of the phenomena existed under ideal conditions. These revised observation statements are used in conjunction with the theoretical models to make predictions about the abstracted physical system. The predictions are then converted into statements about real appearances by just reversing the procedure for changing the original observation statements. In sum, the laws of psychology are no different from any more "basic" law of particle physics or QM. All sciences implicitly hedge their theories by making their laws concern only the abstract models. Theories in psychology and theories in physics are both devised to cover counterfactual versions of some aspect of the world. As a result, their corresponding laws are sensitive only to relations in the models, which may not correspond to actual appearances. Hence, we can see that whether and how ceteris paribus clauses or additional mediating mechanisms are wielded is inconsequential. The psychological "laws" found in definitions (7) and (8) are just as dependent upon abstraction, omission, and reconstruction as the law of gravity or the conservation of momentum.

However, even though Davidson, Fodor, et al. may be misguided, saying that psychological laws and theories are just like any other "more basic" physical law or theory does not answer the motivation behind Davidson's original discussion. Suppose that events c and e are subsumed by the psychological generalization *M* —> *N*. If we be materialists, then we would have to agree that for this particular instance of c and e, there is also a "more basic" generalization that likewise subsumes the events, perhaps idealized differently. How do we determine which generalization to privilege in building models? Saying that psychological laws are just like any other accepted scientific law is not enough. What would be?

Let me be clarify what I am asking. Above, I granted the revision of Searle's point that regularities are in the eyes of the beholder, and we can see them anywhere, and I assumed that in building a physical system, we pick out which regularity or regularities are especially salient. *How we pick* out these patterns is the question I am asking. What I wish to focus upon is what happens *before* the abstract systems are constructed and certain regularities highlighted. What I want to know is: *If it is the case that more than one physical system can subsume each particular set of observed events, then how do we know which physical system to use?* (Or are all equally applicable?) This is not just a question of which model best explains some regularity. Because different systems may subsume the same set of particular events differently—that is, because different systems may emphasize different aspects of the set and, as a result, may project their predicates differently—which *regularity* we should be talking about is the issue. Will psychological predicates end up being *effectively* anomalous in that physical systems defined over those sorts of predicates should not be used in explanation?

Let us return to the example of feature integration. Suppose Mick looks at a display and reports seeing an orange carrot and a blue lake. Without pretending that there are complete theories of feature integration in either psychology or neuroscience, let us see how we might explain this event. We might say something to the effect that Mick's attentional mechanism bound together a triangular shape with the color orange, or we might say something to the effect that the synchronous 40 Hz oscillations in the appropriate cortical neurons bind together the micro-features of the receptive fields of active neurons (Engel et al. 1991). Does focused attention better explain Mick's verbal behavior than synchronous 40 Hz oscillations, or vice versa?

The answer is not clear. Even though we are speaking of a particular instance of a verbal report, how to understand the explanation of that particular event depends upon how we would generalize Mick's behavior. If we take the verbal report to be a token of some conscious psychological event, then oscillating neurons add nothing to the explanation, since there are other means by which to integrate features. On the other hand, if we take the verbal report to be a reaction to neuronal firing patterns, then attention adds nothing to the explanation, since neurons can oscillate without attentional processes.

Not surprisingly, which generalization to use does not admit of a principled answer. If we have a reductive bias, then we might be inclined to generalize over nerve stimulations and brain chemistry . On the other hand, if we lack that sort of bias, then we might be inclined to talk about perceptions and awareness. And which sort of bias to have and what kind of generalizations are best cannot be decided a priori. It all depends upon facts peculiar to the circumstance. If one is teaching Mick how to decrease his reaction time using verbal reinforcement, then knowing that synchronous 40 Hz oscillations bind together active receptive fields may not be useful information. On the other hand, if we are trying to control Mick's perceptual experiences invasively, then understanding the neuronal firing patterns might be very relevant.

Just as Searle, Davidson fails to appreciate the constructivist process of science as well as its pragmatic aspects. Meditating on a well-developed philosophy of science helps to clear their conceptual confusions. However, ridding ourselves of their specific complaints only opens more sophisticated worries regarding how we generalize specific events and how we use those generalizations to build physical systems and abstract models. These questions can still be answered though by realizing that science is largely a social enterprise, and how and what we explain depends a great deal upon who is asking the question of whom and when.

Notes

[1]One should note that "model" here refers to a structure or set of relations. It is not an interpretation function; instead, it refers to the objects themselves that interpretation functions quantify over.

[2]There is some disagreement over whether all scientific explanations answer questions that can be put in the form of a why-question. I shall ignore this dispute in my presentation since its resolution will make no difference to the points I present.

[3]Of course, it is possible for our feature-integration systems to make mistakes, and how and why this occurs is quite interesting. However, taking this fact into consideration would complicate the model beyond what I need for my point. Suffice it to say that I am not giving Treisman's entire story here.

[4]Treisman's feature-integration hypothesis does account for other similar "pop-out" effects; however, they turn on the number of features processed (i.e., whether the map of locations is needed for an answer) instead of a hierarchy of semantic categorization.

[5]In this paper, I am using the notion of computation and of mathematical models interchangeably. This might be a mistake. However, insofar as truly computational models form a subset of mathematical ones, then my arguments should still go through.

[6]I don't intend this distinction to hinge on whether one is a realist. I take it that the problem of applying models is a real problem regardless of one's metaphysical stripe.

[7]This line of argument also works against other instrumentalist views in psychology, e.g., Dennett's intentional stance (Dennett 1987, 1992).

[8]E.g., Kim (1983, 1992a, b), LePore and Loewer (1987, 1989).

References

Armstrong, D.M. (1970), "The Nature of Mind", in C.V. Borst, (ed.), *The Mind/Brain Identity Theory*. London: Macmillan.

__________. (1977), "The Causal Theory of the Mind", *Neue Heft für Philosophie*. 11: 82-95.

Bickle, J. (1993), "Connectionism, Eliminativism, and the Semantic View of Theories", *Erkenntnis* 39: 359-382.

Davidson, D. (1980), *Essays on Actions and Events*. Oxford: Clarendon Press.

Dennett, D. (1987), *The Intentional Stance*. Cambridge, Massachusetts: The MIT Pres.

_______. (1992), *Explaining Consciousness*. Cambridge, Massachusetts: The MIT Press.

Engel, A.K., Konig, P., and Singer, W. (1991), "Direct Physiological Evidence for Scene Segmentation by Temporal Coding", *Proceedings of the National Academy of Sciences of the United States of America* 88: 9136-1940.

Fodor, J.A. (1989), "Making the Mind Matter More", *Philosophical Topics* 17: 59-80.

Kim, J. (1983) "Supervenience and Supervenient Causation", *Southern Journal of Philosophy* 22 (Suppl.): 54.

_____. (1992a) "'Downward Causation' in Emergence and Nonreductive Physicalism", in A. Beckerman, H. Flohr, and J. Kim, (eds.), Emergence or Reduction? *Essays on the Prospects of Nonreductive Physicalism.* New York: Walter de Gruyter, pp. 119-138.

_____. (1992b) "Multiple Realization and the Metaphysics of Reduction", *Philosophy and Phenomenological Research*, LII: 1-26.

Kripke, S. (1981), *Wittgenstein on Rules and Private Language*. New York: Oxford University Press.

LePore, E., and Loewer, B. (1987) "Mind Matters", *Journal of Philosophy* 84: 630-642.

_______________. (1989) "More on Making the Mind Matter", *Philosophical Topics* 17: 175-191.

Lewis, D. (1970), "How to Define Theoretical Terms", *Journal of Philosophy* 67: 427-444.

______. (1972), "Psychophysical and Theoretical Identification", *Australasian Journal of Philosophy* 50: 249-258.

______. (1969), "Review of Art, Mind and Religion", *Journal of Philosophy* 66: 23-35.

Prinzmetal, W. (1981), "Principles of Feature Integration in Visual Perception", *Perception and Psychophysics* 30: 330-340.

Schneider, W. and Shiffrin, R.M. (1977), "Controlled and Automatic Human Information Processing: I. Detection, Search, and Attention", *Psychological Review* 84: 1-66.

Shiffrin, R.M. and Schneider, W. (1977), "Controlled and Automatic Human Information Processing: II. Perceptual Learning, Automatic Attending, and General Theory", *Psychological Review* 84: 127-190.

Searle, J. (1992), *The Rediscovery of Mind.* Cambridge, Massachusetts: The MIT Press.

Shagrir, O. (1991), "Computation", unpublished manuscript.

Smart, J.J.C. (1959), "Sensations and Brain Processes", *Philosophical Review* 68: 141-156.

_______. (1971), "Reports of Immediate Experience", *Synthese* 22: 346-359.

Stabler, Jr., E.P. (1987), "Kripke on Functionalism and Automata", *Synthese* 70: 1-22.

Treisman, A. (1986), "Features and Objects in Visual Processing", *Scientific American* 254: 114b-125.

The Notion of Accuracy in Current Social Perception Research

Barbara Von Eckardt

University of Nebraska–Lincoln

1. Introduction

There are many different kinds of psychology: abnormal, behavioral, clinical, cognitive, developmental, physiological, personality, and social, to name some of the major categories. In recent years, philosophers of psychology (in the sense under discussion today) have focused primarily on cognitive psychology and Freudian psychoanalysis (which cross-cuts abnormal and personality). In this paper, I propose to turn my attention to one of the least discussed of these fields: social psychology. Specifically, I will consider a debate currently raging in the sub-field of social psychology known as "social perception research."

Social psychology is - to quote from a recent textbook - "the scientific study of the thoughts, actions, and interactions of individuals as affected by the actual, implied, or imagined presence of others... . The social emphasis distinguishes social psychology from [other fields of] psychology, and the emphasis on the individual distinguishes it from sociology" (Tedeschi, Lindskold, and Rosenfeld 1985, 4-5).

Social psychology encompasses many sub-fields or research areas. Among these is a sub-field called "social perception" whose aim is to discover how we ordinarily perceive, understand, and explain other people and their behavior (Zebrowitz 1990). In other words, social perception research attempts to empirically investigate aspects of what the psychologists call "naive psychology" and of what philosophers call "folk psychology." Three areas have received primary attention: impression formation, emotion perception, and causal attribution. My concern is with the impression formation literature.

In their everyday lives, people frequently form impressions of other people in the sense of attributing various traits to them. In other words, we often make judgments of the form:

Person P has trait T

on the basis of informal observation of behavior in real life settings. I will call such judgments "trait judgments." For example, we might judge that one of our colleagues is intelligent, energetic, has a good sense of humor, or is self-involved, etc. But how accurate are these judgments?

PSA 1994, Volume 2, pp. 35-46

Psychologists concerned with the study of accuracy have generally recognized that the empirical question of whether people are accurate raises a prior conceptual question, namely, what do we *mean* by saying that a person's judgment is accurate? It has also been noted that this conceptual question is closely related to the question of what we mean by saying that a person's judgment is *true*.

In keeping with this recognition, two attempts have recently been made to taxonomize current research on accuracy into various "philosophical" categories. According to Kruglanski (1989), for example, psychologists have employed three separate "notions" of judgmental accuracy, notions that parallel the three classical theories of truth, viz. correspondence, coherence, and pragmatic. Funder and West (1993) also employ a threefold philosophical taxonomy, albeit a slightly different one. They claim that current accuracy research is "being pursued along three philosophical approaches": realist, constructivist, and pragmatic. Furthermore, they also suggest that these three philosophical approaches have "to some degree...produced" three separate methodological traditions (465). My aim in this paper is twofold. First, I would like to argue that the proposed philosophical taxonomies are problematic and, as a consequence, should be abandoned. Second, I would like to recommend the adoption of an alternative framework which I will call the "minimalist" approach. I will not have the space to argue in favor of this recommendation in any detail. However, I will suggest that this minimalist approach is far less problematic, will do the job that needs to be done, and has the supreme virtue of allowing the researchers to get on with their empirical investigations with a minimum of philosophical fuss and bother. There are serious methodological disagreements among accuracy researchers but these disagreements are best addressed if they are *not* simply accommodated as differences of philosophical "approach".

2. Why the Proposed Philosophical Taxonomies are Problematic

Table 1 summarizes the philosophical taxonomies put forth by Kruglanski, on the one hand, and Funder and West, on the other. Four general problems emerge from reflection on these taxonomies.

(a) The Funder and West taxonomy is a mixture of two kinds of philosophical views.

(b) The proposed taxonomies are not an accurate reflection of the views actually adopted by accuracy researchers.

(c) The pivotal role psychologists have assigned to the notion of a criterion in these frameworks has led to the blurring of important distinctions and the adoption of a mistaken epistemological understanding regarding the assessment of accuracy claims.

(d) Most philosophers today agree that none of the theories of truth being invoked are defensible.

In this section I shall examine each of these points in turn. As a result, the proposed taxonomies will be gradually dismantled. Then in section 3 a more viable alternative will be presented and defended.

A taxonomic mixture. Kruglanski (1989) claims to be distinguishing three separate notions of judgmental accuracy "in parallel to major philosophical conceptions of truth" (395). And, indeed, the philosophical views he mentions - the correspondence theory, the coherence theory, and the pragmatic theory - are *the* three classical theories of truth. The Funder and West scheme, however, while superficially similar and, to some extent, extensionally equivalent in terms of works cited, combines attitudes towards accuracy/truth with attitudes towards the nature of reality. Funder and West's second category, for example, consists of the "constructivist approach" which is characterized as follows:

Kruglanski 1989:

Theory of Truth	Notion of Accuracy
Correspondence: "compares perception to a reality"	"correspondence between a judgment and a criterion" (Funder 1987; Hastie and Raskinski 1988; Kenny and Albright 1987)
Coherence: "internal consistency of beliefs"	"consensus, or interpersonal agreement between judges" (Funder 1987)
Pragmatic: "the veridicality of an idea resides in its apparent ability to work to one's benefit"	"judgments' adaptive value" (McArthur and Baron 1983; Swann 1984)

Funder and West 1993:

Philosophical Approach	Methodological Tradition
Realist: "regards the trait being judged as something that might *really* exist" (Funder 1987)	concern with evidence for trait's existence, including behavior and interjudge agreement
Constructivist (Phenomenal): "emphasizes how reality and perceptions of reality are not easily separated" (Kruglanski 1989)	"concern with the basis on which judgments are made and the way the "same" stimulus can vary according to point of view; also frequently focuses on interjudge agreement
Pragmatic: "people want to know only that which they can use" (Swann 1984)	focuses on "circumscribed accuracy"

Table 1: Proposed Taxonomies

> The "constructivist" approach… emphasizes how reality and perceptions of reality are not easily separated, if they are separable at all. (466)

Clearly, the main theme here is a stance on the realism/anti-realism debate rather than a stance on the <u>nature</u> of accuracy. The same is true of Funder and West's "realist approach" which is described as regarding "the trait being judged as something that might *really* exist" (467).

Approaches to the study of accuracy can, of course, combine views on the nature of reality with the views on the nature of truth. However, in the interests of clarity, it is important to keep these two sets of distinctions straight. Let us, then, introduce the following two, *very* roughly characterized, taxonomies.

> *Theories of Reality*
> Realism: the view that there exists a mind-independent reality.
> Anti-realism: the view that reality is, in some sense, constructed by the mind.
>
> *Theories of Truth*
> Correspondence (traditional version): the view that the truth of a representation (such as a sentence, proposition, belief, or judgment) consists in its "correspondence" with reality.
> Coherence: the view that the truth of a representation consists in its membership in a designated coherent system of representations.
> Pragmatic (standard interpretation): the view that the truth of a representation consists in its expediency.

It is important to note that while both correspondence theorists and pragmatists have tended to be realists and coherence theorists have tended to be anti-realists, these connections are more a matter of natural "fit" than of logical entailment. For example, it is perfectly possible to hold that in some deep metaphysical sense the world we live in is constructed by the mind (perhaps, as Kant thought, by the transcendental ego) and still maintain that the truth of any given judgment, relative to that constructed reality, is a matter of correspondence.

In developing a viable philosophical framework for describing alternative approaches to the study of accuracy, is it important to make room for views on both the nature of reality and the nature of truth? Let me suggest that the former can be dispensed with.

Psychological research by its very nature takes place within a framework of existential assumptions which specify the domain of the field. It seeks, in particular, to investigate people, their behavior, and their psychological states. There is, of course, a deeper metaphysical question about the ontological status of such posits (do people *really* exist?), but that is a question that need not be of concern to psychologists. Instead, all that is required is a commitment to what Fine (1984) has called the "natural ontological attitude", viz. we should accept at face value the things that our scientific theories say exist and not worry about ontological questions at a more fundamental metaphysical level. So, for example, from this point of view, what is at issue in psychology are theoretical questions like: Does semantic memory exist? or: Are there traits?, or even: Are there mental representations? But what is not at issue is whether there are people or whether there is a social or natural environment in which people live.

Incorrect attributions. Tri-fold taxonomic schemes have a certain aesthetic appeal, but, as far as I can see, the middle category in both proposed taxonomiess doesn't correspond with any position adopted, either implicitly or explicitly, by any current accuracy researcher.

Here is how Kruglanski (1989) characterizes his middle "notion".

> Also common is the definition of accuracy as *consensus*, or interpersonal agreement between judges... Consensus represents consistency within an interpersonal array of judgments; hence it resembles the philosophical coherence theory of truth as the internal consistency of beliefs. (396)

Only one work is cited in connection with this approach, namely, Funder (1987). If we now turn to Funder's paper, we find this. Funder considers two "meanings" which laypersons assign to accuracy, one of which is inter-observer agreement and one of which is the ability to predict behavior. He then suggests that the "perspective" of these two meanings.

> …yields an insight into how psychologists might realistically begin to evaluate the accuracy of social judgments: Do they agree with each other, and do they predict behavior? (83)

Now it is certainly true (as well as unfortunate) that Funder uses the word 'meaning.' But it is also clear that his overriding concern is to distinguish (and endorse) two different kinds of *evidence* relevant to the evaluation of accuracy: consensus information and behavioral predictions. Furthermore, in later works, he unequivocally aligns himself with the "realist" approach. There is thus no textual evidence for attributing to him the view that accuracy *means* either consensus or coherence.

Perhaps as a result of feeling uncomfortable with the "coherence" label, Funder changes the middle category in his own taxonomy to "constructivist" and notes that Kruglanski, who is the only researcher cited as an advocate, "sometimes uses the term 'phenomenal'" (Funder and West, 466).

Now is Kruglanski a constructivist? In his 1989 paper, he clearly endorses what he calls the "phenomenalist approach" but there is no mention of "constructivism." So the issue is whether in endorsing the former, he is *ipso facto* endorsing the latter. I think not.

Constructivism, as Funder and West characterize it, is clearly a form of anti-realism. In contrast, although Kruglanski (1989) contrasts his "phenomenal paradigm" with what he calls the "realist paradigm", in fact, the general framework he adopts within which both of these two paradigms are distinguished sounds quite realist, in the philosophical sense. His general accuracy framework is this:

> Consider the definition of accuracy as a correspondence between a judgment and a criterion that constitutes, in turn, some standard setter's judgment. Such a conception of accuracy implies a compound judgment (or metajudgment) that consists of the following simple judgments: (a) the target judgment [for example, a trait judgment], (b) (judgment of) the criterion, and (c) (judgment of) correspondence between judgment and criterion. (401)

I take this to be realist (at least, in the Fine's "natural ontological attitude" sense) because it presupposes the existence of a target, about whom the target judgment is made, a judge, namely, the person making the target judgment, and a standard setter, namely, the person who establishes the criterion of correspondence. It also presupposes that there are judgments being made by these various individuals. There is no suggestion that there is not, at least, this much reality.

The distinction between the realist "paradigm" and the phenomenalist "paradigm", in Kruglanski's sense, is then drawn based on who the standard setter is. He writes:

> When the standard setter is someone other than the subject, accuracy may be investigated from a realist perspective. In other words, the standard is assumed to represent the external reality, and the key question is what may cause the subject's judgment to mirror or deviate from such reality. When the standard setter happens to be the subject him- or herself, accuracy may be investigated from a phenomenal perspective. In such a case the question centers on the *perception* of accuracy, that is, on the degree to which the subject regards two of his or her own judgments (the target judgment and the criterion) as correspondent. (401-402)

In other words, research from a phenomenalist perspective is not concerned with accuracy *per se* at all. Rather, it is concerned with certain *beliefs* about accuracy, namely, the degree to which the judge judges that his own target judgments are accurate. Furthermore, the phenomenalist perspective is not associated with any special definition of accuracy. Accuracy is rather defined in terms of Kruglanski's general framework as "correspondence between a judgment and a criterion."

The moral to be drawn from these remarks is this. If we are interested in devising a taxonomy of approaches to accuracy which accurately captures views that researchers have actually embraced, we can dispense with the middle categories of both schemes, namely, coherence, on Kruglanski's scheme, and constructivism/phenomenalism, on the Funder and West scheme.

The notion of a criterion. It is standard among social psychologists to characterize accuracy in terms of the notion of a criterion. I suspect that this derives from the historical importance to experimental psychology of operationalism combined with the idea that ascertaining the existence of anything always involves measurement. However, employing the notion of a criterion in this way is a mistake, not because it is outright wrong, but because it easily leads to the blurring of important distinctions and the adopting of a mistaken epistemological understanding regarding the assessment of accuracy claims.

I have already quoted a passage from Kruglanski (1989) in which he characterizes accuracy as "a correspondence between a judgment and a criterion." A similar characterization is to be found in an interesting paper by Hastie and Rasinski (1988). They write:

> The concept of accuracy that will be used in this chapter is close to the commonsense notion summarized in an English language dictionary: "(1) having no errors, correct; (2) deviating only slightly but within acceptable limits from a standard" (*American Heritage Dictionary*, 1983). This definition indicates that an analysis of accuracy requires the consideration of three elements: (a) a judgment, response, or assertion, (b) a standard or criterion of the truth; (c) a rule specifying a correspondence relation between the judgment and the criterion. We define error as the converse of accuracy - the discrepancy or deviation between the criterion and the judgment. (193)

Again, although they do not say so explicitly, there is the strong suggestion that the accuracy of a judgment simply *is* the correspondence of that judgment with a criterion. I shall call this the "criterion schema for a definition of accuracy." It will be helpful for the purpose of critical discussion to reformulate it thus: A judgment is accurate if and only if it satisfies criterion C.

Now, why is this conception of accuracy potentially problematic? First, the term 'accurate', as it is ordinarily used, carries with it a certain ambiguity. Characterizing accuracy in terms of the notion of a criterion, in effect, opts for one of the term's associated senses over the other but the selected sense is the wrong sense for the purposes at hand.

Hastie & Raskinski quote from the *American Heritage Dictionary* in support of their concept of accuracy. However, some digging in other dictionaries reveals that there is an ambiguity associated with the term 'accuracy', as it is ordinarily used, which is not captured by the dictionary definition they cite. For example, *Webster's Third New International Dictionary* (1986) defines 'accurate' thus:

> free from error or mistake, especially as the result of care; in exact conformity to truth or to some standard. (14)

In other words, according to ordinary usage, something can be accurate *either* if it conforms to the truth *or* if it conforms to a standard, where a standard is "something established by authority, custom, or general consent as a model or example to be followed" (*Webster's*, 2223). A correct understanding of the disjunction here is not that we are entitled to use the term 'accuracy' in either the standard-sense or the truth-sense of accuracy in *all* contexts. Rather, I think, the disjunction reflects the fact that some uses of 'accurate' involve the standard-sense while others the truth-sense. What about the use of the term 'accurate' in connection with trait judgments? The only appropriate sense in this context is the truth-sense. What we mean by saying that a trait judgment is accurate is that the judgment conforms to the truth, that the person about whom the judgment is being made in fact has the trait being attributed. Authority, custom, or general consent simply don't enter into it.

In sum, the notion of accuracy, in general, can be defined either conventionally (in terms of a standard) or factively (in terms of the truth). What is relevant to the notion of accuracy in the context of assessing trait judgments is the factive sense; the notion of a criterion, however, favors the conventional sense.

A closely related problem arises with respect to the distinction between epistemic and ontological considerations. Suppose we are interested in assessing the accuracy of the judgment that John is intelligent. In other words, suppose we are interested in whether or not the following claim is true:

(J) The judgment that John is intelligent is accurate.

There are two questions we might ask: (a) What do we *mean* by saying that the judgment is accurate? and (b) How can we *tell* if the judgment is accurate? The first is asking for the *truth* conditions of the claim; the second is asking for its *justification* conditions. Truth conditions are, in some sense, metaphysical or ideal. They approach accuracy from God's perspective, as it were. In contrast, justification conditions are epistemically accessible or practical. They approach accuracy from the human perspective.

Consider again (J). Most philosophers would argue that what makes (J) true is that John is intelligent. What would justify our acceptance of (J) is another matter. It might, for example, be that John had a certain score on an intelligence test. Criterion-talk tends to promote thinking about accuracy in terms of justification conditions. However, what is relevant to the *definition* of accuracy are truth conditions.

I do not mean to suggest that the problem of justifying accuracy claims is not an important one. It is perhaps the most serious problem that accuracy researchers must tackle. The point is only that defining what we *mean* by an accuracy claim is different from *justifying* an accuracy claim and we get into trouble if we confuse the two. But that is precisely what criterion-talk tends to do.

Suppose now that we accept this point and resolve to use criterion-talk only in the context of worrying about justification. There is still a problem. Criterion-talk lends credence to the idea that there are justification conditions of a simple sort or, to put it another way, that justification of an accuracy claim is simply a matter of satisfying some simple observable condition. This is an extremely naive view of justification. In trying to ascertain whether the judgment that John is intelligent is accurate, we must gather evidence to determine whether John is, in fact, intelligent. Intelligence is a trait which, if it exists at all, is not directly observable. Rather, it has the epistemic status of being a theoretical posit. Thus, as with any other theoretical posit in science, we can only justify its existence indirectly based on the observation of closely associated, observable phenomena. The difficulty is that the mind is an extremely complex interactive system. As a consequence, there is no reason to believe that any one observable phenomenon - in this case, any behavior - *taken by itself*, will constitute a justification condition for the existence of something as abstract as a personality trait. A person can certainly be intelligent without scoring well on any given intelligence test; in addition, a person can score well on an intelligence test without being intelligent. Of course, depending on the nature of the test, a high score may very well be strong *inductive* evidence of intelligence. But, logically speaking, it can never be more than that. What is needed, as psychologists often recognize, is the convergence of many kinds of evidence.

The third problem with criterion-talk, then, is this. Criteria are most naturally understood as justification conditions. Thus, an attempt to formulate a concept of accuracy in terms of the notion of a criterion can be viewed as an attempt to formulate justification conditions for the accuracy of a trait judgment. However, there are no such conditions (at least in any simple sense). Hence, criterion-talk helps to promote a false understanding of the epistemology of accuracy research.

I have argued that the pivotal role assigned to the notion of a criterion in current discussions of the nature of accuracy tends to promote a false view of both the conceptual problem of defining accuracy and a false view of how to justify accuracy claims. The moral, I think, should be clear. Criterion-talk has got to go.

To summarize the results of the discussion thus far: The two philosophical taxonomies proposed in the recent accuracy literature are problematic in various ways. To rectify those problems I have suggested that an adequate framework should (a) focus exclusively on different approaches to the meaning of accuracy, setting aside issues about realism versus anti-realism, (b) abandon the middle category which concerns the coherence theory of truth, and (c) define accuracy without using the notion of a criterion. Point (b) makes the resulting taxonomy a more accurate reflection of views actually held by researchers; points (a) and (c) are offered in the spirit of philosophical housecleaning.

The result is what philosophers call a "rational reconstruction." According to this reconstruction, there are two approaches to the nature of accuracy, one based on the traditional correspondence theory of truth, and the other based on the pragmatic theory of truth. Formulating these approaches without using the notion of a criterion, we get something like the following:

Correspondence Approach.
A trait judgment is accurate just in case it corresponds with reality.
Pragmatic Approach.
A trait judgment is accurate just in case it is expedient.

I now want to argue that even this taxonomy should be abandoned, not because it is not the best gloss on views currently held, but because the views themselves should be rejected. Most philosophers today agree that neither the traditional correspondence theory of truth nor the pragmatic theory of truth, as standardly interpreted, is philosophically viable. (The same holds for the classical coherence theory but since that is not a view that has actually been embraced by an accuracy researcher, I will not bother to lay out the arguments against it.)

Problematic theories of truth. Obviously, I do not have the space either to canvas all of the standard objections to these theories or to discuss any of them in detail, but let me, at least, sketch a few of the major problems.

The correspondence approach says that the truth (and, hence, accuracy) of a judgment consists in its correspondence with reality. In this century, there have been two attempts to work out this view in greater detail - by Moore, Russell, and Wittgenstein in the first three decades of this century and by Tarski in the 1930's and 1940's (Prior 1967). Most philosophers now agree that the traditional British version is too problematic to be acceptable; the jury is still out on the Tarski version. In this section, I will consider only the former.

On the traditional version, truth is conceptualized as being a relation between two relata. The bearer of truth is generally taken to be a proposition; what makes a proposition true is usually taken to be a fact. Such an approach is quite compatible with the idea of a judgment's being true. A judgment is a mental act of a sort with a certain content. We can view the judgment, as mental act, as true just in case its content is true. But the content of a judgment is nothing but a proposition.

To be adequate the correspondence theory must give a respectable account of what a proposition is, what a fact is, and what the relation of correspondence amounts to. One standard objection to the theory is that traditional correspondence theorists were never able to do any of these things in a satisfactory way. Another objection was this: although the theory has a strong intuitive appeal when it comes to affirmative, categorical propositions, such as that John is intelligent, it becomes far less intuitive in the case of negative propositions, conditional propositions, and modal propositions. Does the truth of the proposition that John is not intelligent also consist in its correspondence with a fact ? How about the proposition that if John were intelligent, he would score well on the SAT exam ? (For further discussion, see Armour 1969, White 1970, Prior 1967).

The pragmatic theory of truth is a set of interrelated doctines to be found in the works of Peirce, Dewey, and James (Ezorsky 1967). Since the details of these doctrines differ in the various authors, I shall focus on James's version since that is the one cited by accuracy researchers.

Among the various claims James makes about truth is that "the true is only the expedient in our way of thinking " (1955, 196). If we take this statement to constitute a claim about what it *means* for something to be true, as the standard interpretation does (Ezorsky 1967), then the pragmatic theory also falls prey to a number of objections. First, there are different ways in which a judgment can be expedient. It can be expedient because it gives rise to predictions which are satisfied, or it can be expedient because it contributes to the "energy, efficiency, or survival" of those who endorse it (Lovejoy 1908).

Second, the idea that the predicate 'is true' simply means 'is expedient' flies in the face of ordinary usage. Clearly, according to Russell (1966), statements of the form 'It is true that p' and 'It is useful to belief that p' are not ordinarily taken to express the same proposition. One measure of this is that the investigations we would undertake to ascertain, say, that it is true that John is intelligent would not ordinarily be considered to be the same investigations we would undertake to ascertain that it is useful to belief that John is intelligent. The former would be focused on John, the latter would be focused on consequences for the believers (Armour 1969).

Third, the theory seems to lead either to a denial of the law of non-contradiction, namely, that a proposition cannot be both true and false at the same time, or to the denial of the law of excluded middle, namely, that every proposition is either true or false. The difficulty stems from the fact that things are not expedient in and of themselves; they are expedient only for someone in a certain context. Who are the relevant parties when it comes to truth? Suppose that we allow relativization to different groups of individuals. Then a proposition could be both true and false at the same time, true because it is expedient for group A and false because it is not expedient for group B. One way to avoid this consequence is to claim that to be true a proposition must be expedient for everyone in the long run. But what if, again, the world of individuals is divided with respect to the expediency of a proposition. Then we would have to say that the proposition is *neither* true or false. But for many propositions, this would be nonsense.

3. An Alternative Approach

Recognition that the traditional theories of truth are problematic has not deterred contemporary philosophers from continuing to worry about the nature of truth. In fact, a host of new theories have sprung up, including many that are, in some sense, successors to the traditional theories. For example, the traditional correspondence view has been succeeded by so-called "semantic" correspondence theories (Tarski 1958, Davidson 1969); remnants of the coherence view are to be found in contemporary epistemic approaches (Rescher 1973, Dummett 1978, Putnam 1981); and a contemporary version of the pragmatic theory can be found in Rorty (1982) and Papineau (1987).

Accuracy researchers who both acknowledge the importance of defining accuracy in an intellectually responsible way and accept the close relationship between accuracy and truth may find this new plethora of theories of truth somewhat discouraging. In this section I shall suggest that there is no need for despair; just as accuracy researchers need not choose between metaphysical realism and anti-realism (because a minimal stance on realism such as Fine's "natural ontological attitude" is sufficient for their purposes), so they also need not choose between competing philosophical theories of truth. There is a minimalist alternative here also, namely, commitment simply to an analogue of what is called "the disquotation convention" or Tarski's "schema T".

Tarski (1944) articulated his schema T in connection with laying down a condition of adequacy for any definition of truth. He formulated it like this:

(T) X is true if and only if p

where 'p' is replaced by any sentence of the language to which the word 'true' refers, and 'X' is replaced by a name of this sentence. For any natural language, there are infinitely many instances of this schema. Instances for English include:

'Snow is white' is true if and only if snow is white.
'Lincoln is the capitol of Nebraska' is true if and only if Lincoln is the capitol of Nebraska.

Tarski did not take (T) in itself to be a theory or (full) definition of truth. Rather, he regarded each instance of (T) as a *partial* definition. In addition, he also suggested that a condition of adequacy for a (full) definition of truth is that all instances of (T) logically follow from it. Other philosophers have recently taken a stronger line. They have argued that there is *nothing to* the concept of truth other than what is expressed by instances of (T) (Leeds 1978, Horwich 1982, 1990, Fine 1984, Soames 1984, Field 1986). Views of this sort have come to be known as "deflationary" theories of truth.

The dispute between deflationary and "inflationary" theories (namely, those that do try to give a definition of truth that goes beyond the disquotation schema) also need not concern the accuracy researcher. Rather, what I want to suggest is that, for purposes of doing accuracy research, simple commitment to an analogue of schema T for judgments will suffice. Whether truth or accuracy can be defined in a more full-blooded way and, if so, what the most adequate full theory of truth is, are questions that psychologists, qua psychologists, need not address.

As (T) makes clear, Tarski applied the predicate 'is true' to sentences. However, analogous schemas can easily be formulated for other bearers of truth. In particular, if we are interested in applying the predicate 'is true' to judgments rather than sentences, we can use the following:

(T)* The judgment that p is true if and only if p

where 'p' is replaced by a sentence. Instances of (T)* would then include:

The judgment that John is intelligent is true if and only if John is intelligent.
The judgment that Susan is charming is true if and only if Susan is charming.

It should now be evident what the minimalist approach to truth is. Why should accuracy researchers accept it? I will only have space to sketch my answer.

Accuracy researchers need *a* theory of accuracy (truth) so that they have a more precise idea of what they are trying to investigate. However, clearly not any old theory of accuracy (truth) will do. Three desiderata come to mind. First, the theory should be philosophically defensible. Second, if possible, it should have some practical value, illuminating or helping to answer the various theoretical, epistemological, and methodological questions connected with the empirical study of accuracy. Finally, again if possible, it should be tolerant of the different kinds of accuracy research (i.e. of Funder and West 1993's "methodological traditions") that psychologists currently engage in. I would regard the first desideratum to be a necessary condition on the acceptability of a theory whereas the second and third are simply desirable features, with the second being more important than the third.

Although, clearly, the basic need for a theory of accuracy would be better served by a full theory as opposed to a partial theory, there is currently no consensus among philosophers on the philosophical defensibility of any of the currently available full theories of truth. There is, however, considerable agreement on the acceptability of Tarski's schema (T). So if a minimalist approach to the nature of accuracy (truth) can satisfy the desiderata of usefulness and tolerance, it will have much to recommend it. It is my contention that it can do precisely that. In particular, it can shed light on talk about different kinds of accuracy, it brings out the importance of the so-called "consistency" controversy over traits (i.e, whether people exhibit sufficiently consistent patterns of behavior to warrant the claim that they even *have* traits), and, it can help psychologists assess the probative status of different kinds of evidence (for example, consensus data versus behavioral data) or different "logics" of argumentation (Hastie and Rasinski 1988). Furthermore, given a minimalist view of the nature of accuracy, it is possible to make sense of all the various kinds of accuracy research currently being engaged in, including that carried out under the banner of the "correspondence" approach, that carried out under the banner of the "pragmatic" approach, and that assigned by Kruglanski and Funder and West, respectively, to their middle categories. What more could psychologists want of an approach to accuracy?

References

American Heritage Dictionary (1983), Boston: Houghton-Mifflin.

Armour, L. (1969), *The Concept of Truth*. Assen: Van Gorcum.

Davidson, D. (1969), "True to the Facts", *Journal of Philosophy* 66: 748-764.

Dummett, M. (1978), *Truth and Other Enigmas*. Oxford: Clarendon Press.

Ezorsky, G. (1967), "Pragmatic Theory of Truth", in P. Edwards, (ed.), *The Encylopedia of Philosophy*. New York: Macmillan.

Field, H. (1987), "The Deflationary Conception of Truth," in G. MacDonald and C. Wright, (eds.), *Fact, Science and Morality*. New York: Blackwell, pp. 55-117.

Fine. A. (1984), "The Natural Ontological Attitude", in J. Leplin, (ed.), *Scientific Realism*. Berkeley: University of California Press, pp. 83-107.

Funder, D. (1987), "Errors and Mistakes: Evaluating the Accuracy of Social Judgment," *Psychological Bulletin* 101: 75-90.

Funder, D.C. and West, S.G. (1993), "Consensus, Self-Other Agreement, and Accuracy in Personality Judgment: An Introduction", *Journal of Personality* 61: 457-476.

Hastie, R. and Rasinski, K.A., "The Concept of Accuracy in Social Judgment", in D. Bar-tal and A.W. Kruglanski, (eds.), *The Social Psychology of Knowledge*. Cambridge: Cambridge University Press, pp. 193-208.

Horwich, P. (1982), "Three Forms of Realism", *Synthese* 51: 181-201.

______. (1990), *Truth*. Cambridge, Mass.: Basil Blackwell.

James, W. (1955), *Pragmatism and Four Essays from The Meaning of Truth*. Cleveland: The World Publishing Co.

Kenny. D.A. and Albright, L. (1987), "Accuracy in Interpersonal Perception: A Social Relations Analysis", *Psychological Bulletin* 102: 390-402.

Kruglanski, A. W. (1989), "The Psychology of Being "Right": the Problem of Accuracy in Social Perception and Cognition", *Psychological Bulletin* 106: 395-409.

Leeds, S. (1978), "Theories of Reference and Truth", *Erkenntnis* 13: 111-129.

Lovejoy, A.O. (1908), "The Thirteen Pragmatisms II," *Journal of Philosophy* 5: 29-39.

McArthur, L.Z. and Baron, R.M. (1983), "Towards an Ecological Theory of Social Perception", *Psychological Review* 90: 215-238.

Papineau, D. (1987), *Reality and Representation*. Oxford: Blackwell.

Prior, A.N. (1967), "Correspondence Theory of Truth" in P. Edwards, (ed.), *The Encyclopedia of Philosophy*. New York: Macmillan.

Putnam, H. (1981), *Reason, Truth and History*. Cambridge: Cambridge University Press.

Rescher, N. (1973), *The Coherence Theory of Truth*. Oxford: Clarendon Press.

Rorty, R. (1982), *Consequences of Pragmatism*. Minnesota: Minnesota University Press.

Russell, B. (1966), *Philosophical Essays*. New York: Simon and Schuster.

Soames, S. (1984), "What is a Theory of Truth?", *Journal of Philosophy* 81: 411-429.

Swann, W.B. (1984), "Quest for Accuracy in Person Perception: A Matter of Pragmatics", *Psychological Review* 91: 457-477.

Tarski, A. (1944), "The Semantic Conception of Truth", *Philosophy and Phenomenological Research* 4: 341-75.

______. (1958), "The Concept of Truth in Formalized Languages", in *Logic, Semantics, Metamathematics: Papers from 1923 to 1938*. Oxford: Oxford University Press, pp. 152-278.

Tedeschi, J.T., Lindskold, S. and Rosenfeld, P. (1985), *Introduction to Social Psychology*. St. Paul: West Publishing Co.

Webster's Third International Dictionary of the English Language Unabridged (1986), Springfield, Mass.: Merriam-Webster.

White. A. (1970), *Truth*. Garden City: Anchor Books.

Zebrowitz, L.A. (1990), *Social Perception*. Buckingham: Open University Press.

What is Psychophysics?[1]

Lawrence A. Shapiro

University of Wisconsin, Madison

1. Introduction

Gustav Fechner published his monumental *Elemente der Psychophysik* in 1860. In the years to follow the book became the object of such intense criticism and such caustic invective that Fechner, prophetically, observed: "The tower of Babel was never finished because the workers could not reach an understanding on how they should build it; my psychophysical edifice will stand because the workers will never agree on how to tear it down" (Stevens 1957, 153). Fechner was right. Here we are, 134 years later, and psychophysics is still with us. Moreover, if it's true that psychophysics thrives on disagreement then likely it will be around for another millennium, for there is currently even less accord about what psychophysics is and whether it is possible than there was when Fechner was alive. Some psychophysicists retain Fechner's view of psychophysics and so claim to be searching for laws relating our sensory experience of the world to physical magnitudes in the world. However, many others prefer to eliminate all talk of sensation in descriptions of their work. For example, Horace Barlow redefines psychophysics in behavioristic terms: "[t]he study of how the subject's report varies with the physical parameters of the stimulus," he tells us, "is called psychophysics" (1982, 3; see also Graham 1952; McKenna 1985). Alternatively, some, like Michel Treisman (1964), have offered a neurological interpretation of psychophysics, according to which psychophysical equations relate neural states to stimuli. Still others make no attempt to redefine psychophysics, but simply reject it out of hand. Gail Hornstein, for example, opines that the existence of psychophysical research is as much an argument for the legitimacy of psychophysics as the existence of parapsychological research is for the authenticity of ESP—as if psychophysical and parapsychological methods are on a par. She concludes: "Psychophysics is to a science of psychological measurement what the Red Queen's words to Alice were to the truth" (1993, 149).

Extricating and evaluating all the various motives anchoring these divergent perspectives is an awesome project, and I shall not attempt it here. Rather, my goal is to scrutinize one very influential attempt to remove sensation from psychophysics, namely C. Wade Savage's (1970). Though the focus will be on Savage, I claim his errors appear regularly in many critical discussions of Fechner's project. Revealing these errors can, I hope, start us in the difficult task of replacing the conflict upon which Fechner's edifice has rested with consensus.

PSA 1994, Volume 2, pp. 47-57

The plan for this paper is as follows. I first describe the genesis of Fechner's law, a law that purportedly relates sensation magnitudes to physical magnitudes. I next turn to a confusion over a notion that plays an integral role in the development of Fechner's law: the just noticeable difference (jnd). When claiming that there is a just noticeable difference, between what things is this difference noticed? Psychophysicists have traditionally assumed that these things are sensations. But, Savage argues, this characterization of the jnd appears to be conceptually incoherent and, in any case, is unnecessary for interpreting the psychophysical methods which appeal to jnds. Denying that just noticeable differences are differences between sensations forces us, Savage thinks, to abandon a conception of psychophysics that contains anything of psychological interest. When we interpret jnds to be jnds between stimuli, psychophysics becomes the study of brute discriminative capacities, where these capacities in human beings do not differ in kind from the discriminative capacities of, e.g., fulcrum balances. In response, I argue that redefining the jnd does not require that we give up Fechner's quest for a psychophysics of sensation. Savage's mistake rests in part upon asking psychophysics to meet standards that would seem unreasonable when applied to other sciences. In part also, Savage is tempted by an understanding of psychophysics that, while in the spirit of Fechner's original proposal, is overly ambitious. Consequently, Savage blames psychophysics for failing to do something it should not pretend to do in the first place.

2. Fechner's Law

Psychophysics began with a law and an inspiration. The law is Weber's law, which tells us that, except at extremes, a just noticeable change in a stimulus is a constant fraction of that stimulus. Stated formally, the law says $dP/P = c$, where P is some physical magnitude, dP is the increase (or decrease) in this magnitude, and c is a constant. Familiar experiences confirm Weber's law. We notice a slight increase in the volume of a soft sound, but the same increase in a blaring noise will go unheard. Likewise, we notice the weight of an additional book in our briefcase, but place the book atop a wheelbarrow full of soil and the burden will not seem any heavier. We notice a teaspoon of sugar added to a cup of coffee, but not to a milkshake. Weber's law tells us that in all of these cases—loudness, heaviness, sweetness—the just noticeable change in a physical magnitude is a constant proportion, *modulo* the particular sensory modality, of the magnitude.

The inspiration Fechner brought to Weber's law is this. While jnds grow in constant proportion to physical magnitudes, jnds *appear* equal. Suppose that to a 53gm weight we must add another gram before a difference in weight is noticed. Suppose, that is, the Weber constant for weights is 1/53. Accordingly, given any weight, we can compute how much we must add to the weight for the change in the weight to be just noticeable. A weight just noticeably greater than 100gms will be 54/53 (100), or 101.900gms. Similarly, the weight that 100gms is just noticeably greater than will be 53/54 (100), or 98.150gms. With the Weber constant in hand, we can construct a table charting jnds above and below the 100gm weight standard.

107.818gms	4 jnds
105.808gms	3 jnds
103.836gms	2 jnds
101.900gms	1 jnd
100.000gms	0
98.150gms	1 jnd
96.383gms	2 jnds
94.648gms	3 jnds
91.271gms	4 jnds

Table 1

Assuming that the jnds mark off equal units of sensation, we can write $dS = c(dP/P)$ where dS is the just noticeable increase (or decrease) in sensation, c is a constant, and P ranges over physical magnitudes. Fechner called this formula the *Fundamental formel*, and, by then integrating and simplifying it,[2] he derived the *Massformel*—what is today known as Fechner's law: $S = k \log P$, where k is a constant. This law tells us that incremental changes in sensation are proportional to logarithmic changes in physical stimuli or, in other words, equal sensation differences correspond to equal stimulus ratios. Fechner called his law a *psychophysical* law because it describes a functional relationship between psychological magnitudes and physical magnitudes, i.e. it is a substitution instance of the form $S = f(P)$.

As the table above indicates, Fechner's law provides a mechanical means by which to measure sensation. Because each jnd corresponds to a unit difference in sensation, if we wish to know the magnitude of a sensation that is greater than the sensation produced by the standard weight of 100gms, we stipulate that the sensory magnitude corresponding to a 100gm weight is zero. Then we need simply to lift weights of greater amounts to count jnds up from the standard until we find a match between the two sensations. The number of jnds up from the standard will count as the value of the sensation. Easier still, we discover the weight that produces a sensation equal to the sensation we wish to measure and we substitute the number of gms of this weight for 'P_x' in the following formulation of Fechner's law: $S = (\log P_x - \log P_0)/\log (54/53)$, where P_0 is 100, i.e. the number of gms of the weight to which a zero sensation has been assigned. With this formula we can derive the value, in terms of jnd units, of the unknown sensation.

3. Between What are JNDs JNDs Between?

Fechner's law introduces a legion of extremely complex questions concerning measurement. We should like to know, for instance, whether the law provides a valid metric scale for sensation and, if so, the power of the scale (is it an ordinal scale?; an interval scale?; a ratio scale?). However, it is not my purpose to delve into these questions here. Rather, I turn now to a question over the nature of the jnd. In talking about jnds we imply that some difference is noticed. But, we may wonder, is this difference a difference between stimuli, sensations corresponding to these stimuli, or both? On the one hand it seems evident that jnds are jnds between stimuli. When noticing a difference between two different weights, one is *a fortiori*, noticing a difference between external objects. Yet, some psychologists have denied this stimulus interpretation of the jnd. "The difference is not a difference of stimuli," Boring tells us. "The difference is a difference in sensation and the entire argument rests upon the empirical fact of Weber's experiments that such differences are noticeable and may even be observable as just noticeable" (1928, 443-444). Boring's reasoning seems to be this. Corresponding to stimuli in the world are our sensations of these stimuli. Changes in the former lead us to notice changes in the latter. Weber's law, accordingly, is a law about our sensations. It tells us by what fraction a given physical magnitude must change in order for there to be a noticeable difference between our sensations of it. Returning to the example of the weights, Boring's claim is that the sensation corresponding to a 100gm weight differs just noticeably from the sensation corresponding to a weight of 101.900gms.

Critics of the sensation interpretation of the jnd, like Savage, tend to characterize sensations as those immediate objects of perception of which we are incorrigibly aware. With such a view in place, it becomes an easy task (and one Savage performs time and again) to draw forth from the sensation interpretation of the jnd various difficulties. For instance, when speaking of jnds as jnds between stimuli, we can define the jnd to be the difference between two stimuli such that any stimulus between the two does not differ noticeably from either. If a weight of 104gms is just noticeably different from a weight of 106gms, then a weight of 105gms will be indiscernible from either weight. To say that two weights are just noticeably different is simply to say that no difference will be noticed between either of these weights and a weight intermediate between them. But, how are we to understand just noticeability for sensations, if, as Savage construes them, sensations are the infallibly and immediately known objects of perception? Suppose a sensation corresponding to a weight of 104gms is just noticeably different from a sensation corresponding to a weight of 106gms. What do we say about the sensation corresponding to a weight of 105gms? Such a sensation would have the odd property of being distinct from the sensations between which it is sandwiched and yet indiscernible from them. Or, perhaps we should deny that there are sensations between just noticeably different sensations. But why should weights of 104 and 106gms produce in us sensations while a weight of 105gms does not? Presumably, we are ordinarily capable of perceiving a weight of 105gms.

Though the conception of sensation Savage adopts is no doubt chosen for the paradoxes it generates, it serves to highlight the fact that Boring surely overstates the case when insisting that jnds cannot be anything but jnds between sensations. Even if one takes the view that we notice sensations one need not doubt that we also notice the external world in virtue of noticing these sensations. Moreover, one needn't think of sensations as the direct objects of perception to believe that psychophysical laws tell us about the relation between sensation and physical magnitudes. Accordingly, in the remainder of this paper I propose not to take sides on the question of the correct interpretation of the jnd. As we shall see, Savage thinks that the mere possibility of offering a stimulus interpretation of the jnd suffices to show that psychophysics is not concerned with sensation. I am willing to grant that jnds might, in fact, mark differences between stimuli; but, I shall respond, this provides no reason for doubting that psychophysical methods can tell us about the relation between the world and our experiences of it.

4. JNDs and the Measurement of Sensation

Earlier I mentioned two methods that one might use to measure sensation by means of jnd units. More detailed consideration of these methods shows that the jnds upon which they rely could simply be jnds between stimuli (the following discussion is adapted from Savage, ch. 8). To see this, let's first state the methods in terms of jnds between sensations.

Method A for measuring sensation in units of jnds between sensations:

1. Having stipulated that a weight of 100gms is to correspond to a zero sensation, present this weight to O.

2. Present to O increasingly larger weights until O identifies a weight that produces a sensation just noticeably greater than the sensation produced by the previously presented weight. Assign to this sensation the numeral $x + 1$, where x is the numeral assigned to the previously presented weight.

3. Repeat step (2) until a sensation is produced in O that matches the sensation we wish to measure.

It should be noted that the tedium of this method can be avoided if we number the weights corresponding to each just noticeably different sensation. With an appropriately numbered series of weights, we can measure O's sensation of weight by choosing the weight that produces in O a sensation of equal magnitude.

Method B for measuring sensation in units of jnds between sensations:

1. Derive the Weber constant for weights, which is 1/53.

2. Stipulate that the sensation corresponding to a weight of 100gms is the zero sensation.

3. Using the formula S = (log P - log 100)/log (54/53), compute in units of sensation jnds the magnitude of the sensation that corresponds to a weight of P grams.

We must now ask about the role jnds between sensations play in Methods A and B. According to Savage, Methods A and B "could proceed quite as well as they do even if there were no perceivable, empirically real sensations produced in the discriminal perception of stimuli" (315). Surely the psychophysicist ought to welcome Savage's claim, for, in itself, it needn't be read as a rejection of sensation *tout court*, but may be only a rejection of a view of sensation that cannot outlive scrutiny in any case. If Savage is right, we ought to be able to measure sensation using jnds between stimuli as units. We need only to rewrite Methods A and B, taking care to replace all pernicious talk of jnds between sensations with talk of jnds between stimuli. Let us do this, calling the reconstrued methods Method A' and Method B':

Method A' for measuring sensation in units of jnds between stimuli:

1. Having stipulated that a weight of 100gms is to count as the zero sensation, present this weight to O.

2. Present to O increasingly larger weights until O identifies a weight that is just noticeably different from the previously presented weight. Assign to this weight the numeral x + 1, where x is the numeral assigned to the previously presented weight.

3. Repeat step (2) until a weight is found that is indistinguishable from the weight whose distance in stimulus jnd units from the zero weight we wish to measure.

Method B' for measuring sensation in units of jnds between stimuli:

1. Derive the Weber constant for weights, which is 1/53.

2. Stipulate that a weight of 100gms is to count as the zero sensation.

3. Using the formula S = (log P - log 100)/log (54/53), compute the number of stimulus jnds between a weight of P grams and the zero stimulus.

To all appearances, Methods A and A' produce identical data. To suggest otherwise is to suppose that the jnd intervals summarized in Table 1 would differ depending upon whether the jnds are jnds between sensations or stimuli. But this is impossible because both methods look to the weights to define the jnd intervals—they differ simply in that Method A assumes that it is the sensations the weights produce rather than the weights themselves that are compared. Likewise, the formulae in Methods B and B' will compute identical numbers of jnd units given the same values for P. In one case it is assumed that the jnds are between sensations and in the other that they are between stimuli.

Savage concludes that the sensation interpretation of the jnd has no essential place in Methods A and B. Hence, the psychophysical method of just noticeable differences can make do with jnds between stimuli. The question to which we now turn is whether this fact implies that psychophysics has nothing to say about sensation.

5. Savage's Critique of Psychophysics

Let us suppose that it is possible to interpret the jnds psychophysicists depend upon to measure sensation as jnds between stimuli. What follows? According to Savage, in choosing to measure sensation in terms of differences between stimuli one relinquishes any claim to be studying sensation. Both jnd methods A' and B' expect from the observer nothing but "perceiving stimuli and comparing them with other stimuli" (314-315). Consequently, it is not, after all, sensation that is measured, but the "[n]umber of just noticeable (stimulus) differences of the stimulus from (stimulus) zero" (315). Hence, Fechner's law can be restated in the following way: $P_d = k (\log P_m - \log P_{m0})$, where P_d is the number of stimulus jnds between a given stimulus and the zero stimulus, P_m is the measured value of the given stimulus, and P_{m0} is the measured value of the zero stimulus. But, restated in this way, Fechner's law is not a *psycho*physical law—not a law of the form $S = f(P)$. Rather, it turns out to have the same form as Weber's law, i.e. $P = f(P)$.

In fact, Savage argues (313-314), Fechner's law and Weber's law share more than just their form—they are merely variants of each other:

> Both laws are based on the measurement of just noticeable differences between stimuli. Every such measurement that tends to confirm, or disconfirm, the one tends to confirm, or disconfirm, the other. And there are, apparently, no other measurements or experiments that tend to confirm or disconfirm either. What reason, then, is there to regard the laws as distinct?

What reason indeed? As should be clear from our earlier discussion of Weber's and Fechner's laws, Fechner's law is just another way of describing the relation between jnds and stimuli that Weber's law defines. Looking again at Table 1, we may express the difference between Weber's and Fechner's laws in the following way. Weber's law tells us that the jnd between two stimuli is some fixed fraction of one of them. Hence, with Weber's law we can extend the columns of Table 1 a row at a time in an effort to discover the number of jnds between the zero stimulus and some distant stimulus. Fechner's law describes the function relating the two columns of the table and so saves us the trouble of climbing rows one at a time in order to reach the jnd value for a given stimulus. So, of course Weber's law and Fechner's law stand or fall upon the same measurements, as Savage claims, because they are simply different mathematical extensions of the data these measurements procure. However, Savage has not made a discovery that will alarm psychophysicists: psychophysicists themselves have already noted that Weber's law and Fechner's law have the same status. This fact is worrisome to the traditional psychophysicist only if Weber's law is not a psychological law—a point I take up in the next section.

Savage believes that once we reject sensation jnds in favor of stimulus jnds and thereby see in a clear light that Fechner's law, like Weber's law, relates only physical variables, the true subject matter of psychophysics reveals itself. Psychophysics becomes the science of human sensitivity. Measurements of jnds provide us with a gauge of sensitivity because sensitivity is just the reciprocal of the jnd: the greater the fraction of a stimulus that must be added or subtracted from the stimulus before a difference is noted, the less our sensitivity. But sensitivity, Savage continues, is not of any psychological interest—it does not involve sensation. The data Table 1 presents "could be obtained for a balance or group of balances," Savage says. "That is to say, sensitivity is a concept that applies equally to balances and human observers of weight" (358). Given that Fechner's law speaks only to sensitivity, it does not recognize the "distinction between psychological and physical dimensions. Therefore, it does not imply that a gap between mind and body has been spanned by a numerical law" (363).

Before responding to Savage's charge that there is nothing psychological about psychophysics, I pause to note that some psychophysicists would welcome Savage's redescription of psychophysics. Asking to what psychophysical statements refer, Horst Gundlach (1993, 145) writes:

> A negative answer first: They certainly do not refer to sensations or other mental phenomena. Consider the weight experiments by E. H. Weber [references omitted]. They are about objects, namely, weights. They explore human capacity to judge differences between weights under specified conditions of exposure without the assistance of instruments. This is then compared with judgements succored by precision balances.

Gundlach, apparently, endorses Savage's picture of psychophysics. Because Weber's law contains only physical variables, it cannot be said to tell us anything about sensation. Hence, Weber's law (and, presumably, Fechner's) can at best tell us about only the sensitivity of a subject, be it human or hardware.

Likewise, S.S. Stevens (1966, 37-38) tenders the following advice:

> . . . I should like to press a precept that seems acutely relevant to the study of perception. When we study the input/output characteristics of ammeters, we do not feel called upon to imagine how it feels to be an ammeter, nor do we try to relate our own experiences to those of ammeters. In the scientific study of man, especially in the study of the operating characteristics of his sensory systems, many pseudo problems can be bypassed if we take the same objective attitude toward the human participant in an experiment as we take toward an ammeter.

As Stevens sees matters, psychophysics can be no more than a science of sensitivity, not simply because its laws relate only physical variables, but because the objectivity of scientific inquiry requires that the human subject be treated no differently from a piece of apparatus. Objectivity in psychophysics means, at least in part, "claiming no privileged view of things merely because we, as experimenters, happen to be human" (1966, 38).

It is time finally to begin untangling the confusions about the nature of psychophysics. The knot has become so large that there is no longer a free end in sight. On the one hand we have a philosopher claiming that Fechner's law relates only physical variables and so reveals nothing of psychological interest. On the other we have psychophysicists who agree with Savage that they could just as well be studying ammeters or balances and yet, in an odd twist, continue to think of themselves as psychologists. Why might a study of sensitivity belong in the realm of psychology? What kind of law is Weber's law? These are the questions to which we must now turn.

6. Why Not a Psychophysics of Sensation?

My goal in this section is modest. I will argue that Savage unfairly dismisses the possibility that psychophysical methods afford measurements of sensation. I characterize this claim as modest because I will not here take any steps toward developing a positive account of sensation to replace the vexed one Savage assumes. Best not to set forth on a laborious journey until one knows that the roads are open.

Savage's conclusion that psychophysics bypasses sensation rests on a number of double standards. We see one such double standard in Savage's claim that because Weber's law contains only physical variables and Fechner's law can be reinterpreted in such a way that it too contains only physical variables, it follows that the laws are not about sensations. In fact, characterizing the variables as physical is tendentious because of our proclivity to contrast the physical with the mental. A less partisan way of making Savage's point is that Weber's law and the reconstrued Fechner's law relate observables with observables. But, anytime an experimenter wishes to investigate the properties of something she cannot directly observe she looks to relations between observables to provide evidence about these properties. This is no less true in chemistry than it is in psychology. Hence, from the uncontested claim that Weber's law relates observables it no more follows that the law cannot be about, or reveal the nature of, sensory experience than it follows that relations of observables cannot tell us something about unobservable chemical processes.

Paradoxically, Savage (1970, 353) is quite willing to infer the existence of an unobservable physiological mechanism from consideration of the observables Weber's law relates:

> Human perceivers may possess a neurological "balancing" mechanism that enables them to perceive weights and weight differences in somewhat the same way as a simple balance does. If so, thresholds can be explained in human perceivers by assuming that something like friction is generated in this mechanism when weights are lifted. This explanation of the threshold would be completely adequate. It could be given without positing any weight sensations in the observer and without assuming even that the observer perceives or is in any other way aware of his perceptual mechanism. Indeed, to posit sensations and to provide a sensationist explanation of thresholds would then be as superfluous and absurd as a comparable explanation for thresholds in fulcrum balances.

Savage cannot have it both ways. If it is illicit to infer the existence of unobservable sensory processes from the relations between observables that Weber's law describes, it should be equally spurious to infer the existence of unobservable physiological mechanisms. That Savage does speculate as to the nature of the mechanism behind Weber's law suggests that his real beef is not with posits of unobservables, but with posits of *psychological* unobservables. But, with no further argument, why should a physiological posit described in wildly metaphorical terms strike us as plausible while a psychological posit should remain beyond consideration?

The illicit inference from the fact that Weber's law relates observables to the fact that it does not describe sensation recurs in Savage's comments about sensitivity. Let us grant that Weber's law describes sensitivity. Savage, Gundlach, and Stevens all seem to think that this removes the psychological element from psychophysics. Given that Weber's law and the reconstrued Fechner's law tell us only about differential thresholds between stimuli, psychophysical methods are as applicable to fulcrum balances and ammeters as they are to human beings. Why, we might take Savage, Gundlach, and Stevens to be asking, is sensitivity a psychological process when talking about sensory systems and not when talking about fulcrum balances and ammeters? Either sensitivity is psychological or it is not, and since it is crazy to suppose that fulcrum balances and ammeters have minds it is likewise crazy to suppose that a person's sensitivity involves anything psychological.

The fallacy in this reasoning is obvious. It is one thing to observe that instruments lacking minds may still display sensitivity; another to claim that sensitivity does not in some cases involve sensation. The point is so apparent that we may wonder how it could have been missed. Stevens, I think, supplies part of the answer to this question when he links objectivity in science to "claiming no privileged view of things merely because we, as experimenters, happen to be human"(1966, 38). To attribute sensory experiences like brightness, loudness, heaviness, etc. to other human beings merely because we, the experimenters, happen to have such experiences is bad science, Stevens thinks, because it requires that we read into psychophysical data more than what's there. We let what we know about our own inner lives infect our interpretation of experimental findings. Better to play it safe and agree with Savage that: "If sensitivity in humans is properly called a psychological dimension, then so is sensitivity in balances; if the term is inappropriate to describe balance sensitivity, it is inappropriate to describe human sensitivity" (359).

But, as already noted, there is nothing wrong with reading into the data more than what's there. This is standard operating procedure in science, where evidence always underdetermines theory. Second and more importantly, when seeking to understand a question such as how human sensory experiences are related to external stimuli it is perfectly appropriate, indeed unavoidable, that we take a privileged view in the design and interpretation of psychophysical methods. If, like Fechner, we take the fact of our own sensory experience of the world to be part of the *explanandum* of psychophysics, there can be nothing illegitimate in incorporating knowledge of our experience in the design and interpretation of psychophysical methods. When studying human sensory systems we should exploit our privileged perspective rather than shun it. Stevens and Savage's cautionary stance is reasonable only when applying psychophysical methods to objects that we have reason to think lack sensory states, or lack sensory states similar to our own—objects like ammeters, fulcrum balances and, perhaps, non–human animals.

One might, I suppose, cry foul at Fechner's helping himself to the "fact" of sensory experience, or doubt the existence of such experience in human beings other than oneself. The former view is inane. There is no question that light sources appear as more or less bright, sounds as more or less loud, coffee as more or less sweet, etc. As I have emphasized, it is difficult to articulate the nature of sensation. Moreover, the challenge of designing methods and scales with which to measure sensation is prodigious. Yet, despite these hurdles, there can be no doubt that we experience the world in particular ways. Psychophysics is the science dedicated to discovering the relationship between these experiences and the world; however dim the prognosis for this endeavor, there is no questioning its intelligibility.

Worries that others may lack sensory experience or may partake in experiences wildly divergent from our own speak to yet another double standard. Granting that a properly stimulated brain is the cause of our sensory experiences, and that like causes produce like effects, qualms about the absence or inversion of these experiences in others fade. These concessions to psychophysics are long overdue and ask of skeptics nothing more than that they hold psychophysics to the same standards other sciences respect. Indeed, concerns about absent or inverted qualia rest on a dualist conception of mind and body—a conception that frees sensation from the shackles of physical instantiation, thus enabling it to violate standardly assumed supervenience relations. But why should we allow supernatural challenges to shake our confidence in psychophysics when like challenges to other sciences would be dismissed with a scoff?

7. Conclusion: Psychophysics, Mind, and Body

I have argued that much of Savage's case against a psychophysics of sensation rests upon holding psychophysics to standards beyond those we would apply to other sciences. Because Weber's and Fechner's laws relate observables, Savage supposes, they cannot provide us with information about unobservables. Or, if we are to allow the common practice of positing unobservables to explain the relation between observables, Savage unfairly requires that these posits be physiological in nature. The reason for this restriction is nowhere stated, but Savage's comparisons of fulcrum balances to human sensory systems suggest that Savage believes there simply is nothing like sensory experience that would help to explain the relations that Weber's law and Fechner's law define. But, to deny that we have sensory experience is absurd. Consequently, even should it turn out that the methods Fechner pioneered for measuring this experience are inadequate, the desire to investigate the relation between sensory experience and physical stimuli remains a reasonable one.

In closing, it is worth reflecting upon the enormous resistance psychophysics has met. Why, if psychophysics does not ask more from its practitioners than other sciences do, have so many seen the need to redraw or reject Fechner's portrait of psychophysics? Perhaps Fechner deserves some of the blame for the hostility with which his program was received. Originally, Fechner defined psychophysics as the "exact science of the functional relations or relations of dependency between body and mind" (Titchener 1905, xxii). Psychologists and philosophers have tended to seize upon this characterization of psychophysics, and have amplified it so that success in psychophysics requires nothing short of a solution to the mind–body problem. Indeed, after redefining Fechner's law, Savage faults it, saying that "[s]ince the law no longer spans the mind–body gap, it loses its former metaphysical significance" (363). But, Fechner never intended his law to "span the mind–body gap." In fact, Fechner distinguished between *outer* psychophysics, which seeks laws relating physical stimuli to our experiences of them, and *inner* psychophysics, which *would* relate sensations to brain states. But, Fechner never proposed a law of inner psychophysics, clearly stating that the law now bearing his name is a law of outer psychophysics. Hence, to saddle psychophysics with the burden of solving the mind–body problem and then to renounce it because it fails to do so is grossly unfair to the project to which Fechner's law belongs. It may be that we will never be able to explain completely how interaction between the brain and physical stimuli produces sensory experience, but the discovery of laws describing the relationship between these things demands no such explanation. When pursuing psychophysics, it is perhaps best for now not to wonder about how a stimulated brain produces sensation, but to take solace in the admirable precedent Newton set when describing what seemed a most improbable force: *hypotheses non fingamus*.

Notes

[1]For helpful comments on earlier drafts of this paper I am grateful to Malcolm Forster, Gary Hatfield, Eric Saidel, and Elliott Sober.

[2]Fechner's integration is now widely believed to be spurious (Luce and Edwards 1958), but this does not impugn the use of jnds to measure sensation, nor does it bear on the debate between Savage and myself.

References

Barlow, H. (1982), "General Principles: The Senses Considered as Physical Instruments", in H. Barlow and J. Mollon, (eds.), *The Senses*. Cambridge: Cambridge University Press, pp. 1-32.

Boring, E. (1921), "The Stimulus Error", *American Journal of Psychology* 32: 449-471.

______. (1928), "Did Fechner Measure Sensation?", *Psychological Review* 35: 443-445.

______. (1950), *A History of Experimental Psychology*, 2nd ed. New York: Appleton-Century-Crofts.

Fechner, G. (1860), *Elemente Der Psychophysik*, Vols. I, II. Leipzig: Breitkopf und Hartel.

Graham, C. (1952), "Behavior and the Psychophysical Methods: An Analysis of Some Recent Experiments", *Psychological Review* 59: 62-70.

Gundlach, H. (1993), "Psychophysics, Its History and Ontology", *Behavioral and Brain Sciences* 16: 144-145.

Hornstein, G. (1993), "The Chimera of Psychological Measurement", *Behavioral and Brain Sciences* 16: 148-149.

Luce, R. and Edwards, W. (1958), "The Derivation of Subjective Scales from Just Noticeable Differences", *Psychological Review* 65: 222-237.

McKenna, F. (1985), "Another Look at the 'New Psychophysics'", British Journal of Psychology 76: 97-109.

Savage, C. (1970), *The Measurement of Sensation*. Berkeley: The University of California Press.

Stevens, S. (1957), "On the Psychophysical Power Law", *Psychological Review* 64: 153-181.

_______. (1966), "Operations or Words?: A Reply to Savage" *Psychological Monographs* 80: 33- 38.

Titchener, E. (1905), *Experimental Psychology*, Vol. II, pt. 2. New York: Macmillan.

Treisman, M. (1964), "Sensory Scaling and the Psychophysical Law", *Quarterly Journal of Experimental Psychology* 16: 11-21.

Part III

FIELDS, PARTICLES AND QUANTUM THEORIES

The History and Philosophy of Quantum Field Theory[1]

Don Robinson

University of Illinois at Chicago

1. Origins

In November of 1925 Born, Heisenberg and Jordan wrote an article together in which they demonstrated that Einstein's energy fluctuation formula could be derived from quantum mechanics. They remark that the equations are subject to reinterpretation. Specifically, the states of radiation oscillators can be reinterpreted as numbers of quanta of radiation. They also connected this latter idea up with Bose-Einstein statistics. Heisenberg wrote to Pauli that it was Jordan who contributed the idea of reinterpreting the terms. This was the first step toward quantum field theory. In August of the following year Dirac derived Einstein's A and B coefficients for induced transitions between states but on the assumption that the electromagnetic field could be treated classically (Dirac 1927). In 1927 Dirac lay the mathematical foundations for quantum electrodynamics. Early that year he combined quantum mechanics, special relativity, and radiation theory in treating the electromagnetic field as if it were an infinite collection of oscillators. By 1928 he had a relativistic theory of the electron (1928a, 1928b).

The further development of quantum field theories were based to a large degree on the method of performing operator substitutions on the equations of special relativity and classical field theories of electromagnetism. The famous Klein-Gordon equation, for instance, results from performing an operator substitution on the variables of the relativistic equation relating energy to mass and momentum. Much of the subsequent development of quantum field theories came from generalizing these equations to higher spins and other interactions.

In the 1930's and 1940's it was discovered that when certain quantities were calculated using quantum electrodynamics, quantities whose values should have been small and finite, the theory yielded infinite values. The sources of these infinities lay in products of powers of the coupling constant and certain integrals over momentum. By the end of the 1940's the so-called renormalization program was in place and techniques were developed that allowed finite values to be extracted from the theory.

Feynman diagrams represent topologically distinct ways a process or transformation can take place. It was shown that a class of Feynman diagrams correspond to any term in the perturbation expansion. Second order terms correspond to diagrams with two interactions, third order terms correspond to diagrams with three interactions, and so on. The essence of renormalization techniques is to proceed term by term in a perturbation expan-

PSA 1994, Volume 2, pp. 61-68

sion until an infinite value arises. When this happens, the term is rendered finite by performing a partial summation of the Feynman diagrams.

Renormalized quantum electrodynamics, the first quantum field theory, yielded extremely accurate predictions for such things as the Lamb shift and the anomalous magnetic moment of the electron. It nevertheless had and continues to have many critics. I will mention some of the criticisms and attitudes before returning to this brief history.

2. Critics of renormalized QED

As early as 1936, Dirac, who laid the mathematical foundations for quantum electrodynamics in 1927 and 1928, was saying that we could give up quantum electrodynamics without regret because of its extreme complexity. Even after the advent of renormalization techniques and in his last writings Dirac said that the resulting was theory was ugly and incomplete (see his 1978 and 1981). His main concern was with the fact that renormalization ignores infinite quantities. He believed that it was alright to ignore small finite quantities but that it was wrong to ignore infinite ones. Of course, renormalized quantum electrodynamics was successful in making very precise predictions. Dirac's response to this was to suggest that this success was perhaps merely a coincidence. Dirac tried, unsuccessfully, to create new foundations for the theory and remained until the end one of QED's harshest critics.

Schwinger agreed with Dirac insofar as he believed the theory was flawed, but his objection was that "The observational basis of quantum electrodynamics is self-contradictory ... To limit the magnitude of interactions while retaining the customary coordinate description is contradictory, since no mechanism is provided for precisely localized measurements" (1958, xvi). Feynman frequently referred to renormalization as a 'dippy process', a 'shell game', and said as recently as 1989 that "it is possible that electrodynamics is not a consistent theory" (Brown and Harré (eds.) 1989, 199). Pauli, who said on many occasions that he refused 'to be renormalized', suggested that "For a real solution to the problem of singularities [renormalization] a step of the same size and significance as that which was taken once before in the twenties might be necessary" (quoted by K. Bleuler in Debrus and Hirshfeld (eds.) 1991).

Given the strength of the convictions concerning quantum field theory, one must wonder why the theories continued to be more fully articulated from the 1950's to the present time. Schweber has remarked that "The defense connection during the 1950's reinforced the pragmatic, utilitarian, instrumental style so characteristic of theoretical physics in the United States" (in Brown, Dresden, and Hoddeson (eds.) 1989, 673). Kragh has described the situation in a similar way. In reference to Dirac, Kragh writes that his "critical attitude toward quantum electrodynamics during the period 1935 to 1947 was neither unique nor particularly remarkable" but that the members of the next generation of physicists "adapted themselves to the new situation without caring too much about the theory's lack of formal consistency and conceptual clarity. The pragmatic attitude of the 'quantum engineers' including Fermi, Bethe, Heitler, and a growing number of young American physicists, proved to be of significant value, but did not eliminate the fundamental problems that continued to worry Dirac, Pauli, and others" (Kragh 1990, 166-167).

Several authors have suggested that Dirac's concerns about renormalized quantum field theories may have been met by supersymmetric string theories which are finite and do not need to be renormalized. The problem here is that such theories are entirely lacking in strong experimental support. In any case, anyone writing about renormalization must address these concerns as they apply to quantum electrodynamics and as they apply to the renormalizable gauge theories which are the subject of the historical sketch that follows.

3. Some more history

In the 1950's and 1960's a great amount of experimental data was accumulated from the new detectors, linear accelerators, and colliders concerning phenomena related to the strong interactions (e.g., resonances) and weak interactions (e.g., parity conservation violations). Although much work went into the articulation of quantum field theoretic representations of this phenomena, great obstacles seemed to stand in the way. Alternative approaches were tried, including S-matrix theory in which certain constraints were placed directly on the scattering matrices in the absence of derivations of their elements from a quantum field theory (see Cushing 1991). Also, some authors followed up on Schwinger's objections to quantum electrodynamics and implemented the quantization of the underlying spacetime (see Prugovečki 1984, 1994). I will also mention the axiomatic approach in which certain fundamental assumptions were made and theorems proven from them. The assumptions are intended to be applicable to any quantum field theory and to date no exact theories of phenomena have been constructed on the basis of these fundamental assumptions (see Velo and Wightman 1973, 1990 and Haag 1992). Michael Redhead's contribution to this symposium is based on certain theorems drawn from this approach.

The articulation of a quantum field theory that could successfully account for the strong and weak interactions as well as electromagnetic phenomena awaited the gauge revolution, which began in the early 1970's and continues to this day. The 'standard model' is the result of 'splicing' together the electro-weak theory of Weinberg-Salam and quantum chromodynamics. It explains neutrino scattering, weak decays, current algebras, and many other phenomena. It is renormalizable as well.

Perturbation theory, which is so useful in connection with quantum electrodynamics, but which gave rise to so many conceptual difficulties, is practically useless when it comes to the strong interactions. In quantum electrodynamics, the coupling constant is approximately equal to 1/137. This means that when we use perturbation expansions in powers of the coupling constant the (renormalized) terms become smaller at higher orders. The strong force is much stronger than the electromagnetic. As a consequence, non-perturbative techniques must be turned to.

The main kinds of non-perturbative techniques involve the classification of classical versions of the relevant equations or putting the theories on a lattice. In the former approach we classify solutions to the classical equations. Exact solutions are then found within each category and a transition is made to quantum field theory by in effect quantizing the solutions obtained for the classical equations. Success has been made on this front in the identification of such things as particle-like solutions known as solitons, magnetic monopoles, and instantons. These particle solutions have interesting features which distinguish them from their classical counterparts, including the fact that they have topological properties which are as yet not well understood (see Rajaraman 1989). In the case of lattices, gauge field theories are put on a lattice (usually of size the order of a fermi) with some minimal distance between space-time points (although continuous time is also used in many cases). Moving to imaginary time gives us a Euclidean metric. Ideally when we take the continuum limit by allowing the spacing to go to zero, we should recover the continuum theory (see Creutz 1983 and the articles collected in Rebbi 1983). Mathematical relations between, on the one hand, lattice formulations of classical theories as well as lattice formulations of spin systems (e.g., the Ising model) and, on the other, lattice gauge theories have facilitated the development of the latter. Several theorems relating these sorts of structures have been exploited in the development of lattice gauge theories (see the review articles of Kogut 1979, 1983).

The effect of this lattice spacing is that when we move from a position representation to the momentum representation, a cutoff on the momenta is in place. This allows for renormalization techniques to be implemented in a simple manner. Gauge theories on a lattice work quite well for bosons but many serious conceptual and calculational difficulties arise for the fermion case. In particular, there is the fermion 'species doubling problem.' When we try to put a single fermion on the lattice we end up in the continuum limit with a doubling for each space-time dimension. Thus, for four dimensions we end up with 16 fermions. There are several ways to overcome this problem, which at first looks like simply an artifact of the lattice formulation but turns out to be connected quite intimately with chiral symmetry violation. Due to the extreme complexity and huge numbers of calculations required by lattice gauge problems, Monte Carlo methods on high-speed computers are used to obtain approximate solutions (see Itzykson and Drouffe 1989 and Binder 1976).

Attitudes toward quantum field theories today range between two extremes. One of these extremes is represented by Pais, who has written that "relativistic quantum field theory is much healthier and much richer in new options than had been thought during the fifties and sixties when, to be sure, quantum electrodynamics looked increasingly successful but the status of meson field theories remained highly problematical" (1986, 551). The other extreme is represented by Prugovečki, who has written that predictive successes of quantum field theory "can represent a somewhat contentious issue if one is not predisposed to an unquestioning conformity to the type of conventional wisdom that has become entrenched in quantum physics during the post-World War II era" (1994, 343).

4. Philosophical foundations

In the past sixty-odd years since the beginnings of quantum theory, the focus of philosophers of science has been almost exclusively on the structures defined by non-relativistic quantum mechanics. In the absence of interactions, quantum field theory defines a vector space, known as Fock space, which is vastly enlarged compared to the Hilbert spaces defined by standard quantum mechanics. Fock space contains a one dimensional space in which the state of the quantum vacuum is represented. In addition to this space, Fock space contains infinitely many infinite dimensional spaces for representing states of one, two, and more particles. It is possible to take linear combinations of states drawn from spaces for different particle numbers and form states of indeterminate particle number. In relativistic quantum field theory (with interactions) the relation between the mathematical structures and those of standard quantum mechanics is not so simple.

The reasons why philosophers of science have focussed almost exclusively on the relatively simpler structures of standard quantum mechanics are not hard to find. First, the interpretive issues can be formulated more accessibly and 'cleanly'. Second, an adequate understanding of the technical problems of quantum field theories (renormalization and so on) and their solutions requires a much greater degree of mathematical sophistication. Nevertheless, quantum field theories do raise new and interesting problems of interpretation not already present in regard to standard quantum mechanics. New conceptual difficulties arise, many of which have received next to no attention from philosophers of physics up to this point. There are two collections of papers from conferences (Brown and Harre (eds.) 1988 and Saunders and Brown (eds.) 1991) and perhaps several dozen papers scattered throughout journals. Many of the problems I have mentioned have not received their due attention in the literature.

Philosophers of physics have up until now focussed on the following problems. There are ontological questions concerned with what quantum field theories tell us about what kinds of systems are being measured. Simon Saunders, in his contribution to this symposium, discusses such matters and raises many important questions concerning the interpretation of quantum field theories. The absence of well-defined unique space-time trajectories, the existence of vacuum state fluctuations, and the absence of non-symmetric states in quantum field theories have all been taken to argue against the possibility of giving quantum field theories an interpretation based entirely on particles. Some work has been done on the 'identity' of indistinguishable particles. One kind of interpretation is based on the notion of quanta. Quanta are simply bundles of properties with no underlying substratum to which the properties could be said to belong. Nick Huggett's contribution to this symposium questions the viability of a quanta interpretation. He argues that the quanta interpretation, insofar as it identifies the way quantum field systems differ from classical systems, takes for granted that classical theories (supposedly about particles) cannot be given a quanta interpretation themselves. Furthermore, he argues that the quanta interpretation, although it might work well in terms of providing some understanding of free (non-interacting) fields, breaks down when extended to interacting fields.

The quantum field theoretic vacuum has been the focus of much research. The vacuum state of a system of quantum fields is capable of acting like a polarizable medium which can make important though extremely small contributions to such things as the Lamb shift and the anomalous magnetic moment of the electron, the great predictive successes of renormalized quantum electrodynamics. Since the quantum vacuum is by definition the state consisting of exactly zero particles, this has been taken by many to point to the inability of particle interpretations to account for phenomena represented by quantum field theory. In axiomatic quantum field theory, it has been shown that correlated fluctuations violate Bell inequalities. In 1982, Michael Redhead argued that quantum field theory could be given an 'extended' particle interpretation (1983). By 1988 he had changed his mind and argued that quantum field theory should be given an interpretation in terms of quantum fields and that particle phenomena should be understood as excitations in those quantum fields (1988). In his contribution to the symposium, Redhead argues on the basis of certain theorems drawn from axiomatic, or generalized, quantum field theory, that quantum field theory is not about particles at all but quantum fields only.

Returning to my survey of philosophical work done on quantum field theory, it should also be noted that some work has been done on the question of the reality of virtual particles, particles that appear in the interior regions of Feynman diagrams. They have very un-physical properties such as violating (sometimes) the Pauli exclusion principle and being emitted and absorbed at exactly the same space-time point. These features have been taken to argue against their physical existence (see Harré 1988, Weingard 1988).

There have been questions raised concerning appropriate formulations of locality principles for quantum field theories. Typically, it is assumed that operators defined at different space-time locations commute with one another. This assumption, termed 'microcausality' is often justified by the claim that to have these operators fail to commute would be to build violations of either causality or some restrictions imposed by special relativity into the theory at the outset. Even with this assumption built into the theory, however, we still get violations of Bell inequalities even by vacuum fluctuations.

Another interesting problem that arises in relativistic quantum theories arises from a dependence upon frame of reference of particle-like localizations. A localization at a spacetime point from one frame of reference has a probability of being localized at distant spacetime points when we move to certain other frames of reference. This point has been particularly stressed by Fleming (see, e.g., his 1988).

The problem of renormalization, the source of so many of the complaints against quantum electrodynamics, has been the focus of several studies. On the one hand, those who see renormalization as an illegitimate practice have had to explain how renormalized quantum electrodynamics could have yielded such accurate predictions. On the other hand, those who see renormalization as unproblematic (in whatever sense) have had to give some explanation for why so many, including Dirac himself, have been so outspoken against it. The central issue is whether renormalized theories are in some sense approximations to the full theory. Recall that renormalization, as discussed above, amounts to taking a cutoff in the momentum integrals. The full theory would presumably require integration over all momenta.

The most pressing issues raised in connection with quantum field theories are concerned with the fact that even the standard model cannot be seen as in any sense as a fundamental theory. At present the values of 18 different parameters have to be written in 'by hand' to obtain a workable theory, whereas in a truly fundamental theory we should require at most one or two. In perturbation theory it is not clear whether the perturbation series itself (as opposed to the series taken merely up to some finite order) fails to converge. Indeed, there are some strong reasons to think that in the case of quantum electrodynamics it does diverge.

Cushing (1991) looks at S-matrix theory from the point of view of models of theory selection. Quantum field theory looked strong at first, then went through a period of uncertainty until the advent of renormalization techniques, then things looked dark again in the 1950's and 1960's, then enjoyed a resurgence since the gauge revolution of the 1970's. Whenever quantum field theory fell out of favor, S-matrix theory (which Heisenberg described as the 'roof' over the foundations of quantum field theory) was turned to. This history speaks against the simplest models of theory selection according to which a theory, once rejected, is never revived. More work needs to be done on other episodes from the history of quantum field theories, such as the fact that the anomalies of electro-weak theory and the anomalies of quantum chromodynamics canceled each other when they were brought together in the standard model. This and many other aspects of the development of quantum field theories call out for further conceptual clarification and philosophical evaluation.

I have tried to give merely a sketch of the history of quantum field theories. Restrictions of space preclude my giving any more than this but the reader is directed to Pais (1989) and Schweber (1994). I have also tried to mention some of the philosophical work that has been done so far on the problems that arise from quantum field theories. The reader is directed to the references I have already cited as well as those cited in the other papers in this symposium. I have tried to bring out the wide range of attitudes for and against quantum field theories and to observe that relatively little work has been done on many important and outstanding issues. This is due to several factors. First, the mathematical complexity of quantum field theories, when compared to that of standard quantum mechanics, together with the apparently widespread belief that no new problems of interpretation or conceptual analysis would arise from quantum field theories. Second, there are the strong negative attitudes toward the mathematical methods that have been applied in renormalized quantum field theories. Finally, there is the fact that the quantum field theory program went through several periods in which the prospects for articulating such theories for the three forces (excluding gravity) looked bleak. I hope that I have been able to explain both why relatively little work has been done on these problems and why it is time we turned our collective attention to these fascinating and pressing issues.

Note

[1] I would like to gratefully acknowledge the support of the Social Sciences and Humanities Research Council of Canada (postdoctoral fellowship 756-92-0294).

References

Binder, K. (1976), "Monte Carlo Investigations of Phase Transitions and Critical Phenomena", C. Domb and M.S. Green (eds.) *Phase Transitions and Critical Phenomena,* Volume 5b. New York: Academic Press.

Brown, H. and Harré, R. (1988), *Philosophical Foundations of Quantum Field Theory*. Oxford: Clarendon Press, Oxford University Press.

Brown, L., Dresden, M., and Hoddeson, L. (1983), *The Birth of Particle Physics*. Cambridge: Cambridge University Press.

_____. (1989), *Pions to Quarks: Particle Physics in the 1950's*. Cambridge: Cambridge University Press.

Cushing, J. (1990), *Theory Construction and Selection in Modern Physics: The S-Matrix*. Cambridge: Cambridge University Press.

Creutz, M. (1983), *Quarks, Gluons and Lattices*. Cambridge: Cambridge University Press.

Dirac, P. (1927), "The quantum theory of the emission and absorption of radiation", *Proceedings of the Royal Society of London* A114: 243-265.

_____. (1928a), "The quantum theory of the electron", *Proceedings of the Royal Society of London* A117: 610-624.

_____. (1928b), "The quantum theory of the electron: Part II", *Proceedings of the Royal Society of London* A118: 351-361.

_____. (1978), *Directions in Physics*. New York: John Wiley and Sons.

_____. (1981), "Does Renormalization Make Sense?", Duke, D. and Owens, J. (eds.), *Perturbative Quantum Chromodynamics*. New York: AIP Conference Proceedings no. 74.

Fleming, G. (1988), "Hyperplane-dependent Quantized Fields and Lorentz Invariance", Brown and Harre (eds.) 1988: 93-116.

Haag, R. (1992), *Local Quantum Physics: Fields, Particles, Algebras*. Berlin: Springer-Verlag.

Harré, R. (1988), "Parsing the Amplitudes", Brown and Harré (eds.) 1988: 59-72.

Itzykson, C. and Drouffe, J. (1989) *Statistical Field Theory* Volume 2: Strong coupling, Monte Carlo methods, conformal field theory, and random systems. Cambridge: Cambridge University Press.

Kogut, J. (1979), "An Introduction to Lattice Gauge Theory and Spin Systems" *Reviews of Modern Physics* 51: 659-713.

______. (1983), "The Lattice Gauge Theory Approach to Quantum Chromodynamics" Reviews of Modern Physics 55: 775-837.

Kragh, H. (1990), *Dirac: A Scientific Biography*. Cambridge: Cambridge University Press.

Pais, A. (1986), *Inward Bound: Of Matter and Forces in the Physical World.* Oxford: Oxford University Press.

Prugovečki, E. (1984), *Stochastic Quantum Mechanics and Quantum Spacetime: Consistent Unification of Relativity and Quantum Theory based on Stochastic Spaces*. Dordrecht: D. Reidel Publishing Company.

_________. (1994), "Foundational Aspects of Quantum Electrodynamics", *Foundations of Physics* 24: 343.

Rajaraman, R. (1989), *Solitons and Instantons*. Amsterdam: North Holland.

Rebbi, C. (1983), *Lattice Gauge Theories and Monte Carlo Simulations*. Singapore, World Scientific.

Redhead, M. (1983), "Quantum Field Theory for Philosophers", P. Asquith and T Nickles. (eds.) *PSA 1982*, East Lansing, Philosophy of Science Association, Vol. 2, pp. 57-99.

Saunders, S. and Brown, H. (1991), *The Philosophy of Vacuum.* Oxford: Clarendon Press, Oxford University Press.

Schweber, S. (1994), *QED and the Men Who Made it: Dyson, Frynman, Schwinger, and Tomonaga*. Princeton: Princeton University Press.

Schwinger, J. (1958), *Quantum Electrodynamics*. New York: Dover.

Velo, G. and Wightman, A. (1973), *Constructive Field Theory*. Berlin, Springer-Verlag.

_ _ _ _ _ _ _ _ _ _ _ _ _ _ _ _ . (1990), *Constructive Field Theory II*. Berlin, Springer-Verlag.

Weingard, R. "Virtual Particles and the Interpretation of Quantum Field Theory", Brown and Harre (eds.), 1988: 43-58.

What are Quanta, and Why Does it Matter?[1]

Nick Huggett

University of Kentucky

1. Introduction

There is an emerging story about many particle quantum mechanics (MPQM) and quantum field theory (QFT) based partly on views inherited from physics, and partly on new work, especially that of Paul Teller and Michael Redhead. Three important steps in the tale go like this—(a) The transition from classical mechanics (CM) to quantum mechanics (QM) involves a significant change in particle metaphysics, (b) QFT cannot be viewed as particulate even in a MPQM sense, although (c) an ontologically enlightening understanding of QFT can be obtained from the occupation representation. Though there is some truth to all of these claims, I wish to argue that, as usually understood, they are in fact false.

The ever present danger in metaphysical debates such as these is that participants will be running around on the same pitch but playing different games; some waving cricket bats at the ball, some aiming for a netball hoop and others trying for a touch–down. In the hopes that we can all play together, or at very least so that others can understand the game which I am playing, I want to briefly describe how I think interpretation of a physical theory can be profitably carried out. What I propose is that the metaphysical implications of a theory be investigated by analysis of its formal models; that is, by demonstrating what properties they have or are consistent with. I am particularly concerned with the spaces of possible states, and with their general structure, independent of specific dynamical systems. What follows is a survey of various philosophically interesting properties that are the consequences of the kinematics of CM, MPQM and QFT. Even if you do not find my suggestion ultimately satisfying, it has the virtue that it gives my metaphysical claims clear meaning—they describe the space of states. To see more clearly how such a programme is to work, I will take up the first point by way of illustration.

2. Individuals in Classical Mechanics

It is a common claim that statistical mechanics reveals an important metaphysical difference between the classical and quantum worlds (see for instance, Dieks 1990, Lavine 1991, Redhead and Teller 1991 and 1992, Reichenbach 1956, ter Haar 1964). Though arguments vary, the underlying intuition is that in many particle systems, say a pair of coins, classical statistics reveal four possibilities (Heads–Heads, Heads–Tails, Tails–Heads and Tails–Tails), but quantum statistics allow only three

PSA 1994, Volume 2, pp. 69-76

(two–heads, one–heads–one–tails and two–tails). On this view classical permutations can produce distinct states, and, intuitively, one can identify a single coin with different properties in qualitatively identical worlds. Thus, commentators suggest, classical coins have a more robust metaphysic of identity than do quantum coins. The two flavours of statistics are often distinguished as Maxwell–Boltzmann and Bose–Einstein respectively, but since I will show that both possibilities are empirically adequate in the classical world, we should avoid such glib use.

The notion of identity at play here needs to be carefully clarified; in the first place to distinguish it from, say, numerical identity, and in the second so that we have a well–defined doctrine to discuss. Fortunately David Lewis (1986) provides us with the notion of 'haecceitism', a property of modal universes of possible worlds such as a space of 'possible states'. To say that the four state universe is haecceitistic means no more or less than this: there is a world, qualitatively identical to the world 'heads–tails', in which the heads–up coin is instead tails–up. In other words, individuals have counter–parts determined in non–qualitative ways. On the other hand, if there is only one heads–tails state the property cannot hold, and so the three–state universe is not haecceitistic. It should be apparent that studying this property realizes my advertised method of interpretation; haecceitism is a property of a universe of possible worlds, and a state space is exactly that. The claim under investigation is that CM entails haecceitism and that QM rules it out: elsewhere (Huggett 1995 and briefly below) I discuss the latter suggestion, here I wish to debunk the former.

Given this clarification, it is perhaps fair to point out that some of the authors cited do not make the explicit claim that CM entails haecceitism. For instance, Redhead and Teller (1991 and 1992) only say that '... we hang on to the idea that quantum 'particles' are classical in having LTI.' (1992, 203) (LTI is 'label transcendental individuality', which at least entails haecceitism, but probably also entails certain other forms of identity that I shall explain below.) They argue that such a notion is inapplicable in QM, and though this quotation proposes that LTI is typically thought to hold in CM, it does not of course imply that CM entails LTI. Fair enough, but let's be clear that haecceitism is not required by CM, and so the fact that it is incompatible with QM should not be that shocking.

In our simple case there is an empirical difference between one–heads–one–tails appearing one time in two and appearing one time in three, but such a description is unrealistic, since real coins have many more degrees of freedom than heads–or–tails. A realistic classical system for our purposes is a genuine gas of atoms with independent canonical positions and momenta. It is for atoms in just such a system that it is supposed that classical identity dissolves in QM; and it is for just such a system that we can see that the supposed classical identity is not an empirical matter.

The generalisations of the four and three state coin state spaces are the full and reduced phase spaces—equivalently the phase and distribution spaces. For n particles each with m degrees of freedom a state is represented in phase space as a point in an n.m dimensional cartesian space. Clearly permutations of single particle positions and momenta yield rotations to distinct points, and hence one can argue that distinct states sometimes differ only in the way that properties are distributed over atoms; in phase space, atoms have identity in the sense under discussion. If we couple this argument with the claim that phase space (when equipped with an indifferent measure) is required to explain observable thermodynamical properties, then we have an empirical argument for haecceitism.

In the reduced phase space any two points related by a permutation are identified as representing the same state—equivalently, states are represented as a distribution over single particle states. Explicitly, states are of the form $(O_1,...O_c)$, where O_i is equal to the number of atoms in the single particle state labelled 'i'. Such a reduced phase can be called a distribution. It is clear that there are no distinct reduced states that differ only by a rearrangement of properties amongst the atoms, and atoms correctly represented in such a way do not have the appropriate flavour of identity. Since it is phase space counting that we are all familiar with in statistical mechanics, and from reflection on toy systems like the coins it is easy to conclude that the reduced phase space is in some way inappropriate for explaining the phenomena of classical thermodynamics, and that it is only when quantum phenomena make themselves felt that such a representation becomes useful. It is equally easy to see that such a conclusion is badly wrong–headed, for there can be no difference in the statistical properties of the two kinds of system.

As is very familiar, we can use binomial coefficients to see that the ratio of distinct phases to any distribution of n atoms over c distinct single particle states is:

$$N_\Gamma(O_1,...O_c):N_Z(O_1,...O_c) = n!/_{i=1}\Pi^c O_i!:1. \qquad \text{eqn 1}$$

Empirical differences between the two representations are supposed to be manifested in statistical properties, ideally, in the frequency with which given distributions occur. Given the difference in counting and assuming identical measures it certainly appears that the two spaces will exhibit such potentially observable differences. For instance, in the coin world there are two distinct heads–tail phases, so that distribution appears one time in two. We shall grant that indeed the data of classical statistical mechanics as inferred from thermodynamics reveals that the correct frequencies are obtained by indifference over phase space. What we shall disprove is the further claim that the indifference in the reduced phase space, with its weaker metaphysical structure fails to predict the same data—the two spaces are, in the relevant cases, empirically equivalent. The point is simple; in classical gases we can make the assumption that all atoms are in distinct individual states, so $O_i \leq 1$. The quickest way to see that this is true is to point out that in a continuum, particle co–incidences are vanishingly unlikely. (And one can make this more rigourous, by deriving statistical properties, for instance the Maxwell–Boltzmann equilibrium distribution $n_{MB}(q) \propto \exp{-E_q/kT}$, directly from the fact that state–cells in distribution space have vanishing volume). On this assumption of 'exclusion' we see:

$$N_\Gamma(O_1,..O_c):N_Z(O_1,..O_c) = n!:1,$$

inserting $0! = 1! = 1$ into eqn 1. Of course, for there are n! distinct permutations of n distinct one–particle states. Hence if there are Z $(=\{n+c-1\}!/n!\{c-1\}!)$ distinct distributions, there are $n!Z$ phases, and the frequency of a given distribution, derived from indifference, in the two representations is:

$$F_\Gamma(O_1,..O_c) = n!/n!Z = 1/Z = F_Z(O_1,..O_c).$$

Of course, since the ratio of distributions to phases is a constant, n! is an irrelevant constant that washes out in frequencies.

Let me emphasise the significance of this result. There are no physical properties that depend on how properties are arranged over particular atoms. At most, properties supervene on the precise distribution of classical continuum canonical coordinates. In the case of a classical gas we are interested in the frequencies with which distribution dependent properties occur, and the maximal information we could in principle obtain is thus the frequency with which a precise distribution occurs. A moment's reflection shows that the frequency with which states of coincidence occur is zero, and that of another moment that the frequency of any remaining distribution is the same in both the full and reduced phase spaces. Thus, in realistic physical situations, the state spaces have identical statistical consequences for distributions, and hence since properties at most supervene on reduced phases, observation can in no way select one over the other. In particular, if the continuum spaces are coarse grained into blocks so that many atoms can be in a single block, the distribution over the blocks is a function of the distribution over the (near) continuum. The frequency of any block distribution is thus derived from the frequencies of the corresponding continuum distributions, and thus by the above result must be the same whichever way we count continuum distributions. This of course means that statistical physics is indeed captured by either space. The result I've given shows this must be true, but it can be simply proved directly as well (Huggett 1995).

There is then nothing here to settle any issue about the metaphysics of atoms, and hence the discussion of quantum mechanics which emphasises the claim that 'identity' evaporates in transition is misguided. Put another way, using the full and reduced phase spaces to explain the difference between Maxwell–Boltzmann and Bose–Einstein counting is inept; the difference between classical and quantum does not lie here. 'Maxwell–Boltzmann' should be reserved for any representation that predicts the correct equilibrium distribution law—as both our spaces do. This is not to say that there are no differences worth mentioning between classical and quantum particles, but I will leave that discussion for another place.

3. Individuals in Quantum Mechanics

The second part of the story we are investigating is the claim that there is another important revolution in the transition from MPQM to QFT. This is for instance assumed in Redhead and Teller (1992); the authors argue that the tensor product formalism is poisoned by the classical notion of identity, LTI, and should be replaced by a 'Fock space description, free of labels and LTI.' (1992, 217) In other words, we need a description without particles. Clearly what they have in mind is the mode excitation representation,

$$|n_1,n_2,...> = (n_1!n_2!...)^{1/2}(a^*{}_1)^{n1}(a^*{}_2)^{n2}...|0>,$$

in which reference is only made to the occupation level of some single particle basis.

No one denies that the QFT formalism, with indistinct particle number, presents new difficulties for atomists, but it is terribly misleading to point to the absence of particle labels as the source of these problems. It is to assume that simply because we don't give a proper name to something, it therefore cannot exist! A much more fruitful way of looking at the question is to again consider the way the world is represented through the state space of the system. If we can show, labels not withstanding, equivalence with a particle representation, then we will have shown the possibility of a particle interpretation.

The relevant result is that an n–particle subspace of, say, symmetrised Fock space is equivalent to the symmetric sector of the n–particle tensor product space; with corresponding mappings of relevant operators. This is a familiar result in non–relativistic QM, see eg Greenberg and Raboy (1981), but I am unaware of any demonstrations in the relativistic domain. In the first place there is no interacting relativistic MPQM, and so physically there is less interest in showing the equivalence. In the second there is a difficulty in constructing a many particle relativistic Schrodinger equation even for the free case. As noted by Smith and Weingard (1987), the Einstein equation, $E^2=p^2+m^2$, and the postulate that the Hamiltonian is the generator of time translations, $H=i\partial/\partial t$, suggests the following free equations of motion:

$$\text{Single particle:} -(\partial/\partial t)^2|\phi_i\rangle = (p_i{}^2 + m^2)|\phi_i\rangle$$

$$\text{Two particle:} -(\partial/\partial t)^2|\phi\rangle = (p_1{}^2 + p_2{}^2 + 2m^2)|\phi\rangle,$$

where $|\phi_i\rangle$ ($i=1,2$) are single particle states, and $|\phi\rangle$ is a two particle linear superposition of products of single particle states, $|\phi_1\rangle|\phi_2\rangle$. Unfortunately, because these equations are quadratic in time, the product form of the joint state is inconsistent with $|\phi\rangle$ and $|\phi_i\rangle$ being solutions of their respective equations of motion.

There is however a way around these problems if one opts to work in the momentum representation,

$$\phi_i(p,t) = \langle p|\phi_i(t)\rangle,$$

for this basis is, of course, diagonal in energy,

$$H\phi_i(p,t) = (p^2 + m^2)^{1/2}\phi_i(p,t) \equiv w_p\phi_i(p,t).$$

Thus our desired, linear, single particle equation of motion is, in this representation,

$$i\partial_t\phi_i(p,t) = H\phi_i(p,t) = w_p\phi_i(p,t).$$

This equation of motion can be used to define a relativistic MPQM, and hence to set–up the desired particle–field equivalence. If we now follow the usual path and demand that the n particle states be symmetrised products of single particle states,

$$\phi(p_1,..p_n,t) = \Sigma_{perms}\phi_1(p_1,t)...\phi_n(p_n,t),$$

we can find a consistent Schrodinger equation, by taking the free hamiltonian to be the sum of single particle hamiltonians acting on the various one–particle states;

$$H_n = H\otimes I\otimes...I + I\otimes H\otimes I\otimes...I + ...\ I\otimes I\otimes...H,$$

which yields,

$$i\partial_t\phi(p_1,..p_n,t) = H_n\phi(p_1,..p_n,t) = {}_{i=1}\Sigma^n w_{pi}\phi(p_1,..p_n,t) \qquad \text{eqn 2}$$

This representation is logically compatible with the claim that the system is comprised of n individuals, each associated with a single particle subspace. This claim will run into trouble with the principle of the identity of indiscernibles for symmetrised states, because the state looks the same from the point of view of any subspaces (eg, if we take the reduced state to be the state of one of these individuals, as Dieks 1990 suggests, then they all have the same state). But we no longer take the identity of indiscernibles as a first principle of natural philosophy, so this is not a problem. It is clear that haecceitism will fail in this case, because permuting identical states amongst individuals of course leads to the same state, but haecceitism is not the last word in individuality. In particular these individuals could be distinct from one another and could be strictly identical across time. The individuation would seem to have to be a brute metaphysical fact, and an ugly one at that, but it is crucial to recognise that the mere form of MPQM does not rule out individuals. This taxonomy of concepts of 'identity' also shows that it would be a mistake to lump all such notions under a single formulation, such as LTI.

So, I urge, if the QFT Fock representation is equivalent to the many particle formalism, then it too is consistent with individuals, whether we express states with or without labels. And such an equivalence is easily obtained, for quantisation of the Klein–Gordon field (see Schweber 1964 for details) reveals that a suitable basis for representing the canonical commutation algebra is,

$$\{|0\rangle, |k_1,...k_n\rangle: n=1,2..\},$$

in which modes are created or destroyed by the familiar creation and annihilation operators, a^*_k and a_k. eg,

$$|k_1,..k_n\rangle = (n!)^{-1/2}a^*_{k1}...a^*_{kn}|0\rangle.$$

Continuing to offer mere highlights of the treatment, the quantised scalar field stress–energy tensor can be expressed as a 'weighted' number operator,

$$H_{KG} = \int d^3k/w_k.w_k a^*_k a_k.$$

Application to an arbitrary state, $|k_1,...k_n\rangle$ yields,

$$H_{KG}|k_1,...k_n\rangle = {}_{i=1}\Sigma^n w_{ki}.|k_1,...k_n\rangle$$

Thus the physical interpretation is that this is a basis of energy eigenstates, with the usual understanding about definite values that goes with it. This of course is exactly the same interpretation given to the n–particle relativistic theory that I developed earlier; and it immediately follows on the assumption that the energy generates time translations that the QFT also has the same equations of motion (eqn 2) as that theory. So, if we map n particle momentum wave functions into field wave functions in n–excitation subspaces, the observables and equations of motion agree. Thus, not only is there a structural equivalence between the representations, they also have the same physical interpretations. It is because of this 'equivalence' that QFT can purport to be a complete theory even in a world that is manifestly particulate. Its formal structure contains elements that are exactly those of a particle theory. Of course, QFT also allows superpositions across n–particle sub–spaces so the equivalence is not full, even if we take MPQM to be the set of all n–particle theories. However, this issue is logically posterior to the question of 'labels' emphasised by commentators such as Redhead and Teller.

Let me spell this out; if it is the switch from labels to excitation level talk which is metaphysically significant then there should be no particles even in the case of free field states of definite number. But in just that case the field state space is the same as that of MPQM, and that is consistent with individualality, (not haecceitism, but in the other senses that I outlined). The representation of QFT has a structure compatible with atomism, and that remains true however you decide to express the states. This result does not mean that we have to accept atomism at this level, but rather that the choice is not forced upon us by the theory itself. If we reject atoms at this level it must be on extra–theoretical grounds.

Let me emphasise that one attempt to give such grounds, that of Redhead and Teller (1991 and 1992) is shown to fail by this equivalence result. As I noted above, they argue that we should abandon MPQM in favour of a Fock representation 'free of LTI'. And the grounds are that in (bosonic) Fock space there are no non–symmetric states, whereas in MPQM there is a 'puzzle' about why such states are never realised. Then, all things being equal, we should prefer the Fock state space, which doesn't allow unactualised possibilities; this is the (no) 'surplus structure' argument. That is, we should prefer no labels and no dubious classical notions of identity. Several comments need to be made about this line of thought. First, my equivalence proof shows that whichever formalism is chosen the same metaphysical options are available, so being 'label free' is just irrelevant. Fock space is compatible with metaphysically distinct 'atoms' that are metaphysically identified through time. To be fair, I have not clearly mapped out how LTI relates to the concepts of identity that I have employed, so perhaps I have not refuted Redhead and Teller's claim. However, we should be clear that they cannot have shown that particles and QM can't go together. Second, the rejection of haecceitism in QM needs no such methodological argument, for, as I explained above, symmetry means that the identity of indiscernibles is violated by every individual. Surplus structure does not show that metaphysically robust individuals are absolutely incompatible with QM, and it is not needed to show that haecceitistic individuals are incompatible with QM.

While I'm discussing this argument, let me just add a couple of comments against Redhead and Teller's use of surplus structure in this instance. First of all, there is no mystery at all about why non–symmetric states are never realised; they are not within the symmetrised Hilbert space that correctly represents the world, and hence do not correspond to physical possibility. Of course,they do exist in the full tensor product space, but this is no problem. To suggest that it is will lead to a similar mystery about non–actualised states in any theory; just expand a complete state space. And the fact that we can express non–symmetric states in the same formalism as the symmetric ones hardly makes them possible in any interesting sense. That fact is no more relevant than the fact that I can represent a particle accelerating beyond the speed of light in four–vector notation. Indeed, surplus structure seems doubly inapplicable in this case, for it is nature, not methodology, that leads us to choose Fock space. There are two significant cases, those in which particle number is conserved, and those in which it is not. In the former, n–particle symmetrised MPQM is adequate and Fock space has radical surplus structure because it contains subspaces corresponding to every possible number of particles, not just n. In the latter case, MPQM is simply false and only Fock space is empirically adequate.

4. How not to Interpret QFT

Finally I want to register my doubts about the value of an interpretation of QFT based upon the occupation representation; a strategy advocated in Teller (1990). These reservations are described in detail in a paper "Interpretations of QFT" (Huggett and Weingard 1994) so I will only sketch them very briefly. First, we think that the occupation representation obscures the connection between relativity and anti–particles. Because it rests on a formulation which is not explicitly covariant (it uses three–momenta not four–momenta) the covariant particle/anti–particle distinction is not apparent. Second, it suggests that we obtain a fermi field by imposing anti–commutation relations on classical, commuting oscillator coordinates, whereas it seems better to say that fermions are the quantum analogues of classical, anti–commuting grassman coordinates. Finally, the oscillator account is significant for free fields, because the excitations are stationary, energy eigenstates. But of course, this is not true in the interacting case, so why is this basis to be preferred to any other? The interacting field does not simply correspond to familiar coupled oscillators. It is not true that every phenomenon of interacting fields can be explained in terms of oscillators. Finally, the oscillator basis sheds no light on the nature of the renormalised propagator, a crucial issue for any interpretation.

The three steps that I have been criticising do not so much constitute an interpretation in themselves, but rather a series of claims about what significant issues need to be accounted for in an interpretation. First, it is supposed that a salient fact about the connection between classical and quantum mechanics is the evaporation of phase space individuality. But this itself can hardly be significant if classical physics holds no commitment to the full phase space. Second, it is supposed that a salient fact about the connection between MPQM and QFT is that since the latter has no particle labels, there is no notion of individuals. But in the relevant way, MPQM and QFT are equivalent, so the issue of labels is a red herring. And finally, BobWeingard and I argue that, attractive as the occupation representation may seem, it simply is not the most significant way of looking at QFT.

Note

[1]I have talked over the ideas in this paper with many people at Rutgers, Princeton, Cambridge and Columbia, and I'd like to thank everyone. I am especially grateful to Paul Teller for his comments on the draft of this paper that I read at the PSA in New Orleans. I did not receive them in time to do them the justice they deserve, but I hope that some of my revisions go some way to address his concerns.

References

Dieks, D. (1990), "Quantum Statistics, Identical Particles and Correlations", *Synthese* **82**: 127–155.

Greenberg, N.I. and Raboy, S. (1982), "One and Two Body Operators on Systems of Identical Particles", *American Journal of Physics* **50**: 148–155.

Huggett, N. (1995), *The Philosophy of Fields and Particles in Classical and Quantum Mechanics, including the Problem of Renormalisation*, PhD thesis, Rutgers University.

Huggett, N. and Weingard, R. (1994), "Interpretations of Quantum Field Theory", *Philosophy of Science* **61**: 370–388.

Lavine, S. (1991), "Is Quantum Mechanics an Atomistic Theory?", *Synthese* **89**: 253–271.

Lewis, D. (1986), *On the Plurality of Worlds*. Oxford: Basil Blackwell.

Redhead, M.L.G. and Teller, P. (1991), "Particles, Particle Labels and Quanta: The Toll of Unacknowledged Metaphysics", *Foundations of Physics* **21**: 43–62.

_ _ _ _ _ _ _ _ _ _ _ _ _ _ _ _ _ _ . (1992), "Particle Labels and the Theory of Indistinguishable Particles in Quantum Mechanics", *British Journal for the Philosophy of Science* **43**: 201–218.

Reichenbach, H. (1956), *The Direction of Time*. Berkeley: University of California Press.

Schweber, S.S. (1941), *An Introduction to Relativistic Quantum Field Theory*. New York: Harper & Row.

Smith, G.J. and Weingard, R. (1987), "A Relativistic Formulation of the EPR Paradox", *Foundations of Physics* **17**: 149–171.

Teller, P. (1990), "Prolegomenon to a Proper Interpretation of Quantum Field Theory", *Philosophy of Science* **57**: 594–618.

ter Haar, D. (1964), *Elements of Statistical Mechanics*. New York: Holt, Reinhart and Winston.

The Vacuum in Relativistic Quantum Field Theory[1]

Michael Redhead

University of Cambridge

1. Introduction

Intuitively the vacuum state of the Universe is the state that would obtain if the space-time arena were emptied of its contents. The idea is that if we removed all the material particles, such as quarks and electrons, together with all the force-carrying particles such as photons and gluons, so there was no matter or force in the Universe, then we would be left with a featureless space-time, the bare arena of physics, and this would be the vacuum.

There are many reasons why such an idea is problematic. On a strict relationist conception of space-time, the procedure envisaged would leave us, not with empty space-time, but literally with nothing. Having removed the relata, the spatio-temporal relations would also disappear.[2] This problem does not arise for space-time substantivalists, but general relativity now raises difficulties. Is there any sense in which we can talk of emptying space-time of gravitation, given the existence of non-trivial vacuum solutions of the Einstein field equations? The whole idea of an independent arena against which physics unfolds is of course expressly denied in general relativity. Another difficulty that arises when we allow accelerated reference frames is the Unruh effect (1976). Here the definition of the vacuum as the absence of particles depends on the state of motion of the observer. So two mutually accelerating observers disagree on whether all the particles have been removed!

In this paper we shall ignore all these problems, and deal only with special relativity and Minkowski space-time. But already this will produce many surprises. We shall begin with the nonrelativistic case, where the intuitive idea works very well and then show how bringing in relativity spoils the intuitive approach.

2. The Vacuum in Nonrelativistic Quantum Field Theory

We rehearse briefly how to quantize the nonrelativistic Schrödinger equation. For simplicity we work at a particular time $t = 0$. Then the field $\psi(\mathbf{x})$ and its Hermitian conjugate $\psi^*(\mathbf{x})$ are interpreted as operators satisfying the equal-time commutation relations

$$[\psi(\mathbf{x}), \psi^*(\mathbf{x}')]=\delta^3(\mathbf{x}-\mathbf{x}') \tag{1}$$

PSA 1994, Volume 2, pp. 77-87

We introduce the number density operator

$$N(\mathbf{x})=\psi^*(\mathbf{x})\psi(\mathbf{x}) \tag{2}$$

To see why $N(\mathbf{x})$ is called a number density define

$$N_{V'}=\int_V N(\mathbf{x})d^3\mathbf{x} \tag{3}$$

Then it is easy to show that N_V has eigenvalues 0,1,2..., and the corresponding eigenstates are interpreted as states in which there are 0,1,3... particles located within the spatial volume V. Moreover,

$$[N_V,N_{V'}]=0 \tag{4}$$

for disjoint V and V'.

So we can simultaneously diagonalize N_V and $N_{V'}$, and in particular achieve a state in which both operators have the eigenvalue zero. We interpret this to mean that there are no particles in V or V'. In particular if V' is the complement of V in the *whole* of space we define the total number operator N as $N_V + N_{V'}$, and the state $|N=0\rangle$ is referred to as the vacuum state. We shall denote it by Ω. It is the *global* vacuum state since the eigenvalues of N represent the total number of particles in the field. But it is also the *local* vacuum state in the sense that it is the zero eigenstate of N_V for all subvolumes V.

So, in a crisp slogan, the global vacuum implies a local vacuum. If there are no particles anywhere in space, then there are no particles present in any local region of space. This sounds like a good candidate for an analytic proposition, but amazingly it is just this nice meshing of the global and the local vacuum which breaks down in the relativistic case.

Another nice feature of the nonrelativistic case is that everything works in an exactly parallel fashion in momentum-space as in position-space.

Thus introducing Fourier transforms

$$\begin{aligned}\psi(\mathbf{x})&=(2\pi)^{-3/2}\int a(\mathbf{k})e^{i\mathbf{k}\cdot\mathbf{x}}d^3\mathbf{k}\\ \psi^*(\mathbf{x})&=(2\pi)^{-3/2}\int a^*(\mathbf{k})e^{-i\mathbf{k}\cdot\mathbf{x}}d^3\mathbf{k}\end{aligned} \tag{5}$$

then $a(\mathbf{k})$, $a^*(\mathbf{k}')$ satisfy a commutation relation

$$[a(\mathbf{k}),a^*(\mathbf{k}')]=\delta^3(\mathbf{k}-\mathbf{k}') \tag{6}$$

which is exactly analogous to (1), and we can introduce a number density operator $N(\mathbf{k})$ in momentum-space defined by

$$N(\mathbf{k})=a^*(\mathbf{k})a(\mathbf{k}) \tag{7}$$

and it is easily checked that the total number operator N can be written indifferently as

$$N=\int N(\mathbf{k})d^3\mathbf{k}=\int N(\mathbf{x})d^3\mathbf{x} \tag{8}$$

the first integral being extended over the whole of **k**-space and the second over the whole of **x**-space.

Moreover we can introduce number operators over subregions of **k**-space, exactly as we did in defining N_V, and check that the global vacuum is also a local vacuum in **k**-space. Curiously enough, this feature *is* preserved in the relativistic case, where the treatments in **k**-space and **x**-space proceed quite differently, unlike the nonrelativistic case we have been considering.

3. The Relativistic Vacuum

It is easiest to start with the momentum-space treatment. Consider as an example, the charged Klein–Gordon field at $t = 0$.

The Fourier transform of the field $\phi(\mathbf{x})$ is now given by

$$\phi(x)=2^{-1/2}(2\pi)^{-3/2}\int\frac{d^3\mathbf{k}}{\omega(\mathbf{k})}\left[a(\mathbf{k})e^{-i\mathbf{k}\cdot\mathbf{x}}+b^*(\mathbf{k})e^{-i\mathbf{k}\cdot\mathbf{x}}\right] \tag{9}$$

where $\omega(\mathbf{k})=\sqrt{m^2+(\mathbf{k})^2}$ and m is the mass parameter associated with the field. $d^3\mathbf{k}/\omega(\mathbf{k})$is an invariant measure in **k**-space. Since ϕ is a scalar, the operators $a(\mathbf{k})$ and $b^*(\mathbf{k})$ are also scalar functions of their arguments. Invariant commutation relations such as

$$\left[a(\mathbf{k}),\, a^*(\mathbf{k}')\right]=\omega(\mathbf{k})\delta^3(\mathbf{k}-\mathbf{k}') \tag{10}$$

are now imposed.

(10) should be compared with (6). Remember that in the nonrelativistic limit $\omega(\mathbf{k})$ is just a constant m. There is a similar commutation relation for b and b^*.

The total number of particles in the field is defined by the operator

$$N^+=\int\frac{d^3\mathbf{k}}{\omega(\mathbf{k})}\; a^*(\mathbf{k})a(\mathbf{k}) \tag{11}$$

while the total number of antiparticles is defined by

$$N^-=\int\frac{d^3\mathbf{k}}{\omega(\mathbf{k})}\, b^*(\mathbf{k})b(\mathbf{k}) \tag{12}$$

N^+ and N^- have the expected eigenvalue spectrum 0,1,2... and the global vacuum is the state $\Omega=|N^+=0, N^-=0\rangle$. It is also a *local* vacuum in **k**-space, exactly as in the nonrelativistic case.

But if we try to represent N^+ and N^- as spatial integrals over number density operators *constructed out of scalar fields*, call them $N^+(\mathbf{x})$ and $N^-(\mathbf{x})$, and construct spatial volume number operators such as

$$N^+_V = \int_V N^+(\mathbf{x})d^3\mathbf{x} \tag{13}$$

and similarly for N^-_V, then disaster strikes[3] in the sense that $[N^+_V, N^+_{V'}] \neq 0$ for disjoint V and V'. Similarly for N^-_V and $N^-_{V'}$.

So defining the total number of particles plus antiparticles by $N = N^+ + N^-$, then it follows that the global vacuum, for which N has the eigenvalue 0, is not the vacuum state for $N^\pm_V$, for any subvolume V.

So what has gone wrong? There are three typical responses in the literature.

(a) $N^\pm_V$ represents virtual particles and antiparticles whereas $N^\pm$ represent real particles. So when there are no real particles present (in the vacuum) then what fluctuates locally is the number of *virtual* particles, so preventing the apparent paradox of saying that when there are no real particles present, then the number of *real* particles is fluctuating locally.

This approach is totally confused. Virtual particles arise in the context of interacting fields and have no place in the interpretation of free fields.

(b) It is possible to construct number density operators that do commute at space-like separation, if we give up manifest covariance of the description. Thus we can introduce so-called Newton–Wigner number densities $N^\pm_{NW}(\mathbf{x})$ for particles and antiparticles and define

$$N^\pm_V = \int_V N^\pm_{NW}(\mathbf{x})d^3\mathbf{x} \tag{14}$$

where

$$N^\pm_{NW}(\mathbf{x}) = \psi^{\pm *}_{NW}(\mathbf{x}) \cdot \psi^\pm_{NW}(\mathbf{x}) \tag{15}$$

and

$$\psi^\pm_{NW}(\mathbf{x}) = (2\pi)^{-3/2} \int \frac{d^3\mathbf{k}}{\omega(\mathbf{k})} a(\mathbf{k}) e^{i\mathbf{k}\cdot\mathbf{x}} \cdot \sqrt{\omega(\mathbf{k})}$$

$$\psi^-_{NW}(\mathbf{x}) = (2\pi)^{-3/2} \int \frac{d^3\mathbf{k}}{\omega(\mathbf{k})} b(\mathbf{k}) e^{i\mathbf{k}\cdot\mathbf{x}} \cdot \sqrt{\omega(\mathbf{k})} \tag{16}$$

It is now easily checked from the commutation relations for a, a^*, b and b^* (compare equation (10)) that

$$[\psi^\pm_{NW}(\mathbf{x}), \psi^{\pm}_{NW}{}^*](\mathbf{x}') = \delta^3(\mathbf{x}-\mathbf{x}') \tag{17}$$

from which it follows that $[N^\pm_V, N^\pm_{V'}] = 0$ for disjoint V and V', exactly as in the nonrelativistic case. It is tempting now to interpret $\psi^\pm_{NW}{}^*(\mathbf{x}) \cdot \Omega$ as states with a single particle or antiparticle located at the point $\mathbf{x}$.

However, Newton–Wigner localization has a number of unattractive features. Localization is now frame-dependent, so if we take a particle say at $\mathbf{x} = 0$ in the rest-frame K, then in a Lorentz-boosted frame K′, the particle will not be Newton–Wigner localized at the origin.

It is easy to show that referred to the boosted frame the state $\psi^{+}_{NW}{}^{*}(0)\cdot\Omega$ becomes $\int d^3\mathbf{x}' F(\mathbf{x}')\psi^{+}_{NW}{}^{*}(\mathbf{x}')\cdot\Omega$, i.e. it is a superposition of states localized at every spatial point $\mathbf{x}'$, referred to the K′-frame.

The amplitude factor $F(\mathbf{x}')$ is given by

$$F(\mathbf{x}')=(2\pi)^{-3}\int d^3\mathbf{k}\, e^{i\mathbf{k}\cdot\mathbf{x}'}\cdot\sqrt{\omega'(\mathbf{k})/\omega(\mathbf{k})}$$

where $\omega'(\mathbf{k})$ is the Lorentz transform of the function $\omega(\mathbf{k})$. If we had $\omega' = \omega = m$ as in the nonrelativistic case, then $F(\mathbf{x}')$ would be just $\delta^3(\mathbf{x}')$, so the boosted state would be localized at the origin. The non-invariance of the localization arises of course from the factor $\sqrt{\omega(\mathbf{k})}$ in equation (16), which is also precisely what is needed to get the nice commutation property (17).

So Newton–Wigner localization is not objective across frames, but even in a *given* frame we can see that Newton–Wigner localization is not really localization at all by computing the expectation value of the charge density $Q(\mathbf{x})$ at the point $\mathbf{x}$ in the state which is Newton–Wigner localized at the point $\mathbf{x}'$. The result does not vanish[4] for $\mathbf{x} \neq \mathbf{x}'$, so the charge on a Newton–Wigner localized state is not itself localized, and this happens, remember, in a single reference frame.

We turn therefore to a third approach for dealing with localized quantities in relativistic quantum field theory.

(c) We have seen how number density operators constructed in an invariant fashion fail to commute at space-like separation. Now it is usual in axiomatic formulations of quantum field theory to impose a microcausality condition on physically significant local observables, *viz* that the associated operators *should* commute at space-like separation. The conclusion of this line of argument is that number densities are not physical observables, and hence we do not have to bother about trying to interpret them. There are lots of local observables such as charge densities, energy densities and so on, which do satisfy microcausality. The *global* number operators $N^{\pm}$ are perfectly respectable physical quantities which commute with global quantities such as the total charge, total energy etc., and taking the case of charge for example, the total charge Q commutes with the charge Q_V in a subvolume V, but it does not follow that $N^{\pm}$ commutes with Q_V (a striking illustration of the non-transitivity of commutativity!). Indeed in eigenstates of $N^{\pm}$ and in particular in the vacuum state, Q_V does not have a sharp value, but exhibits quantum-mechanical *fluctuations*. These vacuum fluctuations of local observables are a characteristic feature of the *relativistic* vacuum, and we shall now proceed to investigate some remarkable properties of these fluctuations in the context of the axiomatic formulation known as algebraic quantum field theory.

4. Algebraic Quantum Field Theory—the Reeh–Schlieder Theorem

The basic idea[5] here is to associate a von Neumann algebra of local observables $R(\mathrm{O})$ with every bounded open region in space-time. In addition we assume a Hilbert space H in terms of which we can represent the action of a space-time translation $\mathbf{a}$ on the algebra $R(\mathrm{O})$ in the form $R(\mathrm{O} + \mathbf{a}) = U(\mathbf{a})R(\mathrm{O})U^{*}(\mathbf{a})$. Here U is a unitary operator acting on H and $\mathrm{O} + \mathbf{a}$ is the image of O under the translation $\mathbf{a}$.

For time-like translations $U(\mathbf{a})$ is exponentiated so as to obtain a Hamiltonian operator which is assumed to be non-negative, i.e. the energy spectrum of the field has no negative elements. In addition it is customary to introduce a global algebra R, defined as the smallest von Neumann algebra containing all the local algebras, and we assume that the representation of R is irreducible and generated by the translates of $R(O)$ for any bounded open set O.

There are two further important properties of the net of local algebras $\{R(O)\}$ which we shall assume:

Isotony: For any two bounded open sets O_1 and O_2,

$$O_1 \subseteq O_2 \Rightarrow R(O_1) \subseteq R(O_2)$$

Microcausality: For all bounded open sets O_1 and O_2, if O_1 and O_2 are space-like related (i.e. every point in O_1 is space-like related to every point in O_2) then every operator in $R(O_1)$ commutes with every operator in $R(O_2)$.

Finally we assume the existence of a global vacuum state Ω, defined to be the unique state which is invariant under every translation operator $U(\mathbf{a})$.

From these meagre postulates it is possible to derive one of the most famous results in axiomatic quantum field theory, the Reeh–Schlieder (1961) theorem. This theorem states that Ω is a *cyclic* vector for $R(O)$ with respect to the Hilbert space H, for *any* O. This just means that $\{A\Omega: A \in R(O)\}$ is dense in H, or in other words, acting on Ω with suitable elements of $R(O)$ we can approximate as closely as we like *any* vector in H. The theorem is remarkable because if O is, for example, the neighbourhood of some particular point in space-time, how could $A\Omega$ approximate an arbitrary state of the field, in particular one which looks quite unlike the vacuum in some distant space-like separated neighbourhood O′, without invoking a gross violation of locality? The explanation of this conundrum is that the vacuum is a highly correlated state, and the Reeh–Schlieder theorem works essentially by exploiting the *correlations* between the local vacuum fluctuations in space-like separated regions. In the next section I shall explain how this works in the case of a grossly simplified model of space-time.

5. Fluctuations and Correlations in the Vacuum

Imagine space-time collapsed to two points, and suppose the Universe consists of just these two points at each of which is located a spin-1/2 particle, and that the quantum state of the Universe is the familiar entangled singlet state of the two particles, which we denote by $\Psi_{singlet}$.

So,
$$\Psi_{singlet} = \frac{1}{\sqrt{2}} \quad (u_1 \otimes v_2 - v_1 \otimes u_2)$$

where u_1, v_1 are the eigenstates of the Pauli spin operator σ_{1z} for particle one with eigenvalues +1 and –1 respectively. Similarly u_2,v_2 are spin states referring to particle two. The Hilbert space for the Universe is just $H = H_1 \otimes H_2$ and each factor is associated with an algebra of spin operators R_1 and R_2.

Now in respect of spin, $\Psi_{singlet}$ is the analogue of the vacuum state Ω as we shall now explain. The local spin operators are all of the form $\sigma_1{\cdot}\mathbf{n}$ ($\sigma_2{\cdot}\mathbf{n}$) for some direction $\mathbf{n}$, and the local projectors P_1, P_2 all project onto the +1 or –1 eigenvectors of $\sigma_1{\cdot}\mathbf{n}$ ($\sigma_2{\cdot}\mathbf{n}$) for some $\mathbf{n}$. Now, from the rotational invariance of $\Psi_{singlet}$ we know that all the local spin operators have zero expectation value, while for all the local projectors $\langle P_1\rangle_{\psi_{singlet}} = \langle P_2\rangle_{\psi_{singlet}} = 1/2$. In other words, on the *average* there is no local manifestation of spin in any direction, but there is a probability of one-half that the local spins will be found pointing along any given direction. So the local spin components are exhibiting fluctuations with perfect mirror-image correlation in any direction.

The situation is remarkably similar to the field theory vacuum. In particular, it is easy to prove a baby version of the Reeh–Schlieder theorem, *viz* that $\Psi_{singlet}$ is cyclic for R_1 (or R_2) with respect to H. Full details can be found in Redhead (1995). Informally the proof exploits the correlations to manipulate the state in H_2 by operations performed on H_1 and vice versa, and hence show how an arbitrary state in H can be generated by operations performed on $\Psi_{singlet}$ which are elements of R_1 or R_2 only.

But can we turn the argument round and show from the Reeh–Schlieder theorem alone the existence of maximal correlations? The answer is yes, although what can be demonstrated is not all the properties of $\Psi_{singlet}$, but just those which make the proof of the Reeh–Schlieder theorem possible.

What we can show is the following

$$\forall P_2, \exists P_1 \text{ s.t. } \mathrm{Prob}^{\Psi_{singlet}}(P_2 = 1 | P_1 = 1) = 1 \tag{19}$$

or equivalently

$$\forall P_2, \exists P_1 \text{ s.t. } \langle P_1, P_2\rangle_{\Psi_{singlet}} = \langle P_1\rangle_{\Psi_{singlet}} \tag{20}$$

The proof proceeds by considering the vector in H produced by projecting $\Psi_{singlet}$ with P_2. This vector, by the Reeh–Schlieder theorem, can also be obtained by acting on $\Psi_{singlet}$ with some operator, call it C_1, selected from R_1. Then it can be shown that one or other of the projectors onto the eigenstates of $C_1^* C_1$ satisfy the condition (20). Of course, in the actual case of $\Psi_{singlet}$, we know that C_1 is itself just the mirror-image projector, so $C_1^* C_1$ is just C_1 itself, and is itself the projector on H_1 whose existence we require to demonstrate! But if we only use the Reeh–Schlieder theorem then we have to use the more roundabout construction as introduced in Redhead (1995).

But in the field theory case we know that the Reeh–Schlieder theorem holds, so we can prove something like (20) for any two space-like related local algebras $R(O_1)$ and $R(O_2)$. The exact statement of the resulting theorem is

$$\forall \varepsilon>0, \forall P_2 \in R(O_1), \exists P_1 \in R(O_1) \text{ s.t. } \langle P_1 P_2\rangle_\Omega > (1-\varepsilon)\langle P_1\rangle_\Omega \tag{21}$$

The epsilonics in (21) arise because cyclicity of Ω only requires that the set of vectors obtained by hitting Ω with elements of $R(O_1)$ is dense in H. Again reference may be made to Redhead (1995) for details of the rigorous proof of (21).

It should be noted, reverting for the moment to the baby Reeh–Schlieder theorem, that satisfaction of (20) corresponds to the maximal value of the correlation coefficient $c(P_1, P_2)$ between P_1 and P_2 subject to fixed values of the marginal probabilities $<P_1>$ and $<P_2>$. It is only when $<P_1> = <P_2>$ that the maximal correlation attains the value 1. This condition *is* satisfied for $\Psi_{singlet}$, but is not true in the field theory case. Indeed there is another famous theorem of axiomatic quantum field theory due to Fredenhagen (1985) which provides a bound on $c(P_1, P_2)$ which falls off exponentially with the minimum Lorentz distance between O_1 and O_2.

Combining Fredenhagen's theorem with (21) shows that for a fixed value of $<P_2>_\Omega$, i.e. of the probability of P_2 occurring in the vacuum state, then the maximally correlated P_1, whose existence is demonstrated in (21), must itself have a probability of occurring that falls off exponentially with the minimum Lorentz distance between O_1 and O_2. The detection of P_1 may become effectively impossible much beyond the Compton wavelength that sets the scale of the exponential decay, not because P_1 fails to be maximally correlated with P_2, in the sense that $\text{Prob}^\Omega(P_2 = 1 \mid P_1 = 1) = 1$, but because the marginal probability $<P_1>_\Omega$ becomes so small that the associated event hardly ever occurs!

As a final remark we note as a simple corollary of the Reeh–Schlieder theorem that Ω is also a separating vector for $R(O)$ in the sense that

$$\forall A \in R(0),\ A\Omega = 0 \Rightarrow A = 0 \tag{22}$$

This enables us to prove in a very simple and direct way that any non-trivial local projector P has non-vanishing expectation value in the vacuum, i.e. that there is a non-vanishing probability that the associated event will occur. Thus defining $p = <P>_\Omega$, we have $p = <P^2>_\Omega = ||P\Omega||^2$. So $p = 0 \Rightarrow P\Omega = 0 \Rightarrow P = 0$, since Ω is a separating vector. Hence arguing contrapositively $P \neq 0 \Rightarrow p \neq 0$. This is illustrated in the $\Psi_{singlet}$ case by reminding ourselves that all the local probabilities are equal to 1/2 which is certainly not equal to zero!

So the picture we have of the vacuum is one in which any possible *local* event occurs with non-vanishing probability, so all local magnitudes exhibit vacuum fluctuations, but at the same time these fluctuations are intricately correlated at every distance scale.

6. Nonlocality and the Vacuum

In this section we want to discuss the question whether the vacuum correlations can be used to argue for nonlocal action-at-a-distance in the interpretation of relativistic quantum field theory, and hence to create a putative tension with the requirements of relativity, which led to the demonstration of the correlations in the first place!

Let us rehearse briefly the situation in nonrelativistic quantum mechanics, taking again the familiar example of two spin-1/2 particles in the state $\Psi_{singlet}$. We assume either realism (R) asserting that spin components have sharp values in $\Psi_{singlet}$ or antirealism (A) asserting that they do not. We introduce two versions of locality adapted to the R and A options respectively.

LOC_R: This principle prohibits the transition from one sharp value to another sharp value of a local observable initiated by some event at space-like separation.

and

LOC_A: This principle prohibits bringing a sharp value into existence at space-like separation.

Then the Einstein–Podolsky–Rosen argument (1935) asserts

$$A \Rightarrow \neg LOC_A \tag{23}$$

while the Bell argument (1964), assuming the violation of the Bell inequality, asserts

$$R \Rightarrow \neg LOC_R . \tag{24}$$

So whether we assume realism or antirealism in the interpretation of quantum mechanics, we are committed to some form of nonlocality. For the sake of argument we shall assume this conclusion to be correct[6] in the nonrelativistic case. We now want to see whether similar conclusions apply in the case of the relativistic vacuum.

Taking the case of the realistic interpretation of the locally fluctuating magnitudes, it is well-known that the Bell argument can be reproduced in the vacuum state.[7] So (24) still seems to hold. It is worth remarking, however, that even if the Bell inequality were not violated, so allowing the possibility of a common cause explanation of the correlations by events in the overlapping backward light-cones of the correlated events, this would still not give an acceptable local explanation of the correlations. This is because the vacuum is time-translation invariant, so any common cause events employed to explain correlations at a later time, are themselves inevitably involved in correlations that themselves need explaining, so either we embark on an infinite regress of explanation, or simply accept the correlations as 'brute facts'. So the issue of violating the Bell inequality does not seem so crucial in the vacuum state for assessing whether acceptable causal explanations of the correlations can be given.

Let us turn now to the antirealism option, and the question of formulating the EPR argument in the vacuum state. We recall briefly how the argument works in the nonrelativistic case. Measuring the spin component in any direction for one of the space-like separated spin-1/2 particles enables us to predict the result of the antiparallel measurement on the second particle, due to the perfect mirror-image correlations of $\Psi_{singlet}$. Applying the EPR criterion for identifying an element of reality allows us to infer the existence of a sharp value for the spin component on the second particle. Since on the antirealist assumption the sharp value did not exist prior to the measurement on the first particle, it must have been brought into existence by that measurement, a violation of LOC_A, so (23) follows. The argument appears to fail in the relativistic case with measurements at space-like separation, where the lack of an invariant time order prevents the unambiguous application of the EPR criterion in terms of reliable prediction. However, the EPR criterion can also be given a counterfactual formulation, if a measurement *were* to be made on the second particle, then the correlated value *would* be found, licensing the existence of the element of reality in question.[8] It has been argued recently by Ghirardi and Grassi (1994) that the counterfactual criterion is still available in the relativistic case, and in particular we shall apply it to the case of the maximal correlations in the vacuum described in section 5. Thus we consider a measurement made in a region O_2 that reveals the result one for the projector P_2, and ask the counterfactual question, if we also measured P_1 in the space-like separated region O_1, that by (21) is maximally correlated with P_2, would the result also be one? If the answer is yes, then according to the Ghirardi–Grassi approach, P_1 has a sharp value, which is not the case in the vacuum state (remember that $1-P_1$ is also a projector in $R(O_1)$ and hence P_1 must have a non-vanishing probability of yielding the value zero in the vacuum, as well as a non-zero value of yielding the value one). So we seem again to have demonstrated a violation of LOC_A. But here we must be very careful. To licence the argument for violating LOC_A, we must ensure that if we did measure P_1, this would not affect the outcome, *viz*, one, for the measurement of P_2. So we must invoke a principle which we call LOC_{M-O} which prohibits measurement outcomes being affected by other measurement procedures performed counterfactually at space-like separation.

Then the full argument reads

$$A \wedge LOC_{M-O} \Rightarrow \neg LOC_A \tag{25}$$

or

$$A \Rightarrow \neg LOC_{M-O} \vee \neg LOC_{A} \quad (26)$$

If we want to preserve LOC_A this can be done by giving up LOC_{M-O}. But now we can argue that violating LOC_{M-O} in a counterfactual *indeterministic* setting is perfectly acceptable, and involves no spooky causal action, but just arises on a very natural reading of the truth conditions for tensed counterfactuals in the presence of indeterminism. The argument here is exactly the same as that brought by Hellman (1982) and Redhead (1983) against the Stapp (1971) proof of the Bell inequality.

If this argument is accepted then the antirealism option does appear to offer an escape from the nonlocality argument, and hence to allow peaceful coexistence between quantum field theory and special relativity.[9]

Notes

[1]I am grateful to David Malament for prompting me to think about these issues in the first place.

[2]By strict relationism here, we are denying that relations between possible events could be constitutive of space-time.

[3]For details of the calculation see, for example, Henley and Thirring (1962, 44–45) who deal with the neutral Klein–Gordon field.

[4]See Wightman and Schweber (1955, 831).

[5]For full details of the algebraic approach see Horuzhy (1990).

[6]For an overview of the controversies surrounding this conclusion see Redhead (1991).

[7]See for example Summers and Werner (1985) and Landau (1987).

[8]For further discussion see for example Wessels (1981).

[9]This is also effectively asserted by Ghirardi and Grassi, although they are not specifically concerned with quantum field theory. However, their argument for this conclusion is essentially different from the one presented here. A detailed critique of the Ghirardi–Grassi argument can be found in La Riviére and Redhead (1995).

References

Einstein, A., Podolksy, B. and Rosen, N. (1935), "Can Quantum-Mechanical Description of Physical Reality be Considered Complete?", *Physical Review* 47: 777–80.

Fredenhagen, K. (1985), "A Remark on the Cluster Theorem", *Communications in Mathematical Physics* 97: 461–463.

Ghirardi, G.C. and Grassi, R. (1994), "Outcome Predictions and Property Attribution: The EPR Argument Reconsidered", *Studies in History and Philosophy of Science* 25: 397–423.

Hellman, G. (1982), "Stochastic Einstein–Locality and the Bell Theorems", *Synthese* 53: 461–504.

Henley, E.M. and Thirring, W. (1962), *Elementary Quantum Field Theory*. New York: McGraw-Hill.

Horuzhy, S.S. (1990), *Introduction to Algebraic Quantum Field Theory*. Dordrecht: Kluwer.

Landau, L.J. (1987), "On the Non-classical Structure of the Vacuum", *Physics Letters* A123: 115–118.

La Riviére, P. and Redhead, M.L.G. (forthcoming), "The Relativistic EPR Argument: A Critique of Ghirardi and Grassi" in J. Cushing, A. Fine and S. Goldstein (eds), *Bohmian Mechanics: An Appraisal.* Dordrecht: Kluwer.

Redhead, M.L.G. (1983), "Relativity, Causality and the Einstein–Podolsky–Rosen Paradox: Nonlocality and Peaceful Coexistence", in R. Swinburne (ed.), *Space, Time and Causality*. Dordrecht: Reidel, pp. 151–189.

__________. (1991), "Nonlocality in Quantum Mechanics", *The Aristotelian Society*, Supplementary Volume LXV, 119–140.

__________. (1995), "More Ado about Nothing", *Foundations of Physics* 25: 123–137.

Reeh, H. and Schlieder, S. (1961), "Bemerkungen zur Unitäräquivalenz von Lorentzinvarianten Feldern", *Nuovo Cimento* 22: 1051–1068.

Stapp, H. (1971), "S-Matrix Interpretation of Quantum Theory", *Physical Review* D3: 1303–1320.

Summers, S.J. and Werner, R. (1985), "The Vacuum Violates Bell's Inequalities", *Physics Letters* A110: 257–259.

Unruh, W.G. (1976), "Notes on Black-Hole Evaporation", *Physical Review* D14: 870–892.

Wessels, L. (1981), "The "EPR" Argument: A Post-Mortem", *Philosophical Studies* 40: 3–30.

Wightman, A.S. and Schweber, S.S. (1955), "Configuration Space Methods in Relativistic Quantum Field Theory. I", *Physical Review* 98: 812–837.

A Dissolution of the Problem of Locality[1]

Simon Saunders

Harvard University

1. Introduction

Relativistic quantum theory poses a number of conceptual problems over and above the non-relativistic mechanics. From a purely mathematical point of view it is also much more sophisticated. Even the kinematic theory poses considerable difficulties: locality, antimatter, negative energy, and charge are already systematically linked in ways that cannot simply be paraphrased. A further complication is that in the midst of this structure we have what is usually called the Newton-Wigner representation (or, in the case of the Dirac theory, the Foldy-Wouthuysen representation), in which fields and states are no longer covariantly described and where the "local" self-adjoint quantities (NW-local observables) do not obey microcausality, but only satisfy equal-time commutators with respect to a particular inertial frame. If we pass to this represenation, we obtain at a stroke the basic structure of non-relativistic quantum field theory; it is not too hard to descend from that to a many-particle mechanics, and to recover the usual definitions of localization.

Given this it is not surprising that NW-locality presents something of an enigma; for if it is relevant to particle positions, and if the latter are what are observed in the laboratory—at least in the low-energy limit of particle-detection phenomenology—then the events that we see do not appear to have a covariant description, in direct conflict with relativity. If, on the other hand, it is not relevant to particle positions, then one wonders what it can possibly signify, and why it is there. It is not an ad hoc construction.

Something similar can be said of the "particle concept". In view of the difficulties of making sense of particle positions, it is sometimes said that the particle concept should be abandoned. The two are surely connected, but first and foremost the concept "particle" appears in the mathematics of QFT at the level of a Fock-space representation, where the Hilbert-space action of the fields is given in terms of creation and annihilation operators. Along with this comes the distinction between positive and negative energy, matter and antimatter, and the two signs of charge. I doubt that we can do without Fock-space methods in field theory and solid-state physics. If we abandon the particle concept, what then are the Fock-space states, and how are they related to observed phenomena?

PSA 1994, Volume 2, pp. 88-98

In trying to say something about the concept of locality in RQT we cannot avoid these questions, but a good deal of the concrete formalism—and the physics—will be suppressed. The advantage, in contrast to the line I have taken in earlier assays on this problem (Saunders 1992, 1991), is that an underlying *philosophical* difficulty to the notion of localization can be cleanly separated-off from the more technical problems. This is what we shall try to do here.

Let me begin with a careful statement of the problem of locality as I understand it. It is to determine a correlate, in the language of RQT, to observed laboratory phenomena. In non-relativistic theory we suppose, in a suitably idealized sense, that what is observed are particle positions, defined in terms of eigenstates of position, or better, in terms of states non-vanishing over a small region of space (i.e. with support in the region of the observed phenomena). Equivalently, what are measured are projections (or time-ordered sequences of projections), in terms of which the position operator can be defined. The correlates to observed phenomena are either states localized in this sense or, in slightly more sophisticated terms, subspaces of Hilbert-space or projections.

The "philosophical" business just referred to is about giving up this picture. It is not just that we need an alternative; we also need to understand what is wrong with it, and why it has so strong a hold on the imagination. The difficulty is that the idea is so simple; we think of a particle as a wave, which is localized in a box if the wave is zero outside of the box. Few of us entirely dispense with this intuition.

Then why give it up?—Here is another way of posing the problem of localization: What is the relativistic analog to this machinery? For there is no such system of projections and localized states which transform covariantly, and no covariant position operator or configuration-space Born interpretation. At the level of states, there is no covariant representation at all where the states have positive energy and bounded support (we shall consider the analogous statement for projections shortly). If we appeal to the NW-representation, the state is only required to be square-integrable, and it can certainly vanish over open subsets of space; but its support does not transform as a subset of a spacelike hyperplane, and the associated projections do not satisfy microcausality. If these are what are measured by local laboratory operations, then the failure of microcausality implies that the *statistics* of remote experiments will be modified by experiments performed locally, albeit that the effect is small, independent of the particular local outcomes[2].

I see no real option but to abandon this picture of locality (and the NW-representation with it). We therefore embrace the second horn of the dillema remarked on above. To adress the problem of locality, we shall hold on to those parts of the measurement postulates that underlie the non-relativistic framework, namely the projection postulate and the eigen-vector-eigenvalue link. Some assumptions of this kind cannot be avoided, because we ask for correlates to *what is observed* (so that this is an *epistemological* question). It is true that the measurement problem follows on behind, but our immediate interest is with the contrast between relativistic and non-relativistic theory, not the measurement problem *per se*.

2. The Hergerfelt-Malament Theorem

We have rejected the NW-apparatus of localization because the NW-states, number operators, and creation and annihilation operators are non-covariant and do not respect microcausality. A slightly more general statement is possible: given an *irreducible* representation, there is no other definition of localization satisfying natural and simple constraints, for all the states and projections of this kind have been classified (Newton and Wigner 1949, Wightman 1962, Varadarajan 1973), and they all share exactly the same properties. In the case of free systems, in particular, the matter is settled. But a more general result is due to Hergerfelt, applicable to interacting fields as well. To state this, we need to introduce some definitions and terminology.

We suppose we have a map $\Delta \mapsto A(\Delta)$ from open bounded subsets Δ of Minkowski space M to an algebra $A(\Delta)$ of linear operators on a complex Hilbert space **H**. We further suppose we have a continuous, unitary representation $U(\underline{a})$, $\underline{a} \in \mathbf{M}$ of the translation subgroup of the inhomogeneous Lorentz group (**M** is Minkowski space). By Stone's theorem it follows that for each 1-parameter family of translations $\tau\underline{a}$ (with $\underline{a}$ fixed and $\tau \in \mathbf{R}$) there exists a self-adjoint operator $H(\underline{a})$ on **H** such that

$$U(\tau) = \exp(-i\tau H(\underline{a})). \qquad (1)$$

The *energy* is the generator of translations in time, i.e. for timelike $\underline{a}$. It is *bounded below* if its spectrum has a lower bound. Suppose now that there is in addition a map P: $\Delta \mapsto P(\Delta)$ to projections in $A(\Delta)$ such that

$$\Delta_1, \Delta_2 \text{ spacelike} \Rightarrow P(\Delta_1)P(\Delta_2) = P(\Delta_2)P(\Delta_1) = 0. \qquad (2)$$

We shall call this a *placing condition*. The intended interpretation of $P(\Delta)$ is "system is localized in Δ"; the placing condition expresses the idea that given this, it follows that the system cannot also be localized elsewhere. Microcausality (for the P's) follows in turn from Eq.(2).

We can now state Hergerfelt's result. It is that given translational covariance and the energy condition, the placing condition implies that $P(\Delta)=0$ for all Δ. But is the placing condition of Eq.(2) anyway too stringent? It is stronger than microcausality. Some (e.g. Fleming 1988) advocate that we allow superluminal propagation, in the sense that a particle localized at Δ_1 can also be localized at spacelike Δ_2, but that this can be understood according to a modified notion of covariance ("hyperplane-dependent covariance"). It is hoped that this project could be carried through consistent with microcausality, despite the superluminal propagations.

Hyperplane-dependence is, however, a red-herring, as Malament (1995) has recently demonstrated. Choose unit timelike $\underline{a} \in \mathbb{M}$ and let X: $\mathbf{M} \mapsto \mathbf{R}^4$ be an inertial coordinate system with $X(\tau\underline{a})=(\tau,0,0,0)$. For each τ, denote by X_τ the hyperplane with coordinates (τ,x,y,z). $\{X_\tau\}$ is then a family of parallel spacelike hyperplanes parameterized by τ. For each X_τ, Δ with non-empty intersection denote $X_\tau \cap \Delta$ by Δ_τ. In place of Eq.(2), we impose the weaker condition:

$$\Delta_\tau \Delta'_\tau = \emptyset \Rightarrow P(\Delta_\tau)P(\Delta'_\tau) = P(\Delta'_\tau)P(\Delta_\tau) = 0 \qquad (3)$$

(note that Δ_τ and Δ'_τ lie on the *same* hyperplane). This is surely the absolute minimum that is required. Note that it no longer implies microcausality, so we need a separate postulate for this. It can likewise be weakened so as to apply only to the family of hyperplanes $\{X_\tau\}$ fixed throughout; we must, however, allow for different values of τ:

$$\Delta_\tau \cap \Delta'_\tau \text{ spacelike} \Rightarrow [P(\Delta_\tau), P(\Delta'_{\tau'})] = 0. \qquad (4)$$

We can now state:

Theorem 1 (Malament):

For fixed $\underline{a}$, X, $P: \Delta_\tau \mapsto P(\Delta_\tau)$, if:

(i) $U_{\underline{a}}P(\Delta_\tau)U_{\underline{a}}^{-1} = P(\Delta_\tau + \underline{a}), \in \mathbf{M}^4$ (covariance under translations).
(ii) The generator $\boldsymbol{H}(\underline{a})$ given by Eq.(1) is bounded below.
(iii) Microcausality, in the sense of Eq.(4).
(iv) Hyperplane-dependent placing-conditions, in the sense of Eq.(3).
Then $P(\Delta_\tau) = 0$ for all Δ_τ.

The full Lorentz symmetries (particularly the boosts) are therefore irrelevant to the question of localization; indeed, it was always clear from the free-field case (NW-localization) that hyperplane-dependence *per se* does not solve the problem of the failure of microcausality for the NW-number density operators.

3. The Reeh-Schlieder Theorem

There is another theorem, which makes use of the same underlying mathematical machinary, that bears directly on the central problem. We return to the general framework: we have an assignment, to each open bounded subset Δ in **M**, of a local algebra $\mathbf{A}(\Delta)$ of operators on a complex Hilbert space **H**. There are a variety of ways of doing this, but the precise details will not matter very much. Suppose further that we have a continuous unitary representation of the full inhomogeneous Lorentz group, and that the local algebras transform covariantly under this. Given that the energy is bounded below, if now Ω is a translationally-invariant state in **H** (i.e. the vacuum state) there follows:

Theorem 2 (Reeh-Schlieder)[3]

For any open bounded set Δ in **M**, the set of vectors $\{A\Omega; A \in \mathbf{A}(\Delta)\}$ is dense in **H**.

(A state Φ of the form $A\Omega/\|A\Omega\|$, $A \in \mathbf{A}(\Delta)$ with Δ an open bounded set will be called *local*.) In consequence, it is easy to see that the local algebras do not contain creation or annihilation operators, or any number density operator:

Corollary

Let $P(\Delta)$ be a projection in $\mathbf{A}(\Delta)$; then

(i) $P(\Delta)\Omega=0 \Rightarrow P(\Delta)=0$.
(ii) $P(\Delta)\Omega=\Omega \Rightarrow P(\Delta)=\mathbb{I}$.

The Reeh-Schlieder theorem says that any state can be arbitrarily well-approximated by local states associated with any bounded open set Δ. Redhead has provided a useful and perhaps illuminating parallel between the vacuum and the rotationally-symmetric EPR state for a system of two spin-1/2 particles. However this is of little assistance in understanding the difference between relativistic and non-relativistic theories *vis-à-vis* the concept of locality. The Reeh-Schlieder theorem is a purely relativistic result.

In fact the Reeh-Schlieder theorem was completely unexpected. It was discussed widely when it appeared, leading to Segal's proposal (see e.g. Segal 1964) to use what turned out to be NW-localized states and operators in building up the local operator algebras. This particular line of reasoning was rejected, for reasons that should by now be quite clear, but no very good consensus emerged as to the real import of the theorem. From the corollary there is the obvious indication that no local measurement can distinguish the vacuum state from other states with certainty, and surely, as Streater and Wightman say, "it can be interpreted as meaning that it is difficult to isolate a system described by fields from outside effects"; there are, however, more specific implications for our puzzle.

For one the theorem and the corollary apply to a much wider class of states than the vacuum. The theorem is true of any state $\mathbf{\Phi}$ with bounded energy (Haag 1991 II.5.3); therefore statements analogous to (i) and (ii) apply, and there can be no non-trivial local projection $P(\Delta)$ which has $\mathbf{\Phi}$ has its eigenstate. Given background states of this kind, it follows that a macroscopic object localized in Δ cannot be associated with a local projection in $\mathbf{A}(\Delta)$ by means of the eigenvalue-eigenvector link or the projection postulate.

The conclusion is not so surprising when we recall that neither can localized states in NRQT have bounded energy. But there is another class of states, ruled out by a similar argument, that seems to have nothing to do with considerations of this kind, namely what we have called local states:

Theorem 3

Let Φ be of the form $A\Omega/\|A\Omega\|$, $A\in\mathbf{A}(\Delta')$, with Δ' an open bounded set. For $\in\mathbf{R}$ and unit spacelike vector $\underline{a}\in\mathbb{M}$, then for any open bounded set Δ and projection $P(\Delta)\in\mathbf{A}(\Delta)$:

$$\lim_{\lambda\to\infty} \langle\Phi,P(\Delta+\lambda\underline{a})\Phi\rangle=0 \Rightarrow P(\Delta)=0.$$

Proof

Whatever the sets Δ, Δ', $\lim_{\lambda\to\infty} [A,P(\Delta+\lambda\underline{a})]=0$ by microcausality. Therefore:

$$\begin{aligned}&\langle\Phi,P(\Delta+\lambda\underline{a})\Phi\rangle \longrightarrow \langle\Omega,A^*AP(\Delta+\lambda\underline{a})\Omega\rangle/\|A\Omega\|^2 \longrightarrow\\ &\quad\langle\Omega,A^*A\Omega\rangle\langle\Omega,P(\Delta+\lambda\underline{a})\Omega\rangle/\|A\Omega\|^2 = \langle\Omega,P(\Delta+\lambda\underline{a})\Omega\rangle.\end{aligned}$$

where the penultimate step follows by the cluster decomposition theorem (Streater and Wightman 1964, Th.3.4). By translational invariance of the vacuum,

$$\langle\Omega,P(\Delta+\lambda\underline{a})\Phi\rangle \longrightarrow \langle\Omega,P(\Delta+\lambda\underline{a})\Omega\rangle = \langle\Omega,U(\lambda\underline{a})P(\Delta)U(\lambda\underline{a})^{-1}\Omega\rangle = \langle\Omega,P(\Delta)\Omega\rangle$$

By hypothesis the LHS converges to zero; therefore $\langle\Omega,P(\Delta)\Omega\rangle=0$ and $P(\Delta)$ is identically zero by the Reeh-Schlieder theorem.

It follows that for local states there can be no $\iota\in\mathbf{R}$ and no projection $P(\Delta)\in\mathbf{A}(\Delta)$ satisfying:

$$\langle\Phi,P(\Delta)\Phi\rangle = 1 \tag{5}$$

$$\underline{a}\geq\iota \Rightarrow \langle\Phi,P(\Delta+\lambda\underline{a})\Phi\rangle=0\,. \tag{6}$$

A fortiori there can be no projection in $\mathbf{A}(\Delta)$ with the intended interpretation "localized in Δ", for then it would follow "*not* localized in $\lambda\underline{a}+\Delta$" (for sufficiently large λ).

Increasingly the argument seems to have nothing to do with the concept of *particles* at all, although it is easy to see that the placing condition (Eq.(2)) of the Hergerfelt-Malament theorem is ruled out in consequence. Indeed, suppose Eq.(2) is satisfied.

Define

$$\Phi=P(\Delta_\tau)/\|P(\Delta_\tau)\Omega\|.$$

It follows that Eq.(5) is trivially satisfied for $\Delta=\Delta_\tau$. Choose $\iota\in\mathbf{R}$ such that $\iota\underline{a} + \Delta_\tau$ is spacelike to Δ_τ. Then:

$$\lambda\geq\iota \Rightarrow P(\Delta\ )P(\Delta\ +\lambda\underline{a}) = 0.$$

Therefore for $\lambda\geq\iota$,

$$0=<\Phi,P(\Delta_\tau)P(\Delta_\tau+\lambda\underline{a})\Phi>=<P(\Delta_\tau)\Phi,P(\Delta_\tau+\lambda\underline{a})\Phi>=<\Phi,P(\Delta\ +\lambda\underline{a})\Phi>$$

and Eq.(6) follows as well. For this reason the condition of Eqs.(5),(6) can be considered a *weak* placing condition. Its intuitive significance is anyway quite clear.

4. Diagnosis

The conclusion is hardly fatal to the concept of locality. We can always suppose that the state is non-local, retaining weak-placing conditions in consequence. But it would be odd to insist on a we-know-not-what in remote (spacelike) vicinities, in order to so much as describe the localized phenomena that we see right before our eyes. I think we have presented reasons enough to conclude that the difficulty is more general than the particle concept *per se*. The reason why we are inclined to insist on Eq.(2) (or Eqs.(5),(6)) is because of the silent partner—the *thing* which is localized in Δ. This *very thing* is not also localized in $\Delta+\lambda\underline{a}$. But it does not matter very much that it is a particle; it could as well be a "system" or "charge", or even a "laboratory phenomenon", which is after all what we are interested in.

It is, however, not so clear that it could be an *event*. The question of localization concerns the correlates to what is observed; might these (what I have been calling "phenomena") be better understood as events? Of course it is easy to slide from the one to the other, for the event might be a time-slice of the world-line of the apparatus, which is usually thought of as a thing; but that is all the more reason to take care with the distinction. For consider: we cannot say that one and the same localized *event* does not occur in two different places, but only that one and the same *kind* of event does not occur in two different places. And stated in this way, it is by no means clear that it should be true, or that that can be what we are trying to say. "Same kind as", unlike "identical to", is as it stands a purely qualitative notion. Given that a description applies to one event, it is rather likely that there is another event to which it also applies, somewhere, and at some time.

For all that, there are surely events of so special a kind that we expect that there is only *one* such event—in the careers of individual persons, for example. That may be so; but it would be entirely misconceived to build this into an *algebraic* constraint on projections, independent of the state entirely—as in Eq.(2). Equally, it would be odd, in that case, to require that the state be specified in terms of the structure of the allegedly unique event alone. Whether or not the event is, in fact, unique, will surely depend on the state elsewhere. That is, there may be a role for weak-placing conditions, depending on the state[4], but not for the strong-placing condition, which is independent of the state altogether.

But the important point is not that the notion of locality, satisfying the weak-placing conditions, can be defended by appeal to non-local states, but that there is no reason to insist on the placing condition in the first place. This and *a fortiori* the strong-placing condition is only compelling given that we are in the grip of a certain picture, according to which the thing that I see cannot, as a matter of logic, also be somewhere else entirely[5]. We think there is an essence, an underlying identity, which is there before us, rather than a particular event or sequence of events of such-and-such a kind. This is the picture that must be given up. Here as elsewhere relativity requires the language of events, not of things.

This does not mean we are never entitled to make the sort of inferences licensed by the strong-placing condition. On the contrary, the condition of Eq.(2), with subsets Δ of the reals replacing space-like regions, is built into the basic principles of quantum mechanics, including RQT. It arises as an expression of the principle of non-contradiction, true enough, but concerning the values of dynamical variables. That is, if it is true that "the value of q lies in the interval $\Delta_1 \subseteq \mathbb{R}$", then it cannot also be true that "the value of q lies in the interval Δ_2", when $\Delta_1 \cap \Delta_2 = \emptyset$, and indeed the projections defined by q (via the spectral theorem) necessarily commute and are necessarily disjoint in that case. The variable plays the same role that "the system" or "the particle" played before ("value of q lies in Δ", "position of system is in Δ_τ"); it is only when we have a position operator that we can express the fact that if the system is at one place, then it, this very same thing, is not at another. But this is not how space-time coordinates are introduced in field theory, and there is no satisfactory position operator in RQT.

5. Proposal

The conclusion, although not the whole story, is that we should look for correlates to localized events, not to localized things, and that there is no *a priori* ground for the inference from the fact that event ***E*** occurs, to facts about other events elsewhere, like or unlike to ***E***. This is not to say that there may not be contingent reasons, based on previous experience and explicit theorizing; if I see someone just like Adam step out of the living room, I do not expect to see someone else just like Adam still inside, whether or not either of them is Adam. To take a case of a somewhat different kind, if a nearby clock reads 3.15, that is reason to suppose that other clocks in the neighborhood will also read 3.15, give or take a bit. This is the sort of thing we learn as children; as rules of practical reasoning they are essential, but that does not mean they should be built into the equations of physics. What we have found is that these rules in practice work, not because Adam falls under a theory of identity and "thinghood" which guarantees, with the appearance of logical finality, the strong-placing condition, and not because clocks measure "the time", which is a global instant everywhere, so that it is one and the same thing that is measured by other clocks. In both cases we have only an instance of the weak-placing condition, where, in effect, we use background knowledge to make guesses as to the global state, consistent with Th.3.

We may, that is, abandon the strong-placing condition altogether, and hold on to the weak condition only in special cases, consistent with Th.3. The way is open, in particular, to make use of local self-adjoint quantities (local observables) constructed out of the fields themselves.

I have said nothing about this so far, but I trust the strategy is familiar. Because self-adjoint, we can apply the spectral theorem to obtain associated projections. These are to be the correlates of local events. If it is thought that this solution is too quick, that it makes the entire discussion up to now somehow pointless, it should be added that in the relativistic case the eigenstates of such projections are non-vanishing everywhere in space. Indeed, the only point of our discussion is to see that that is just as well, that so far from being the only way to make sense of locality, the link between the support of the state in configuration space, and the region of localization, this link is not even desirable.

6. The Particle Concept

The connection might, however, be considered "essential" to the particle concept, so that what is proposed is exactly to abandon the particle concept, as Wald (1994) and Malement (1995) recommend. It does follow from our proposal that the concept of particle has no direct role to play in the description of local events, that it is essentially a global concept. I do not see that this means we should abandon it. A related point is that giving up the strong-placing condition, on the basis that it has nothing to do with the concept of a localized event, is to deny that particles are distinguishable on grounds other than some structure to events. After all, when we conclude from the fact that "the particle is in Δ" to the fact that "the particle is not in Δ'", the warrant is that we speak of *the very same particle*, as reflected in the use of the definite article. Clearly, if we only permit descriptions of local events, we should say "a particle in Δ" etc., and only given particle distinguishability—that whatever the events elsewhere, none of them can be an instance of this very particle before me—would the inference be warranted. Giving this up is to give up "particle identity", and perhaps this is essential to the particle concept as well. That may be so; but it is hardly a new argument. We have known from the very beginnings of quantum mechanics that particles must be understood as indistinguishable (this from the statistics). The argument would apply equally to NRQT.

At this point we should get clear on how relativity makes a difference; for the link in dispute, between the support properties of the state and locality, can be upheld in the non-relativistic case. A certain technical apparatus is then available, consistent with the intuitive idea of a "localized" wave-function, which is "confined" to a certain region of space. With this the strong-placing condition also follows. But the strong-placing condition is inherently non-local, when viewed as a condition on the descriptions of events, and indeed draws on intuitions of unique and individualizable things. These are in turn, according to an epistemology based on the concept of events, learnt by applications of the *weak* placing conditions, by learning to guess the global state, with respect to features at the focus of our senses. We learn to get this roughly right a good deal of the time.

But now if the strong-placing condition is inherently non-local, it seems not only can we dispense with it, but that it cannot possibly hold. That is, it should not hold even in the non-relativistic case, despite the fact that there we have a perfectly legitimate position-operator whose projections satisfy Eq.(2), so that the support of the state defines the locality. We appear to have a contradiction.

To resolve this we need to go a little more into the nature of the Fock-space representation, and how it is that a field can be interpreted as a many-particle mechanical system. The essential point is that n-particle operators (and in particular 1-particle operators) are only defined with respect to *subspaces* of Fock space. This decomposition is inherently global, for it depends on the total number operator, involving a global integration over the number density operators. Only once this is done can we hope to have weak-placing conditions. In the non-relativistic case indeed these are obtained for the number density operators, which (because they commute with the total number operator) also leave invariant each n-particle subspace. If we then consider this particular n-particle state space as the entire Hilbert space of the system, the weak-placing is in effect independent of the state, for now every state is an n-particle state. The global operation with which we began, the decomposition of Fock space into n-particle subspaces and the selection of one of these, slips entirely from view. More than that—in the non-relativistic case and choosing the 1-particle subspace—the weak-placing implies the strong condition of Eq.(2)[6].

Our conclusion is that we never do have strong-placing conditions unless we restrict down to an n-particle quantum mechanics; equally, that then and only then can we hope to have position operators (and not just number densities); but most important, that the inferences licensed by placing in all cases derive from an appeal to global knowledge of the state. Therefore, the placing conditions cannot possibly constrain the description of local events, just because we seek only to describe what is local.

That does not, of course, mean that global assumptions cannot be used in the case of particular models. That is after all (if our proposal is correct) what non-relativistic mechanics comes down to; a theory which mixes global and local concepts in devious but effective ways, in the right application. The same is true of our everyday reasoning in terms of things. What is remarkable, in RQT, is that the notion of locality is so deeply imbedded in the structure of the theory that there can be no precise sense in which this mix can be obtained, on pain of violation of microcausality.

This can easily be seen in free-field theory. Although we can as before consider the global decomposition of the Fock-space into n-particle subspaces—including the particle-antiparticle distinction—the latter are not stable under the action of the number density operators. Nor do the densities commute with the total number operator, nor do they satisfy microcausality, not even at a single time. If there are going to be any weak-placing conditions involving particle number, they will have to concern global constructions that have no direct relation to the correlates to local events.

Modulo certain equivocations concerning the normal-ordering and other renormalization procedures, what *are* local observables are local integrals of the stress-energy tensor densities and charge-current 4-vector densities, particularly the time-components, the energy or charge density. With these, or rather with their associated projections, we can indeed satisfy weak-placing conditions given the total state. We can even try to follow the same route as in the non-relativistic theory, down to an analog of the position operator. What we run up against is exactly the difficulty of interpreting negative-energy states, and defining a positive-definite norm. There is no non-trivial n-particle relativistic quantum mechanics, precisely because no local observables commute with the total number operator, and there is no n-charge RQT other than the standard field theories, restricted to the n-charge superselection sector. Nor can we appeal to number subspaces (with definite particle and antiparticle number), to obtain weak-placing conditions for the charge densities, for the latter do not commute with the number operators. In this way we are systematically blocked from arriving at a strong-placing condition as an expression of locality. That is as it should be, for a placing condition is an inherently non-local concept.

It is another matter as to how we are to explain the *success* of non-relativistic methods. Evidently what is needed is the *approximate* validity of weak-placing conditions, for certain sorts of states, arrived at by systematically translating non-relativistic n-particle states into relativistic analogs in the low-energy regime. Surely here the NW-representation plays an important role. I take it that a treatment of approximate weak-placing is necessary to prove the adequacy of the present proposal. That is a matter for further and more technical work[7].

I will conclude with a remark aimed at a different audience. There are obviously points of contact with Russell's use of Fregean quantification theory, with its apparatus of individuation as provided by the variable, in establishing the "true" logical form of names and definite descriptions. In effect, by reading "the author of *Waverley*" as having the logical form "there is an x such that x wrote *Waverley* and for all y, if y wrote *Waverley* then y is identical to x", definite descriptions explicitly constrain the entire logical space and are in that sense global descriptions. Insofar as this must be rejected in the definition of correlates to local events in RQT—and this is surely a theory of reference—the point may bear on wider issues in the philosophy of language and reference. Indeed, the problems we have considered resemble a number of issues in the debate over "internal" and "external" relations, which so exercised Russell and 19th century idealists and which led Russell to the theory of denoting in the first place[8].

Notes

[1]I would like to thank David Malement and Gordon Fleming for a number of illuminating discussions.

[2]The result is due to Lders (1951) (I am grateful to David Malement for this reference): following the experiment to measure X, we should use the mixture over the outcomes weighted with the corresponding probabilities. The expectation value of other self-adjoint operators will be modified in consequence unless they commute with X. The proof is easy.

[3]For a precise statement and proof of the theorem in the case of the unbounded polynomial algebra in the smeared fields, see Wightman and Streater (1964, Th.4.2); for a C*-algebra approach, see Emch (1972).

[4]And consistent with Th.3. What is required is that the "global state of affairs" is represented by a state which is not a local state; and that is a perfectly reasonable presumption. In that case the thing can be before me *and* elsewhere.

[5]It is true that if it is before me it cannot be elsewhere and not before me; but this applies equally if we replace "it" by an indefinite description, in terms of relations of events.

[6]The action of the density operator, restricted to the 1-particle subspace of Fock space, is the same as the multiplicative action of delta-functions (Saunders 1992); the smeared analogs include, in particular, the multiplicative action of characteristic functions, hence the strong placing condition.

[7]There are a variety of abstract strategies, directed at a characterization of particle states in terms of coincidence measurements (characterized by local observables), which do not make use of the NW methods: see e.g. Enss (1975). I take it approaches of this kind are in line with our proposal, and that the point of NW-theory is to understand the non-relativistic limit (it is in this sense a "footprint" of NRQM, in roughly the sense of Post 1971).

[8]The use of the variable in the theory of reference is elegantly summarized in Quine (1990, Chap.2). For Russell's theories of denoting, see Hylton (1990).

References

Emch, G. (1972), *Algebraic Methods in Statistical Mechanics and Quantum Field Theory*. New York: Wiley Interscience.

Enss, V. (1975), “Characterization of Particles by Means of Local Observables”, *Communications in Mathematical Physics* 45: 35-52.

Fleming, G. (1988), “Lorentz Invariant State Reduction, and Localization”, *Proceedings of the Philosophy of Science Association* 2: 112-26.

Hergerfelt, G.C. (1974), “Remark on Causality and Particle Localization”, *Physical Review* D22: 377.

Haag, R. (1992), *Local Quantum Physics*. Berlin: Springer-Verlag.

Hylton, P. (1990), *Russell, Idealism, and the Emergence of Analytic Philosophy*. Oxford: Clarendon Press.

Lüders, G. (1951), “*Über die Zustandsänderung durch den Messprozess*”, *Annalen der Physik* 8: 322-28.

Malement, D. (1995), “In Defence of Orthodoxy”, in R. Clifton, (ed.), *Reality and Experience*. Dordrecht: Kluwer.

Newton, T. and Wigner, E. (1949), “Localized States for Elementary Systems”, *Reviews of Modern Physics* 21: 400-406.

Post, H. (1970), “Correspondence, Invariance, and Heuristics: In Praise of Conservative Induction”, *Studies in History and Philosophy of Science* 2: 213-55.

Quine, W.V. (1990), *In Pursuit of Truth*. Cambridge: Harvard University Press.

Saunders, S. (1992) “Locality, Complex Numbers, and Relativistic Quantum Theory”, *Proceedings of the Philosophy of Science Association* 1: 365-80.

______. (1991), “The Negative-energy Sea”, in S. Saunders and H. Brown, (eds.), *The Philosophy of Vacuum*. Oxford: Clarendon Press.

Segal, I. (1964), “Quantum Fields and Analysis in the Solution Manifolds of Differential Equations”, in W. Martin and I. Segal, (eds.), *Analysis in Function Space*. Cambridge, MIT Press.

Streater, R. and Wightman, A. (1964), PCT, *Spin and Statistics, and All That*. Reading: Addison-Wesley.

Varadarajan, V. (1970), *Geometry of Quantum Theory*, Vol.2. Princeton: Van Nostrand.

Wightman, A. (1962), `Localizability of Quantum Mechanical Systems', Reviews of Modern Physics 34: 845-72.

Wald, R. (1994), *Quantum Field Theory in Curved Spacetime and Black Hole Thermodynamics*. Chicago: University of Chicago Press.

Part IV

FEMINIST PERSPECTIVES ON SPECIAL SCIENCES

Methodological Norms in Traditional and Feminist Philosophy of Science

Elizabeth Potter

Mills College

This essay explores one of the fundamental ways in which feminist methodology in philosophy of science differs from most standard philosophy of science. Methodology in general arises from goals which the methods are designed to reach. Feminist goals in philosophy have been scandalous precisely because they are avowed political interventions into what has been considered a cool, apolitical academic activity. Another way to put this point is that feminism self–consciously inserts certain moral and political values into an activity considered to be neutral among moral and political values; it advocates a moral and political point of view in an area presumed to be objective in the sense that it is without any point of view. And precisely because the goals of feminist efforts in philosophy of science are moral and political ones, they appear inimical to the central goals of philosophy of science itself—the morally neutral and apolitical production of theories about how science works. Thus, an evaluation of feminist methodology must begin with an examination of the place of non–cognitive values in the philosophy of science.

Traditional philosophies of science have adopted many norms and values that are reflected in their methodologies, but here I am concerned with only two such norms: (1) many philosophies of science have taken as a norm or set a high value on the freedom of science from non–cognitive values. The norm that science should be free of non–cognitive values arises from the factual assumption that good science is free of non–cognitive values. And (2) these philosophies of science adopt the methodological norm that the philosophy of science should reflect the (non–cognitive) value neutrality of good science. That is, good philosophy of science should proceed methodologically in ways that reveal the production of good science to be free of non–cognitive values. I will argue below against this standard methodological norm and for the norm that good philosophy of science should allow us to see that and how good science might not and need not be neutral among non–cognitive values.

Let us begin with a brief discussion of the vexed question whether science is "value–free". Few dispute the influence that political, economic and other values have upon the choice of hypotheses to be investigated by scientists—influence often exercised by the institutions financing research. Too, most of us recognize that non–cognitive values influence or even determine the use of scientific hypotheses once they have been established. But the area of greatest concern to philosophers is the technical work establishing the hypothesis, closely connected to what is sometimes called the "content" of the hypothesis or theory, and the issue is whether this work, like the inception and use of hypotheses, is ever influenced by non–cognitive values.

PSA 1994, Volume 2, pp. 101-108

In 1981 Carl Hempel accepted the distinction between cognitive and non–cognitive values (he dubbed them "epistemic" and "non–epistemic") and argued that the content of scientific work like Kepler's laws is free of all values. The essay in which he made this point resurrected the argument of Richard Rudner (1953) locating the entrance of values into scientific method at the point of scientific decisions over acceptance of hypotheses. Rudner argued that the scientist qua scientist makes value judgments, for once he has determined the probability of a hypothesis, the scientist must still decide to accept it and his decision will take account of how important it is not to make a mistaken decision, e.g. when scientists at a pharmaceutical firm decide that the probability based on the evidence of a drug's being both safe and effective is high enough to accept the hypothesis that 'the drug is safe and effective.' Hempel argued that scientists use as desiderata in their decisions to accept hypotheses or theories such epistemic values as contribute to the objectives of scientific inquiry, that is, to the improvement of scientific knowledge. His list of epistemic values includes the theory's being probably true, rich in informational content, closely fitting experimental data, having predictive power, simplicity and compatibility with established theories in related fields. Ultimately, he suggested that these desiderata constitute the goal of science. But Hempel rejected the entrance of values, both epistemic and non–epistemic, into what he called the "content" of a hypothesis:

> Since it is often said that science presupposes value judgment, let me stress that epistemic judgments of value do not enter into the content of scientific hypotheses or theories; Kepler's laws, for example, do not presuppose or imply any value judgments at all—either epistemic or of other kinds. But epistemic valuation does enter into the acceptance of hypotheses or theories in this sense: the assertion that a given hypothesis H is acceptable in a given knowledge situation implies that the acceptance of H possesses a greater expectable epistemic value for science than does the acceptance of any rival hypothesis that may be under consideration. (Hempel 1981, 398)

Kepler's laws, and by analogy other scientific laws and hypotheses, do not, according to Hempel, presuppose or imply any value judgments at all—either epistemic or of other kinds. Hempel makes it clear here that the connection between a law or hypothesis and a value must be one of necessity. On this reading, Hempel requires that the value(s) be part of the meaning or definition of the law or hypothesis and he assumes that if B is part of the "content" or meaning of A, then a necessary or analytic connection exists between A and B. Thus, to show that Kepler's laws presupposed some gender values, feminists would have to prove a necessary or analytic connection between the laws and those gender values. But there are other ways for values to" enter into the content of scientific hypotheses or theories." Kepler's laws might as a matter of historical fact contain terms that connoted values for some people at a given place and time, for example, for Kepler and others in the Sixteenth Century. Just such a connection is to be found between certain religious and political values and both the principle of the inertia of matter and the principle of hylozooism in the Seventeenth Century. These scientific hypotheses or theories had social meanings in the sense that, for Robert Boyle and others, these hypotheses had religious and political connotations (J.R. Jacob 1977, J.R. and M.C. Jacob 1980, Rattansi 1968 and 1972 and Potter 1989 and 1993). Given this sort of possibility for the connection between values and Kepler's laws, Hempel's claim that Kepler's laws do not contain any value judgments would be a claim that, as a matter of historical fact, the laws did not presuppose, in the sense of "connote to anyone," any values. But whether Kepler's laws contained any values in this sense is a matter of fact to be empirically determined through a case study. We will return below to the problems facing attempts to do these case studies.

The historical importance of Hempel's 1981 essay is that in it he made the turn to a pragmatic, decision–theoretic model of science and set out a list of cognitive values on the basis of which he thought scientists should decide among hypotheses. Ultimately, he stipulated that the goal of science just is to choose theories that ever better satisfy the cognitive values (1981, 404). Thus, his definition of the goal of science is normative, based on his argument that to be rational, scientific decisions must accord with cognitive values. It is not descriptive, based on an empirical survey of actual scientific practice. And the unstated assumption driving his argument is that if non–cognitive values were to enter scientists' decisions among theories, the result would be bad science. Such decisions would be irrational, inconsistent with the goal of science, the improvement of scientific knowledge. On Hempel's view, non–cognitive values have no place at all in good scientific work. As we have seen, he canvasses only two possible locations for values: in the decision to accept a hypothesis, and in the (analytic) "content" of a hypothesis or theory. He argues that, while cognitive values have a place in decisions among hypotheses, neither cognitive nor non–cognitive values have a place in the content of hypotheses; good science, such as that found in Kepler's laws, is value–free.

But decision–theoretic philosophies of science can reveal possible ways in which non–cognitive values might influence good scientific decisions. These philosophies include the decision theoretic models of science offered by Mary Hesse (1974), Bas Van Fraassen (1980) and Ron Giere (1988). Here I will describe only Hesse's Network Model of scientific theories in enough detail to make it clear how she allows us to see whether and when non–cognitive values influence scientific decision–making.

Hesse understands a scientific theory as a system of laws which has a very complex relation to nature. When the scientist establishes a law, Hesse argues, he classifies phenomena on the basis of resemblances among them. Any scientist is, then, constantly faced with decisions as to whether two things are similar enough to be classed together. But since phenomena are similar in some respects and different in others (none are identical; they differ at least in occurring at different times or occupying different locations), the question becomes, "Which respects are more important, the similar ones or the dissimilar ones?" When the data are all in—here observations of the respects in which phenomena do and do not resemble one another—decisions must be made about which data are significant. This is a fundamental case of "interpreting the data." Data alone, observations alone, do not determine a law or generalization; for example, we observe that whales swim in the water and so are like fish; but we also observe that they are live-bearing like mammals. Are they fish or mammals? Because similarity is not transitive, a decision must be made on grounds other than observed similarity. That is, b may resemble a and b may resemble c, but a and c do not therefore resemble one another; how, then, should we classify b? As an a or as a c? Since any decision here is underdetermined by the data, it has to be determined on other grounds.

One criterion at work in such a case is logical coherence throughout the system; however, we cannot claim that this criterion alone is sufficient to account for theory production. Scientists do not always decide between conflicting observations on the grounds that one generalization provides coherence with the greatest number of other generalizations. The problematic generalization may instead be the occasion to decide that most of the generalizations in the theory are wrong.

At this point, the mainstream philosophers who adopt a Network Model argue that scientists either do or should have recourse to cognitive virtues. Scientists hold or should hold certain assumptions about what constitute good systems of laws or "good theories." Just so, Quine has argued, the assumptions that good theories are "conservative" or are "simple" guide the scientist to make the decision that conserves most of what has been held true in the past, or the one that makes the system simpler (Quine 1978). We have seen Hempel's list of "epistemic virtues" above. Hesse refers to the virtues as "coherence conditions" and argues that they include assumptions such as the goodness of symmetry and of certain analogies, models and so on (Hesse 1974, 52). However, feminists, as critical science scholars, want to know, not what mainstream philosophers of science think scientists should do, but what scientists actually do. That is, we need to be able to look and see what assumptions scientists actually hold to when they decide between conflicting generalizations. The feminist working hypothesis is that the assumptions guiding classificatory decisions may be androcentric or sexist.[1]

Thus, feminist concerns lead to an extension of the Network Model by recognizing gender (as well as class, race and other) assumptions as "coherence conditions." Symmetry, favored analogies and models, like the traditional cognitive virtues, are still "technical" considerations, suitable for an internalist account of scientific theory production. But an extended model shows us how androcentric or sexist assumptions influence the construction of scientific theories. At least for those cases in which a particular generalization is underdetermined by the data, the decision as to which generalization to adopt must be based on other grounds than simple observation. Because all the generalizations in a system are logically interrelated, the adoption of one of a pair of conflicting generalizations will have repercussions throughout the system and throughout related systems. The assumption of technical coherence conditions or cognitive virtues can determine which repercussions are desirable, but so can the assumption of some other principle, for instance that male behavior is the norm, that male behavior is crucial to evolution, that hierarchies are functional, that hierarchical models are better than nonhierarchical ones or that women should be kept in a secondary social position. The suggestion here is that feminist studies of scientific work should look carefully at the constraints affecting the choices scientists make between conflicting generalizations. On a Network Model each generalization in the system is—at any given time, though not at all times—corrigible, so there is nothing theoretically to prevent us from discovering that even the most innocent choice is constrained ultimately by an androcentric or sexist assumption.

The flexibility of any system of generalizations means that choices among generalizations can be made that allow at once some degree of empirical adequacy, of coherence, of fruitfulness, simplicity, faithfulness to preferred analogies or models and the maintenance of androcentric or sexist assumptions. Thus, the model makes it clear that even good scientific theories, by all the traditional criteria, can be androcentric or sexist in the sense that a sexist or androcentric assumption constrains the distribution of truth values throughout the system. The flexibility of theoretical systems also allows the possibility of new and different theory constructions. Theories could be constructed that base classificatory decisions on feminist assumptions instead of antifeminist ones. The maintenance of a feminist assumption, such as the assumption that women were significant in human evolution or that nonhierarchical, organismic models are better than hierarchical ones, or that women and men should be allowed equal social positions, would have repercussions throughout the classificatory system and would still allow, just as nonfeminist assumptions have, some degree of empirical adequacy, of coherence, of fruitfulness, simplicity, faithfulness to preferred analogies or models, and so on.[2] Finally, we should note that while the Network Model shows that some coherence condition(s) must be used by scientists, none— including non–cognitive coherence conditions such as those mentioned above—operates necessarily or always or even most of the time. Science scholars must look at each case to determine which coherence conditions scientists employed.

Ron Giere's decision theoretic model of science also allows us to see how non–cognitive values can influence scientific decision–making. And Giere is quite clear about the influence of non–cognitive values upon scientific work: he points out that we must recognize not only that scientists value correct outcomes more than mistakes, but also that they are not indifferent to the choice between two correct outcomes. His decision theory matrix allows us to account for the fact that "actual scientists do not value the two correct decisions equally or regard the two mistakes with equal anxiety. That is, a scientist will normally prefer that the one model be accepted rather than the other . . . ." (Giere 1988, 163)

Since these models of science show us how science and values can be connected, the remaining question is an empirical one: whether there are any examples of instrumentally good scientific decisions influenced by non–cognitive values. Clearly, only empirical investigation which does not beg the question by assuming at the outset that good science is non–cognitively value neutral can determine whether cases of good science are or are not neutral. And, indeed, studies that are methodologically agnostic about the non–cognitive value neutrality of good science have produced plausible case histories revealing the influence of moral, religious and other non–cognitive values upon good science.

Thus, the conclusion that any science influenced by non–cognitive values is instrumentally bad science is either empirically premature or question begging.

The possibility that good scientific work is sometimes influenced by moral or political values runs directly against common scientific parlance in which "good science" means instrumentally good science that is non–cognitively value–neutral. The assumption is that all instrumentally good science is (non–cognitively) value–neutral, from which it would follow that any scientific work influenced by non–cognitive values (good or bad) is instrumentally bad science and is dubbed "biased" science. The assumption that science must be morally neutral is based on the recognition that bias often clouds one's judgment, causing poor data selection, poor interpretation of data, and so on; therefore, bias is supposed always to produce instrumentally bad science. That is, a theory chosen for biased reasons is supposed not to fit the facts, so experiments or technology based on the theory would not work. However, to make my point about the compatibility of good science and non–cognitive values, let us make a distinction between bias and other non–cognitive values: if 'bias' refers to the influence of a value that leads in a particular case to bad scientific work, the question is whether that same value always leads to instrumentally bad science; is that value always a 'bias'? We need to make room for 'non–biasing, non–cognitive values'. This is a bit like the distinction between murder and other killing of people. Murder and bias are already bad. Murder is morally bad and bias is instrumentally bad. Of course, non–cognitive values have led to many cases of instrumentally bad science; these values are 'biases' and these cases show us that 'bias' leads to bad science. But the point is that it ain't necessarily so. And Hesse's Network Model shows why it isn't necessarily so.

As a norm, the proposition, "good science is morally neutral" is a rule–of–thumb for scientists. It tells them that their values might function as biases and might cloud their judgment; the norm alerts them to prevent that from happening. But as a rule–of–thumb, the proposition is consistent with the recognition that moral and political values need not cloud their judgment, but can be made compatible with empirical adequacy and other cognitive values. Thus, as a factual claim, "(all) good science is morally neutral," is either false or tautological.

This gives philosophers of science a reason to think carefully when choosing between the methodological norm that (2) philosophy of science should hold good science to be neutral among non–cognitive values and the norm that (2') philosophy of science should allow us to see whether and how non–cognitive values influence good science. Indeed, whether a philosophy of science adopts (2) or (2') will determine in advance whether that philosophy of science could account for cases of good science that are influenced by non–cognitive values.

The decision theoretic models produced by Hempel, Hesse and other philosophers lie at the more descriptive end of the spectrum between normative and descriptive philosophies of science. They attempt to describe activities of actual scientists, including their decisions among hypotheses, more or less accurately. Therefore some degree of empirical adequacy is necessary for their success. Giere states explicitly that a good philosophy of science should be empirically adequate in describing the decisions of scientists. Noting that recent sociology of science shows scientists using "professional and other broader interests" as well as traditional cognitive virtues to make their decisions, Giere says, "Since scientists obviously have both professional and social interests, any model of scientific decision making that restricted consideration to some supposed set of 'scientific values' would stand little change of fitting the actions of real scientists." (Giere 1988, 163) Moreover, he says, "As I understand it, a cognitive theory of science need not deny the importance of these other interests. If it did, it could not be an adequate theory of science." (Giere 1988, 165) It would not be empirically adequate to the facts about scientists.

Moreover, in its descriptive aspects, a philosophy of science is similar to a history or sociology of science and, with them, similar to work in natural science: all must decide which facts in the case under consideration are relevant and must be accounted for. The problem becomes one of determining whether an account is empirically adequate enough; and here is a point at which non–cognitive values can influence a philosophy of science as well as history, sociology and the natural sciences themselves. Which facts are included in an account of events depends in part upon the assumptions, interests and values of the philosopher or historian. If, for example, he assumes from the outset that gender politics are irrelevant in the work to establish or justify a hypothesis, the philosopher or historian is in danger of overlooking their operation if they are present. And if he depends upon case studies conducted by other scholars, the philosopher is at their mercy and risks acquiescing in selections they made on the basis of their norms and values. This problem is particularly acute when the norm guiding their choice of facts is the moral neutrality of good science. Unless the philosopher does his own historical case studies, he can be misled by case studies written under the influence of the value–neutrality norm of good science, for these studies are not likely to mention any non–cognitive values at work in the context of justification. Compare, for example, studies of Robert Boyle's work on early modern atomic theory by J.B. Conant (1970) and Marie Boas (1952 and 1976) with those studies by James Jacob (1977) and by Steve Shapin and Simon Schaffer (1985). Conant simply omits the role Boyle's political and religious commitments played in the production of Boyle's Law of Gases and, although Boas does mention those commitments, she never connects them with Boyle's work on air pressure.

Regardless of who does the case study, we are unlikely to find a smoking gun, that is, a scientist claiming or admitting outright that non–cognitive values influenced his theory choice—consider how unusual was Newton's remark, "When I wrote my treatise upon our Systeme I had an eye upon such Principles as might work with considering men for the beliefe of a Deity & nothing can rejoyce me more than to find it usefull for that purpose." (Newton 1959–1967, 233) The usual case is not one in which the historical record is crystal clear; instead, we get indications of some sort. But how strong must the indications be to require philosophical notice? When can the philosopher ignore them? Let us suppose a case study published by a young feminist historian in the journal, *Social Studies of Science*. Is a philosophy of science descriptive enough if it ignores the indications put forward in the account? Or suppose the philosopher does his own primary research upon one of the paradigm cases in the history of science and uncovers indications that in their interpretation of the experimental data, the scientists in the case were influenced by political considerations. In making the decision to include or exclude these indications from the case history which his philosophy must explain, the philosopher of science can be influenced by the desiderata of good history or sociology of science, by philosophical desiderata, by professional interests and by direct social and political interests or by background assumptions that include socially or politically significant interests or values. In fact, since neither the desiderata of history of science nor the desiderata of the philosophy of science are well defined, their application is also open to the influence of non–cognitive values. (This point is precisely analogous to the controversial claim that the desiderata of science are not well defined and so are always open to negotiation.)

But whether and how the philosopher chooses to take account of indications that non–cognitive values influenced the work he is examining will depend upon whether he has chosen as norms that (1) good science is neutral among non–cognitive values and, consequently, that (2) good philosophy of science reflects (1) the non–cognitive value–neutrality of good science. These norms will guide him to omit the indications from his case history and thus to produce a philosophy of science that reproduces the picture of good scientific work as neutral among non–cognitive values. Thus, the choice to adopt or reject (1) and (2) is fundamental for philosophers of science because, if we adopt them, we will construct or choose a philosophy of science which will reinforce them; and if we reject them, we will construct or choose a philosophy of science reinforcing the alternative norms: (1') that good science need not be neutral among non–cognitive values and (2') that good philosophy of science can make clear how non–cognitive values might influence good scientific work.

Failing an *a priori* argument for the claim that good science is neutral among non–cognitive values, and considering the small but growing bibliography of case studies refuting that claim, I suggest that we reject (2) the norm that good philosophy of science should assume that good science is neutral among non–cognitive values and adopt the alternative norm (2') that good philosophy of science should allow us to see whether and how non–cognitive values influence good science. This is the methodological norm feminist philosophy of science adopts in order to pursue one of its scandalous goals, viz. determining whether and when gender politics influence good scientific work.

Notes

[1]David Bloor (1982) argues that coherence conditions should include any social interests that influence the choice a scientist makes between competing hypotheses. Although he never mentions gender considerations, he might include androcentric or sexist social interests as coherence conditions. But there is a problem with the notion of "social interest" here: a woman scientist might well adopt a sexist or androcentric coherence condition even when it is against her social interest to do so. Cf. also Longino (1990), esp. Ch. 3. On the model set out here, what she refers to as "background assumptions" determine scientists' classificatory decisions.

[2]The sociobiological theories of Sara Hardy, Nancy Tanner and Adrienne Zihlman provide an excellent illustration of this point. Cf. (Hardy 1981), (Tanner 1981), (Tanner and Zihlman 1976) and (Zihlman 1978).

References

Bloor, D. (1982), "Durkheim and Mauss Revisited: Classification and the Sociology of Knowledge", *Studies in History and Philosophy of Science* 13: 267-297.

Boas, M. (1952), "The Establishment of the Mechanical Philosophy", *Osiris* 10: 412–541.

_ _ _ _ . (1976), *Robert Boyle and Seventeenth–century Chemistry*. Millwood: Kraus Reprint Co.

Conant, J.B. (1970), *Robert Boyle's Experiments in Pneumatics*. Cambridge, Ma.: Harvard University Press.

Giere, R.N. (1988), *Explaining Science*. Chicago and London: University of Chicago Press.

Hardy, S.B. (1981), *The Woman That Never Evolved*. Cambridge: Harvard University Press.

Jacob, J.R. (1977), *Robert Boyle and the English Revolution*. New York: Burt Franklin and Co., Inc.

Jacob, J.R. and Jacob, M.C. (1980), "The Anglican Origins of Modern Science: The Metaphysical Foundations of the Whig Constitution", *Isis* 71: 251-267.

Longino, H. (1990), *Science As Social Knowledge*. Princeton: Princeton University Press.

Newton, I. (1959–1977), Letter to Richard Bentley in H.W. Turnbull, (ed.), *The Correspondence of Isaac Newton* III. Cambridge.: Cambridge University Press, p. 233.

Potter, E. (1989), "Modeling the Gender Politics in Science", in N. Tuana, (ed.), *Feminism and Science*. Bloomington and Indianapolis: Indiana University Press, pp. 132–146.

_ _ _ _ . (1993), "Gender and Epistemic Negotiation", in L. Alcoff and E. Potter, (eds.), *Feminist Epistemologies*. New York: Routledge, pp. 161–186.

Quine, W.V. (1978), "The Web of Belief", New York: Random House.

Rattansi, P.M. (1968), "The Intellectual Origins of the Royal Society", *Notes and Records of the Royal Society* 23: 129-143.

_ _ _ _ _ _ _ _ . (1972), "The Social Interpretation of Science in the Seventeenth Century", in Peter Mathias, (ed.), *Science and Society 1600–1900*. Cambridge, U.K.: Cambridge University Press.

Rudner, R. (1953), "The Scientist Qua Scientist Makes Value Judgments", *Philosophy of Science* 20: 1–6.

Shapin, S. and Schaffer, S. (1985), *Leviathan and the Air Pump: Hobbes, Boyle, and the Experimental Life*. Princeton: Princeton University Press.

Tanner, N. (1981), *On Becoming Human*. Cambridge: Cambridge University Press.

Tanner, N. and Zihlman, A. (1976), "Women in Evolution, Part I: Innovation and Selection in Human Origins", *Signs* 1: 585-608.

Van Fraassen, B.C. (1980), *The Scientific Image*. Oxford: Clarendon Press.

Zihlman, A. (1978), "Women in Evolution, Part II: Subsistence and Social Organization Among Early Hominids", *Signs* 4: 4-20.

Methodological Issues in the Construction ofGender as a Meaningful Variable in Scientific Studies of Cognition[1]

Phyllis Rooney

Oakland University

1. Introduction: Situating Questions and Meanings

There are many reasons why my "special science," psychology—and more specifically cognitive psychology—lends itself to particularly fruitful feminist philosophical analysis. Many central questions in feminist philosophy of science and feminist science studies are well illuminated there, especially those that are reflected in specific methodological issues. For example, in feminist science critiques tensions have arisen about the role of empiricism: many stress the importance of paying careful attention to certain strictures of empiricist methodology (close attention to accuracy in data collection, hypothesis formation, replication of "findings" about sex differences, and so on), yet concerns have also been raised about empiricism as an overall feminist epistemological framework—specifically, concerns about whether such a framework can adequately entertain the most transformative feminist political projects. I think such tensions in feminist science criticism are best addressed by paying close attention to their deployment in particular working contexts of feminist science. This question concerning empiricism can be seen as one of a set of background questions motivating my particular examination of important developments in feminist psychology in the last two decades.

A significant part of my discussion involves elucidating what can best be described as a major shift in the theoretical appropriation of *gender* as a meaningful working concept in the psychological study of sex/gender differences, a shift largely propelled by feminist work in psychology. This, in brief, involves a reappraisal of the traditional appropriation of gender as a straightforward marker of individual difference (as a subject variable), and a shift toward an emphasis on gender as a significant site of ongoing situated social regulation and power asymmetry. I will examine some of the specific methodological commitments highlighted by such a shift, and I will show how such commitments have important implications for studies on gender and cognition, and, indeed, for scientific studies of cognition more generally.

This specific focus marks an especially fruitful confluence of questions, some of which I develop more extensively elsewhere. As part of an ongoing project I am especially taken with the question of gender, rationality, and cognition. I am not simply interested in questions about whether purported claims of gender differences in cognitive capacities are well substantiated; more fundamentally, I seek to reevaluate the philosophical assumptions presupposed in framing such questions as meaningful.

PSA 1994, Volume 2, pp. 109-119

The more relevant questions that then emerge are questions about how gender difference assumptions have informed and reinforced particular conceptions of cognition and cognitive capacities, in some cases helping to constitute the scientific circumscription of the cognitive capacities in question (Rooney 1995). Even the notion that *gender is a meaningful variable* in scientific studies of cognition can be seen to motivate particular mutually reinforcing conceptions of both gender and cognition. For example, rendering gender meaningful as the actual or possible site of relatively stable individual intrapsychic measurable traits (cognitive or else) both reinforces and is reinforced by an understanding of cognitive capacities as "inner," as distinct, stable, isolable traits or proficiencies. The shift to an understanding of gender as a significant site of social regulation, as situationally reinforced and maintained, propels important questions about corresponding shifts in our understanding of cognition and cognitive context, especially in gender and cognition studies. While these latter questions have not yet been fully explored I will examine (in section 3) some recent studies that point in fruitful directions.

When I draw attention to the construction of gender as a "meaningful variable" I am not equating meaningfulness with significance. Specific statistical criteria indicate when a given variable (factor) is "significant" with respect to a given explanatory context. However, in order for a factor to be deemed "significant," certain suppositions about the meaningfulness of that factor must already be in place: certain broader explanatory frameworks, specific understandings of what that factor is (which can be translated into appropriate scientific measures of the factor in question), and certain kinds of expectations about how that factor, if deemed significant, will figure into the specific explanations at issue. Some of the feminist critiques of particular findings in psychology are, as we will see, appropriately directed to the establishment of gender as a "significant" variable in specific contexts. Yet ultimately such critiques draw attention to this broader "meaningfulness" question, which in turn inevitably draws critical attention to the theoretical construction of gender itself. However, questions about the theoretical construction of gender, in turn, cannot be neatly separated from gender issues in broader sociocultural arenas—how gender is rendered salient in such arenas is in turn a question of substantial social and political import as feminist theorizing, generally, continues to show.

The "continuum" I am pushing here, from the contextually well-circumscribed methodological criterion of "significance" to ever broader senses of "meaningfulness," is deliberately designed to prompt parallel associations with a "continuum" between the rational, cognitive, epistemic dimensions of science on the one hand and the social, non-epistemic dimensions of science production on the other, a "continuum" that is a matter of some discussion in the long-standing debate about the rational and the social in science. While the specific focus of my paper precludes the full development of the relevance of my specific case study to this broader question, that question is also clearly there in the background. Elsewhere I have challenged a specific articulation of the separation of the rational from the social in science—that which has been argued in terms of a distinction between epistemic and non-epistemic values (Rooney 1992). In addition, I argued there that the full philosophical import of feminist work in science and science studies is constrained by strict adherence to an epistemic values/non-epistemic values distinction, and that a significant part of that work shows (or has the potential to show) how "non-epistemic" values can inform the constitution of fundamental concepts, questions, and methodologies in specific science projects and can thereby inform the constitution and deployment of "epistemic" values like simplicity and fruitfulness in those same projects. I intend to further that argument in this paper by means of a more detailed exploration of one area of feminist science: by drawing attention to various suppositions involved in particular appropriations of gender in cognitive psychology, by arguing that these appropriations are reflected in specific constitutive methodological criteria of research programs, and by noting that these various suppositions about gender involve social and cultural assumptions that may be visible as such only now. Once feminists propose alternative models of gender they draw attention to the network of theoretical, social, and political commitments involved in choosing one such model over another.

A significant part of section 2 is devoted to critical reflection on *gender* as a theoretical construct in psychology—a theoretical construct that is reflected in nontrivial methodological criteria in research on sex/gender differences. In section 3 I focus on two recent studies on gender and cognition that illustrate the experimental significance of the shift in understandings of gender (discussed in section 2), and I argue that they also draw critical attention to the significant possibilities such research holds for expanding our understanding of the situated nature of cognition.

2. Toward New Models of Gender in Psychology Research

In her 1981 review of feminist criticism of research methods in psychology, Grady notes several recurring areas of concern. These include: kinds of topics chosen for research, subject selection (sometimes males only and/or males taken as the "norm"), "findings" of sex differences taken as explanations rather than as starting points for scientific inquiry, greater frequency of reports of positive findings regarding sex differences (in some cases supporting the perception that such findings are well-established—thus delaying necessary replication studies), greater emphasis on means than on variance (distribution for each gender and significant overlap of genders) in reports of findings—thereby distorting the the nature of the difference findings. Grady thinks that many of these kinds of methodological problems can be resolved by more meticulous attention to the canons of scientific research. Yet, she suggests, there are also situations where more is required, where a feminist political awareness is needed to uncover "the extent to which sexist institutions prescreen any proposed subject population" (p. 634). She illustrates this with a relatively simple example that I think draws attention to some central critical issues we need to examine.

At the turn of the century the greater representation of retarded males in mental institutions was interpreted by Darwinists as evidence of superior male *variability* (which in this case meant the greater numbers of males at both the upper and lower ends of mental and intellectual ability). It was later pointed out, however, that different social and economic conditions for women and men provided the selection criteria for this observed numerical sex difference: women were more likely to find placement in lower paying occupations at the time, lower subjective standards of intelligence were projected on women, and so on. Grady notes: "The demonstrated 'sex difference' then was not one of mental abilities at all but of different social and economic conditions for the sexes" (p. 635). It is important to note here that the "sex difference" was presumably well demonstrated, that is, based on accurate counting and appropriate determination of the significance of sex distributions. Yet, this also nicely illustrates how data point nowhere by themselves, how they acquire their specific status as "evidence" only with respect to working hypotheses in going theoretical frameworks. In this case we see that the different explanatory frameworks suggested are inextricably linked to *different appropriations of gender*. In the first case, gender attaches straightforwardly to individual persons as the locus of fundamental, "inner," relatively stable traits (biological or mental)—gender is, in effect, unproblematically a subject variable. In the second case, it is social and economic conditions that differentially impact individuals in a gender-schematic society that provide the working context of gender in the explanatory framework. Grady concludes about these kinds of examples: "psychology as a research endeavor has tended to be satisfied with results that locate sex differences within the individual *whether arrived at by 'nature' or 'nurture'* rather than in the situation or social structure" (p. 635, my emphasis).

This example highlights some key elements in a shift in conceptions of gender encouraged by work in feminist psychology in the past two decades. 1974, in fact, marked a landmark year in feminist psychology. It was the year that Maccoby and Jacklin published their comprehensive work, *The Psychology of Sex Differences*, in which they examined over 1400 published studies on sex differences. They concluded that studies conducted to that point supported only four clear differences between males and females: in the area of cognition, male superiority in mathematical and visual-spatial abilities and female superiority in verbal ability; in the area of social behavior, males were reported to be more aggressive (Maccoby and Jacklin 1974). This work marked a summing up of previous research, yet it also helps to delineate somewhat different feminist projects that subsequently developed with sex differences research. These projects are not entirely distinct, yet they do emphasize somewhat different research strategies and methodological and epistemological critiques: (A) stresses feminist reassessment of research design and methodology, along with replication studies to find out if these reported differences "hold up"; (B) foregrounds critiques of the specific construction of gender that these studies both subscribe to and reinforce, and propels the critical development of new models of gender. (A) is a critique that specifically focuses on what is said *about* gender, and can also be seen as largely *reactive*, while (B) directs attention to *gender* itself and the way it is represented in psychological theory, and can be seen as more *proactive*. In the literature (A) and (B) are sometimes presented as being in tension with one another, in part because they are seen to subscribe to different epistemological frameworks: (A) drawing on the methodology of feminist empiricism and (B) on what is generally (though sometimes ambiguously) called "social constructionism."[2]

(A) and (B) can, however, be seen to be significantly compatible projects (if not mutually supporting in places) especially when critical reflection within the general purview of (B) draws upon crucial results obtained within the general framework of (A). This is especially the case when sex difference claims (reexamined within (A)) were not found to "hold up" with specific modifications in experimental situations. Among the kinds of modifications that altered results were the following: changing the sex of the experimenter, changing instructions with tasks but keeping the tasks essentially the same (instructions seemed to draw differentially on gender stereotypes), changing the situational contexts from public to private settings or vice versa (as also supported by findings that people seem to conform more to gender roles and stereotypes in public settings), changing the sex and/or status composition of groups in cases where group behavior and interaction were involved (Deaux 1984, Deaux and Major 1987; Hare-Mustin and Marecek 1990). As one researcher noted in summing up this work, what had been "established" sex differences began to acquire a "now you see them, now you don't" quality! (Unger 1990, 107). Many other factors in cognitive and behavioral contexts—status and power differentials linked to race and class, for example—emerged as important variables working independently *or*, more significantly, in conjunction with gender, directing the functioning of gender as a salient variable. This work, in effect, directed attention to the significance of gender in terms of ongoing situational constructions and definitions, and it also encouraged a more refined attunement to the way situations are complexly constructed along multiples axes of social/power relations.

It is important to stress what this "new" conception of gender does *not* involve, though it might initially be confused with it—something which will also help explain the somewhat shifting uses of the terms "sex" and "gender" in these discussions. "Sex" is generally taken to refer to the biological "given" that distinguishes individuals as female or male. Many feminist theorists have subscribed to the use of "gender" as distinguishing the cultural overlay, the psychosocial concomitants of biological sex. Where gender differences were thought to be significant, feminists were largely seen to stress explanations involving (long-term) socialization rather than biology. However, according to this more recent shift in feminist understandings of gender, *both* of these accounts (the biological-determinist and the socialization-determinist, or any combination thereof) subscribe to the same model of gender—that is, as an attribute of persons who have relatively stable traits understood as developmental achievements caused by *distal* factors of nature and/or long-term socialization. The shift, instead, is toward understanding gender and gender-related traits as *situationally* encouraged, reinforced, and defined, and thus significantly explained by *proximal* factors of ongoing social regulation, of identity- and power/status-maintenance in gender-schematic cultural contexts.

This shift, however, also confounds the simplicity of the earlier sex/ gender distinction. Unger (1990, 107-113) specifically addresses this problem of terminology in feminist psychology. She notes that the assumed or "given" dichotomy based on biological criteria is not entirely unproblematic, since one can argue that there are more than two sexes in terms of the many biological criteria of sex, and one can meaningfully ask about deep cultural investments in constructing sex as a dualism rather than a continuum. What is even more obviously problematic, however, is the way this dualism has been carried over into scientific appropriations of "gender" as also automatically a meaningful dualism: thus, for example, in studies assessing differences in (non-biological) behavioral, psychological, or cognitive traits it is assumed meaningful to divide people into female-gender and male-gender as defined by "the" biological criterion (whether one does or does not project a biological explanation of possible differences). It is precisely the way in which this "meaningfulness" is appropriated or established that I think is key to assessing the full radical potential of feminist work in this area of psychology. Feminists are not saying that gender differences are not meaningful. On the contrary, they are committed to uncovering the *full meaningfulness* of a whole network of gendering systems, a network which centrally includes deep and persistent social regulation by gender dichotomy. The standard delineation of such regulation as encouragement into specific "social roles" is barely a beginning. More fundamentally, as feminist research is showing, in cultures with a deep commitment to gender dichotomy, gender functions as a basic category in perception and cognition, and in the construction of social reality. It influences how we perceive, react to, evaluate others and ourselves, how we structure and assess situations—all of which is informed on an ongoing basis by the subtle or not-so-subtle regulatory practices that sustain gender dichotomy and coherence. (It can be argued that this dimension of gendering is largely invisible because we do it so automatically: it is only when there is an uncertainty, a situation where we are unable to determine the sex/gender of someone and get stuck in responding to them, that we realize how deeply committed we are to gender categorization in our fundamental cognitive and behavioral organization.) Many feminists stress this dynamic, ongoing, socially regulated and sustained *process* view of gender when they appropriate "gender" as "doing gender," as "the processes and structures of gendering" (Fine and Gordon 1992, 9), or in drawing from Sherif's definition of "gender" as "a scheme for the social categorization of individuals" (Sherif, 1982).

Examining the full meaningfulness of deep and persistent social regulation by gender dichotomy has far-reaching implications for the psychological study of gender, and I will return to some of these implications below. One should not assume here, however, that, working with new conceptions of gender, feminists are saying that biological and/or socialization factors can never appear in explanatory hypotheses concerning cognition and behavior. What they are saying is that granting central significance to this "scheme for the social categorization of individuals" significantly reframes biological and socialization explanations. For example, it is less than obvious what would be involved in discovering a "purely biological" determinant or correlate of a specific behavior or trait, since, among other things, the theoretical construction and significance of biological categories now emerges as contested ground in feminist critiques. Similarly, one cannot say that long-term socialization is made to disappear. However, a gender-specific developmental trait normally assigned to socialization is not to be understood simply as a static *fait accompli,* but is likely to be appropriated more along the lines of a flexible dispositional network that is realized and granted significance and meaning in ongoing gender-laden and gender-reinforcing contexts.

Our attention is drawn to some of the specific methodological issues at stake in new theoretical appropriations of gender by noting key methodological problems in "traditional" sex differences research which were uncovered by feminist analyses, and which, as argued above, in significant part also propelled new understandings of gender. (This also challenges [in this case at least] the still common perception that feminist research is motivated largely by the imposition of feminist "political" values and programs "from without," with minimal attention given to "established" empirical data and appropriate methods of research.) Sophisticated methodological critiques abound in the feminist literature. Some of these were noted above, with special attention given to discoveries about how sex differences disappeared with slight modifications in task characteristics and experimental situations—this will be illustrated further below. Such critiques should also be considered in light of important meta-methodological observations, especially those derived from statistical techniques of "meta-analysis" where all of the studies relating to a specific behavior or trait are analyzed together. For example, Maccoby and Jacklin (1974) noted that, with the exception of the four traits mentioned, "findings" of sex differences were no more significant than "difference findings" that would emerge by chance from similar studies conducted on two groups chosen at random (pp.3-4). In addition, even with traits where sex-related differences seemed to appear regularly, there is an upper limit of about 5% on the percentage of total variability in a given behavior that can be predicted on the basis of sex. This, clearly, has raised questions about the explanatory power of sex-of-subject as a "main effect" in scientific studies of social and cognitive behavior (Deaux 1984). Such meta-analyses help foreground critical issues in the construction of the meaningfulness of sex/gender (as a subject variable), and they acquire special significance in light of Unger's meta-methodological observation: "Although no adequate theoretical justification for what determines a relevant or irrelevant psychological category has ever been formulated, biological sex has long been an unquestioned psychological variable" (1990, 110).

What, then, are some of the research implications of this alternative conception of gender as process and interaction, as situationally configured by social relations, as encouraged or mandated by various forms of social categorization and regulation? At the very least, this work challenges the priority of a "traits" view of behavior (traits as stable characteristics that people carry around "inside") *particularly when* that obscures or grants minimal attention to situational constraints on behavior that significantly construct or grant meaning to the behavior in question. This is certainly the case with so-called gender-specific traits and gender-laden situations or contexts, but this applies just as well to many other kinds of behavior and interaction informed by power and status, however those are constituted in different cultural contexts. Through producing more refined models of experimental contexts that reveal the impact of such social relations on individual and group behavior (including cognitive behavior), such work also supports what many feminists see as one of the goals of *feminist* research: to contribute to social activism by producing knowledge that can be used to inform more effective models of social change. The almost exclusive construction of gender-as-individual-difference (as in the relentless fixation on sex differences with sexed-individuals the carriers of stable traits), on the other hand, as Fine and Gordon argue, "functions inside psychology as a political and scientific diversion away from questions of power, social context, meaning, and braided subjectivities" (1992, 8).

To facilitate experimental design Deaux and Major (1987, 372) have presented a relatively detailed model in research on "gender-related behavior", that is designed to direct further study of "the degree to which gender-related behavior is variable, proximally caused, and context dependent" (yet a model that is also presented as a "supplement to existent models of sex differences" [p. 369]). It is important to note that this model is well supported by copious references to studies that indicate the significance of the many factors influencing gender-related behavior that they depict. Citing work from social psychology, they "believe that the enactment of gender primarily takes place within the context of social interaction, either explicitly or implicitly" (p. 370). They also view social interaction as a process of identity negotiation, which interweaves, in particular, processes of self-verification (maintaining self-conceptions) and processes of self-presentation ("commit[ting] to certain identities or selves that seem most suitable or most potentially rewarding in a particular situation" [p. 371]). They specify many aspects of a situation that can make gender-related issues salient, and these include: belief systems of those involved (which can trigger the functioning of social stereotypes), situational cues, and gender-related schemata of the individuals involved and the situation. (Individuals can be more or less gender schematic, that is, draw more or less on gender as a behavioral and cognitive organizational tool.)

While this model provides a helpful map indicating how various factors stressed in this newer conception of gender might be translated into an experimental context, Deaux and Major refer to it as a model to "understand the complexity and variability of *social* behavior" (p. 384, my emphasis). However, this social behavior involves cognition at just about every turn, in the way people perceive, reflect, modify beliefs, and in the way they can be said to "know" situations, themselves, and others, particularly in social interaction. Despite this emphasis on social behavior and cognition, we can meaningfully ask whether aspects of this model would also apply to the "enactment of gender" with respect to "non-social" cognition—typically presented as isolated-individual-solving-a-puzzle, the type traditionally privileged by philosophers as "pure" cognition, and also favored by those psychologists who project cognition as ideally studied with individuals performing cognitive tasks in the laboratory, removed from the "noise" of social context. There are various possibilities that such a question opens up here. One possibility might involve arguing that this new situational view of gender applies primarily (or only) to contexts of social interaction (as Deaux and Major seem to suggest), that gender as socially/situationally constrained does not impact "pure" cognition. However, as mentioned earlier, such a view has been challenged by studies (with isolated "pure" cognizers) that indicate that "situational" changes in tasks (changes in format and instructions, for example) yield different results with respect to gender significance. In pursuing this question with an examination of two recent studies on gender and cognition I will also raise questions about the social cognition/ non-social cognition division that is often presupposed in these discussions. While, clearly, a full exploration of this issue goes well beyond the scope of this paper, the studies I examine help us to see how new models of gender incorporated into the scientific study of gender and cognition are thereby providing new experimental models of cognition, and are advancing, in particular, the notion that "non-social" cognition is also in significant ways situated.

3. Two Recent Studies on Gender and Cognition

The two studies I examine here are very relevant to this discussion since they address two areas of active debate concerning gender differences in the last decade: moral reasoning and spatial ability. Moral reasoning provides an especially appropriate arena to examine the impact of situation on cognition. Clopton and Sorell's (1993) study is specifically designed to examine the "stable versus situational" question which has been a relatively consistent question of concern in critiques of Gilligan's (1982) work—a work that was an important catalyst for the debate on gender and moral reasoning. The concern has been that "Gilligan's theory may derive from a bias that exaggerates differences in disposition between women and men and overlooks differences in social structure, such as power differentials, that press for different behavior in the two sexes" (Clopton and Sorell 1993, 86; Mednick 1989). Clopton and Sorell restricted their study to female and male parents of both handicapped children and nonhandicapped children, and moral dilemmas were restricted to real-life parenting situations. No significant gender differences were found in "moral reasoning orientation scores" when the dilemmas were restricted in this way. They cite other studies which indicate that gender differences are more likely to be found in cases where there is no restriction on the specific kinds of dilemmas respondents may draw from in their responses. Respondents are then likely to draw from their life experiences, and differences in reasoning in such cases may have more to do with "differences in men's and women's daily lives... [than with] differences in stable intrapsychic characteristics" (pp. 99-100). Situational effect, then, and especially as it pertains to gender, refers not just to the immediate situations evoked or constructed by moral dilemmas, but can also include life "situations" more broadly.

The notion of "situated cognition" pertains especially well to moral reasoning, yet many might argue that this is because moral reasoning is by definition social-situational. Moral deliberation necessarily involves situations (actual or projected) characterized by some form of social interaction, where the potential to help or harm others is especially salient. However, there is much that such gender studies can contribute to expanding our understanding of moral deliberation: new models of gender, in particular, can significantly contribute to an appreciation of the full situational placement of moral agents, who might, in some contexts, have their range of responses limited by the persistent deployment of sociocultural stereotypes (a limitation that should not be seen to apply to women only). Questions remain, however, about whether new conceptions of gender and related models of situated cognition can apply to types of cognition that might not readily be assessed as "social."

Two studies on gender and spatial cognition by Sharps et al. (1993, 1994) raise issues that I will argue pertain quite directly to this question. These studies were designed to examine the impact of changes in instructional and stimulus conditions in mental image rotation (MIR) and spatial memory tasks (the latter in the 1993 study only). Gender differences in performance outcomes changed (and in some cases were eliminated) when changes were made in instructional format (but the "pure cognitive construct" or task remained the same). In particular, women performed better and as well as men when the spatial character of the task was de-emphasized in the instructions; in another case, women did not perform significantly less well with stereotypically "masculine" instruction items such as the flying of military aircraft and the navigation of naval vessels (less well, that is, than they did with "non-masculine" instructions), but the men performed "at a higher level" with such instructions. The authors conclude that studies that indicate that men do better than women at spatial tasks need to be rethought, particularly in terms of the operation of "contextual variables" like the diminished motivational capacity of women in sociocultural contexts where they are surrounded by beliefs like "women have trouble with road maps" and where they are subject to "implicit sociocultural stereotyping" that can promote "the negative feelings of women toward spatial cognitive capacities that may violate culturally mediated feminine self-concepts" (1994, 414).

Studies such as those by Sharps et al. which pay particular attention to "contextual variables" that may differentially impact women and men are clearly consistent with research projects that seek to incorporate newer conceptions of gender as involving ongoing social constructions that are situationally-sensitive in many respects, from immediate situations to broader sociocultural contexts. They also draw attention to the possible operation of gender stereotypes as socioculturally promoted, as ongoing, and as impacting self-conceptions, operating even in "isolated" individual cognitive activity. Sharps et al. note that their study should not be taken as anything like a final determination of the impact of "contextual factors" on gender and spatial performance—the full elucidation of these possible mechanisms "represents a formidable task for the future." However, their study does provide an illustration that enables some specific claims about the theoretical appropriation of gender as a relevant variable in scientific studies of cognition. Two experiments, one with the "highly spatial" instructions and the other with the "nonspatial" instructions, yielded difference performance levels for the women in relation to the men—with the "nonspatial" instructions there was no significant gender difference (Sharps et al., 1993). But, if this is the case, then gender (as a subject variable that is normally assigned by sex) is not an irreducible "main effect" variable in what Sharps et al. present as a reasonable causal explanation that draws from these performance differences, *even though* gender bears a high correlation with the factor that is: that factor is really better articulated more along the lines of a distinction between C-persons and D-persons, where C-persons are, on the whole, subjected to stereotypes and cultural self-conceptions of forms x and y...which are likely to be triggered in situations like p and q..., and B-persons are not (or are subjected to other stereotypes and self-conceptions). (Some theorists now like to describe gender as a "carrier variable" which suggests that gender might be more fruitfully construed as a useful marker of relevant situational constraints.) Thus, how one constructs relevant variables in causal explanatory hypotheses (designed to explain differences among individuals) is a nontrivial methodological matter, and in some cases can make the difference of forestalling a confusion between description and explanation. If a gender difference is established or suspected in a specific case, and gender is automatically appropriated into a causal explanation as an irreducible or main-effect subject variable rather than as a "carrier" variable, there is a danger that a description will simply be confused with an explanation. Lott (1990) articulates this point cogently: "If average differences between some women and men are attributed to the persons rather than to the differential experiences that are correlated with them, then gender is seen as the cause of behavior, and description is confused with explanation" (p. 70).

The full potential for enhanced models of cognition that draw significantly on newer models of gender in gender and cognition studies has, to my knowledge, not yet been significantly explored. Sharps et al., in fact, seem to stop short of what I think are some noteworthy possibilities suggested by their studies. They assert, for example, that the "contextual factors" in question (triggered by manipulations of instructional and/or stimulus format) are "noncognitive factors" that influence performance on a task, that detract from abilities, or that can inhibit "access" to the full range of capabilities. When such "contextual factors" are operating, they seem to suggest, we are not getting a direct measure of specific cognitive abilities, where these are understood as "raw abilities," as the processing involved in "the basic 'hardware' of cognition," as "the pure cognitive construct alone" (1994, 421,423). But elsewhere they seem to waver somewhat in their projection of a pure core of cognition that can be separated (theoretically at least) from the many factors of cognitive context, or a "core" that clearly divides these factors into those that pertain to the "pure" cognitive processing at hand and those that do not (though these latter may pertain fundamentally to modes of expression and performance). They write: "A relatively recent tradition in cognitive psychology, that of 'situated cognition,' may be useful in the interpretation of these results. This viewpoint holds that cognitive processes are not reifiable, disembodied functional entities operating in isolation... The processes involved in spatial cognition do not operate in isolation, but instead function interactively with other situational and organismic variables, in attempts by individuals to solve problems posed by given situations or environments." (1993, 79; 1994, 422). (It is somewhat ironic that such remarks are emerging from the psychologists' laboratories which may well be the the only place where one could reasonably imagine spatial cognition (or any other cognitive capacity for that matter) operating "in isolation.") Such an approach to cognition is, of course, not unknown in our own philosophical tradition—it bears a distinct resemblance to pragmatist conceptions of cognition.

In short, the kinds of issues raised by critical feminist reflection on studies on gender and cognition point not simply to alternative models of gender but also to alternative models of cognition that can help sustain more expansive understandings of the situational placement of individuals in a whole range of cognitive activity. Clearly, feminist research is not suggesting that we abandon the scientific study of gender and cognition. Seeking to develop a better understanding of the interaction of gender and context (cognitive or else) is quite consistent with a range of positions on the long-term goals of feminism, some of which seek the elimination of gender as a fundamental organizing principle of society. Whether all feminists agree on this or any other articulation of a long-term goal for feminism is not at issue here. Feminists surely will agree, however, that sustained and careful reflection on the construction and meaning of gender must be incorporated into scientific projects on gender and cognition, that such work has fundamental methodological implications for the study of gender and of cognition, and that there are clear social (and yes "political") commitments involved in seeking to advance the study of cognition in light of such work—and also in continuing to ignore or marginalize it.

Notes

[1] I am grateful to my fellow symposiasts Lynn Hankinson Nelson, Jack Nelson, and Elizabeth Potter for their encouragement with this project, and also to Abigail Stewart and Rhoda Unger for their encouragement and guidance in my exploration of the literature in feminist psychology.

[2]Sometimes the term "social constructionism" is used to stress the social construction *of gender*, the idea that gender is maintained by all kinds of social inscriptions and regulations. This is the sense of "constructionism" that Bohan (1993), for example, contrasts with "essentialist" construals of gender. Sometimes the term is used more specifically to refer to an epistemological stance about the construction *of theories*, the view that scientific theories (including theories of gender) are informed by the interests and values of science practitioners, that such theories inevitably bear the marks of their sociocultural backgrounds. This, for example, is the sense of "constructivism" that Hare-Mustin and Marecek (1990) use when they stress that "our understanding of reality is a representation...Representations of reality are shared meanings" (p. 27); this they also contrast with a "positivist" interpretation. These two senses are not necessarily in opposition to one another, though their connections (with respect to theories of gender specifically) sometimes need to be worked out more clearly.

References

Bohan, J.S. (1993), "Regarding Gender: Essentialism, Constructionism, and Feminist Psychology", *Psychology of Women Quarterly* 17:5-21.

Clopton, N.A. and Sorell, G.T. (1993), "Gender Differences in Moral Reasoning: Stable or Situational?", *Psychology of Women Quarterly* 17: 85-101.

Deaux, K. (1984), "From Individual Differences to Social Categories: Analysis of a Decade's Research on Gender", *American Psychologist* 39(2): 105-116.

Deaux, K. and Major, B. (1987), "Putting Gender into Context: An Interactive Model of Gender-Related Behavior", *Psychological Review* 94(3): 369-389.

Fine, M. and Gordon, S.M. (1992), "Feminist Transformations of/despite Psychology", in M. Fine (ed.), *Disruptive Voices: The Possibilities of Feminist Research.* University of Michigan Press, pp. 1-25.

Gilligan, C. (1982), *In A Different Voice: Psychological Theory and Women's Development.* Harvard University Press.

Grady, K.E. (1981), "Sex Bias in Research Design", *Psychology of Women Quarterly* 5(4): 628-636.

Hare-Mustin, R.T. and Marecek, J. (eds.) (1990), *Making a Difference: Psychology and the Construction of Gender.* Yale University Press.

Lott, B. (1990), "Dual Natures or Learned Behavior: The Challenge to Feminist Psychology", in Hare-Mustin and Marecek (1990)

Maccoby, E.E., and Jacklin, C.N. (1974), *The Psychology of Sex Differences.* Stanford University Press.

Mednick, M.T. (1989), "On the Politics of Psychological Constructs: Stop the Bandwagon, I Want to Get Off", *American Psychologist* 44(8): 1118-1123.

Morawski, J.G. (1994) *Practicing Feminisms, Reconstructing Psychology: Notes on a Liminal Science*. University of Michigan Press.

Rooney, P. (1992), "On Values in Science: Is the Epistemic/Non-Epistemic Distinction Useful?", *PSA 1992*, Volume 1, D. Hull, M. Forbes, and K. Okruhlik (eds.). East Lansing: Philosophy of Science Association, pp. 13-22.

_______. (1995), "Rationality and the Politics of Gender Difference", *Metaphilosophy* 26 (1&2): 22-45.

Sharps, M J. Welton, A.L. and Price, J.L. (1993), "Gender and Task in the Determination of Spatial Cognitive Performance", *Psychology of Women Quarterly* 17: 71-83.

Sharps, M.J. Price, J.L. and Williams, J.K. (1994), "Spatial Cognition and Gender: Instructional and Stimulus Influences on Mental Image Rotation Performance", *Psychology of Women Quarterly* 18: 413-425.

Sherif, C.W. (1982), "Needed Concepts in the Study of Gender Identity," *Psychology of Women Quarterly* 6(4): 375-398.

Unger, R.K. (1989), *Representations: Social Constructions of Gender*. Baywood Publishing Company.

_______. (1990), "Imperfect Reflections of Reality: Psychology Constructs Gender", in Hare-Mustin and Marecek (1990).

Feminist Values and Cognitive Virtues[1]

Lynn Hankinson Nelson
Rowan College of New Jersey

Jack Nelson
Temple University

1. Introduction

Commonly-cited criteria for the assessment of hypotheses, research projects, and theories include empirical adequacy, simplicity, conservatism, explanatory power, generality of scope, fecundity, reproducibility, and interconnectedness with other going theories. The list of criteria for good scientific practice typically includes objectivity (though what objectivity comes to is much disputed), respect for evidence, open mindedness, and tentativeness. Feminist scientists and science scholars have of late proposed additional and, in some cases, alternative criteria (e.g., Biology and Gender Study Group 1989, Bleier 1984, Fausto-Sterling 1985, Haraway 1978, Keller 1983 and 1985, Longino 1994, and Nelson 1990). We here consider the nature and rationale of some of these proposed criteria, focusing on several articulated by Helen Longino. A research program in neuroendocrinology investigating a hormonal basis for alleged sex-differentiated lateralization and feminist critiques of this research serve as our case study.

In two recent discussions, Longino proposes a list of standards or criteria which she takes to be related to feminist values, finds characteristic of the practices of feminist scientists, and recommends as criteria for guiding the assessment of and/or choice between individual hypotheses, research programs, and theories (Longino 1990 and 1994). The most traditional of these standards is empirical adequacy, which Longino parses as "agreement of the observational claims of a theory or model with observational and experimental data, present, retrospective, or predictive" (Longino 1994, 476). Additional values and/or criteria shaped by these "come into play" in the assessment of theories, hypotheses, and models, Longino contends, because "empirical adequacy is not a sufficient criterion of theory and hypothesis choice" (ibid., 477). The criteria that Longino links to feminist values and the practice of feminist scientists are ontological heterogeneity, complexity of relationships, diffusion of power, applicability to current human needs, and novelty (ibid., 477-479).

In response to the question, "What is specifically feminist or gendered about these standards?", Longino maintains that the rationale for feminist inquirers to adopt them is that "one of the effects they all have in one way or another is to prevent gender from being disappeared". Each makes gender "a relevant axis of investigation" and this feature gives each "its status as feminist" (ibid., 481). The "non-disappearance of gender" is itself described by Longino as "a bottom line requirement of feminist knowers"

PSA 1994, Volume 2, pp. 120-129

in the evaluation of cognitive standards", its intent "to reveal or prevent the disappearing of the experience and activities of women and/or to prevent the disappearing of gender" (ibid., 481). Hence, we take it to be Longino's view that this requirement constitutes an over-arching criterion for the evaluation and choice of other standards (e.g., ontological heterogeneity) to be used in the assessment of theories and research. We also take it to be Longino's view that this bottom-line requirement and the other standards she links to feminist values are criteria for good science *simpliciter*—and that science as currently practiced by feminists is a model for good science.

We here explore two of the standards Longino proposes: "ontological heterogeneity", which, as she describes it, "permits equal standing for different types, and mandates investigation of such difference" (ibid., 477); and "complexity of relationships", which Longino describes as "taking complex interaction as a fundamental principle of explanation" and valuing models in which "no factor can be described as dominant or controlling and that describe processes in which all active factors influence the others" (ibid., 478). The question we ask is whether there is reason to consider these to be criteria of good science. Our attention to these two criteria reflects our sense that, of those Longino proposes, these and "the non-disappearance of gender requirement" are the most plausible candidates for criteria of good science rather than, say, of an enlightened social policy about science. That said, we found that we disagree about whether ontological heterogeneity and complexity of relationships can be construed as criteria of good science and sketch our disagreements below. We also note that, contra our question, Longino maintains that these and the other criteria she proposes "can't be dichotomized into cognitive or social criteria" because, for feminist inquirers, each criterion is related to the bottom line requirement of the non-disappearance of gender (ibid., 480-481; see also Longino 1990, Chap. Nine). We delay specific discussion of this claim and the bottom line requirement until our concluding remarks.

2. Research on sex-differentiated lateralization

A current hypothesis in neuroendocrinology is that androgens have an organizing effect on male fetal brains, causing right-hemisphere dominance in the processing of visuo-spatial information, a dominance related in some of the investigations we summarize to "superior performance" of male laboratory animals "in spatial contexts" and "superior performance in mathematics" among human males.[2] (We use quotes because what constitutes such performance and contexts are often not sufficiently specified in the research we are summarizing.)

In a study investigating correlations among migraine, left-handedness, immune-system disorders, and learning disabilities (the last three suggested by earlier research to be more common in men and boys than in women and girls), Geschwind and Behan (1982) proposed that testosterone slows the development of the left hemisphere cortex *in utero*.[3] As this effect "will usually be greater in males because the fetal testes secrete testosterone", the hypothesis was described as an explanation of "the biological foundations of laterality"—specifically, of right-hemisphere lateralization in men and boys (ibid., 5099). Two earlier studies were cited as primary support for the hypothesis. Diamond et. al (1981) had reported that two areas of the cortex of male rat brains are 3 percent thicker on the right side than the left (an asymmetry not found in female rats), and hypothesized that the thickness was related to lateralization. Drawing on a hypothesis current in empirical psychology and reproductive endocrinology—that right-hemisphere lateralization would increase visuo-spatial ability—Diamond et al suggested that such lateralization would better enable male rats to interact with female rats during estrus (Diamond et al 1981, 266).

Geschwind and Behan's extrapolation of Diamond et al's results and hypothesis to humans was supported by appeal to a study by Chi et al (1977) which reported that two convolutions of the right hemisphere of human fetal brains develop several weeks earlier than do corresponding convolutions of the left. Geschwind and Behan proposed that the differential rate of development reported by Chi et al is caused by testosterone, i.e., the latter causing the slower development of the left hemisphere. They did not link right-hemisphere lateralization to mathematical ability in this study, but when describing this research in *Science*, Geschwind suggested that the effects of testosterone *in utero* can produce "superior right hemisphere talents, such as... mathematical talent" (Kolata 1983, 1312). And two years later Geschwind and Behan (1984) continued the investigation of the role of "male hormones" in determining laterality and appealed to a study by empirical psychologists reporting "a marked excess of males" among mathematically gifted children, as further support for the hypothesis that "male hormones" cause right-hemisphere lateralization (Geschwind and Behan 1984, 221).

Feminist biologists critical of the hypothesis that androgens cause right hemisphere dominance, and via this superior spatial and mathematical abilities, argue that there is no basis for positing the relationship between lateralization and thickness in the areas of the right hemisphere of male rat brains that Diamond et al initially suggested. Without this, they argue, there is no basis for the hypothesis that androgens cause right-hemisphere lateralization (see, e.g., Bleier 1984, 1988). They also point out that the "higher-level" hypothesis of sex-differentiated lateralization assumed by Geschwind and Behan relies on additional hypotheses which are a matter of some controversy in empirical psychology, including that there are sex differences in cognitive abilities and that such differences (assuming they are established) have a biological foundation (compare, e.g., Kinsbourne 1980 and McGlone 1980). And they question the rationale of looking for such a foundation, given that changes in cultural expectations and educational policies appear to be closing the gap between girls and boys in mathematical performance (a gap sex-differentiated lateralization was to explain), and in light of a substantial body of research documenting differences in relevant socialization for girls and boys (Bleier 1984, 1988; Fausto-Sterling 1985; Rosser 1982, 1984; see also Longino 1990 and Nelson 1990).

Feminist scientists have also charged that results are often misrepresented in research into sex differences (see, e.g., Bleier 1984, 1988; and Fausto-Sterling 1985). Recall, for example, that Geschwind and Behan (1982) appealed to the differential development of hemispheric convolutions in human fetal brains reported by Chi et. al (1977) as supporting the hypothesis that testosterone causes right-hemisphere dominance. What it failed to note was that Chi et al reported the differential development in *both* female and male brains and stated explicitly that investigators "could recognize no difference between male and female brains of the same gestational age" in the measurement of 507 human fetal brains of 10-44 weeks gestation (Chi et al 1977, 92)—a result obviously undermining the hypothesis that androgens cause the differential development.[4]

On the basis of both lines of criticism, a number of feminist scientists have concluded that research into a hormonal basis for sex-differentiated lateralization such as that just outlined is intellectually bankrupt, was never warranted by the available evidence, and was motivated by social and political interests (e.g., Bleier 1984, 1988; and Fausto-Sterling 1985).

Considered in isolation, a hypothesis positing a hormonal basis for sex-differentiated lateralization does seem unwarranted. Given the nature of the topic and the relationship between the assumptions informing it (that, e.g., males are superior in mathematics and in spatial contexts) and gender stereotypes, given as well a staggering list of differences in "female" and "male" brains proposed on the basis of (an equally staggering amount of) research in the history of science, and given cases in which results were reported in ways at least misleading of which we have cited one example, its driving force can easily be seen, as many critics have seen it, as largely political. But we suggest that there was evidential warrant for Geschwind's and Behan's hypothesis and briefly summarize some of it here.

In neuroendocrinology, research questions center on the organizing and activating effects of hormones on the brain (their effects on neural events and physiology) and (via the brain) on behavior and cognitive abilities. Sex differences have functioned as a baseline for the investigations of these relationships and as a cornerstone for the broader hypotheses about them which define the discipline, *given* the assumption that there are "male" hormones and "female" hormones (androgens and estrogens, respectively), and the broader assumption of sexual dimorphism. Further, both the "male/female" dichotomy and other hypotheses shaping investigations of sex-differentiated lateralization traversed three research traditions.

In reproductive endocrinology, research into relationships between hormones and the brain began as efforts to understand the mechanisms (thought to be hormonal but involving neural events) that regulate ovarian function. In the 1960's, studies suggested that hypothalamic neurons respond cyclically in female rats and regulate pituitary functions, and that the presence of androgens in male rats blocks the cyclic response. This hypothesis was subsequently tested and apparently confirmed through the injection of both females and males with androgens (but see Bleier 1979, 1984, and Rosser 1982, 1984, for critiques of these tests). While the role of estrogens was not similarly investigated—indeed, while the effects of hormones designated as "female" have received far less attention in these investigations—the blocking effects were taken as evidence that male hormones "organize" hypothalamic neurons in such a way that *rat brains become sexed*: i.e., the presence of androgens organizes "a male brain", a female brain "results from" their absence (Harris and Levine 1965; see also Bleier 1984, 1988; Fausto-Sterling 1985; and Longino 1990).[5]

Also in the 1960's, investigators in neuroanatomy, endocrinology, and empirical psychology began intense study of cerebral dominance, its biological foundations, and its functional effects (see Geschwind and Galaburda 1984, 1-8). Some investigations looked for structural asymmetries in the human brain and by the 1970's several were reported, including a larger left temporal operculum, an asymmetry in the architectonic areas, and asymmetries in the content of several transmitter substances and in the rates of development of the hemispheres—this last result one of those to which Geschwind and Behan's 1982 study appealed (see, e.g., the Introduction to Geschwind and Galaburda 1984, 1-8). Concurrently, investigators in reproductive endocrinology and empirical psychology were attempting to relate these and other structural asymmetries to functional asymmetries. Asymmetries in the temporal operculum and architectonic areas, for example, were found to be related to language function and to the lateralization of language to the left hemisphere (Galaburda 1984; and Geschwind and Behan 1984).

Relationships between investigations into causal relationships between androgens and brain morphology, cerebral dominance, behavior, and cognitive capacities, were forged concretely four years before Geschwind and Behan's 1982 proposal that androgens cause right-hemisphere dominance. Reproductive endocrinologists reported morphological sex differences (in size and number of neurons) in areas of rodent brains associated with the regulation of estrous cyclicity and a sex difference in a group of neurons related to the ability of males of some bird species to sing, and related both sex differences to androgens (Gorski et al 1978 and Gorski 1979). The first of these studies announced that "the concept of the sexual differentiation of brain function is now well established" while acknowledging that its mechanisms were not yet understood (Gorski et al 1978, 334). And Gorski 1979 reported the instigation of a search for "a clear morphological signature of sexual differentiation in the brain" (Gorski 1979, 114).

This background indicates that Geschwind's and Behan's hypothesis and the research they undertook on its basis were neither far fetched nor purely politically motivated. Rather, these represented a synthesis of research questions and results in several research traditions. But the criticisms feminist scientists have leveled against this hypothesis and the research serving as its background reveal a substantial role for naive and unquestioned assumptions about gender differences in behavior and capacities, as well as a fair dose of androcentrism.

We have noted that feminist scientists question the existence of the cognitive differences the research we have outlined is purported to explain. Feminist biologists also criticize the emphasis placed on so-called male hormones, pointing out that conclusions can not be drawn from studies apparently establishing their organizing and/or activating effects until a similar amount of research is devoted to the organizing effects of estrogen (see, e.g., Bleier 1979, 1984, 1988; Fausto-Sterling 1985; Rosser 1982, 1984; see also Longino 1990 for an overview of these critiques). Many also challenge the labeling of androgens and estrogens as "male" and "female", noting that males and females produce both hormones and that there are continuous conversions among the three families of sex hormones (e.g., Bleier 1984). Feminist scientists also point to experimental results indicating complex and often non-linear interactions between cells, and between cells and the maternal and external environments, during every stage of fetal development. On the basis of these several arguments, they maintain that the isolation of so-called "male" hormones as causing fairly remote effects is unwarranted (Bleier 1984 and 1988, Fausto-Sterling 1985, and Rosser 1982 and 1984).

Hence, while we maintain that there was evidential warrant for Geschwind and Behan's hypothesis of a hormonal basis for sex-differentiated lateralization, both the hypothesis and the other investigations into sex differences summarized here appear far less viable or promising in light of the critiques advanced by feminist scientists. Further, we maintain that the evidential warrant for the feminist critiques we have summarized is also constituted by a broad matrix of current hypotheses, research, theories, and assumptions—including (but not exhausted by) assumptions and theories informed by values and practices in the broader social and political context, particularly those shaped by feminism.

3. Ontological Heterogeneity and Complexity of Relationships: Two Views

The case study just outlined is particularly appropriate for considering Longino's criteria of complexity of relationships and ontological heterogeneity. One apt criticism of the investigations into a biological basis for alleged sex differences we have outlined is that they persistently and consistently posited and assumed simple linear causal relationships (e.g., between hormones and cognitive capacities) and lumped together such disparate behavior as rat maze-negotiating behavior and mathematical problem solving. The feminist critiques we have summarized suggest that had researchers been looking for and expecting more complex interconnections, causal relations, and categories, their questions, experiments, and results would have been *different* and, it now seems, *better*.

A similar point can be made concerning the criterion of ontological heterogeneity and what Longino calls "the non-disappearance of gender" requirement. Investigators in reproductive and neuroendocrinology have focussed by and large on the effects of androgens. Had they widened their investigations to include estrogen, and not taken what they categorized as "male" hormones, behavior, and capacities to be the most interesting phenomena, their questions, experiments, and results might have been quite different. It is now reasonable to think they might have been more circumspect in drawing conclusions based on studies which focussed almost exclusively on the organizing and activating effects of androgens. So, too, were the criterion of heterogeneity at work, the assumption consistently made of strong analogies between rat brains and human brains, and between rat and human behavior, might have been recognized as in need of substantive articulation as well as substantial qualification. Finally, as the feminist critiques we have outlined indicate, sexual dimorphism serves as a baseline assumption in many of these investigations: it has shaped the categorization of hormones, the assumption that gender is a sufficient variable in research devoted to establishing and/or explaining sex-differentiated cognitive abilities, and the assumption that differences between women and men are of more significance than differences among each group. In these cases, it seems clear that more heterogeneity and more critical attention to the role of assumptions about sex and gender in shaping research questions were called for—i.e., would have led to better research questions, better experimental design, more sophisticated construals of results, and so on.

And it may be that one of the major lessons of the debates that have occurred in the last forty years in the biological sciences and the philosophy of biology is that biology is not simple, its categories and causal processes are complex, its objects and relationships heterogeneous. This way of describing the lesson, and cases such as that just summarized, might well lead one to accept Longino's ontological heterogeneity and complexity of relationship standards as criteria of good science.

But one of us remains unconvinced. This author readily admits the truism that no theory should posit ontological homogeneity where there is heterogeneity, simplify relationships between elements of its domain in ways which mask significant relationships, or lump together, by means of broad categories, elements whose differences are important for understanding the area of nature being studied. But this truism, the author continues, is compatible with a sensible injunction to avoid heterogeneity and complexity where they are not needed. The reasonable criticism, on this author's view, of the research of Geschwind and Behan and that which served as the research background for their hypothesis, is not that simple causal models were used, but that *unduly* simple causal models, *unduly* simple categories, and an *unduly* simple ontology (e.g., excluding estrogen), were used. Finally, this author notes that one of the criticisms of this research area involves the positing of "sexed brains" when there was inadequate reason for using a sexual classification. This is surely a case where the more complex classification system (two kinds of brains) produced worse, not better, science.

This author does agree that scientists have at times assumed simplicity where there is in fact great complexity, but finds it hard to see why we should purposely seek to complicate the domain of a single theory and/or the causal relations with which it is concerned where doing so yields no gain in predictive power, no broader scope, no greater conformity with other going theories, etc. Moreover, this author thinks that while the notion of simplicity is itself very complicated, some sense probably can be given to it and, accordingly, to the traditional criterion of simplicity. That is, whether or not we accept simplicity as a theoretical virtue, the claim 'the simpler the better' *makes sense* when said of ontologies, hypotheses, and theories. On the other hand, 'the more complex the better' does *not* seem to make sense. There is *no end point* to complexity; for any theory of any given complexity, we can always produce one which is more complex but has the same observational consequences.

The other author is not convinced that the criteria, complexity of relationships and ontological heterogeneity, cannot function as standards of good science, and questions whether the standards do come to simply "the more complex the better", as well as whether the issues involved concern choosing between two theories whose observational consequences and/or domains *are the same*. On this author's view, the rationale for the standards of heterogeneity and complexity as they function in the practice of feminist scientists seems not to be that more complicated stories about a *given* domain are better—but rather that there is reason to prefer *more complex domains* and the more complex theories that go with them, an issue returned to below. This author also questions the asymmetry the first maintains between simplicity and complexity, suspecting that determining the *appropriate* degree of simplicity is as relative to a broader context of current theories (i.e., that its force is not simply "the simpler the better") and as resistant to formalization as the first author claims of complexity and heterogeneity.

That said, this author does find aspects of Longino's arguments for these criteria troubling, particularly the implicit distinction between them and empirical adequacy. (Recall, for example, that these criteria are introduced as part of a list of criteria to be used *in ad-*

dition to empirical adequacy.[6]) Many of the arguments offered by feminist scientists to the point that an openness to complexity in natural relationships and domains is necessary to good science, suggest that what Longino calls "ontological heterogeneity" and "complexity of relationships" function as features of a broadened notion of empirical adequacy—one commensurate with views about the relationships actually obtaining in natural/biological processes—and that concern for such adequacy is motivating their being put forward as criteria for good methodologies, models, theories, and so on.

Consider, for example, the critiques of linear and hierarchical models of gene action offered by feminist biologists Ruth Bleier, Ruth Hubbard, and Evelyn Fox Keller. These scientists argue that uni-directional models of gene action—models which posit discrete effects of discrete genes in, for example, cellular protein synthesis—oversimplify and, hence, distort or obscure, what are more complex biological processes (Bleier 1984, Hubbard 1982, Keller 1983). Similarly, Keller's suggestion that "order" should replace the narrower emphasis on "law-like" relationships, involves an argument to the point that the latter emphasis has served to focus attention on *a subset of natural relations* (Keller 1983 and 1985). So, too, the critiques of the assumption of sexual dimorphism offered by feminist biologists noted above involve arguments that the assumption bifurcates what is actually *a continuum* of physiological, chromosomal, and hormonal traits (e.g., Fausto-Sterling 1985). Finally, feminist critiques of the abstraction of gender as a variable in research devoted to establishing or explaining sex-differences (e.g., in cognitive abilities), include arguments to the point that this abstraction results in an emphasis on differences between women and men which are in fact less statistically significant than are the differences among each group. In each of these cases, the criterion of empirical adequacy is part and parcel of arguments for criteria of complexity and heterogeneity, not separable from these. Moreover, implicit in the foregoing is the point that these criteria have cognitive force which is distinguishable from their social force (i.e., the issue of the empirical adequacy of linear, hierarchical models of gene action is distinguishable from the role such models play in underwriting biological determinist theories), a point returned to below.

Secondly, this author notes that the last three decades suggest that an injunction to be open to heterogeneity and complexity of relationships would, as in the research programs considered above, make for better research questions and better hypotheses in areas of physics, the biological sciences, primatology, archeology, bio-behavioral sciences, and the social sciences. But one implication of their emergence *at this time* is that theoretical virtues and other criteria for good science evolve concomitantly with views about how best to arrive at empirically adequate models and theories—views *in turn dependent on* a current state of science (e.g., recognized domains, problems faced by earlier models, and so on). Hence, it seems plausible to view the applicability of these standards (like that of simplicity, on this author's view) as broadly context-specific.

4. The Non-disappearance of Gender.

We conclude with a brief discussion of what Longino describes as the bottom line requirement for feminist knowers, the standard of the non-disappearance of gender. We agree with Longino that at the moment, a fairly long moment to be sure, gender is an important category for science—a category which the sciences cannot ignore for reasons that emerged above. But we note that one result of feminist scholarship is that gender is an historically-specific and socially-constructed category whose relationship to other categories, social relations, and practices is more complex than was recognized even in feminist theory two decades ago. From this perspective, it is not clear that attention to gender is necessary to good science in every context; the value attributed to its non-disappearance seems clearly to be context-specific.

We also agree with Longino that the non-disappearance of gender has now both obvious cognitive force (i.e., can be expected to contribute to more empirically adequate theories and research in many areas) and obvious social force (i.e., can be expected to contribute to more enlightened social policies about science). And we agree that, in cases such as that here considered and many others focussed on by feminist scientists and science scholars, its cognitive and social virtues are deeply entangled. Because of such cases, it is now reasonable to expect that less sexist or androcentric science would promote less sexist social policies, and that a less sexist society will lead to less sexist and androcentric science—and we grant that understandings of this general insight are dynamic and as yet incomplete.

But, we remain tempted by the view that the cognitive and social virtues involved are, in the end, separable and should continue to be construed as such—i.e., that a distinction between the epistemic and social *formulations and rationale* of the non-disappearance of gender criterion is both possible and important. Briefly put, the feminist case against research into a hormonal basis for alleged sex differences in lateralization is not exhausted by the *social and political implications* of such investigations and/or by the role of social and political context *in shaping and/or motivating them*. The full case requires an appeal to the standard of empirical adequacy and to the relationships *between that standard* and what Longino calls "the non-disappearance of gender", showing that attention to the construction of the category 'gender' and its role in research is as much a criterion of good science as it is a criterion of an enlightened social policy.

Notes

[1]We are grateful to Peter Machamer, Elizabeth Potter, Phyllis Rooney, and the audience at the symposium, "Feminist Perspectives on the Special Sciences", for instructive criticisms of an earlier version of this paper.

[2]Our summary of this research relies on a special issue of *Science* (Vol. 211, 20 March 1981) which included review essays of research into sex differences (we draw on Ehrhardt and Meyer-Bahlburg 1981; MacLusky and Naftolin 1981; and Wilson et al 1981); as well as Bleier 1984 and 1988, Chi et al 1977, Diamond et al 1981, Fausto-Sterling 1985, Geschwind and Behan 1982 and 1984, Geschwind and Galaburda 1984, Gorski 1978, Gorski et al 1979, Harris and Levine 1965, Hubbard 1982, and Longino 1990. A more extensive analysis is undertaken in Nelson (forthcoming) and the next several paragraphs parallel that discussion.

[3]Migraine is more common in females; the association Geschwind and Behan claimed in this case was with left-handedness (though, of course, they went on to relate left-handedness to testosterone).

[4]Chi et al studied 207 serially-sectioned brains and photographs of an additional 300 brains provided by the Collaborative Perinatal Project (Chi et al, 86).

[5]Harris and Levine 1965 which maintained this, did, in fact, also investigate the role of estrogens; but such investigations have been the exception rather than the rule (see, for an overview, Longino 1990, Chapters Six and Seven).

[6]Longino's arguments for the insufficiency of empirical adequacy indicate that she does maintain such a distinction. One argument appeals to underdetermination, which Longino parses as the thesis that "the data serving as evidence for hypotheses or theories are not sufficient to support a hypothesis or theory to the exclusion of alternatives" (Longino 1994, 474); hence, Longino argues, these other standards come into play when choosing between alternatives. A second argument is to the point that when the criterion of empirical adequacy is applied, the range of data is already determined (ibid., 482); hence, Longino seems to view the criterion of heterogeneity as applying to a (prior?) choice of domains.

References

Biology and Gender Study Group. (1989), "The Importance of Feminist Critique for Contemporary Cell Biology", in N. Tuana (ed.), *Feminism and Science*. Bloomington and Indianapolis: Indiana University Press, pp. 172-187.

Bleier, R. (1979), "Social and Political Bias in Science: An Examination of Animal Studies and Their Generalizations to Human Behaviors and Evolution", in R. Hubbard and M. Lowe (eds.), *Genes and Gender II*. New York: Gordian.

______. (1984), *Science and Gender*. New York: Pergamon.

______. ([1986] 1988), "Sex Differences Research: Science or Belief?", in R. Bleier (ed.), *Feminist Approaches to Science*. New York: Pergamon.

Chi, J.G., Dooling, E.C., and Giles, F.H. (1977), "Gyral Development of the Human Brain", *Annals of Neurology*, 1: 86-93.

Diamond, M.C., Dowling, G.A., and Johnson, R.E. (1981), "Morphologic Cerebral Cortical Asymmetry in Male and Female Rats", *Experimental Neurology 71*: 261-268.

Ehrhardt, A.E. and Meyer-Bahlburg, H.F.L. (1981), "Effects of Prenatal Sex Hormones on Gender-Related Behavior", *Science 211*: 1312-1318.

Fausto-Sterling, A. (1985), *Myths of Gender: Biological Theories about Women and Men*. New York: Basic Books.

Galaburda, A.M. (1984), "Anatomical Asymmetries", in N. Geschwind and A.M. Galaburda (eds.), *Cerebral Dominance: The Biological Foundations*. Cambridge, MA and London: Harvard University Press, pp. 11-25.

Geschwind, N. and Behan, P. (1982), "Left-handedness: Association With Immune Disease, Migraine, and Developmental Learning Disorder", *Proceedings of National Academy of Sciences 79*: 5097-5100.

________________. (1984), "Laterality, Hormones, and Immunity", in N. Geschwind and A.M. Galaburda (eds.), *Cerebral Dominance: The Biological Foundations*. Cambridge, MA and London: Harvard University Press, pp. 211-224.

Geschwind, N. and Galaburda, A.M. (eds.) (1984), *Cerebral Dominance: The Biological Foundations*. Cambridge, MA and London: Harvard University Press.

Gorski, R. (1979), "The Neuroendocrinology of Reproduction: An Overview", *Biology of Reproduction 20*: 111-127.

Gorski, R., Gordon, J.H., Shryne, J.E., and Southam, A.M. (1979), "Evidence for a Morphological Sex Difference Within the Medial Preoptic Area of the Rat Brain", *Brain Research 148*: 333-346.

Haraway, D. (1978), "Animal Sociology and a Natural Economy of the Body Politic", *Signs 4*(2): 21-60.

Harris, G. and Levine, S. (1965), "Sexual Differentiation of the Brain and Its Experimental Control", *Journal of Physiology 181*: 379-402.

Hubbard, R. (1982), "The Theory and Practice of Genetic Reductionism—From Mendel's Laws to Genetic Engineering", in S. Rose (ed.), *Towards a Liberatory Biology*. London: Allison and Busby.

Keller, E.F. (1983), *A Feeling for the Organism*. New York: W.H. Freeman.

______. (1985), *Reflections on Gender and Science*. New Haven: Yale.

Kinsbourne, M. (1980), "If Sex Differences in Brain Lateralization Exist, They Have Yet to be Discovered", *The Behavioral and Brain Sciences 3*: 241-42.

Kolata, G. (1983), "Math Genius May Have Hormonal Basis", *Science 222*: 1312.

Longino, H.E. (1990), *Science as Social Knowledge*. Princeton: Princeton.

________. (1994), "In Search of Feminist Epistemology", *The Monist 77,* 4: 472-485.

MacLusky, N.J. and Naftolin, F. (1981), "Sexual Differentiation of the Central Nervous System", *Science 211*: 1294-1311.

McGlone, J. (1980), "Sex Differences in Brain Asymmetry: A Critical Survey", *The Behavioral and Brain Sciences 3*: 215-263.

Nelson, L.H. (1990), *Who Knows: From Quine to a Feminist Empiricism*. Philadelphia: Temple.

________. (forthcoming), "A Feminist Naturalized Philosophy of Science", *Synthese* (Special Issue on Feminism and Science).

Rosser, S. (1982), "Androgyny and Sociobiology", *International Journal of Women's Studies 5*: 435-444.

_____. (1984), "A Call for Feminist Science", *International Journal of Women's Studies 7*: 3-9.

Wilson, J.D., George, F.W., Griffin, J.E. (1981), "The Hormonal Control of Sexual Development", *Science 211*: 1278-1284.

Part V

DO EXPLANATIONS OR PREDICTIONS (OR NEITHER) PROVIDE MORE EVIDENTIAL SUPPORT FOR SCIENTIFIC THEORIES?

Dynamics of Theory Change: The Role of Predictions[1]

Stephen G. Brush

University of Maryland, College Park

"What did the President know and when did he know it?"

Senator Howard Baker, Watergate hearings, 1973

1. Introduction

Why do scientists accept or reject theories? More specifically: why do they change from one theory to another? What is the role of empirical tests in the evaluation of theories?

This paper focuses on a narrowly–defined question: in judging theories, do scientists give greater weight (other things being equal) to successful *novel predictions* than to successful deductions of previously–known facts? The affirmative answer is called the "predictivist thesis" (Maher 1988).

It is primarily philosophers who are interested in this question, and they have treated it mostly as a normative or logical problem. Can the writings of historians of science tell us how scientists have treated novel predictions in the past? Until recently historians have rarely addressed this point. There is a need for historical research designed to answer such questions, and philosophers must apply the same critical scrutiny to historical arguments for their claims that they apply to logical arguments.[2]

I don't claim that philosophy of science must be validated by history of science. Normative or logical studies of the relations between theory and evidence are perfectly legitimate activities for philosophers—as valuable as any other intellectual exercise. My remarks are addressed only to practitioners of "naturalistic" philosophy of science—to those who agree with the "metacriterion" formulated (though not accepted) by Imre Lakatos (1974, 246):

> a rationality theory ... is to be rejected if it is inconsistent with accepted "basic value judgments" of the scientific community. (Lakatos 1974, p. 136)

2. Novel Predictions in the Philosophy of Science

During the past two decades "novel prediction" has played a prominent role in three areas of the philosophy of science: (a) the quasi–historical "methodology of scientific

---

PSA 1994, Volume 2, pp. 133-145

research programmes" developed by Imre Lakatos and his followers; (b) the "problem of old evidence" in Bayesian analysis; and (c) the "miracle argument" for scientific realism.

(a) The *Lakatos methodology of scientific research programmes*

Imre Lakatos (1970) introduced a temporal element into the assessment of theories: a series of theories or a "research programme" should be judged "progressive" or "degenerating" according as later theories are more or less successful than earlier theories in the series. "Success" means, primarily, confirmed novel predictions.

But the application of his methodology to specific historical cases soon showed that it was unreasonable to claim that *only* novel predictions can provide evidence for a theory; scientists obviously do count the explanation of already–known facts in judging a theory. Lakatos's methodology failed to satisfy his metacriterion. His followers tried to rescue it by changing the definition of "novel." They suggested that a previously–known fact might be considered "novel" with respect to a hypothesis if it was not used in constructing that hypothesis. Thus, the advance of the perihelion of Mercury could be counted as a successful novel prediction for Einstein's general relativity since, according to Zahar (1973), Einstein did not use that fact in constructing his theory.

Then John Earman and Clark Glymour (1978) examined Einstein's unpublished correspondence, and found a 1915 letter to Arnold Sommerfeld which strongly suggested that Einstein did in fact use the known behavior of Mercury's perihelion in choosing his field equations for general relativity. Citing this example, Michael Gardner (1982) and others argued that "use" definitions of novelty that can be implemented only by detailed historical research in unpublished documents cannot be used to explain the rational evolution of science; after all, other scientists could not have known at the time whether Einstein had used the Mercury behavior to construct his theory.

Other definitions of "novelty" have been proposed and used by philosophers to evaluate the empirical support of theories. But I have not yet found any evidence that these definitions have any basis in the behavior of scientists.

(b) *Bayesian analysis*

Clark Glymour suggested that Bayesian analysis implies an extreme predictivist thesis: "the absurdity that old evidence cannot confirm new theory" (1980, 86). According to Glymour's interpretation of traditional Bayesian analysis, only novel predictions can test a theory, contrary to actual scientific practice. Hence Bayesian analysis is refuted by the Lakatos metacriterion: it is inconsistent with accepted judgments of the scientific community. Deborah Mayo (1988) reached the same conclusion for the opposite reason: scientists do (she claims) give greater weight to novel predictions but Bayesian analysis does not, hence Bayesian analysis is inadequate. Daniel Garber (1983) and others have agreed that old evidence does count in science, and that Bayesian analysis can be formulated in a manner that is consistent with this fact. Colin Howson (1984) argues that Bayesian analysis is valid because it *does* give "high supportive power" to "any novel facts it predicts" but nevertheless rejects the claim that old evidence counts less than new (Howson 1989).

These and other philosophers have defended all four possible positions: Bayesian analysis is (i) valid because it favors novel predictions, (ii) valid because it does not favor novel predictions, (iii) invalid because it favors novel predictions, and (iv) invalid because it does not favor novel predictions. If we knew whether scientists actually favor novel predictions we could eliminate two of those positions.

(c) The *miracle argument for scientific realism*

Hilary Putnam wrote: "the typical realist argument against idealism is that it makes the success of science a *miracle*." How can theories of electrons, space–time and

DNA "correctly predict observable phenomena if, in reality, there are no electrons, no curved space–time, and no DNA molecules"? If these entities don't exist it is a miracle that a theory assuming their existence successfully predicts phenomena (1978, 18–19). This became known as the "miracle argument" for scientific realism, and has generally (but not always) been taken to mean that the success of *novel* predictions is incomprehensible unless one assumes that the theory generating the prediction refers to something in the real world.[3]

It takes only an elementary knowledge of the history of science to recognize that several successful novel predictions have come from theories now considered incorrect. This was forcefully pointed out, with many examples, by Larry Laudan (1981). In response to Laudan's critique, realists have retreated to weaker versions of the miracle argument (Leplin 1984, 204, 213; Carrier 1993) or have argued that the old false theories really refer to entities that do exist (according to current theory) rather than to what their authors said they did (Kitcher 1993, 144).

3. Does Novelty Make a Difference?

Before we can use historical examples to test the predictivist thesis, we have to take account of an unfortunate linguistic confusion. In ordinary language "predict" means "foretell" or "prophesy," implying a statement about future events. But physicists (and many other scientists) currently use the word to mean "deduce from a theory" whether before or after the fact is known or has occurred. Occasionally one finds the phrase "predict in advance" used to specify prediction of a future event, and sometimes the context indicates that this is what is meant, but very little use is made of terms like "retrodiction" or "postdiction."[4]

While a few philosophers have recognized this usage most still want to distinguish *novel* from other predictions. Since we have to name the distinction in order to discuss whether it is important, I support this as a general term, but I don't think much is to be gained by adopting one of the more restrictive definitions of novelty advocated in the discussion of Lakatosian research programmes. There is still no suitable phrase for *non*–novel predictions. "Accommodation" seems too pejorative. Lacking a better term I will use "retrodiction."

"Explanation" is sometimes said to be the alternative to prediction, offering intellectual understanding as opposed to the pragmatic power to manipulate nature. I prefer not to use this term because I am uncomfortable with the way philosophers of science often define it: as deductive derivation from the basic assumptions of a theory (Achinstein 1991, 6). Thus what philosophers mean by explanation is just what scientists mean by prediction! In this sense relativity and quantum mechanics explain a large number of facts—yet they use basic assumptions that are themselves very hard to understand, even for those scientists who have been most successful at developing such "explanations" (Feynman 1967, 129).

The fact that physicists frequently do not distinguish novel prediction from retrodiction suggests that they don't ascribe much importance to novelty. Yet in their *popular* writings they often celebrate successful predictions such as Einstein's light bending and Mendeleev's new elements. Since "prediction" means "novel prediction" in popular discourse, and it's not always clear whether an author is using a word in the technical or popular sense, we cannot easily infer whether scientists believe the prediction was more important just because it was novel. In order to isolate the novelty factor, I try to find cases in which the same theory made both novel and non–novel predictions (preferably at the same time and of the same importance).

For the sake of argument I grant that (a) the publicity generated by a successful novel prediction may lead scientists to *pursue* a theory that they would otherwise ignore; (b) a novel prediction may stimulate experiments designed to test the theory and thus contribute more to the advance of knowledge than a retrodiction; (c) published statements may not reveal the "real reasons" why scientists choose one theory over another.[5]

Nevertheless I suggest that it is useful to focus on technical publications and science textbooks (rather than popular works or unpublished correspondence and interviews) in order to learn how a discipline articulates a public position on the evaluation of a theory, and how this position is passed on to students.

4. Evidence from case histories

I summarize here the results of my study of 8 case histories in physical science, 6 of them completed (Alfvén's plasma theories, general relativity, the big bang cosmology, Dirac's relativistic quantum mechanics, Yukawa's meson theory of nuclear forces, Gell–Mann's 8–fold way) and two still in progress (Heisenberg–Schrödinger quantum mechanics and Mendeleev's Periodic Law).

I. Acceptance despite failed predictions

According to Julian Simon (1990, 1981), Malthusian theories about the effect of population increase on resources and the standard of living fall into this category. He argues that such theories continue to be supported by scientists even though they are inconsistent with known data and all their specific novel predictions have turned out to be wrong. If he is correct, this would be a strong counterexample to the predictivist thesis.

II. Rejected despite successful novel predictions

Hannes Alfvén developed an electromagnetic plasma theory of space and solar system physics from which he deduced several novel predictions. Most of them were confirmed but some were falsified or still remain in dispute. Even though he won the Nobel Prize in Physics for his work, his theory has been rejected by most space scientists, not because of its falsified predictions but because its basic premises and procedures are considered unsatisfactory. When Bibhas De used one of the confirmed phenomena to predict that the planet Uranus would be found to have rings, his paper was rejected for publication by *Icarus*, a major astronomy journal, and was rejected again when it was resubmitted after the Uranian rings were discovered. This is the example that originally led me to undertake this research on predictions (Brush 1990).

III. Acceptance independent of confirmation of novel predictions

In 1925 Werner Heisenberg proposed his "matrix mechanics" theory of the atom, and in 1926 Erwin Schrödinger proposed a "wave mechanics" theory; shortly thereafter the two theories were shown to be mathematically equivalent (at least with regard to their observational consequences) and they are now considered different versions of a single theory, "quantum mechanics," also formulated in a more abstract way by P. A. M. Dirac. Now acknowledged to be the foundation for theories of the properties of atoms, molecules, radiation, gases, liquids, solids and metals, quantum mechanics is the most important physical theory of the 20th century.

Confirmation of novel predictions played essentially no role in the acceptance of quantum mechanics by physicists. Most researchers active in atomic physics had already accepted the theory before 1929, although its interpretation and technical details continued to be debated for another decade. Because of this rapid acceptance, it is almost correct to say that quantum mechanics was accepted before there was time to confirm any of its novel predictions.

Of course the new quantum mechanics was based on earlier theories—Einstein's light–quantum, Bohr's atomic model, and de Broglie's matter–waves—which did make successful novel predictions. But it was a much more general and powerful theory than its predecessors, and had philosophical consequences that had only been hinted at previously. Given the instrumentalist flavor of the writings of its advocates—especially Heisenberg and Bohr—one might have expected that the new theory would have been put forward with strong claims about its confirmed novel predictions—but that was not the case. Instead, they argued that quantum mechanics accounted at least as well for the facts explained by the old theory, explained several anomalies that its predecessor had failed to resolve, and gave a single consistent method for doing calculations in place of a collection of *ad hoc* rules. Even after 1929 physicists did *not* ascribe any extra weight to the handful of experiments that could now be called confirmations of novel predictions.

As far as I can determine, the earliest novel predictions of quantum mechanics were (1) the intensities of Stark components in the spectra of hydrogen and helium (i.e., lines shifted by an external electric field); (2) the scattering of pairs of identical particles.

(1) Schrödinger's calculation of the intensities of Stark lines in the hydrogen spectrum was confirmed in 1928 by J. Stuart Foster and Laura Chalk. (They had published a preliminary announcement of some of their results in October 1926, showing rough agreement with Schrödinger's predictions but giving so few details that this experiment could hardly be regarded as a crucial confirmation.) The result also supported Schrödinger's assumption that the line intensity depends on the *square* of the wave function amplitude rather than just the amplitude (as proposed by P. Epstein); this was an important point in the physical interpretation of the theory (Gingras 1981). But the Foster–Chalk paper was not cited in any major physics journal before 1930 except by Foster himself (Small 1981).

In 1927 Foster also confirmed the wave–mechanical predictions for the intensities of Stark lines in helium (though it is not clear from his paper whether he made the observations before or after he had done the calculations). There were no explicit citations of Foster's 1927 paper before 1929 in major physics journals (Small 1981), and I have so far found only one mention of it in a book. Foster himself, though an important figure in the development of Canadian physics, is rarely mentioned in histories of quantum mechanics; if he helped Heisenberg and Schrödinger win their Nobel Prizes, they left no acknowledgment on the public record, nor did he claim a major role for himself in the quantum revolution.[6]

(2) In 1930 N. F. Mott calculated from wave mechanics the angular distribution of the scattering of identical particles (at a 45° angle it is twice as great as for non–identical particles). The confirmation of Mott's prediction came too late to influence the acceptance of the theory;[7] like Schrödinger's Stark effect prediction, it is rarely mentioned in the extensive literature on quantum mechanics and on its history and philosophy.

IV. Retrodiction counts as much as novel prediction

The 1919 eclipse test of Einstein's general theory of relativity was an important event, not only in the history of science but also in the history of the philosophy of science. It led Karl Popper, impressed by the contrast between excessively flexible (hence untestable) doctrines like psychoanalysis and Marxism, and relativity—boldly risking death by a crucial experiment on the gravitational bending of light—to declare falsifiability an essential property of a scientific theory.

Light bending turns out to be a good case for examining the claim that novel prediction is a better test of a theory than retrodiction (Brush 1989). There is a large amount of scientific and popular literature dealing with this case, so that one can hope to draw conclusions about the behavior of an entire scientific community, not just a handful of specialists.

Moreover, one can judge the weight ascribed to light bending by comparison with two other tests that were discussed at the same time: the advance of the perihelion of Mercury and the gravitational redshift of spectral lines. The former was a well–known discrepancy that theorists had failed to explain satisfactorily despite several decades of work; Einstein managed to calculate the observed effect within the observational error without introducing any arbitrary parameters.

The redshift was, like light bending, a novel prediction from general relativity theory, but its observational confirmation was still in doubt in the 1920s and remained so for several decades. I will therefore ignore it and inquire simply whether scientists considered that light bending was better evidence than Mercury's orbit because it was a *novel* prediction.

The confirmation of the light–bending prediction did draw an enormous amount of attention, among scientists as well as the public, to Einstein's theory. Physicists were forced to look more closely at a radical theory they might otherwise have ignored.

But the technical literature during the years after the eclipse test has frequent references to the "three predictions" of general relativity and in particular to the "prediction" of the perihelion advance of Mercury. As already mentioned, scientists often use the word "prediction" without implying novelty; in this case, lumping together novel and non–novel predictions strongly suggests that novelty is not considered significant.

Most of the published comments by physicists during the first two or three years after the 1919 eclipse test indicated that light bending and the Mercury perihelion advance counted equally strongly in favor of general relativity. It later became clear to the experts that the Mercury effect was *stronger* evidence than light bending. In part this was because the observational data were more accurate—it was very difficult to make good eclipse measurements, even with modern technology—and in part because the Mercury orbit calculation depended on a "deeper" part of the theory. The novelty of the light–bending prediction seems to count for little or nothing in these judgments.

There is even some indication that, rather than light bending providing better evidence because it was a novel prediction, it actually provides less secure evidence *for that very reason* (cf. Weinberg 1992, 288)—at least in the years immediately following the announcement of the eclipse result. Physicists recognized that the result might be explained by more than one theory. In fact, advocates of competing theories argued that if they could retrodict light bending, their theories would get just as much support from its discovery as did Einstein's theory. Far from being discounted for failing to predict light bending in advance, they argued that their theories should be *preferred* over Einstein's because they did not have to invoke fantastic notions such as space–time curvature.

Because the Mercury discrepancy had been known for several decades, theorists had already had ample opportunity to explain it from Newtonian celestial mechanics and had failed to do so except by making implausible *ad hoc* assumptions. Einstein's success was therefore immediately impressive; it seemed unlikely that another theory would subsequently produce a better alternative explanation. It was a few years before Einstein's supporters could plausibly assert that no other theory could account for light bending, and this phenomenon therefore counted as evidence in favor of Einstein's theory over the others.

V. Acceptance after novel prediction is confirmed, but...

There are 3 well–known cases of new particles predicted from theories (Brush 1993b): the positron (from Dirac's relativistic quantum theory); the meson (from Yukawa's theory of nuclear forces); and the omega–minus, Ω^- (from Gell–Mann's SU3 or "8–fold way" symmetry group theory). In each case physicists accepted the theory within two or three years after the discovery of the predicted particle. But, while the successful predictions certainly forced physicists to give serious consideration to those theories, there is no convincing evidence that within the context of such consideration, a theory that merely retrodicted the particles would be any less acceptable, other things being equal.

In each case, the original theory that predicted the particle was soon replaced by another theory. Perhaps most remarkable is the case of the positron, which Dirac proposed as the "anti–particle" of the electron. The existence of an anti–particle followed directly from his equation, provided one accepted his interpretation of "holes" in a sea of negative–energy states as particles with the opposite charge and positive energy. But Dirac's theory was replaced by quantum electrodynamics, in which the existence of anti–particles was not deduced but simply postulated.

Also in this category is the "big bang" cosmology of Friedmann, Lemaître and Gamow (Brush 1993a). Alpher and Herman, and later Gamow, predicted from this theory the existence of a cosmic microwave background, with a Planck frequency distribution corresponding to a temperature a few degrees above absolute zero. The rival "steady state" cosmology of Bondi, Gold and Hoyle did not entail that consequence. Soon after the discovery of the background radiation in 1965, astronomers abandoned the steady state theory in favor of the big bang.

Again, it is not clear whether the big bang theory, once it was revived by this successful prediction, got credit for novelty; steady–state advocates argued that if they could somehow retrodict the new phenomenon from their theory, they would be entitled to just as much credit for it. After they failed to do so, the big bang was accepted.

The cosmology case also shows the influence of Karl Popper's falsificationism on scientists. Bondi and Gold (but not Hoyle), citing Popper as a guide to scientific methodology, promised that they would abandon their theory if any reliable evidence were found that the large–scale properties of the universe were different in the past than they are now. When the cosmic microwave background provided evidence for a much hotter early state, they kept their promise. So falsificationism works if you believe in it.

VI. Novelty does count—a little

Patrick Maher asserted that "scientific practice accords well with the predictivist thesis" but in support of that assertion he presented only a single example: Mendeleev's periodic table. In 1871 Mendeleev predicted the existence and properties of three elements needed to fill gaps in the table. Two of them, gallium and scandium, were discovered in the 1870s; the third, germanium, was found in 1886. Scientists, previously skeptical, now acclaimed Mendeleev's Periodic Law, and in 1882 the Royal Society awarded him its Davy Medal. According to Maher, the number of elements in the table had increased by only a relatively small number—from 62 to 64—so we must conclude that scientists were more impressed by the novel predictions of 2 elements than by the larger number of elements accommodated by the table (Maher 1988, 273, 274). As Peter Lipton says, using the same example to support his version of the predictivist thesis, "sixty accommodations paled next to the two predictions" (1990, 51; see also Lipton 1991).

The Maher–Lipton claim gives us a semi–quantitative version of the predictivist thesis: predicting a new element is worth more than 31 times as much as accommodating a known one. Unfortunately Maher and Lipton give no documentation for their claim. Did the Royal Society award the Davy Medal to Mendeleev because of his successful novel predictions? Perhaps some evidence for this assertion can be found, but the most obvious source refutes it. The citation for the award does not even mention those predictions! Instead, it discusses the "foundations of a general system of classification of the elements," lists the atomic weights of 15 elements *not* including gallium or scandium, remarks on "the marvelous regularity with which the differences of property" of the sequence from lithium to fluorine are reproduced in the sequence from sodium to chlorine, and mentions the graphs of physical properties such as atomic volume plotted against atomic weight. Moreover, the Davy Medal was awarded jointly to Lothar Meyer, who was responsible for the atomic volume graph but did not successfully predict new elements. Thus if we are to believe the public announcement, the Davy Medal was awarded for accommodation, not for prediction (Spottiswoode 1882).

But Maher and Lipton may still be correct about the Periodic Law in a broader sense. Eric Scerri is currently preparing a detailed study of this case (Scerri 1994). My own survey of chemistry text–books and articles in the late 19th century suggests that many chemists did give some credit for novelty; they considered that, other things being equal, the prediction of a new element and its properties counted more than fitting a known element into the table. But not 31 times as much!

Mendeleev himself asserted that he regarded the chemists who discovered these elements "as the true corroborators of the periodic law. Without them it would not have been accepted to the extent that it now is" (1902, 26). A few other scientists made similar statements about the importance of these successful predictions in establishing the law.

Nevertheless almost every discussion of the periodic law in 19th–century chemistry textbooks, including Mendeleev's, gives much more attention to the correlations of properties of the known elements with their atomic weights than to the prediction of new ones. Frequently the reader is given the impression that the periodic law is *established* by these correlations, and then *applied* to make predictions.

Among the applications of the periodic law was the *correction* of atomic weights of known elements, such as beryllium and uranium. Mendeleev argued that in order to fit into his table, Be should have atomic weight 9 (rather than the value 13.8 proposed by some chemists), and U should be 240 (rather than 120). Such revisions had considerably more practical significance for chemists than the discovery of Ga, Sc, and Ge.

The reason why these predicted new elements were less important to chemists than the known elements that were correlated by the periodic law is the same reason why they had not already been discovered before 1869: their abundance at the earth's surface is very small. Of course this doesn't mean that rare elements are necessarily unimportant (cf. radium). But in late 19th–century chemistry books these elements get little space; sometimes it is said that they are of interest mainly because of the fact that Mendeleev predicted them.

While chemists differed on the relative importance of prediction and accommodation, it seems fair to approximate the consensus in 1890 as follows. The reasons for accepting the periodic law were, in order of importance: (1) it accurately describes the correlation between physicochemical properties and atomic weights of nearly all known elements; (2) it has led to useful corrections in the atomic weights of several elements; (3) it has yielded successful predictions of the existence and properties of new elements.

VII. Novelty is crucial

Are there any cases in which a theory was accepted *primarily* because of its successful predictions of novel facts, and would not have been accepted if those facts had been previously known? Some textbook presentations of the "scientific method" imply that this is the norm in science. So far I have found no examples in this category, but I'm still looking.

5. Are theorists less trustworthy than observers?

One reason why some philosophers and scientists want to give more credit to novel predictions is presumably their suspicion that theorists may be influenced in reaching their conclusions by knowledge of the phenomena to be explained. But have we forgotten so soon the phenomenon of "theory–dependence of observations" widely discussed a generation ago by philosophers of science? Isn't it just as likely that observers will be influenced in reporting their results by knowledge of theoretical predictions of those results? (This has been suggested in the case of light bending by Everitt 1980 and others.) Doesn't the predictivist thesis imply a double standard for theorists and observers, based on a discredited empiricist conception of science with its "neutral observational language"? Wouldn't it be just as reasonable to give more weight to observations performed before rather than after a theoretical prediction?

6. Conclusions

Novel predictions played essentially no role in the acceptance of the most important physical theory of the 20th century, quantum mechanics. As evidence for general relativity, light bending did not get more weight because of its novelty.

In several other cases (cosmic microwave background, positron, etc.), acceptance of a theory followed a successful novel prediction but was not necessarily due to its novelty. In another case scientists refused to accept a theory (Alfvén's) regardless of the success of its predictions.

One case gives limited support to the predictiveness thesis: novel predictions did have some evidential value in the establishment of the Periodic Law, though most chemists did not consider them as important as the success of the Law in organizing and revising knowledge about the known elements.

The predictivist thesis gains little empirical support from the history of science. Any attempt to rescue it by redefining novelty in terms of what the theorist knew, when he knew it, and what he did or could have done with the information puts the philosopher in the position of a Watergate investigator without a Deep Throat.

Notes

[1]I thank Lindley Darden and Frederick Suppe for valuable criticism of earlier drafts; useful suggestions and comments have been received from Laurie Brown, David Cassidy, Max Jammer, Helge Kragh, Larry Laudan, Edward MacKinnon, Arthur Miller, Helmut Rechenberg, Eric Scerri, and Katherine Sopka. Louis Brown first called my attention to the significance of Mott scattering as a novel prediction of quantum mechanics.

My research has been supported by the National Science Foundation, the National Endowment for the Humanities, the Institute for Advanced Study (Princeton), the Andrew W. Mellon Foundation, and the University of Maryland General Research Board.

[2]To assert that evidence must be critically scrutinized does not imply that a positivist or hypothetico–deductive method should be used to test methodological claims. This kind of criticism has been used by some philosophers to avoid giving serious consideration to a major project which does exactly what I am proposing (Donovan, Laudan and Laudan 1988).

[3]See the collection of articles edited by Leplin (1984) and especially Leplin's remark on page 217 which rejects the position, apparently taken by Putnam, that *any* empirical success supports realism. The novelty issue is discussed by Leplin (1982), Musgrave (1988), Carrier (1991), Meehl (1992), Petroni (1993). An earlier example (without the word "miracle") in connection with Mendeleev's Periodic Law is in Darrow (1927, 48).

[4]See the explicit statement by Margenau (1950, 105). Biologists and geologists do not follow the practice of physicists here, and occasionally complain about the ambiguous use of the word "prediction" (Mayr 1985, 49; Strahler 1987, 15). But I have found occasional instances in the social sciences of "prediction" or even "forecast" being used to deduce known facts (Gurr and Lichbach 1986).

[5]These issues are discussed in my published papers on cases in physics and astronomy (Brush 1989; 1990; 1993a; 1993b). Of course one cannot assume that what a scientist says in a letter or interview is any more than a second approximation to the "real reason," taking published writings as the first approximation. Most statements by historians and philosophers about the reasons for theory change are only a *zero–order* approximation, based on essentially *no* evidence. I am currently using the quantum mechanics case to test the assumption that the reasons for theory–choice given in published writings are the same as those given in correspondence and interviews; unlike most other cases, a large quantity of unpublished material is easily available at the Center for History of Physics in College Park.

[6]Schrödinger later called this the "earliest quantitative achievement of quantum mechanics" (1952, 235) without explicitly citing the work of Foster and Chalk; he did not even mention his prediction of Stark intensities in his Nobel Lecture or in other expositions of quantum mechanics. Heisenberg recalled, but only in an unpublished interview (1963), that Foster's work on the empirical testing of quantum mechanics was "very exciting."

[7]It did however impress Ernest Rutherford, according to Mott's later recollections (1962).

References

Achinstein, P. (1991), *Particles and Waves: Historical Essays in the Philosophy of Science*. New York: Oxford University Press.

Brush, S.G. (1989), "Prediction and Theory Evaluation: The Case of Light Bending", *Science* 246: 1124–1129.

_______. (1990), "Prediction and Theory Evaluation: Alfvén on Space Plasma Phenomena", *Eos: Transactions of the American Geophysical Union* 71: 19–33.

_______. (1993a), "Prediction and Theory Evaluation: Cosmic Microwaves and the Revival of the Big Bang", *Perspectives on Science* 1: 565–602.

_______. (1993b), "Prediction and Theory Evaluation: Subatomic Particles", *Rivista di Storia della Scienza* [2] 1, no. 2: 47–152.

Carrier, M. (1991), "What is wrong with the Miracle Argument?", *Studies in History and Philosophy of Science* 22: 23–36.

_______. (1993), "What is right with the Miracle Argument: Establishing a Taxonomy of Natural Kinds", *Studies in History and Philosophy of Science* 24: 391–409.

Darwin, C.G. (1931), *The New Conceptions of Matter*. London: Bell & Sons.

Donovan, A., Laudan, L. and Laudan, R. (eds.), (1988), *Scrutinizing science: Empirical Studies of Scientific Change*. Boston: Kluwer.

Earman, J. and Glymour, C. (1978), "Einstein and Hilbert: Two Months in the History of General Relativity", *Archive for History of Exact Sciences* 19: 291–308.

Everitt, C.W.F. (1980), "Experimental Tests of General Relativity: Past, Present and Future", in *Physics and Contemporary Needs*, volume 4, Riazuddin (ed.) New York: Plenum, pp. 529–555.

Feynman, R.P. (1967), *The Character of Physical Law*. Cambridge, MA: MIT Press.

Garber, D. (1983), "Old Evidence and logical omniscience in Bayesian confirmation Theory", in *Testing Scientific Theories,* J. Earman (ed.). Minneapolis: University of Minnesota Press, pp. 99–131.

Gardner, M.R. (1982), "Predicting Novel Facts", *British Journal for the Philosophy of Science* 33: 1–15.

Gingras, Y. (1981), "La Physique à McGill entre 1920 et 1940: La Réception de la Mécanique Quantique par une Communauté Scientifique Péripherique", *HSTC Bulletin* 5 (1): 15–39. Reprinted in *Science, Technology and Medicine in Canada's Past*, R. A. Jarrell and J. P. Hull (eds.). Thornhill, Ontario, Canada: Scientia Press (1991), pp. 105–128.

Glymour, C. (1980), *Theory and Evidence*. Princeton:Princeton University Press

Gurr, T.R. and Lichbach, M.I. (1986), "Forecasting Internal Conflict: A Competitive Evaluation of Empirical Theories", *Comparative Political Studies* 19: 3–38.

Heisenberg, W. (1963), Interviews with Thomas S. Kuhn. Tapes 50b and 52. Archive for History of Quantum Physics. Transcript at Niels Bohr Library, Center for History of Physics, College Park, MD.

Howson, C. (1984), "Bayesianism and support by novel facts", *British Journal for the Philosophy of Science* 35: 245–51.

______. (1989), "Accommodation, Prediction, and Bayesian Confirmation Theory", in *PSA 1988*, vol. 2. East Lansing, MI: Philosophy of Science Association, pp. 381–392.

Kitcher, P. (1993), *The Advancement of Science*. New York: Oxford University Press.

Lakatos, I. (1970), "Falsification and the Methodology of Scientific Research Programmes", in *Criticism and the Growth of Knowledge*, I. Lakatos and A. Musgrave (eds.). New York: Cambridge University Press, pp. 91–196.

_____. (1974), "Popper on Demarcation and Induction", in *The Philosophy of Karl Popper*, P.A. Schilpp (ed.). La Salle, IL: Open Court, pp. 241–273.

Laudan, L. (1981), "A Confutation of Convergent Realism", *Philosophy of Science* 48: 19–49.

Leplin, J. (1982), "The Historical Objection to Scientific Realism", in *PSA 1982*, volume 1, East Lansing: Philosophy of Science Association, pp. 88–97.

Leplin, J., (ed.) (1984), *Scientific Realism*. Berkeley: University of California Press.

Lipton, P. (1990), "Prediction and Prejudice", *International Studies in the Philosophy of Science* 4, no 1: 51–65.

_ _ _ _ _ . (1991), *Inference to the Best Explanation.* London & New York: Routledge.

Maher, P. (1988), "Prediction, Accommodation, and the Logic of Discovery", in *PSA 1988*, volume 1. East Lansing: Philosophy of Science Association, pp. 273–285.

Margenau, H. (1950) *The Nature of Physical Reality.* New York: McGraw–Hill.

Mayo, D. (1988), "Brownian Motion and the Appraisal of Theories", in A. Donovan, L. Laudan and R. Laudan (eds.) (1988), pp. 219–243.

_ _ _ _ _. (1991), "Novel Evidence and Severe Tests," *Philosophy of Science* 58: 523–552.

Mayr, E. (1985), "How Biology differs from the Physical Sciences", in *Evolution at a Crossroads*, D.J. Depew and B.C. Weber (eds.). Cambridge: MIT Press, pp. 49–63.

Meehl, P.E. (1992), "The Miracle Argument for Realism: An important Lesson to be Learned by Generalizing from Carrier's Counter–examples", *Studies in History and Philosophy of Science* 23: 267–82.

Mendeleev, D. (1902), *The Principles of Chemistry*, Volume 2, Part 3. 2nd English ed. New York: Collier.

Mott, N.F. (1962) "Notes by Prof. Mott on his Personal Experiences of the Development of Quantum Physics." Unpublished memoir in Archive for History of Quantum Physics. Copy at Niels Bohr Library, Center for History of Physics, College Park, MD.

Musgrave, A. (1988), "The Ultimate Argument for Scientific Realism", in *Relativism and Realism in Science*, R. Nola (ed.). Boston: Kluwer, pp. 229–252.

Petroni, A. (1993), "Conventionalism, Scientific Discovery and the Sociology of Knowledge", *International Studies in Philosophy of Science* 7: 225–240.

Putnam, H. (1978), *Meaning and the Moral Sciences.* London: Routledge & Kegan Paul.

Scerri, E.R. (1994), "Prediction, Accommodation and the Periodic Table", preprint.

Schrödinger, E. (1952), "Are there Quantum Jumps?", *British Journal for the Philosophy of Science* 3: 109–123, 233–242.

Simon, J.L. (1980), "Resources, Population, Environment: An Oversupply of False Bad News", *Science* 208: 1431–1437.

_ _ _ _ _ _. (1981), *The Ultimate Resource.* Princeton, NJ: Princeton University Press.

_ _ _ _ _ _. (1990), *Population Matters: People, Resources, Environment, and Immigration.* New Brunswick, NJ: Transaction Publishers.

Small, H. (1981), *Physics Citation Index 1920–1929.* Philadelphia: Institute for Scientific Information.

Spottiswoode, W. (1882), President's Address, *Proceedings of the Royal Society of London* 34: 302–329.

Strahler, A.N. (1987), *Science and Earth History. The Evolution/Creation Controversy*. Buffalo: Prometheus.

Weinberg, S. (1992), *Dreams of a Final Theory*. New York: Pantheon.

Zahar, E. (1973), "Why did Einstein's Programme supersede Lorentz's?", *British Journal for the Philosophy of Science* 24: 95–123, 223–262.

Empirical and Rational Components in Scientific Confirmation[1]

Abner Shimony

Boston University

A Perspective

A common device in popular presentations of science is a sequence of views from cosmic to terrestrial to local to microscopic, thereby placing the subject to which the program is devoted in a proper perspective. I wish to use an adaptation of this device to place the announced topic of our panel — "Do Explanations or Predictions Provide More Evidential Support for Scientific Theories?" — in perspective. My four steps, from the largest to the smallest scale, are the following:

1. A brief summary of the world view suggested by the discoveries of the natural sciences and by philosophical reflections on them;
2. a consideration of the methodology for scientific investigation, upon assumption that this world view is approximately correct;
3. the formulation of a version of Bayesian scientific inference satisfying the desiderata of step 2;
4. the topic of our panel — explanation vs. prediction.

1. Sketch of a World View

Plato's grand division of facts into generalities and contingencies has been maintained by modern science, e.g., the contrast between differential equations and boundary conditions, the contrast between symmetries and the breaking of symmetries. Furthermore, the dichotomy is elaborated as a hierarchy, according to which laws at the n level result from the conjunction of laws at the n-1 level with contingencies. The hierarchical organization of generalities is not just a matter of deductive subordination, for there is a great role of chance in the emergence of specialized levels in the hierarchy. Immense stretches of time, immense numbers of partially autonomous elements, hence immense numbers of combinations, added to the stochastic character of the fundamental laws, ensure that the universe has an evolutionary history.

Humankind emerged after many stages of the hierarchical organization of the universe had been achieved: the cooling that permits the formation of nucleons and hydrogen; the genesis of stars that could serve as furnaces for synthesizing heavier ele-

---

PSA 1994, Volume 2, pp. 146-155

ments; the fortuitous development of a terrestrial environment in which the molecular experiments of prebiotic evolution could be carried out; the subsequent biotic evolution, establishing both biological types and the biological laws governing them; the evolution of higher animals governed by even more derivative and specialized laws. The evolutionary point of view is exhibited not only phylogenetically but ontogenetically, in the articulation of the nervous systems of higher animals (Edelman's "neural Darwinism") and in trial and error learning processes.

The enterprise of the natural sciences is the establishment and correction of the world view just sketched and the filling in of details whenever the outline is reliable. The enterprise is carried out by human beings, with all their limitations deriving from relative size, from spatio-temporal localization, from imperfections of sensory equipment, and from peculiarities of information processing in the brain and mind. The scientific world view sketched in the first two paragraphs of this Section was presented from an Olympian standpoint, but the enterprise of science is carried out by non-Olympians. It seems to me that the fundamental question for philosophically minded historians of science to address is this: how could the world view of science, with its wonderful coherence and reliability, be achieved by non-Olympians? The constructive and cooperative work of an entire profession is required to come close to an adequate answer to this question. I hope that the remarks on methodology in the next two Sections will be useful, albeit infinitesimally, in this great project. It should be added that the universe must probably satisfy certain conditions of knowability for any human methodology to work. For example, a radical breakdown of the invariance of fundamental physical laws under spatial and temporal translation would preclude extrapolations from locally obtained data. Hence, if the laws of physics change as the universe ages, the change must be gradual if it is to be discovered — which is another way of saying that temporal invariance is maintained at a sufficiently general level. There are also scientific questions, intricately entangled with philosophical ones, about the possibility of definite limitations of human faculties. I am an optimist that "the Idols of the Cave" are corrigible by enlightened methodology, despite weighty arguments to the contrary, but a discussion of this matter is beyond the scope of the present paper.

2. Methodology

Let us suppose that the sketch of a world view presented in Section 1 is correct, but that the details completing the sketch are unknown. What methodology is appropriate for investigations within the assumed framework? In this Section I shall list unsystematically some of the components of an adequate methdology.

(i) The methodology should abstain from anything like the intuitive induction proposed in the last chapter of Aristotle's "Posterior Analytics." The reliability of intuitive induction presupposes a world view radically different from that of Section 1 — a metaphysics of substantial forms and a theory that the intellect can grasp the forms of substances after sufficient empirical exposure. In the world view of Section 1, human beings are the products of a long evolution, with a highly derivative and special place in the hierarchical structure of the universe. Hence there is no reason to credit the human intellect with a capability of intuiting the forms that govern the fundamental level of nature, and furthermore there is no direct exposure of human sensory faculties to individual entities on the fundamental level.

(ii) In lieu of direct insight — intellectual or empirical or both combined — into matters of fact remote in time, space, or scale from ordinary human experience, indirect inference is essential. The ontological underpinning of indirect inference is the existence of causally established correlations between facts in the domain of interest and elements of human experience. These correlations in turn are based upon the hierarchical structure of the universe assumed in the scientific world view. Of course the details of the correlations are not known without much knowledge of the hierarchical structure, which is a large part of the enterprise of the natural sciences. In the absence of knowledge of these correlations there is no substitute for hypotheses of sufficient specificity that deductions can be made about the results of observation.

(iii) Since other influences than the facts of primary interest enter into the causal chains that terminate in observational data, an important component of methodology is the disentanglement of unwanted influences that are massive enough to be identified and controlled. Some of these influences are in the physical environment, some are in instruments, and some are in the sensory and intellectual equipment of the observers. The disentanglement of these influences is the methodological procedure of preventing or correcting systematic errors. When systematic errors are suspected but not identified, they can be sought by the well known methods of "trouble shooting." When they are identified, their effects can often be diminished by shielding or by improvement of instruments or can be "subtracted out" from the data.

(iv) Also entering in the causal chains that eventuate in observational data are innumerable small influences, resulting partly from the existence of innumerable semi-autonomous entities in the natural world and partly from the stochastic character of fundamental natural laws, both of these being aspects of the world view sketched in Section 1. Random errors are the consequences of many tiny influences that cannot be individually controlled. To some extent the random errors can be diminished by physical means, e.g., cooling the apparatus in order to reduce thermal noise. The intellectual instrument for dealing with random errors and setting reasonable upper bounds upon them is probability theory, of which error theory is a subdiscipline.

(v) The hierarchical structure of the universe and the highly special place of human beings imply that any scientific program that aims at comprehensiveness must cultivate what may be called "a strategy of ascent" — that is, a strategy that subdivides the scientific enterprise into manageable small steps and nevertheless envisages ways of integrating small increments of knowledge into a systematic view. There can be no a priori design of a strategy of ascent, because neither the obstacles nor the opportunities can be foreseen. It has been suggested that the scientific enterprise is analogous to the game of Twenty Questions, whereby localization in the space of possibilities is achieved in a finite number of steps; but the analogy is inadequate, because Twenty Questions presupposes a set of categories that are deployed in the process of exploration, whereas the categories of the scientific enterprise are discovered en route. It is not even the case that a strategy of ascent always moves from the levels of the hierarchy of the universe closest to the scale of human beings to the more remote levels (Aristotle's formula of moving from "first in the order of knowing" to "first in the order of being"), because it often happens that precise knowledge of laws on a microscopic scale precedes precise knowledge of laws on a human scale. A strategy of ascent is essentially an exploratory, open-minded, undogmatic, self-critical, tenacious, painstaking, and patient use of human intelligence. If this characterization is reminiscent of the pragmatism of Peirce and Dewey, that is not an accident. It may be objected that a strategy of ascent aims to be a logic of discovery. This not my intention, since I am concerned with the logic of confirmation of hypotheses. But if it should happen that the incorporation of a strategy of ascent into confirmation theory will provide some heuristics for the proposal of fruitful hypotheses, that is a bonus to rejoice over.

3. Rational and Empirical Elements in Bayesian Confirmation Theory

Bayesian confirmation theory takes as its fundamental concept the epistemic probability function P(x/y), which is a real-valued function of a pair of propositions (x,y), with y required not to be self-contradictory. P(x/y) roughly means "the reasonable degree of belief in x, if y is the total evidence." There are different schools of Bayesian confirmation theory, differing primarily in the interpretation of the adjective "reasonable." The logical probabilists (especially Keynes and Carnap) maintain that there is an objectively definite reasonable degree of belief, founded somehow on the logical relation between x and y. The personal probabilists (Ramsey, DeFinetti, Savage) recognize no condition for reasonableness other than "coherence" (an extension of the concept of consistency), and therefore they allow different persons to have their own probability functions, none more reasonable than the others. My own interpretation (1970, modified somewhat in 1993) is intermediate between these two extremes, and I shall argue below that it incorporates methodological component (iv), a strategy of ascent, in a natural manner.

That the function P(x/y) satisfies the standard probability axioms has been established in various ways, which I shall not review. These axioms entail the following, called Bayes's theorem:

$$P(h/e\&b) = [P(h/b)P(e/h\&b)]/P(e/b).$$

This theorem does not depend upon the epistemic character of h,e, and b, but its methodological importance emerges when h is a hypothesis, b is the background of general information and assumptions (not always completely articulated), and e is a body of specific and definitely articulated evidence. P(h/b) is called "the prior probability of h," P(e/b) is "the prior probability of e," and P(e/h&b) is "the likelihood of e, given h and the background." An immediate corollary is an equation expressing the ratio of the posterior probabilities of two hypotheses h and h' in terms of the ratio of thelr prior probabilities and the ratio of the likelihoods of e given one and the other hypothesis:

$$P(h/e\&b)/P(h'/e\&b) = [P(h/b)P(e/h\&b)]/[P(h'/b)P(e/h'\&b)].$$

The first four of the five methodological components of Section 2 fit well into Bayesian confirmation theory generically. Component (i), the abstention from intuitive induction, is exhibited in two ways: first, there need be no sensory presentation of the entities involved in h, because the empirical evidence e may be linked to these entities by long causal chains; secondly, the conclusion regarding h is not the recognition of its necessity, which was supposed to be the consummation of intuitive induction, but only its high probability given the evidence, or perhaps only a higher probability than its rival hypotheses h', h'', etc., possess.

Component (ii), indirect reasoning, is captured well by Bayes's theorem and its corollary. Typically it is the likelihood P(e/h&b) that is calculated directly, and then the posterior probability P(h/e&b) is obtained indirectly by Bayes's theorem after reasonable assumptions are made about the prior probabilities P(h/b) and P(e/b); or the ratios of posterior probabilities are obtained via the corollary, which has the obvious advantage of dispensing with the evaluation of P(e/b). The classical archetype of indirect reasoning is the hypothetico-deductive method, which is not explicitly probabilistic and yet can be understood as a special application of Bayes's theorem in the following way. Suppose that h&b contains sufficient information to deduce e by logical and mathematical means alone (which in practice means that b contains a considerable body of auxiliary information about such things as boundary conditions and the absence of important perturbations). Under this ideal condition the axioms of probability yield P(e/h&b)=1, and then Bayes's theorem simplifies to

$$P(h/e\&b) = P(h/b)/P(e/b).$$

The posterior probability is increased over the prior probability of h by a factor that is the inverse of the prior probability of the evidence e, and this inverse is a reasonable measure of how "striking" the supporting evidence for h is. Thus the frequently emphasized importance of "striking" evidence in hypothetico-deductive confirmation has a straightforward Bayesian explanation.

Methodological component (iii), the disentanglement of influences, is not manifest in generic Bayesian confirmation theory, because of the compactness and generality of the formalism, but it lurks just below the surface in typical applications.

Typically h asserts a law governing some natural domain or asserts that some factor plays a crucial role in some phenomenon, while e is specific data concerning the phenomenon. If the hypothetico-deductive method is used, then e must be deduced from h&b, which places a great burden on b. For the deduction to be valid b must assert the non-occurrence of systematic errors and hence the "normal operation" of instruments and sense organs. How strong the assumption of "normal operation" is may be seen from Wilson's instructions for trouble-shooting (1951, Sections 5.6 and 6.6) — e.g., look for uncontrolled thermal and mechanical flows, stray electro-magnetic fields, noise sources in the apparatus, slippage of alignments, corrosions of parts, distortions of amplification, and failure of registration. The background b is, of course, not incorrigible, and the occurrence of unexpected or anomalous empirical evidence e is a stimulus to unpack and articulate the assumptions contained in b and then to check them. Finally, it should be added that the disentangling of influences is generally important for reliable calculation of likelihoods, not just in the extreme case of the hypothetico-deductive method when the likelihood is unity.

As to methodological component (iv), the probabilistic treatment of random errors, there is no need to say much, since epistemic probability is the central concept of Bayesianism. It may be worth remarking, however, that when a treatment of ontic probabilities or propensities is available, as in parts of error theory, there is no reason why it cannot be assimilated by a theory of epistemic probability. If, for example, h asserts that a loaded die has the propensity 1/4 to turn up the number six, and e asserts that a six will turn up on a given toss, which according to the background b is not an atypical toss, then a reasonable evaluation of the likelihood is $P(e/h\&b)=1/4$. The function P is unequivocally understood as an epistemic probability function in spite of this assimilation.

I wish to devote special attention to methodological component (v), the strategy of ascent, since it points preferentially to the version of Bayesian confirmation theory that I have named "tempered personalism." This version was essentially proposed by Harold Jeffreys (1961), but it is presented with some variations in two of my papers (1970, 1993). Although Jeffreys was nominally a logical probabilist, he recognized that there is much less consensus concerning prior probabilities than likelihoods. He also noted that if all possible hypotheses are admitted in an investigation, then any one of them would receive only an infinitesimal prior probability, and consequently Bayes's theorem would preclude any hypothesis from achieving a substantial posterior probability upon a humanly accessible body of evidence. To deal with these two difficulties, Jeffreys effectively suggested a localized, relativized, and pragmatic trreatment of prior probabilities that abandons the logical interpretation of epistemic probability. He supposed that at any given time there is only a finite set of hypotheses $h_1,...,h_n$ seriously proposed by the scientific community concerning a phenomenon of interest. To these one can add the "catch-all" hypothesis h_{n+1} that is the negation of the disjunction of these n hypotheses; it is the hypothesis that something else, not yet specified, is the case. The background b can be taken to be the common body of knowledge and assumptions of the scientific community at the specified time, which would include a survey of the seriously proposed hypotheses concerning the matter in question. Jeffreys does not prescribe definite values of the prior probabilities $P(h_i/b)$ for the selected set of hypotheses, and in this way he has moved toward the libertarian position of the personalists. But he does prescribe open-mindedness towards each h_i ($i = 1,...,n+1$): each $P(h_i/b)$ should be sufficiently high for the possibility to be kept open that the posterior probability of h_i will be greater than that of all of its rivals on a moderate and humanly achievable body of evidence. This rule I call "the tempering principle," In addition to offering a solution to the two difficulties posed by Jeffreys, tempered personalism has a number of virtues as a via media between logical probabilism and personalism (Shimony 1970, Section 3). It appears, however, to have a serious weakness — the obscurity of the phrase "seriously proposed." Unless the phrase is clarified, the tempering principle appears vacuous. But if there is clarification, it seems hard to avoid the two extremes of a liberal construction, in which case too many hypotheses would have non-negligible prior probability, or a strict construction, which seems to build dogmatism and establishmentarianism into scientific methodology.

I believe that the strategy of ascent suggests a guide to a golden mean between these undesirable extremes. Before trying to spell out what this guide suggests, I want to give an example in which the scientific community seems to have exhibited collective wisdom in its recognition of a set of seriously proposed hypotheses. I shall cite Franklin's penetrating studies (1986, 1993) of the physics community's acceptance of the experiment of Christenson, Cronin, Fitch, and Turlay (1964) and their inference that CP-invariance is violated in certain weak interaction processes. In this experiment the evidence consists of data from scintillation counters and Cerenkov counters in an apparatus designed to look at decays of long-lived neutral kaons K^0_2 into pairs of pions, and the hypothesis of primary interest h is the violation of CP. Since h is contrary to a deeply held symmetry principle, it is not surprising that many alternatives were proposed to explain the anomalous evidence e. Franklin (1993, 262-263)) gives the following summary:

> In the actual practice of science, however, the limits placed on the hypothesis space do not seem very stringent. Thus, when the experiment of Christenson et al. (1964) detected K^0_2 decay into two pions, which seemed to show that CP symmetry (combined particle-antiparticle and space inversion symmetry) was violated, no fewer than ten alternatives were offered. These included (1) the cosmological model resulting from the local asymmetry of matter and antimatter, (2) external fields, (3) the decay of the K^0_2 into a K^0_1 with the subsequent decay of the K^0_1 into two pions, which was allowed by the symmetry, (4) the emission of another particle, "the partino," in the K^0_2 decay, similar to the emission of the neutrino in beta decay, (5) that one of the pions emitted in the decay was in fact a "spion," a pion with spin one rather than zero, (6) that the decay was due to another neutral particle, the L, produced coherently with the K^0, the existence of a "shadow" universe, which interacted with our universe only through the weak interactions and that the decay seen was that of the "shadow" K^0_2, (8) the failure of the exponential decay law, (9) the failure of the principle of superposition in quantum mechanics, and (10) that the dacay pions were not bosons. As one can see, the limits placed on alternatives were not very stringent.

I wish to raise two questions concerning this fascinating passage. The first is whether Franklin is correct in saying, "As one can see, the limits placed on alternatives were not very stringent.". My own answer is that indeed the ten hypotheses are far-ranging within the space of possibilities roughly mapped out by the elementary particle physics of the epoch, but that they concretely sample little of that space. Franklin does not put the catch-all hypothesis — that something else is true — in his list, and for good reason: the catch-all offers no target for an experimental test. But the futility of trying to test the catch-all does not prevent it from occupying most of the space of logical possibilities, when a reasonable measure is defined on that space. Buried in the catch-all are frivolous and captious hypotheses about coincidences, strange curves that fit the data points, delusions, conspiracies, frauds, etc., and also buried there are the hypotheses of the elementary particle physics of the future, which may differ considerably from contemporary physics. The former group of specifications is disregarded because of silliness, the latter because of inaccessibility.

My second question is whether all the hypotheses in Franklin's list are "reasonable" enough to warrant testing. Do they deserve to be recognized as seriously proposed? My own answer is yes, all of them are reasonable, at least in the sense of promising some kind of understanding rather than giving trivial summaries of data. One of them, (2), is just the sort of hypothesis that has to be raised in the process of trouble-shooting. Some of them — (1), (9), and (10) — offer grand vision, the first within the accepted framework of the time, the other two outside this framework. (One of the radical proposals, (9), had intrigued me when I read about it in Kabir (1968), since limiting the superposition principle is one avenue for solving the quantum mechanical measurement problem.) Some hypotheses on the list — (3), (4), (5), and (6) — are analogues of historically successful hypotheses in elementary particle physics. The reasonableness of (8) stems from a recognition of the subtle assumptions and approximations needed for the standard quantum mechanical derivation of the exponential law. Only (7) looks spooky at first, but the more detailed presentation by Franklin (1986, 96) dissipates that first impression.

Both the list of hypotheses for coping with the CP problem and the general considerations of a strategy of ascent in Section 2 point to a rough criterion for a hypothesis to be seriously proposed: it should promise understanding. But what is understanding? The strategy of ascent suggests that a partial answer to this question is obtained by reflection upon those scientific achievements of the past that have proven to be robust under repeated examination, application, and integration with other achievements. But this answer cannot be complete, for it relativizes the criterion of "seriously proposed" to the established "normal science," in Kuhn's terminology. The conception of a strategy of ascent also includes the recognition of novel types of understanding that are extrapolations or modifications or distillations or transformations from those modes of understanding that are exemplified in normal science. It is important to remind ourselves at this point that we are not now discussing the criteria for acceptance of a hypothesis, since that requires the calculation of posterior probabilities when empirical evidence is obtained. We are considering the criterion for admitting a hypothesis into the limited set to which the Bayesian machinery is applied. Some of the hypotheses on Franklin's list, that were taken seriously as ways of preserving CP invariance, were quite radical departures from the physics of the time, as was the hypothesis that CP is violated. The moral is, I believe, that thoughtful investigators, immersed in their disciplines, have a good sense of what constitutes a promise of understanding, and that sense is derivative somehow from knowledge of past achievements but is not confined by them. I do not pretend to have an explanation for the psychology of intelligent assessment that reaches beyond the confines of established paradigms. Some ingredients are plausible, such as analogy, formal beauty, and an adumbration of theoretical unification. But even without an explanation we can acknowledge the historical (and hence empirical) fact that intelligent scientists on the frontiers of their disciplines often recognized that radical hypotheses offered promise, even before they were confirmed.

Bayesian confirmation theory generically has a rational element, namely the axioms of the calculus of probability, which can be established a priori in (at least) three different ways. There is also an empirical element in Bayesian confirmation theory, in that the posterior probability of a hypothesis depends upon evidence. Over and above these obvious propositions, both rational and empirical elements are introduced by tempered personalism in the process of selecting the seriously proposed hypotheses to which the Bayesian machinery is applied, and these elements are intricately entangled. There is an element of rationalism in the condition that a seriously proposed hypothesis should promise some kind of understanding. But since it seems hopeless to lay down a priori the criteria for understanding, these criteria are unavoidably largely distilled from empirically succesful scientific theories. But in the dialectic of rationalism and empiricism the latter does not unequivocally have the last word, because of the historical fact that research workers are sometimes able to discern new kinds of promises of understanding. Does this last turn in the dialectic entail a partial retraction of the abstention from intuitive induction, which was the first methodological thesis of Section 2? I think not, because we are not here concerned with the ultimate judgment concerning a scientific proposition, which Aristotle said was the grasping of its necessity, but something more tentative and elusive — a judgment of plausibility, promise, and being on the right track.

4. Explanation vs. Prediction

I hope that the foregoing long excursion into science, metaphysics, and methodology has provided a perspective for examining the primary question posed to this panel: how much, and why, does the evidential support of a hypothesis by a body of observations depend on the temporal relation between the observations and their theoretical derivation? In other words, does a prediction weigh more than an explanation (i.e., a post-diction), and if so, why?

It is useful to reformulate the question in order to make it more amenable to a Bayesian treatment. If the temporal relation is known, call it e', and write the evidence e as a conjunction e'&e", where e" is the content of the observations, without reference to the time when they were made. Now the question of explanation vs. prediction can be reformulated: is it the case or not that

$$P(h/e''\&b) = P(h/e'\&e''\&b) \ ?$$

Rewriting the right hand side with a new application of Bayes's theorem yields the equivalent question: is it the case or not that

$$[P(h/b)P(e''/h\&b)]/P(e''/b) = [P(h/e'\&b)P(e''/h\&e'\&b)]/P(e''/e'\&b) \ ?$$

Since it is reasonable that P(h/b)=P(h/e'&b) — for why should the prior probability be affected by chronology? — the question reduces to the validity of

$$P(e''/h\&b)/P(e''/b) = P(e''/h\&e'\&b)/P(e''/e'\&b) \ . \qquad *$$

We shall call this expression Eq.*. It cannot be assessed in one swoop. Various cases must be considered, according to the content of the temporal proposition e' and some other considerations.

Suppose e' asserts that the observational data were obtained subsequent to the theoretical analysis of evaluating the probability of e" given h, the extreme case being the prediction of e" on the basis of h and b. Since the outcome of the observations is unknown at the time of the analysis, it surely is reasonable to equate the numerators on the right and left hand sides of Eq.*. But the equality of the denominators is a delicate matter. If part of the content of b is the high reputation of the theorists who proposed h and who calculated the likelihood of e" given h, and another part of b is the profound importance of h should it turn out to be correct, then there are psychological influences that may drive the experimenter towards finding e". Observation may be not only theory-laden but ambition-laden! Unless b contains further information of correctives to the possible psychological systematic error in the experiment (e.g., the reputation for scrupulous honesty and care of the experimenters), then a personal probability evaluation might easily yield

$$P(e''/e'\&b) >> P(e''/b).$$

Thus the evidence e" may not be as "striking" given the temporal proposition e' as it would be without e', and the evidential support of h by e" may actually be diminished by knowing that the experimental result was predicted.

Now consider the case in which e' asserts that the analysis of the relation between h and e" was performed after the observations yielding e". Then the denominators in Eq.* can reasonably be taken to be equal, but what of the numerators? At first glance one might think that they too are equal, since the temporal proposition e' is irrelevant to the logical relation between h and e". But this thought presupposes that the logical and mathematical operations in the evaluation of the likelihood are impeccable. Hacking (1965) has warned against this assumption and has proposed a "slightly more realistic" personal probability theory in which limitations of calculating time are taken into account. In the spirit of Hacking's proposal I suggest that the general psychology of actual calculating be considered, including the tendency to trim approximations in the direction of a desired result. In other words, a systematic error may occur in calculations and conceptual analysis just as much as in manipulations of apparatus. Hence, the actually calculated likelihoods may satisfy the inequality

$$P(e''/h\&e'\&b) >> P(e''/h\&b),$$

and therefore the actually calculated posterior probability P(h/e&B), with temporal information buried in e, may be high but unreliable. The apparent evidential support for h would then be poisoned by a systematic calculational error. As in the preceding paragraph, this pessimistic conclusion could be avoided if b contains information establishing the honesty and reliability of the people performing the calculations and conceptual analysis.

My conclusion concerning the question of explanation vs. prediction is that either may go astray, because of different kinds of systematic errors, but if these errors are controlled and corrected, perhaps by auxiliary investigations, the temporal information e' does become irrelevant.

One final reflection is partly historical and partly conceptual. We know that Popper, who was particularly insistent upon the weightiness of prediction relative to explanation (1968, 242-247), was also much preoccupied with the obscurity of concepts in the human sciences. He was correctly suspicious of typical analyses of the logical relations between hypotheses and data in these sciences, especially when the observational data antedated the formulation of a hypothesis or the analysis of its implications. I do not agree, however, with his sweeping denigration of explanation in favor of prediction. If conceptual control is achieved in the human sciences, then hypotheses could be supported equally well by predictions and explanations, provided, of course, that the characteristic systematic errors of these two operations are eliminated.

Note

[1]This research was supported by the National Science Foundation, grant no. SBE-9223678.

References

Aristotle (1941), "Posterior Analytics", in R. McKeon (ed.) *The Basic Works of Aristotle*. New York: Random House.

Carnap, R. (1962), *Logical Foundations of Probability*, 2nd ed. Chicago: University of Chicago Press.

Christenson, J.H., Cronin, J.W., Fitch, V., and Turlay, R. (1964), "Evidence for the 2-pi decay of the K^0_2 meson", *Physical Review Letters* 13: 138-140.

DeFinetti, B. (1937), "*La prevision: ses lois logiques, ses sources subjectives*", *Annales de l'Institut Henri Poincare'* 7: 1-68.

Dewey, J. (1938), *Logic: the Theory of Inquiry.* New York: Henry Holt.

Edelman, G. (1987), *Neural Darwinism.* New York: Basic Books.

Franklin, A.(1986), *The Neglect of Experiment*. Cambridge UK: Cambridge University Press.

Franklin, A. (1993), "Discovery, pursuit, and justification", *Perspectives in Science* 1: 252-284.

Hacking, I. (1967), "Slightly more realistic personal probability", *Philosophy of Science* 34: 311-325.

Jeffreys, H. (1961), *Theory of Probability*, 3rd ed. Oxford: Clarendon Press.

Kabir, P.K. (1968), *The CP Puzzle*. New York and London: Academic Press.

Peirce, C.S. (1934), *Collected Papers*, vol. 5. Cambridge: Harvard University Press.

Keynes, J.M. (1921), *A Treatise on Probability*. London: Macmillan.

Popper, K.R. (1968), *Conjectures and Refutations.* New York and Evanston: Harper and Row.

Ramsey, F.P. (1931), "Truth and probability", in *The Foundationsof Mathematics and Other Logical Essays*. London: Rutledge and Kegan Paul.

Savage, L.J. (1954), *Foundations of Statistics.* New York: Wiley.

Shimony, A. (1970), "Scientific inference", in R. Colodny (ed.), *The Nature and Function of Scientific Theories*. Pittsburgh: University of Pittsburgh Press, pp. 79-172. Reprinted in A. Shimony (1993), *Search for a Naturalistic World View*, vol.1. Cambridge UK: Cambridge University Press.

Shimony, A. (1993), "Reconsiderations on inductive inference", in *Search for a Naturalistic World View*, vol.1. Cambridge UK: Cambridge University Press, pp. 274-300.

Wilson, E.B. (1951), *An Introduction to Scientific Research*. New York: McGraw-Hill.

Explanation v. Prediction: Which Carries More Weight?

Peter Achinstein

Johns Hopkins University

1. The Historical Thesis of Evidence

According to a standard view, predictions of new phenomena provide stronger evidence for a theory than explanations of old ones. More guardedly, a theory that predicts phenomena that did not prompt the initial formulation of that theory is better supported by those phenomena than is a theory by known phenomena that generated the theory in the first place. So say various philosophers of science, including William Whewell (1847) in the 19th century and Karl Popper (1959) in the 20th, to mention just two.

Stephen Brush takes issue with this on historical grounds. In a series of fascinating papers he argues that generally speaking scientists do not regard the fact that a theory predicts new phenomena, even ones of a kind totally different from those that prompted the theory in the first place, as providing better evidential support for that theory than is provided by already known facts explained by the theory. By contrast, Brush claims, there are cases, including general relativity and the periodic law of elements, in which scientists tend to consider known phenomena explained by a theory as constituting much stronger support than novel predictions.[1]

Both the predictionist and the explanationist are committed to an interesting historical thesis about evidence, viz.

> *Historical thesis*: Whether some claim e, if true, is evidence for an hypothesis h, or how strong that evidence is, depends on certain historical facts about e, h, or their relationship.

For example, whether, or the extent to which, e counts as evidence for h depends on whether e was known before or after h was formulated. Various historical positions are possible, as Alan Musgrave (1974) noted years ago in a very interesting article. On a simple predictionist view (which Musgrave classifies as "purely temporal") e supports h only if e was not known when h was first proposed. On another view (which Musgrave attributes to Zahar (1973) and calls "heuristic"), e is evidence for h only if when h was first formulated it was not devised in order to explain e. On yet a third historical view (which Musgrave himself accepts), e is evidence for some theory T only if e cannot be explained by a "predecessor" theory, i.e., by a competing theory which was devised by scientists prior to the formulation of T. These views, and other variations, are all committed to the historical thesis.

PSA 1994, Volume 2, pp. 156-164

Is the historical thesis true or false? I propose to argue that it is sometimes true, and sometimes false, depending on the type of evidence in question. Then I will consider what implications, if any, this has for the debate between Brush and the predictionists.

Before beginning, however, let me mention a curious but interesting fact about various well–known philosophical theories or definitions of evidence. As Laura Snyder (1994) points out in a perceptive paper entitled "Is Evidence Historical?", most such theories, including Carnap's (1962) a priori theory of confirmation, Hempel's (1945) satisfaction theory, Glymour's (1980) bootstrap account, and the usual hypothetico–deductive account, are incompatible with the historical thesis. They hold that whether, or the extent to which, e is evidence for, or confirms, h is an objective fact about e, h, and their relationship. It is in no way affected by the time at which h was first proposed, or e was first known, or by the intentions with which h was formulated. Defenders of these views must reject both the predictionist and the explanationist claims about evidence. They must say that whether, or the extent to which, e supports h has nothing to do with whether e was first formulated as a novel prediction from h or whether e was known before h and h was constructed to explain it.

Accordingly, we have two extreme or absolutist positions. There is the position, reflected in the historical thesis, that evidence is always historical (in the sense indicated). And there is a contrasting position, reflected in certain standard views, that evidence is never historical. Does the truth lie at either extreme? Or is it somewhere in the middle?

2. Selection Procedures

Suppose that an investigator decides to test the efficacy of a certain drug D in relieving symptoms S. The hypothesis under consideration is

h: Drug D relieves symptoms S in approximately 95% of the cases.

The investigator may test drug D by giving it to persons suffering from S and by giving a placebo to other persons suffering from S (the "control group"). In deciding how to proceed, the investigator employs what I will call a "selection procedure," or rule, determining how to test, or obtain evidence for, an hypothesis, in this case determining which persons he will select for his studies and how he will study them.

For example, here is one of many possible selection procedures (SP) for testing h:

SP 1: Choose a sample of 2000 persons of different ages, sexes, races, and geographical locations, all of whom have symptoms S in varying degrees; divide them arbitrarily into 2 groups; give one group drug D and the other a placebo; determine how many in each group have their symptoms relieved.

Now, suppose that a particular investigator uses this (or some other) selection procedure and obtains the following result:

e: In a group of 1000 persons with symptoms S taking drug D, 950 persons had relief of S; in a control group of 1000 S–sufferers not taking D but a placebo none had symptoms S relieved.

The first thing to note about this example is that whether the report e supports hypothesis h, or the extent to which it does, depends crucially on what selection procedure was in fact used in obtaining e. Suppose that instead of SP1 the following selection procedure had been employed:

SP 2: Choose a sample of 2000 females aged 5 all of whom have symptoms S in a very mild form; proceed as in SP1.

If result e had been obtained by following SP2, then e, although true, would not be particularly good evidence for h, certainly not as strong as that obtained by following SP1. The reason, of course, is that SP1, by contrast with SP2, gives a sample that is varied with respect to two factors that may well be relevant: age of patient and severity of symptoms. (Hypothesis h does not restrict itself to 5 year old girls with mild symptoms, but asserts a cure–rate for the general population of sufferers with varying degrees of the symptoms in question.)

This means that if the result as described in e is obtained, then whether, or to what extent, that result confirms the hypothesis h depends crucially on what selection procedure was in fact used in obtaining e. That is, it depends on an historical fact about e: on how in fact e was obtained. If e resulted from following SP1, then e is pretty strong evidence for h; if e was obtained by following SP2, then e is pretty weak evidence for h, if it confirms it at all. Just by looking at e and h, and even by ascertaining that e is true, we are unable to determine to what extent, if any, e supports h. We need to invoke "history."

To nail down this point completely, consider a third selection procedure:

SP 3: Choose a sample of 2000 persons all of whom have S in varying degrees; divide them arbitrarily into 2 groups; give one group drugs D and D' (where D' relieves symptoms S in 95% of the cases and blocks possible curative effects of D when taken together); give the other group a placebo.

Consider once more result e (which, again, let us suppose, obtains). In this case e supports h not at all. And, again, whether this is so cannot be ascertained simply by examining the propositions e, h, or their "logical" relationship. We need to know an historical fact about e, viz. that the information it (truly) reports was obtained by following SP3.

So far then we seem to have support for the historical thesis about evidence. Can we generalize from examples like this to all cases. Can we say that for any true report e, and any hypothesis h, whether, or to what extent, e is evidence for h depends upon historical facts about how e was obtained? No, we cannot.

Consider another very simple case. Let e be the following report, which is true:

e = In last week's lottery, 1000 tickets were sold, of which John owned 999 at the time of the selection of the winner; this was a fair lottery in which one ticket was selected at random.

h = John won the lottery.

In an attempt to obtain information such as e to support h different rules or "selection procedures" might have been followed, e.g.,

SP 4: Determine who bought tickets, and how many, by asking lottery officials.

SP 5: Determine this by standing next to the person selling tickets.

SP 6: Determine this by consulting the local newspaper, which publishes this information as a service to its readers.

Let us suppose that following any of these selection procedures results in a true report e. (And, as in the symptoms case, we may suppose that following any of these procedures is a reasonable way to establish whether e is true.) But in this case, unlike the drug example, which selection procedure was in fact followed is completely irrelevant in determining whether, or to what extent, e is evidence for h. In this case, unlike the drug example, we do not need to know how information e was obtained to know that e (assuming it is true) is very strong evidence for h. Nor do we need to know any other historical facts about e, h, or their relationship. (In particular, contrary to both the predictionist and explanationist views, we do not need to know when e was first known relative to when h was first formulated; i.e., we do not need to know whether e was explained or predicted. But more of this later when these two historical views are examined more fully.) Accordingly, we have a case that violates the historical thesis of evidence.

Since examples similar to each of the two above can be readily constructed, we may conclude that there are many cases that satisfy the historical thesis of evidence, and many others that fail to satisfy it. Is there a general rule for deciding which do and which do not?

Perhaps our two examples will help generate such a rule. In the drug case the evidence report e is historical in an obvious sense: it reports the results of a particular study made at some particular time and place. But this is clearly not sufficient to distinguish the cases, since the evidence report e in the lottery case is also historical: it reports facts about a particular lottery, who bought tickets, and when. So, I submit, what distinguishes the cases is not the historical character of the evidence, but something else.

I shall say that a putative evidence statement e is *empirically complete* with respect to an hypothesis h if whether, or to what extent, e is evidence for, or confirms, h depends just on what e reports, what h says, and the relationship between them. It does not depend on any additional empirical facts—e.g., facts about when e or h were formulated, or with what intentions, or on any (other) facts about the world. In the drug example, e is not empirically complete with respect to h: whether, or to what extent, e supports h depends on how the sample reported in e was selected—empirical information not contained in e or h.[2] By contrast, in the lottery example, e is empirically complete with respect to h: whether, and to what extent, e supports h in this case does not depend on empirical facts in addition to e. To determine whether, and how much, e supports h in this case we do not need any further empirical investigation. To be sure, additional empirical inquiry may unearth new information e' which is such that both e and e' together do not support h to the same extent that e by itself does. But that is different. In the drug but not the lottery example information in addition to e is necessary to determine the extent to which e itself supports h. In the drug case we cannot legitimately say whether or to what extent the report e supports the efficacy of drug D unless we know how the patients described in e were selected. In the lottery case information about how purported evidence was obtained is irrelevant for the question of whether or how strongly that evidence, assuming its truth, supports h.

So we have one important difference between the two examples. Is this enough to draw a distinction between cases that satisfy the historical thesis of evidence and those that do not? Perhaps not. There may be cases in which e is empirically incomplete with respect to h, but in which empirical facts needed to complete it are not historical. Consider

e = Male crows are black.

h = Female crows are black.

One might claim that whether, or the extent to which, e supports h in this case depends on empirical facts in addition to e. If, e.g., other species of birds generally have different colors for different sexes, then e does not support h very much. If other species generally have the same color for both sexes, then e supports h considerably more. But these additional facts are not "historical," at least not in the clear ways of previous examples. (I construe "other species of birds generally have different colors for different sexes" to be making a general statement, and not to be referring to any particular historical period.) If this is granted, then we need to add a proviso to the completeness idea above.

There are cases (including our drug example) in which a putative evidence claim e is empirically incomplete with respect to an hypothesis h, where determining whether, or to what extent, e supports h requires determining the truth of some historical fact. I shall speak of these as historical evidence cases. They satisfy the historical thesis of evidence. By contrast, there are cases in which a putative evidence claim e is empirically complete with respect to hypothesis h (e.g., our lottery case); and there may be cases in which a putative evidence claim e, although empirically incomplete with respect to h, can be settled without appeal to historical facts (possibly the crow example). Cases of the latter two sorts violate the historical thesis of evidence. What implications, if any, does this hold for whether predictions or explanations provide better confirmation?

3. Predictions v. Explanations

Let us return to the original question proposed by Brush. Do predictions of novel facts provide stronger evidence than explanations of old one, as Whewell and Popper claim? Or is the reverse true? My answer is this: Sometimes a prediction provides better evidence for an hypothesis, sometimes an explanation does, and sometimes they are equally good. Which obtains has nothing to do with the fact that it is a prediction of novel facts or that it is an explanation of known ones.

To show this, let us begin with a case that violates the historical thesis of evidence. Here it should be easy to show that whether the putative evidence is known before or after the hypothesis is formulated is irrelevant for confirmation. Let the hypothesis be

h = This coin is fair, i.e., if tossed in random ways under normal conditions it will land on heads approximately half the time in the long run.

e = This coin is physically symmetrical, and in a series of 1000 random tosses under normal conditions it landed on heads approximately 500 times.

We might reasonably take e to be empirically complete with respect to h. Accordingly, whether e supports h, and the extent to which it does, does not depend on empirical facts other than e. In particular, it does not depend on when, how, or even whether e comes to be known, or on whether e was known first and h then formulated, or on whether h was conceived first and e then stated as a prediction from it. Putative evidence e supports hypothesis h and does so (equally well) whether or not e is known before or after h was initially formulated, indeed whether or not e is ever known to be true.

So let us focus instead on cases that satisfy the historical thesis of evidence. We might suppose that at least in such cases explanations (or predictions) are always better for confirmation. Return once again to our drug hypothesis:

h = Drug D relieves symptoms S in approximately 95% of the cases.

Consider now two evidence claims, the first a prediction about an unknown future event, the second a report about something already known:

e_1 = In the next clinical trial of 1000 patients who suffer from symptoms S and who take D approximately 950 will get some relief.

e_2 = In a trial that has already taken place involving 1000 patients with S who took D (we know that) approximately 950 got some relief.

On the prediction view, e_1 is stronger evidence for h than is e_2. On the explanation view it is the reverse. And to sharpen the cases let us suppose that e_2, by contrast to e_1, was not only known to be true prior to the formulation of h, but that h was formulated with the intention of explaining e_2. Which view is correct? Neither one.

Let us take the prediction case e_1 first. Whether, and to what extent, e_1 (if true) supports h depends on empirical facts in addition to e_1. In this case it depends on the selection procedure to be used in the next clinical trial. Suppose this selection procedure calls for choosing just 5 year old girls with very mild symptoms who in addition to D are also taking drug D' which ameliorates symptoms S in 95% of the cases and potentially blocks D from doing so. Then e_1 would be very weak evidence for h, if it supports it at all. This is so despite the fact that e_1 is a correct prediction from h, one not used in generating h in the first place. By contrast, suppose that the selection procedure used in the past trial mentioned in e_2 is much better with respect to h. For example, it calls for choosing humans of both sexes, of different ages, with symptoms of varying degrees, who are not also taking drug D'. Then e_2 would be quite strong evidence for h, much stronger than what is supplied by e_1. In such a case, a known fact explained by h would provide more support for h than a newly predicted fact would.

Obviously the situations here can be reversed. We might suppose that the selection procedure used to generate the prediction of e_1 is the one cited in the previous paragraph as being used to generate e_2 (and vice versa). In this situation a newly predicted fact would provide more support for h than an already explained one.

In these cases what makes putative evidence have the strength it does has nothing to do with whether it is being explained or predicted. It has to do with the selection procedure used to generate that evidence.[3] In one situation—whether it involves something that is explained or predicted—we have a putative evidence statement generated by a selection procedure that is a good one relative to h; in the other case we have a flawed selection procedure. This is what matters for confirmation—not whether the putative evidence is being explained or predicted.

4. Brush Redux

Brush is clearly denying a general predictionist thesis. By contrast he cites cases in which scientists themselves regarded known evidence explained by a theory as stronger support for that theory than new evidence that was successfully predicted. And he seems to imply that this was reasonable. He offers an explanation for this claim, viz. that with explanations of the known phenomena, by contrast with successful predictions of the new ones, scientists had time to consider alternative theories that would generate these phenomena. Now, even if Brush does not do so, I want to extend this idea and consider a more general explanationist view that is committed to the following three theses that Brush invokes for some cases:

(1) A selection procedure for testing a hypothesis h is flawed, or at least inferior to another, other things equal, if it fails to call for explicit consideration of competitors to h.

(2) The longer time scientists have to consider whether there are plausible competitors to h the more likely they are to find some if they exist.

(3) With putative evidence already known before the formulation of h scientists have (had) more time to consider whether there are plausible competitors to h than is the case with novel predictions.

I would challenge at least the first and third theses. In my first example, selection procedure 1 for the drug hypothesis does not call for explicitly considering competitors to that hypothesis. Yet it does not seem flawed on that account, or inferior to one that does. However, even supposing it were inferior, whether or not a selection procedure calls for a consideration of competitors is completely irrelevant to whether the putative evidence claim is a prediction or a known fact being explained. In the case of a prediction, no less than that of an explanation, the selection procedure may call for a consideration of competitors.

For example, in our drug case, where h is "Drug D relieves symptoms S in approximately 95% of the cases," and e is the prediction "In the next clinical trial of 1000 patients suffering from symptoms S who take D, approximately 950 will get some relief," the selection procedure to be used for the next clinical trial might include the rule

> In conducting this next trial, determine whether the patients are also taking some other drug which relieves S in approximately 95% of the cases and which blocks any effectiveness D might have.

Such a selection procedure calls for the explicit consideration of a competitor to explain e, viz. that it will be some other drug, not D, that will relieve symptoms S in the next trial. This is so even though e is a prediction. Moreover, to respond to the third thesis about time for considering competitors, an investigator planning a future trial can have as much time as she likes to develop a selection procedure calling for a consideration of a competing hypothesis. More generally, in designing a novel experiment to test some hypothesis h as much time may be spent in precluding competing hypotheses that will explain the test results as is spent in considering competing hypotheses for old data.

5. Thomson v. Hertz

Finally, let me invoke an example more recognizably scientific. It involves a dispute between Heinrich Hertz and J.J. Thomson over the nature of cathode rays.[4] In experiments conducted in 1883 Hertz observed that the cathode rays in his experiments were not deflected by an electrical field. He took this to be strong evidence that cathode rays are not charged particles (as the English physicist William Crookes had concluded), but some type of ether waves. In 1897 J.J. Thomson repeated Hertz's experiments but with a much higher evacuation of gas in the cathode tube than Hertz had been able to obtain. Thomson believed that when cathode rays pass though a gas they make it a conductor, which screens off the electric force from the charged particles comprising the cathode rays.[5] This screening off effect will be reduced if the gas in the tube is more thoroughly evacuated. In Thomson's 1897 experiments electrical deflection of the cathode rays was detected, which Thomson took to be strong evidence that cathode rays are charged particles.

Here, however, I want to consider the evidential report of Hertz in 1883, not of Thomson in 1897. Let

> e = In Hertz's cathode ray experiments of 1883 no electrical deflection of cathode rays was detected.
>
> h = Cathode rays are not electrically charged.

Hertz took e to be strong evidence for h. In 1897 Thomson claimed, in effect, that Hertz's results as reported in e did not provide strong evidence for h, since Hertz's experimental set–up was flawed: He was employing insufficiently evacuated tubes. To use my previous terminology, Thomson was claiming that Hertz's selection procedure for testing h was inadequate.[6]

Here we can pick up on a point emphasized by Brush. Hertz, we might say, failed to use a selection procedure calling for considering a competitor to h to explain his results (viz. that cathode rays are charged particles, but that the tubes Hertz was using were not sufficiently evacuated to allow an electrical force to act on these particles). But—and this is the point I want to emphasize—in determining whether, or to what extent, Hertz's putative evidence e supports his hypothesis h, it seems to be irrelevant whether Hertz's e was a novel prediction from an already formulated hypothesis h or an already known fact to be explained by h. Hertz writes that in performing the relevant experiments he was trying to answer two questions:

> Firstly: Do the cathode rays give rise to electrostatic forces in their neighbourhood? Secondly: In their course are they affected by external electrostatic forces? (Hertz 1896, p. 249)

In his paper he did not predict what his experiments would show. Nor were the results of his experiments treated by him as facts known before he had formulated his hypothesis h. Once he obtained his experimental result he then claimed that they supported his theory:

> As far as the accuracy of the experiment allows, we can conclude with certainty that no electrostatic effect due to the cathode rays can be perceived. (p. 251)

To be sure, we might say that Hertz's *theory* itself predicted some such results, even if Hertz himself did not (i.e., even if Hertz did not himself draw this conclusion before getting his experimental results). But even if we speak this way, Hertz did not claim or imply that his experimental results provide better (or weaker) support for his theory because the theory predicted them before they were obtained. Nor did Thomson in his criticism of Hertz allude to one or the other possibility. Whichever it was—whether a prediction or an explanation or neither—Hertz (Thomson was claiming) should have used a better selection procedure. This is what is criticizable in Hertz, not whether he was predicting a novel fact or explaining a known one.

I end with a quote from John Maynard Keynes (1921, p. 305), whose book on probability contains lots of insights. Here is one:

> The peculiar virtue of prediction or predesignation is altogether imaginary. The number of instances examined and the analogy between them are the essential points, and the question as to whether a particular hypothesis happens to be propounded before or after their examination is quite irrelevant.

Notes

[1]To what extent Brush wants to generalize this explanationist position is a question I leave for him to answer. There are passages in his writings that strongly suggest a more general position. For example: "There is even some reason to suspect that a successful explanation of a fact that other theories have already failed to explain satisfactorily (for example, the Mercury perihelion) is more convincing than the prediction of a new fact, at least until the competing theories have had their chance (and failed) to explain it" (1989, p. 1127). In what follows I consider a generalized explanationist thesis.

[2]For Carnap (1962) and others, every e is empirically complete with respect to every h. For these writers, whether, and the extent to which, e confirms h is an a priori matter.

[3]Cf. Mayo (1991).

[4]See Achinstein (1991), Essays 10 and 11; also Buchwald (1994), ch. 10.

[5]See Thomson (1897), p. 107.

[6]Lord Rayleigh (1942, pp. 78–9), in a biography of Thomson, made the same claim: "He [Hertz] failed to observe this [electrical] effect, but the design of his experiment was open to certain objections which were removed in a later investigation by Perrin in 1895, directed to the same question. Perrin got definite evidence that the rays carried a negative charge. J.J. Thomson, in a modification of Perrin's experiment showed that if

the Faraday cylinder was put out of the line of fire of the cathode, it acquired a charge when, and only when, the cathode rays were so deflected by a magnet as to enter the cylinder." [Note Rayleigh's claim that Perrin (and Thomson) got "definite evidence" that cathode rays carry a negative charge, whereas, by implication, Hertz's experiments did not give "definite evidence" concerning the question of charge.]

Acknowledgement: I am indebted to Laura J. Snyder for very helpful discussions, and to Robert Rynasiewicz for trying to convince me of the error of my ways.

References

Achinstein, P. (1991), *Particles and Waves*. New York: Oxford University Press.

Brush, S. (1989), "Prediction and Theory Evaluation: The Case of Light Bending," *Science* 246: 1124–29.

Buchwald, J. (1994), *The Creation of Scientific Effects*. Chicago: University of Chicago Press.

Carnap, R. (1962), *Logical Foundations of Probability*. Chicago: University of Chicago Press, 2nd ed.

Glymour, C. (1980), *Theory and Evidence*. Princeton: Princeton University Press.

Hempel, C. (1945), "Studies in the Logic of Confirmation," *Mind* 54: 1–26, 97–121.

Hertz, H. (1896), *Miscellaneous Papers*. London: Macmillan.

Keynes, J.M. (1921), *A Treatise on Probability*. London: Macmillan.

Mayo, D. (1991), "Novel Evidence and Severe Tests," *Philosophy of Science* 58: 523–52.

Musgrave, A. (1974), "Logical versus Historical Theories of Confirmation," *British Journal for the Philosophy of Science* 25: 1–23.

Popper, K. (1959), *The Logic of Scientific Discovery*. London: Hutchinson.

Rayleigh, R. (1942), *The Life of Sir J.J. Thomson*. Cambridge: Cambridge University Press.

Snyder, L. (1994), "Is Evidence Historical," *Scientific Methods: Conceptual and Historical Problems,* P. Achinstein and L. Snyder, eds. Malabar, Florida: Krieger.

Thomson, J.J. (1897), "Cathode Rays," *The Electrician* 39: 104–108.

Whewell, W. (1847), *The Philosophy of the Inductive Sciences*. New York: Johnson Reprint, 1967.

Zahar, E. (1973), "Why Did Einstein's Programme Supercede Lorentz's," *British Journal for the Philosophy of Science* 24: 95–123, 223–62.

Part VI

SEARCH HEURISTICS, EXPERIMENTATION, AND TECHNOLOGY IN MOLECULAR AND CELL BIOLOGY

Deciding on the Data: Epistemological Problems Surrounding Instruments and Research Techniques in Cell Biology[1]

William Bechtel

Washington University in St. Louis

1. Introduction: Data vs. Artifact

The primary focus of philosophy of science in this century has been on theories and theoretical knowledge. Except for concern about whether phenomenal reports or reports of objects and events should count as data reports and whether data might be theory-laden and what consequences that might have for objectivity of science, data have been taken to be relatively unproblematic. But for scientists, questions about what are the data are often of paramount concern. Such controversies often overshadow controversies over theories or explanatory models. Scientists' questions about data, moreover, do not turn on the philosophical questions just identified. Instead, for scientists, the overriding question is whether purported data is actually informative about the phenomenon in nature under investigation or whether it represents an artifact; that is, whether it was so much the product of the procedures used to generate the data that it could not be interpreted as providing information about the underlying phenomenon.

A major reason for scientists' worries that data might constitute artifacts and not provide information in the manner desired is that the generation of data is typically the result of procedures designed to transform radically the phenomenon under investigation so as to generate the data. The question facing scientists is to determine whether the results of these transformations still give correct information about the original phenomenon or not. There are a variety of reasons why it is frequently hard to make such assessments. First, there are often a large number of intervening steps between the original phenomenon and the results that are construed as data. Each of these steps is potentially a point that could give rise to an artifact. Second, many procedures are extremely brutal since one often has to transform radically the phenomenon to achieve interpretable results. Third, there is often very little knowledge about how exactly the procedures work. Theories of the procedures are often arrived at only after the procedures have been accepted and widely employed. Thus, at the time the procedures are being developed and evaluated there is little understanding of precisely what consequences they have. Last, it is often the case that procedures are extremely sensitive to the details of the way in which they are carried such that slight variation in procedures may alter the results, sometimes significantly. Accordingly, attempts to replicate the procedures by others may not generate the same result, suggesting that it was the details of the procedures that generated the results, not the underlying phenomena.

PSA 1994, Volume 2, pp. 167-178

The epistemological problems in determining whether the result of an experimental intervention should be treated as data are often hidden from view. Once a community of scientists accepts a procedure as veridical, approved ways of performing it are worked out and published in laboratory manuals and methods books. They become what Latour (1987) calls *black boxes*. This is why they are not frequently noted in philosophical accounts of science. If, as philosophers, we want to understand the reasoning scientists use in arriving at data (and perhaps someday engage in normative evaluation of that reasoning) we must attend to the periods when new procedures are being worked out and examine the arguments given by scientists for regarding the results as generating useful data or artifacts. By examining how new procedures are constructed and evaluated we can gain insight into the epistemological tools scientists employ.

In this paper I shall proceed by developing a case study of new experimental procedures that initially generated a great deal of controversy as to whether they were generating artifacts. These were the procedures for developing electron micrographs of cells so as to reveal intracellular organization. Electron microscopy was one of several investigatory techniques that were introduced in the 1940s and further developed in the 1950s which made it possible to investigate seriously biological processes at the subcellular level. Previously, biologists were largely limited to studying processes at the level of whole cells (e.g., observing processes of cell replication), or at the level of biochemical reactions within cells which transpired in aqueous media. Only relatively large objects within the cell, such as the nucleus or the mitochondrion, or objects like chromosomes, which could be easily stained, were accessible to study with light microscopy), and the means for studying them was relatively limited (e.g., by establishing correlations between their behavior and the behavior of whole cells). With the introduction of electron microscopy along with other techniques such as cell fractionation, spectrography, etc., the intracellular level became an active area of scientific investigation, both with regard to morphological structures found there and their functional significance. Drawing upon researchers trained in a number of other disciplines, cell biology emerged as a distinct field of biological inquiry (see Bechtel, 1993).

2. Case Study: Developing Procedures for Electron Microscopy of Cells

By the time biologists began to use the electron microscope to look at cellular material, it was already a well-established instrument in physics and fairly sophisticated accounts of its operation had been developed (Marton, 1968). However, putting an instrument to use in a new field often requires new procedures to deal with special problems. In particular, to use the electron microscope to study intracellular structures required developing procedures for working with cells in a vacuum, means for producing extremely thin specimens, and ways for enhancing contrast. The various strategies devised for satisfying these requirements opened up the potential for generating artifacts since each required quite brutal actions upon the cell using techniques whose consequences were largely unknown. The researchers developing these techniques were generally quite aware of the potential for artifacts, and the manner in which they argued for or against various techniques provides a good example of how such dialogue proceeds and is resolved.

a. Placing specimen in a vacuum

The most brutal transformations of the cell required for electron microscopy stem from the need for the specimen to be in a vacuum, requiring normally aqueous cells to be dehydrated. Most frequently this was done by chemical means, using substances like alcohol to displace water. The problem is that removal of water causes shrinkage and distorts the shape of the cell. Generally the drying is done by placing the specimen on a film, helping to maintain the shape in two dimensions, but raising the prospect of even more radical distortion in the third dimension. These distortions could affect both the overall cell and organelles within it, which could be particularly problematic insofar as shape was one of the criteria used to identify organelles. Even more critically, the chemicals used for drying may interact in various ways with cell constituents and drying may cause dislocation of material (e.g., cause smaller constituents to be deposited around larger ones), thereby potentially giving false information about where organelles are located.

Researchers were particularly attentive to the possibility that chemical dehydration might alter the shape and location of structures which electron microscopy was introduced to determine. One way to appraise whether artifacts are being produced is to compare the results of a new technique with already developed techniques considered to be reliable. Here the most obvious comparison was with light microscopy, but one of the problems is that many of the structures imaged in electron micrographs are not even visible using light microscopes. The reason why biologists were eager to use the electron microscope was that it could provide images beyond the limits of resolution of the light microscope. A second approach is to develop alternative procedures that accomplish the same result in a different way. In this case, investigators did develop a second means of drying the cell, freeze-drying. This involves quickly freezing the specimen and reducing the partial pressure of water in the atmosphere surrounding the cell below that of water in the specimen, leading to the direct transfer of water molecules to gas. Researchers expected this approach to yield superior results to ordinary chemical drying for, in addition to reducing the opportunities for distortion and dislocation, it did not remove the water soluble constituents of the cell. But it has the disadvantages of being more difficult and producing specimens that are extremely fragile.

In this case, comparison of results indicated that freeze-drying did not produce significantly different results from ordinary chemical drying. Despite a great number of published statements of concern about the potential for artifacts as a result of how the cell was dried, little evidence materialized that chemical drying did introduce serious artifacts. (For a example comparative study discounting any significant differences between chemical drying and freeze-drying of vertebrate nerve fibers, see Fernández-Morán 1952; for a contemporary review of chemical and freeze-drying techniques, see Bell 1952.)

b. Generating thin specimens

A second problem facing researchers attempting to use the electron microscope with cells stemmed from the need for thin specimens. Otherwise too few electrons could penetrate the specimen to generate an image. With specimens as thick as whole living cells there was too much scattering of electrons to produce useful images. This problem was sufficiently serious that initial attempts to use the electron microscope to study biological materials were restricted to specimens thinner than normal cells, such as viruses and bacteria, and products liberated from cells by procedures such as cell fractionation. But the goal of many researchers was to determine the nature of structures within cells. A variety of tactics were employed to generate specimens sufficiently thin to be used in electron microscopy. One was to make a replica or cast of the surface of a specimen. This was often coupled with shadow casting, in which a beam of metal atoms, such as gold or palladium, were directed at the specimen surface from an angle, causing a build up on one side of any build up on the surface, which would be caused by structures projecting from the surface (Williams and Wyckoff, 1944). This technique, however, was useful only with structures which projected from the specimen surface.

For electron microscopy to achieve its potential in giving high resolution images of the internal structures within cells, some way had to be found to make images from electron beams directed through the cell. Two strategies were pursued. The first was to develop techniques of microtomy that could slice specimens sufficiently thinly. Microtomes were already used to slice specimens for light microscopy. However, those microtomes generally could only produce specimens 1μ in thickness. For electron microscopy with the microscopes available in the 1940s and early 1950s, however, specimens .2μ thick, and preferably only .1μ thick, were needed. Numerous researchers set about designing new microtomes and techniques for their use. For the most part, this was an engineering task. It required devising ways of cutting very thinly without distorting the material being cut. One of the first techniques was to cut wedges, which would be thin at their boundaries. For many purposes (e.g., determining the concentration of particular chemical substances at different locations in the cell, slices of constant thickness were required. In the attempt to develop slices of constant thickness, different mechanical means of advancing the specimen towards the blade were tried, including cantilevers and rocking arms; in many respects a procedure of gently heating the specimen proved more successful than mechanical advances (Cosslett, 1955). Researches explored such things as different types of embedding materials and different blades. Much of the research focused on devising glass blades, and researchers developed preferences for different sorts of glass (Robertson 1987). Among the more important contributions was developing ways of avoiding a return stroke of the blade, which increased chances for distortions at the cutting surface (see Bretschneider 1952, and Porter and Blum 1953).

By the early 1950s the challenges in developing thin slices had been solved and it turned out that the numerous variations in technique, such as between using metal and glass blades, did not generate noticeable differences. But before thin sectioning had advanced to the point of producing useful micrographs, an alternative had been developed. Porter, intimately familiar with the process of tissue culture, recognized that cells grown in tissue culture spread out on the medium on which they are grown and thus are thinner than normal cells. This suggested that it might be possible to produce an electron micrograph of a tissue-cultured cell without microtomy. Working with Fullam, an industrial electron microscopist, Porter produced such a micrograph of a cell cultured from an explant of the gizzard derived from a 14-day-old chick embryo (Porter, Claude, and Fullam 1945). While the center part of the image was too dark to detect any detail, due to the thickness of the specimen, the edges were far less dark and one could detect structure. Porter identified the structure as a "lace-like reticulum" consisting of interconnected strands and vesicles of small dimensions (100 to 150 mμ) and relatively low density. Prior to the advent of electron microscopy the idea that there had to be a cytoskeleton to give structure to the cell was popular (see, e.g., Needham 1942); thus it was natural for Porter to interpret the lace-like reticulum as this cytoskeleton and hence an actual part of the cell. Over the next several years Porter continued to develop the techniques of electron microscopy of tissue-cultured cells and identified a similar structure in a variety of other cell-types which could be grown in a manner suitable for electron microscopy. Porter and Kallman (1952) named the structure the "endoplasmic reticulum" since the appearance of vesicles suggested a reticular structure and they were generally not seen in the thinnest margins of the cell but only in the inner region or endoplasm.

Researchers developing electron micrographs from tissue slices also noticed a structure in what was, in light microscopy, generally known as the *ground structure* or *basophilia* of the cell, due to the fact that it stained with basic dyes. But they did not perceive it as vascular but as pairs of membranes (Sjöstrand 1953) or filaments (Dalton 1953). The reason for the different perception is straight-forward: working with slices of cells, researchers only saw the vesicles when they lay in the plane of the slice; otherwise they would appear at best as vacuoles. But researchers at the time did not know this, and interpreting the doubled-membranes or filaments as part of the endoplasmic reticulum required accepting the results of Porter's method of developing electron micrographs from tissue-cultured cells.

There were, though, good reasons to resist Porter's interpretation. The whole procedure of growing cells in tissue-culture was extremely difficult and delicate: the cells had to be grown on Formvar-covered coverslips, then peeled from the glass surface and transferred under water to the grids that could be placed in the electron microscope. Porter (1987) reports that he only succeeded about half of the time, and, partly as a result of his early work transplanting cell nuclei from one species of frog to another, he was a master of such delicate operations. As a result, the technique was not adopted by others. Moreover, there was reason to suspect artifacts. To begin with, the environment in which cells are cultured is very different from that in which cells normally develop, creating potential for abnormal structure. Second, when this was combined with the poorly understood procedure for fixing the cells with osmium tetroxide, it seemed likely that an appearance such as Porter produced could be an artifact. In fact, in their subsequent comparative study of thin-sliced preparations and tissue-cultured preparations, Palade and Porter (1954) noted that while the thin spreading of the cell was an advantage in generating an alignment of the structure into two dimensions, thus rendering it more perspicuous, it also introduced a distortion of what they then took to be the character of the actual structure in the cell.

One researcher who vociferously took issue with Porter was Sjöstrand, who observed in tissue slices only paired membranes and contended that the structures were neither endoplasmic nor reticular: "These cytoplasmic membranes are included in a variety of cytoplasmic structures that are called the 'endoplasmic reticulum' by Porter. As there does not exist any exoplasm in tissue cells of this kind and as the structure generally does not represent a reticulum and as no really strict morphologic definition has been presented by Porter for his endoplasmic reticulum, this name seems rather unspecific and useless." Sjöstrand proposed instead a purely descriptive characterization: "Realizing that a name should be descriptive either of form, of function, or of both, these membranes will be referred to as α-cytomembranes. . . . *The α-cytomembranes are defined as about 50-Å-thick membranes to one side of which opaque irregularly shaped particles with a mean diameter of about 150 Å are attached. These membranes bound irregularly formed, closed, and in most cases very flat spaces.*" He then explicitly links the definition to the means of generating the image: "This definition refers to their appearance after osmium fixation" (1956a, 273). (Sjöstrand proceeds similarly with other constituents of the cell, including the cell wall—β-cytomembranes—and the Golgi apparatus—γ-cytomembranes.)

The fact that the two claims about cell structure were based on two different techniques led to attempts to link the results of the two techniques. One of the most obvious ways of doing so is to examine a number of tissue slices that have been cut in series. Porter and Blum (1953) (also Palade and Porter 1954) claimed that reconstructing a series of slices showed that the apparently isolated components in tissue slices were part of a continuous structure. Palade and Porter conducted a detailed examination in which they examined whole cultured cells, slices of cultured cells, and slices of ordinarily prepared fixed cells. In the slices of ordinary fixed cells they too found only "scattered independent elements." They appealed to the fact that "The same 'broken down' appearance is encountered, however, in cultured cells when examined in sections" as "good evidence that the appearance mentioned is the result of sectioning" (1954, 647). Although it took some time, and was undoubtedly aided by the development of a suggestive account of the functional significance of the endoplasmic reticulum (see below), Porter's interpretation was, by the end of the decade, generally accepted.

c. *Enhancing Contrast*

In electron microscopy, the image is generated by the scattering of electrons by objects in the path of the electron beam so that they do not reach the photographic plate. The number of electrons reaching the plate is determined by the amount of matter in the path, where amount of matter is the product of the number of atoms and their atomic weight (Cosslett, 1955). The challenge for electron microscopy stems from the fact that the atoms in biological material tend to be of roughly the same molecular weight; accordingly they will all scatter electrons equivalently. What is needed in order to produce micrographs with sufficient contrast to differentiate cellular constituents is a means of inducing contrast by having specific materials within the cell absorb heavy elements which will scatter electrons more effectively.

A readily available means of accomplishing this was provided by a widely used fixative from light microscopy, osmium tetroxide (used already by Marton in a micrograph of a plant leaf in 1934). Osmium vapors were used by Porter *et al.* in developing their first micrographs of tissue-cultured cells in 1945 and the sharpness of the resulting images indicated that it adequately fixed the cell and that osmium deposits highlighted what were taken to be intracellular structures. They and other investigators also explored a number of other classical fixatives, such as Flemming's solution and formalin, but these did not produce as detailed images and were interpreted as causing changes in submicroscopic structure (Cosslett, 1955). Just knowing that osmium tetroxide could generate images of high detail was, however, not sufficient. The conditions of its application turned out to affect what images were produced. Palade (1952), for example, conducted a systematic study of the effects of osmium fixation at different pH's, and concluded that a buffered solution maintaining a pH of 7.3 to 7.5 generated the best (most detailed) results. Palade's results were widely accepted and his procedure adopted, but at first there was dissention. Sjöstrand, for example, claimed "the pH of the osmium tetroxide seems not to be so important as he [Palade] originally claimed. Variation of pH within a wide range from pH 4, and in some cases even pH 2, to pH 8 does not substantially affect the result in many tissues… . Most of the great differences of the quality of fixation described by Palade (1952) in his study at a low resolution seem to represent various degrees of post-mortem changes." (1956b, 459) Sjöstrand in fact argues that Palade's interpretation of one of the new constituents of the cell that Palade claimed to have identified with micrographs developed using his improved fixation techniques, the cristae or infoldings of the mitochondrial membrane, was flawed in part due to allowing post- mortem swelling by not fixing the cell quickly enough. He also faulted Palade for not noting the importance of variations in the tonicity of the solution: "The osmium tetroxide solution of Palade is strongly hypotonic and in several cases … hypotonic solutions of osmium tetroxide produce a more or less marked swelling of the cells" (1956b, 459).

Eventually the mode of action of osmium was discovered (it reacts principally with phospholipid membranes, unsaturated lipids, and reactive groups of some proteins). But this information was not available at the time researchers concluded that osmium tetroxide was a suitable fixative and stain. The interesting question is how, in the absence of theoretical principles, researchers determined which fixatives generated correct results, and which induced artifacts. One criterion involved comparison with results from other visualization techniques, such as light microscopy of living cells grown in tissue-culture and techniques such as phase contrast and polarization microscopy. However, this does not address the question of whether artifacts are induced in the detail beyond what these other techniques can reveal. Another was the plausibility of the images. Cosslett (1955, 520-1), for example, comments: "It is in general assumed that pronounced granularity of the contents of cell or nucleus, or thickening of membranes, is a sign of bad fixation, but there can be no certainty that these criteria are correct without a great deal more experience." A third approach was comparison with other stains. Light microscopists, for example, had found it useful to develop multiple stains which would react selectively with cellular constituents of specific biochemical constitution so as to identify the chemical constitution and gain clues as to the functional significance of different cell structures. Osmium seemed to react quite generally with intracellular structures, thus providing no differential information. None of the other available fixatives seemed to be yielding even plausible images. As a consequence, investigators such as Cosslett (1955, p. 513) called for comparative experimental investigation of different potential stains, as well as techniques for drying and fixing preparations.

In the late 1950s and 1960s other fixatives were introduced for electron microscopy, such as glutaraldehyde and permanganate (see Mercer and Birbeck, 1972 for a review). But about each one there was some reason to suspect they were introducing artifacts. Thus, Cosslett stated "In general, the conclusion has to be that there is no perfect fixative. Each causes some type of artifact, while giving good preservation of other structures… . There is obviously great scope for differences of opinion over what is 'real' and what is artifact in any set of results" (Cosslett, 1971, 129).

The problems of interpreting results of enhancing contrast with substances such as osmium tetroxide is well illustrated in a very short-lived controversy over the reality of the

Golgi apparatus. Palade and Claude (1949a, b) claimed that the Golgi apparatus was itself an artifact of fixation with osmium tetroxide or other fixatives used in demonstrating the Golgi apparatus. The basis for their claim is that they showed that it was possible artificially to create myelin figures that resemble the Golgi from lipids in refringent droplets via a process of slow fixation, which locally reduces pH. Since the Golgi apparatus was one of the most familiar structures in the cell from the days of light microscopy, Palade and Claude's charge of artifact drew quick responses, one of the most effective of which was due to Bensley (1951). He did not take issue with Palade and Claude's evidence of the ability to create structures similar to the Golgi artificially. Rather, a major part of Bensley's argument consists in showing that the Golgi apparatus appears with other techniques, including direct observation on living cells and with freeze-dried preparations. Palade and Claude did not return to the issue; as a result of multiple means of identification, the Golgi apparatus continued to be accepted as a cell organelle.

3. Means of Evaluating New Techniques

In the case study presented in the previous section I identified a number of points in the techniques for doing electron microscopy at which researchers worried about the potential generation of artifacts and identified some cases in which there were controversies over whether the results obtained were indeed artifacts. We need to turn now to a more analytical discussion of the question of how scientists evaluated whether in fact those results were artifacts or whether the techniques could be taken as reliable indicators of underlying phenomena. I will identify several such criteria scientists employed and ways in which they figured in the controversies described in the previous section. A great deal of evaluation of new techniques occurs before results are ever made public as scientists in a laboratory determine whether the results they are generating have any significance and should be made public. The criteria scientists employ in these evaluations are not directly revealed in public activities such as arguments in journal publications. However, once they do go public with their results, and are challenged, scientists bring forward a number of criteria in support of the informative value of their techniques, and it stands to reason that many of these criteria are also among those that figured in their private evaluations.

One of the criteria is simply whether there are any determinate results. This means, in part, that the results can be reproduced. If they cannot be regenerated, that is good grounds for thinking that the results that were obtained were accidental occurrences or noise. But even more is required: there must be a suggestive structure in the results. When Porter produced his first micrographs of tissue-cultured cells, he was impressed by the fact that there seemed to be a clear and regular pattern in the micrographs which he could take as evidence of a lace-like reticulum running through most of the part of the cell that generated any image. His opponents, such as Sjöstrand, were equally impressed by the regular patterns that suggested paired membranes, which appeared in their micrographs of sliced specimens. The fact that something occurs regularly and with sufficient structure is initially a compelling reason to think that the technique is producing evidence of something real. Of course it could turn out that the regular result was the result simply of something in the technique; for instance, the regular globular structure that early 19th century microscopists such as Dutrochet saw in cells turned out to be the result of chromatic aberrations in the lenses of their microscopes. Nonetheless, a definite structure is at least worthy of investigation, and in order to discount the evidence as artifactual, one often needs an account of how it was generated. Accordingly, when Palade and Claude tried to discredit the Golgi apparatus, they needed to produce evidence to indicate how it might be artificially produced.

Having results determinate enough to suggest that they reveal something about the phenomenon under study merely opens the inquiry into whether the results are artifactual or not. Since scientists typically do not have, at the time, a sufficiently developed theoretical framework concerning the procedures employed in producing the results, they must invoke indirect measurers. As I noted earlier, one of the measures most frequently employed is to compare the results of the new technique with either other already accepted techniques or with new techniques. Thus, it was important for Porter in introducing micrographs made through tissue culture to point out that at least one structure known from light microscopy could be identified in the micrographs, the mitochondrion.

Agreement with previously accepted procedures, however, can only be a starting point in evaluating a new technique. First, it is always possible that the old procedures, no matter how widely accepted, were themselves generating artifacts. But more importantly, the interest in the new procedures is that researchers hope to gain evidence that goes beyond the limits of the old procedure. Beyond mitochondria, the Golgi apparatus, and a basophilic staining substance, light microscopy could not provide information about the internal structure of the cytoplasm of the cell. The most important contribution of the electron microscope was to provide information about sub- microscopic structures for which there was no comparison with results produced with the light microscope. Instead researchers had to compare one new technique with another (either designed to perform the same function, as in the cases I discuss here, or another function, such as cell fractionation, which offered information based on biochemical segregation of possible cell components). It was for this reason that investigators were concerned to compare chemically dehydrated cells with freeze-dried cells. The concern that chemical preparation was distorting the cell and thus creating artifacts was significantly overcome by this comparison. Similarly, many researchers expressed great concern during the period when most electron microscopy relied on osmium tetroxide as the only fixative. Porter and other microscopists had compared osmium tetroxide with a number of other fixatives, but these did not produce very determinate results. In this case, the criterion of producing determinate results sufficed to override the fact that other techniques could not yield comparable results. But, as evidenced by numerous comments in the published literature, investigators were uncomfortable with this situation and called for investigations into other possible fixatives (see, e.g., Cosslett, 1955, Sjöstrand, 1956b, Wyckoff, 1959).

The reasons why this way of justifying results is so compelling is that the different techniques generally do not rely on the same processes which might potentially be introducing distortions. It seems unlikely that two different procedures would give rise to the same artifact; it is far more likely that they would generate different results. Whewell spoke of *consilience of inductions* when one had different reasoning strategies that generated the same result while Wimsatt (1981) speaks of theoretical models being *robust* when, using different assumptions, they generate the same or very similar results. While we recognize that each inference, or each assumption in a model, is fallible, if two or more different procedures triangulate on the same result, that suggests that the inferences or assumptions, however mistaken they might be, did not in this case generate errors. Robustness is, for many scientists, the strongest criterion of what is real in or about the world. But determining whether two techniques are providing consilient or robust results is not always straight-forward. I noted above the importance of identifying mitochondria in his first micrographs for Porter, but such identifications can themselves be problematic. A structure such as the mitochondrion both appears differently and behaves differently (e.g., stains differently) under different preparations. Hence, there is always a question of whether one is correct in identifying the results of two different procedures as the same. This problem is brought out nicely in the controversy over whether the cell contained pairs of membranes relatively short in length or a continuous reticular structure. Porter and Palade had to make the case that the paired membranes seen in tissue slice preparations were parts of the more continuous structure seen in tissue-culture preparations by using the intermediate case of slices of tissue-cultured cells.

A further problem stems from the possibility that two procedures that seem quite different in fact rely on a common element which generates an artifact. An example of how a common element enters into two quite different processes is that even with freeze-drying of cells, where the need for fixation is avoided, there is still a need for contrast enhancement. For many years the best contrast enhancement was obtained with osmium tetroxide, the same compound used as a fixative with chemically dried cells. This raises the possibility that the apparent consilience of results between chemically dehydrated preparations and freeze-dried ones is due to the use of osmium tetroxide in both processes. In this instance, researchers discounted the possibility of osmium tetroxide causing false consilience since the osmium tetroxide was not functioning in the same way: "It may be assumed that osmium tetroxide acting on living cells and on dead dried cells (that is under different conditions) would not produce identical artifacts" (Sjöstrand 1956b, 527). But such an assumption is, of course, fallible.

As important as determinate results and consilience are, they are not the only factors scientists appeal to in attempting to demonstrate that their results provide real data about the phenomena under investigation. A third factor is whether any sense can be made of the results, whether the results can be integrated into a theory or model of the phenomena. In the case of the cristae of the mitochondria, Palade was quick to point out that the oxidative processes associated with the mitochondria had long been recognized to require membranes. Warburg (1913) had taken oxidative reactions to depend upon surfaces, and, based upon repeated attempts to extract and reconstitute the system responsible for oxidative phosphorylation (Keilin and Hartree 1949), numerous researchers (e.g., Green, Loomis, and Auerbach 1948; Lehninger 1951) had concluded that the process was intimately connected with a membrane in which the responsible enzymes were embedded in particular arrangements. Thus, Palade immediately proposed that enzymes might be embedded in the cristae he claimed to have found: "It may be assumed that they are arranged in the proper order in linear series or chains—a disposition comparable in design and efficiency to an industrial assembly line. Such enzymatic chains have to be built at least partially in the solid framework of the mitochondria [the cristae] because some of the component enzymes, namely succinic acid dehydrogenase (succinoxydase) and cytochrome *c* oxydase, are known to be insoluble and structure bound" (Palade 1952, 439).

Similarly, Porter was eager to establish a functional significance for the endoplasmic reticulum, initially by linking it to proposals for a cytoskeleton. One of the contributions of work with thin sections was the discovery of particles (Palade 1953, Porter 1954) on substantial portions of the endoplasmic reticulum, which came to be called the *rough endoplasmic reticulum* (see Sjöstrand's characterization of his α-cyto-membranes above). Palade and Siekevitz (1956), based largely on biochemical studies establishing the high level of RNA in these particles, proposed a role for them in protein synthesis. Porter pointed to the apparent connections between the smooth endoplasmic reticulum and pores in the nuclear membrane and, while recognizing it to be speculative, considers the possibility that this was a means for the migration of relatively large particles from the nucleus to the cytoplasm: "The significance of the close morphological association between the inner membrane of the nuclear envelope and the peripheral chromatin is at this time impossible to assess, as are also the various observations suggesting that the cytoplasmic part of the system is derived from the envelope by outgrowth, by replications … , or by the formation of blebs… . Though their meaning is unclear, these observations have prompted the somewhat vague proposal that the ER through its cytoplasmic patterns and pathway serves as a vehicle for the transfer of genetic information to the cytosome" (1961, 654). The reason for mentioning this proposal is that it gives reason for thinking that the endoplasmic reticulum should be a continuous system, not just dissociated pairs of membranes distributed throughout the cytoplasm. Thus, the potential for integration with an emerging theory or model adds credibility to the sets of techniques that produced the information initially.

4. Conclusion

In this paper I have used a case study to identify some of the criteria scientists employ to distinguish informative data from artifacts: determinate results, consilience or robustness, and incorporation into theoretical models. Each of these criteria is fallible, and scientists might compensate for the failure of one to apply by application of another. Determining precisely how such judgments are made requires even more micro-level study than was presented here. Determining the generality of these criteria in scientists' actual adjudication of whether one has data or artifacts requires more comparative studies. But these criteria seem to be ones employed by scientists, and hence ones philosophers should take seriously and consider further.

Note

[1]Support for this research was provided by the National Endowment for the Humanities (RH- 21013-91), and is gratefully acknowledged.

References

Bechtel, W. (1993), "Integrating Sciences by Creating New Disciplines: The Case of Cell Biology", *Biology and Philosophy*, 8: 277-299.

Bell, L.G.E. (1952), "The Application of Freezing and Drying Techniques in Cytology", *International Review of Cytology* 1: 35-63.

Bensley, R.R. (1951), "Facts versus Artifacts in Cytology: The Golgi Apparatus", *Experimental Cell Research* 2: 1-9.

Bretschneider, L.H. (1952), "The Electron-microscopic Investigation of Tissue Sections", *International Review of Cytology* 1: 305-322.

Cosslett, V.E. (1955), "Electron Microscopy", in G. Oster and A. W. Pollister, (ed.), *Physical Techniques in Biological Research, Vol. 1, Part A. Optical Techniques*. New York: Academic. pp. 461-531.

________. (1971), "Electron Microscopy", in G. Oster, (ed.), *Physical Techniques in Biological Research, Vol. 1, Part A. Optical Techniques*. New York: Academic. pp. 71-156.

Dalton, A.J. (1953), "Electron Microscopy of Tissue Sections", *International Review of Cytology* 2: 403-417.

Fernández-Morán, H. (1952), "The Submicroscopic Organization of Vertebrate Nerve Fibres: An electron Microscope Study of Myelinated and Unmyelinated Nerve Fibres", *Experimental Cell Research* 3: 282-359.

Green, D.E., Loomis, W.F., and Auerbach, V.H. (1948), "Studies on the Cyclophorase System I." *Journal of Biological Chemistry* 172: 389-403.

Keilin, D. and Hartree, E.F. (1949), "Activity of the Succinic Dehydrogenase-cytochrome System in Different Tissue Preparation", *Biochemical Journal* 44: 205-218.

Latour, B. (1987), *Science in Action: How to Follow Scientists and Engineers Through Society.* Cambridge, MA: MIT Press.

Lehninger, A.L. (1951), "The Organized Respiratory Activity of Isolated Rat-liver Mitochondria", in J. Edsall, (ed.), *Enzymes and Enzyme Systems*. Cambridge, MA: Harvard University Press. pp. 1-14.

Marton, L. (1968), *Early History of the Electron Microscope.* San Francisco: San Francisco Press.

Mercer, E.H. and Birbeck, M.S.C. (1972), *Electron microscopy: A Handbook for Biologists.* Oxford: Blackwell Scientific Publications.

Needham, J. (1942), *Biochemistry and Morphogenesis.* London: Cambridge University Press.

Palade, G.E. (1952). "The Fine Structure of Mitochondria", *Anatomical Record* 114, 427-451.

_ _ _ _ _ _ . (1952), "A Study of Fixation for Electron Microscopy", *Journal of Experimental Medicine* 9: 285-297.

_ _ _ _ _ _ . (1953), "A Small Particulate Component of Cytoplasm," *Journal of Applied Physics* 24: 1419.

Palade, G. E. and Claude, A. (1949a), "The Nature of the Golgi Apparatus. I. Parallelism between Intercellular Myelin Figures and Golgi Apparatus in Somatic Cells," *Journal of Morphology* 85: 35-69.

_ _ _ _ _ _ _ _ _ _ _ _ _ _ _ _. (1949b), "The Nature of the Golgi Apparatus. II. Identification of the Golgi Apparatus with a Complex of Myelin Figures", *Journal of Morphology* 85: 71-111..

Palade, G.E. and Porter, K.R. (1954), "Studies on Endoplasmic Reticulum", *Journal of Experimental Medicine* 100: 641-655.

Palade, G.E. and Siekevitz, P. (1955), "Liver Microsomes: An Integrated Morphological and Biochemical Study," *Journal of Biophysical and Biochemical Cytology* 2: 171-200.

Porter, K.R. (1954), "Electron Microscopy of Basophilic Components of Cytoplasm," *Journal of Histochemistry and Cytochemistry* 2: 346-375.

_ _ _ _ _ _ . (1987), "Electron Microscopy of Cultured Cells", in J. E. Pauly, (ed.), *The American Association of Anatomists, 1888-1987. Essays on the History of Anatomy in America and a Report on the Membership—Past and Present.* Baltimore: Williams and Wilkins. pp. 59-67.

Porter, K.R. and Blum, J. (1953), "A study in Microtomy for electron Microscopy", *The Anatomical Record* 117: 685-710.

Porter, KR., Claude, A. and Fullam, E (1945), "A Study of Tissue Culture Cells by Electron Microscopy", *Journal of Experimental Medicine* 81: 233-246.

Porter, K.R. and Kallman, F.L. (1952), "Significance of Cell Particulates as seen by Electron Microscopy," *Annuals of the New York Academy of Science* 54: 882-891.

Robertson, J.D. (1987), "The Early Days of Electron Microscopy of Nerve Tissues and Membranes," *International Review of Cytology* 100: 129-201.

Sjöstrand, F.S. (1953), "Electron Microscopy of Mitochondria and Cytoplasmic Double Membranes", *Nature* 171: 30-32.

_ _ _ _ _ _ _ . (1956a), "Electron Microscopy of Cells and Tissues", in G. Oster and A.W. Pollister, (ed.), *Physical techniques in biological research.* New York: Academic. pp. 241-298.

_ _ _ _ _ _ _ . (1956b), "The Ultrastructure of Cells as Revealed by the Electron Microscope", *International Review of Cytology* 5: 455-533.

Williams, R.C. and Wyckoff, R.W.G. (1944), "The Thickness of Electron Microscopic Objects", *Journal of Applied Physics* 15: 712-716.

Wyckoff, R.W.G. (1959), "Optical Methods in Cytology", in J. ßBrachet and A.E. Mirsky, (eds.), *The Cell: Biochemistry, Physiology, Morphology*. New York: Academic Press. pp. 1-20.

Wimsatt, W.C. (1981), "Robustness, Reliability, and Overdetermination", in M.B. Brewer and B.E. Collins (eds.), *Scientific Inquiry and the Social Sciences.* San Francisco: Jossey-Bass, pp. 124-163.

Warburg, O. (1913), "Über sauerstoffatmende Kornchen aus Leberzellen und Über Sauer- stoffatmung in Berkfeld-Filtraten wässeriger Leberextrakte", *Pflügers Archiv für die gesamte Physiologie des Menschen und der Tierre* 154: 599-617.

Reasoning Strategies in Molecular Biology: Abstractions, Scans and Anomalies[1]

Lindley Darden
University of Maryland at College Park

Michael Cook
Rockefeller University

1. Introduction

In the spring of 1994, Lindley Darden spent five months as a visitor in Joshua Lederberg's Laboratory for Molecular Genetics and Informatics (MGI) at Rockefeller University. Michael Cook is a Research Associate in the MGI Lab. This paper discusses reasoning strategies at use in that lab. In Part I, Lindley Darden recounts her experiences in the lab and discusses reasoning strategies that she observed in use there. In Part II, Michael Cook presents a technique of methodical hypothesis generation in the light of an anomaly for a model.

Part I by Lindley Darden

2. Overview of Reasoning Strategies

The reasoning strategies to be discussed in this paper are reasoning in hypothesis formation, reasoning in experimental design, and reasoning to generate hypotheses in the light of an anomaly. More specifically, the reasoning strategies may be characterized as (1) abstraction-instantiation (Darden, 1987; 1991; Darden and Cain, 1989), (2) the systematic scan (Lederberg, 1965), and (3) modular anomaly resolution (Darden, 1991; 1992; forthcoming). All three of these strategies play roles in the reasoning about molecular genetics experiments in the MGI Lab.

3. Experiment Planning

The research focus of one group at the MGI Lab during the spring of 1994 was the question of how conformational states of DNA relate to DNA's susceptibility to mutagenesis. More specifically, the research focused on the relation of transcription and mutagenesis. (This research program is related to the controversial topic of adaptive mutation, but a discussion of that topic is beyond the scope of this paper. It is a fascinating idea that the genes that are being actively used, that is, being actively transcribed, may have the opportunity to change more, presumably in a non-directed way. On the topic of adaptive mutation, see Foster, 1993; Keller, 1992; Sarkar, 1991; Thaler, 1994.)

A more specific hypothesis investigated by the lab group is that DNA that is being actively transcribed (genes that are being expressed) will be in a state which renders that

PSA 1994, Volume 2, pp. 179-191

section of the DNA molecule more susceptible to alteration by mutagens (Davis, 1989). During DNA transcription, the DNA double helix is "open," that is, the Watson-Crick base pairs are separated and the DNA is single-stranded inside the bubble produced by the RNA polymerase enzyme that is copying the DNA into RNA. The hypothesis is that DNA in this state is more vulnerable to mutagens than when it is tightly packed.

One version of an abstract skeletal model of this process is as follows:

```
DNA=>"open DNA"=>(more) lesions=>production of mutants=>detect mutants
   |              |                                         |
   induce         introduce                                 repair?
   transcription  mutagen                                   replication
```

When transcription (gene expression) is induced in DNA, then the DNA double helix opens. The Watson-Crick base pairs separate, as the messenger RNA is produced. The hypothesis is that during such transcription the DNA is more susceptible to mutagens, so that if a mutagen is present, then more lesions (mutations) will be caused in the transcribing genes than in other portions of the DNA. In order to detect those mutations, bacteria are allowed to grow and the mutant colonies observed. So, between the possible effect of the mutagen and the detection of the mutant, DNA replication must occur. A possible confounding factor is the repair of mutations that is known to occur during DNA replication. If the mutations are repaired before being detected, then the hypothesized effect may be occurring but it may not be measured or the amount measured may be less than the amount that occurred.

The design of an experimental system that provides a good instantiation of this skeletal model has been a focus of research in the MGI Lab for several months. Thus a reasoning strategy for designing an experimental system may be characterized: develop an abstract skeletal model of steps (known and hypothesized) in the process under study; instantiate the variables in the model. For example, choose a particular gene in a particular organism that can be induced; determine what mutations in that gene are to be the focus of the mutagen and how the mutations can be detected; determine what mutagen is to be used; and so on for all the abstract components of the skeletal model. The realization of this instantiation in laboratory work results in an actual experimental system. This reasoning strategy provides a method for reasoning from a hypothesis to a skeletal model (an elaboration of the steps of a process in which the hypothesized step plays a role) to an experimental system.

The traditional philosophical account from the hypothetico-deductive (H-D) method totally obscures this reasoning. Recall the steps in the traditional H-D account—conjecture hypothesis, plug in initial conditions, derive prediction, test prediction. The step of designing an experimental system that will provide a good test of the hypothesis is totally obscured. No clues are given as to how such a design is made. Yet this is an important reasoning task of scientists. Hans Rheinberger (1992) argued for the importance of the concept of an experimental system in the history and philosophy of molecular biology, although he did not discuss the reasoning in constructing such experimental systems.

Thus, the reasoning to be discussed here is the elaboration of this abstract model and its instantiation in a laboratory experimental system. To give the game away a bit: the prediction that genes undergoing transcription will show an increase in the rate of mutagenesis has been tested in several experimental systems, one of which will be discussed in detail. The prediction has not yet been confirmed; the failed prediction constitutes an anomaly. Reasoning to resolve this anomaly is discussed in Part II by Michael Cook.

4. The Systematic Scan

Reasoning about this skeletal model often employs a reasoning strategy that was devised by Lederberg and is frequently used by the lab group—the systematic scan

(Lederberg, 1965; see also Zwicky, 1967). Before showing a role that this strategy played in the design of an experimental system, it is useful to characterize the general strategy. Given a problem, find one approximate solution to it. Then examine the solution to find constants that can be converted into variables. If the variables are numeric, then the scan could potentially go from minus infinity to plus infinity. Construct a set of solutions and aggregate subsets at appropriate grains of resolution. Evaluate the subsets and choose one; then evaluate the sets within that subset to choose which particular solution to pursue.

A key issue in using the scan method is to identify the variables and to determine the range of the variables in order to construct sets and subsets of types of solutions. Most powerfully, the sets and subsets should not be a mere heap but should be constructed via a vector or a matrix with orthogonal axes. The choice of variables to construct the axes, and thus the sets, is a key to success of the systematic scan method. One must have good items, constructed in a systematic way, in order for the scan to be productive.

Philip Kitcher (1993) advocates a method of reasoning about types of hypotheses and the use of eliminative induction to narrow consideration to one of them. However, he does not attempt to develop a method for systematic generation of alternative hypotheses and talks vaguely of prior constraints providing the alternatives. Kitcher, as well as most of his colleagues in twentieth century philosophy of science, neglects the reasoning in hypothesis generation. This systematic scan method is a useful addition to Kitcher's view of scientific methodology.

For some problems, given a set of variables and the range of their values, one can do a complete scan, that is a scan that is exhaustive and non-redundant. Lederberg wrote the algorithm for the first expert system, DENDRAL, which could exhaustively generate all possible three-dimensional chemical structures for a given chemical formula. Thus, the search space for a problem has all possible topological connections of the atoms (Lindsay, Buchanan, Feigenbaum, and Lederberg, 1980; 1993).

A complete scan will typically have too many possibilities to consider all of them explicitly. With regard to actual experimental design, the problems are too vague and the possible solutions too little specified to have any confidence that one is doing a complete scan. The looser application of the systematic scan method involves a question: what are all the possible solutions to a problem that come to mind or that can be extracted from a search of the scientific literature? Or, another way of posing a question: what is the set of which the single instance that I have found is a member? Would some other member of the set be better than the current instance under consideration?

5. Scanning and Instantiation to Produce an Experimental System

The task now is to see how these reasoning strategies of abstraction-instantiation and the systematic scan are related, and how their use results in the design of an experimental system. The most abstract level is the abstract hypothesis, which is elaborated to produce an abstract skeletal model of a process. The abstract model can be further elaborated with additional steps or various steps can be left as implicit. Then, variables that must be instantiated are identified and a scan of the range of possible values of the variables is made. Finally, one value for each variable is specified and a fully instantiated experimental system results. Recall the transcription-mutation skeletal model to be instantiated:

```
DNA=>"open DNA"=>(more) lesions=>production of mutants=>detect mutants
|                 |                                     |
induce            introduce                          repair?
transcription     mutagen                            replication
```

In the reasoning to develop an instantiation of the transcription-mutation skeletal model, a scan has been made of possible mutagens. A number have been used in actual experiments. Much of this scanning occurred before I (Lindley Darden) arrived at the Lederberg lab. Various criteria were used to generate this list and to choose the best candidates. The one that was the focus of study during my visit was EMS (ethylmethane sulfonate).

In addition to the choice of mutagen, other necessary components for constructing an experimental system that instantiates the skeletal model are a gene that is (1) able to have its expression induced and (2) has mutations that can be easily and rapidly detected. The *lac* operon of *E. coli* is a system of choice because it is so well understood and because it has been engineered to be a versatile laboratory tool. (In the late 1940s and early 50s, Lederberg pioneered in the study of *lac* mutants and in developing laboratory methods for their manipulation. See Brock, 1990.) No scanning of other genetic systems as alternatives to the *lac* operon system occurred during the period of my visit to the MGI Lab. Lederberg, in reflecting on their earlier decisions, suggested that they "scanned in their heads" before beginning the current line of research focused on the *lac* operon.

As Jacob and Monod (1961) had worked out in the 1960s, the *lac* operon in *E. coli* bacteria has three structural genes that produce enzymes. The one of interest here is the *lac Z* gene that produces the enzyme β-galactosidase, which functions to break down the sugar lactose. In the absence of lactose, β-galactosidase is not produced. But if lactose is added to the system, it induces the production of the enzymes that break it down. In order to explain this induction phenomenon, Jacob and Monod postulated the existence of another gene, the *lac I* gene, that produces a repressor. If no lactose is present, the repressor prevents transcription of the *lac* operon. If lactose is added, then lactose forms a complex with the repressor, freeing the genes to begin transcription. However, if the *lac Z* gene is mutated, then no functional β-galactosidase is produced, even if an inducer is present.

Since the 1960s, the *lac* operon has been extremely well-studied. Numerous experimental techniques have been developed to make the *lac* operon very useful in genetic experiments. Of particular interest to us is the gratuitous inducer, the chemical, isopropyl-thio-β-D-galactoside, called IPTG. IPTG induces transcription of the *lac* operon genes in the absence of lactose, the normal inducer; but, unlike lactose, IPTG is not itself affected by the enzymes that are produced. Another engineering feat is the development of strains of bacteria that do not have the *lac* operon on their chromosomes. In such strains, the *lac* genes can be altered in various ways and introduced into the bacteria on plasmids, which are extra-chromosomal bits of DNA. (Historians and sociologists recently have discussed the engineering of laboratory artifacts for experimental purposes and the *lac* operon certainly qualifies.)

A major task for geneticists is strain construction. Mutations are moved from one strain into another to create a desired combination of mutations. The reasoning in strain construction is an important topic in a study of reasoning in genetics, but time will not permit pursuing that topic here. (Michael Cook and David Thaler are designing an expert system to plan bacterial genetic experiments and do strain constructions.)

In the strain construction for the mutagenesis experiments, the MGI Lab group used a strain in the lab (labeled A70) which lacks the entire *lac* operon on its chromosome and also lacks the gene for making the amino acid proline; the strain is designated "delta *lac pro*." The strain is also resistant to streptomycin. A set of strains of bacteria were engineered and supplied by Claire Cupples (formerly at UCLA, now in Montreal) (Cupples and Miller, 1989; Cupples et al., 1990). Cupples's strains are designated as derivatives of an *E. coli* strain (P90C) which is delta *lac proB* on the chromosome. The Cupples's strains also contain a sex factor (a plasmid, which is a piece of DNA separate from the bacterial chromosome) specifically engineered with *lac* mutants, designated: F' *lac I- Z- proB+*. The F' is a plasmid that carries a gene for making proline and has a specific *lac* Z- mutation. Cupples created six strains with different *lac* Z- mutations at a critical site (residue 461) in the *lac Z* gene; this is a critical site for the gene to produce a functional enzyme (β-galactosidase). Each strain has a specific known base substitution that must be restored to the normal DNA codon (GAG, codes for glutamic acid) in order to get the wild type phenotype (i.e., functional enzyme).

Note how the molecular level gets used in engineering a plasmid to go into a strain for a genetic experiment. Schaffner (1993), when he isn't discussing his formal reduction model, correctly notes such "intertwining" of the genetic and the biochemical levels in biology and medicine. It is interesting to note that this is the first point in the experimental design that DNA sequences become relevant. Most of the work is done at the genetic level, or at a level in between the gene (considered as a functional unit that produces an enzyme) and the detailed DNA sequence; this intermediate level is the level of the three-dimensional, conformational state of DNA during transcription. Investigation of the lowest level, the sequence level, can be deferred during the planning and execution of the genetic experiments. DNA sequencing of the mutants would be done only after a positive result in the genetic experiments.

In addition to the bacterial chromosome, which does not have the *lac* operon genes, and the F' plasmid with the specific *lac* Z- mutants, the engineered strain also contains another plasmid, called pZC21, which carries the *lac I* gene. Having *lac I* means that the *lac* repressor is produced, and, thus, the *lac Z* gene is repressed unless an inducer is present. This engineered bacterial strain for use in the mutagenic experiments is thus (A70) delta *lac pro*/F' *lac Z-pro+*/pZC21*lac I+ ampR*.

The skeletal model can now be instantiated to produce one specific experimental system:

lac Z- DNA=>"open DNA"=>(more) lesions=>production of mutants=>

"open DNA"	(more) lesions	production of mutants
induce transcription with IPTG	introduce mutagen EMS	repair? replication

=> detect mutants by growth on E lac medium (medium without lactose)

After scanning for possible values of the variables and the instantiation of each, a detailed experimental system is designed. The DNA is the *lac* Z- gene on the F plasmid. The *lac* Z- gene is inducible, because *lac I+* is present and is producing the repressor. Transcription is induced by adding IPTG to the medium: the IPTG interacts with the repressor and allows transcription to begin. A mutagen, EMS, is then put into the medium. The prediction is that more mutations (lesions) in the *lac* Z- gene will be produced in a system in which transcription is induced than in a system where transcription has not been induced.

The mutation that is being detected after subjecting these bacteria to the mutagen EMS is the reversion of *lac* Z- to *lac* Z+. In other words, a dysfunctional gene is being mutated and what is detected are those mutants which restore functionality to the gene. What is actually detected is evidence for the activity of the enzyme that the gene produces. The presence of the enzyme is detected because the bacterial colony will grow on a minimal medium with lactose as its food (that is, carbon) source; the functional enzyme is necessary for lactose metabolism.

A complete instantiation of the skeletal model results in a detailed experimental system in which transcription is induced in the mutant *lac* Z- gene on the F' plasmid by IPTG, the mutagen is EMS, and growth of colonies on a minimal medium with lactose indicate that a *lac* Z+ reversion occurred. The control system has no IPTG and thus has very little transcription of the *lac Z* gene. (There is a small amount of residual activity in normal cells without inducer, but that may be neglected in these experiments.)

Raphael Stimphil (a technician in the MGI Lab) kindly supplied me with his detailed protocol from one of the mutagen experiments:

> Two cultures of CC102pZC21 were grown overnight in NCE(.2%)Glucose 100ug/ml Amp +/- 0.5mM IPTG at 37°C. The cultures were diluted 1:10 in fresh medium of the same composition +/- 0.5 mM IPTG, and grown to an optical density at 600 nm of 0.2 at 37°C. They were aliquoted 1 ml each in microcentrifuge tubes on ice. Ethylmethane Sulfonate (EMS) was added to 35mM and incubated at 37°C for the indicated time periods. The mutagen was neutralized with 2-Mercaptoethanol to 35mM. Survival was assessed on NCE(.2%) glucose plates, and mutagenesis on NCE(.2%) lactose. Plates were incubated at 37°C, and counted after 48hrs.

Raphael continued: "there were other variations to this protocol, mainly in the temperature at which mutagenesis was carried out...with this protocol I [Raphael Stimphil] was not able to observe any difference between repressed and induced. There was another protocol through which I could observe a 1.6 fold higher yield of *lac*+ revertants when the operon was induced. However, I have not been able to widen the gap (get more of an effect) between repressed and induced. This was the starvation protocol: cells were starved for 4hrs +/- 0.5 mM IPTG were mutagenized with DES (Diethyl Sulfate)."

6. Experimental Results—An Anomaly

Thus, the EMS experiments showed increases too small to be persuasive, or to be a useful foundation for further work, given the underlying sampling and other sources of statistical variance. If the hypothesis is correct that mutagenesis increases during transcription and if this experimental system is a good test of that hypothesis, then more *lac Z*+ revertants would have been expected consistently in the presence of IPTG. So, the data do not match the prediction of the model that a consistent increase in revertants would occur in the cells that were subjected to the mutagen during transcription. This lack of agreement between the prediction and the data constitutes an anomaly.

7. Reasoning in Anomaly Resolution

I (Lindley Darden) participated in discussions in which the MGI Lab group did anomaly resolution. (It was great fun for me to watch scientists using some of the anomaly resolution strategies that I had proposed hypothetically in my book but had never seen scientists actually using, especially the strategy of considering each module of a model and generating alternatives to each one. Also, I saw how the process of anomaly resolution led to uncovering previously implicit assumptions, and I sometimes nudged the group to make their implicit assumptions explicit.)

As I have argued elsewhere, reasoning in anomaly resolution is, first of all, like a diagnostic reasoning process (Darden, 1990; Darden, 1991, Ch. 12; Darden, 1992). That is, it is analogous to debugging a computer program, to determining a mechanical failure in a car, to diagnosing a disease. One must find locations in the model which may be failing. Secondly, after localization, anomaly resolution is a redesign process, like engineers designing a new part to prevent failure in the future (Karp, 1990). The model must be redesigned to avoid the failure.

Such anomaly resolution reasoning involves three major factors: the modular representation of the failing system, the nature of the anomaly, and the reasoning strategies to localize and to fix the failure. (These reasoning strategies are interestingly similar to the reasoning strategies of decomposition and localization, discussed by Bechtel and Richardson (1993).)

This particular anomaly provided geneticists with less positive guidance in localization than others that I have examined (see, for example, the discussion of linkage anomalies in Darden, 1991, Ch. 9). What happened here is simply the lack of an effect, when one had been predicted. One could conclude that the original hypothesis—that genes undergoing transcription show an increased mutation rate—has been disproved. But such a conclusion is premature. Whether this particular experimental system is an adequate test is a prior question. Efforts were made to reason about the experimental details and tinker with them.

Collectively in lab meetings and individually by email, we outlined the skeletal model in more detail and considered what could be going wrong at each step. Lederberg and I tend to draw pictures of processes with sequential steps (these correspond nicely, I think, to what Ken Schaffner (1993) calls "causal, mechanistic models" and Bechtel and Richardson (1993) call the "causal components" of systems). (On the role of visualization in his hypothesis formation, see quotations from Lederberg in Judson, 1980, pp. 184-186.)

Lederberg said in one email message during this anomaly resolution process:

> We probably want to expand this [the skeletal model] to at least 2-fold more detail, and try to attack any of the steps. This model expansion is too case specific to lend itself to exhaustive enumeration. But for each step we could try to construct "all the possible ways" that it could be wrong, or experimentally bolstered or tested.

Michael Cook elaborated the model by stating assumptions in sentences and performing systematic permutations on the sentences. He discusses these reasoning strategies in Part II.

Part II by Michael Cook

8. Hypothesis Generation Based on a Technique Suggested by A Model for Defense Mechanisms

Scientific discussions are often devoted to explaining experimental results. Over the past year we had a series of lab meetings in which we tried to explain why a certain expected effect was not observed. In this context, I (Michael Cook) outlined a method for systematically generating such explanations, based on a technique suggested by Patrick Suppes and Hermine Warren in a different context (Suppes and Warren, 1975).

The first step is to abstract a verbal model of the knowledge we are working with in the lab. Although the underlying biochemical models are highly technical, it is necessary to verbalize the basic principles, and much of the discussion in our meetings is an exercise in just that. In one particular case, I suggested the following sentences as a summary of the relevant knowledge, based on diagrams put on the whiteboard by Joshua Lederberg:

BACKGROUND KNOWLEDGE:
(1) Transcription opens DNA.
(2) EMS mutates DNA.
(3) IPTG induces transcription.
HYPOTHESIS:
(4) EMS has better access to open DNA than closed DNA.
PREDICTION:
(5) IPTG will result in more mutation in the transcribed gene.

The first three statements are considered to be "well known," whereas the fourth statement is a working hypothesis. The fifth statement is a prediction.

Experiments were performed, and the predicted result (statement 5) was not observed. In analyzing this, we questioned the hypothesis, but we also ended up questioning the background knowledge. As the discussion progressed I suggested the above model as an abstracted summary of our assumptions.

Once a verbal model is made explicit, one can generate explanations as to why the expected effect was not observed by systematically transforming the sentences in the model. This technique was used in a paper by Suppes and Warren (1975), which represents defense mechanisms as transformations of propositions. (For example, the thought "I hate my mother" gets transformed to: "I love my mother" or to "My mother hates me" or to "My husband hates my mother." Suppes and Warren enumerate a set of such transformations and correlate them with known defense mechanisms.)

When we don't see the expected effect, we generate possible explanations by systematically varying our assumptions. This is done sentence by sentence as follows:

(a) Negate the sentence. (DENIAL)
(b) Substitute a new variable for an existing one. (DISPLACEMENT)
(c) Insert a new clause in the chain. (RATIONALIZATION)
Comment on (c): The new clauses are generally of the "Yes, but..." variety.

They acknowledge the truth of the sentence, but add a new sentence whose function is to suggest why the original sentence did not result in the expected observation. This process is reminiscent of the "qualification problem" described in expert systems literature: a "rule", such as "all birds fly" is constantly being qualified to account for reality: penguins, ostriches, baby birds, wounded birds, dead birds, comic strip birds, Kentucky Fried Chicken, etc. It often happens that when a rule-based system is applied to a real problem, the exceptions start to drown out the original simplicity and modularity of the initial rule set (see Genesereth, 1987).

Here are some illustrative examples of inserted clauses. Case 1: Transcription opens DNA. Yes, but something is closing the DNA, e.g., a single-strand binding protein. Case 2: IPTG induces transcription. (a) Yes, but something (the EMS?) is preventing the IPTG from doing its job. (b) Yes, but something (the EMS?) is "stalling" the transcription. Case 3: EMS has better access to open DNA than closed DNA. Yes, but repair enzymes repair open DNA more efficiently than closed DNA.

Often the insertion of new clauses amounts to bringing in the possibility of side-effects, or exogenous variables that have not been considered but are in fact relevant. This of course is especially prevalent when dealing with *in vivo* systems.

Thus, four sentences and three transformations leads to twelve basic "explanations." It takes non-trivial semantic processing to perform the transformation, and to interpret it in terms of the result to be explained. The twelve transformed sentences, with some discussion, are listed below. Not all twelve are equally meaningful or suggestive, but they are all listed for completeness.

(1) Transforming "Transcription opens DNA":

(a) Transcription does not open DNA. Perhaps the "transcription bubble" image is misleading? Sri Sastry pointed out that the "openness" of the complex is inside the enzyme that is doing the transcribing (the RNA polymerase), which thus may protect the transcribed DNA from the action of the mutagen.

(b) Something else opens DNA. For instance, "breathing," namely the normal opening and closing of DNA base pairs. This would explain the negative result, since then both untranscribed and transcribed DNA would be open, hence similarly susceptible to mutagenic effects of EMS.

(c) Another variable is canceling out the effect of open DNA. This variant suggested the possibility of single-strand binding proteins binding to the exposed strands of the transcription bubble, protecting the DNA from the EMS.

(2) Transforming "EMS mutates DNA."

(a) EMS does not mutate DNA. The issue of the mutagenic effect of EMS must certainly be looked at, although it is not in dispute. But perhaps the conditions of the experiment are insufficient to get maximum effects?

(b) Something else mutates DNA. This idea doesn't seem relevant to the situation at hand, because mutagenesis was detected in these very experiments, and not detected in controls in which the EMS was left out.

(c) Another variable is canceling out this effect. For instance, EMS might mutate the DNA, but repair enzymes might repair the damage.

(3) Transforming "IPTG induces transcription."

(a) IPTG is not inducing transcription (or: not noticeably). This led to the speculation that the so-called glucose effect—the presence of glucose inhibits expression of the *lac* gene even in the presence of inducer—may be at work here.

(b) Something else is inducing transcription. This is hard to interpret.

(e) Another variable is canceling out this effect. For example, EMS/IPTG interactions.

(4) Transforming "EMS has better access to open DNA than closed DNA."

(a) EMS has better access to closed DNA. This doesn't seem likely, as there is no observed difference.

(b) Something else has better access to open DNA. (Again, repair enzymes.)

Or: EMS has better access to open DNA in *replication*, and this effect swamps out the one we are looking for, because all the DNA would be affected equally, not just the *lac* Z- gene.

Or: EMS has better access to the nucleotide precursors and it is they which are mutated before incorporation into the DNA during replication. This would explain why there was no observed difference between transcribed and untranscribed DNA because all the nucleotides would be just as likely to be affected.

These last two possibilities are, strictly speaking, not derived from the original sentence by substitution. They were pointed out by David Thaler, who observed that if "open" DNA is really an important variable, then DNA undergoing replication is a strong candidate for susceptibility to mutagenesis, because replicating DNA (as well as transcribing DNA) is open. In fact, these effects may be much stronger than transcription effects, and may swamp out any such examples. In addition, precursor nucleotides in some sense are the most "open" of all (since they are not yet bound to any DNA) and may be the most subject to mutagenesis. These questions have opened up many interesting subsequent and ongoing discussions in our group.

(c) Another variable is canceling out this effect. Again, single stranded binding proteins; or IPTG/EMS interactions.

This list covers the results of several hours of joint brainstorming in the lab, and can be derived "mechanically" by applying transformations to the verbal model. I put "mechanically" in quotes, because there are many semantic nuances involved here, and much contextual knowledge. The point is, though, that given the model, there are rules for using it to generate hypotheses, and the need for "insight" is reduced, although not eliminated.

Two additional points need to be made about this hypothesis generation method. First, this approach depends on the formulation of the four statements in the model. Thus, if I said: "Transcription makes DNA more susceptible to mutation," we would not be locked into the model of "open." Not surprisingly, generating the representation of the model is a significant part of the task. Secondly, the transformations are syntactic, but their rationalization must be done by a human. For example, "something else opens the DNA" doesn't generate the concept of "breathing." But adding "something else" (namely a confounding variable) can act as a catalyst for thinking of an instantiation, namely breathing.

How to be certain we have covered all the bases? How systematic was our scan? As usual, answering that question is hard. We can perhaps begin to be certain that we have covered all the bases vis-a-vis our model; the one door into the greater outside universe is the ability to insert new sentences. This allows us to generate other variables not in the model, and think about them without fully instantiating them.

The question is, which variables are likely to be important? Choosing variables on which to focus can be a hard problem. A fruitful line of investigation might be to find heuristics used in variable choice. Once the choice to focus on a particular set of variables is made, the universe of discourse is defined, and work can begin: model-building, model-fitting, model-testing, etc.

It is interesting to note that the use of defense mechanisms in hypothesis generation is not that far-fetched. After all, "rationalization" is in the basic catalog of defense mechanisms, and it is also true that science does attempt to "rationalize experience." That the same word is used for both activities—"making up excuses" and "generating hypotheses"—is more than just a pun, and points out a general pattern in human psychology. Moreover, perhaps defense mechanisms are not necessarily neurotic, as the phrase tends to connote. For example, Lakatos lists as one of the elements of his "positive heuristics": Defend the ramparts of your theory (Lakatos, 1970).

More can be said along these lines. The process of more fully articulating the model on which the experiment is based can be compared to abreaction, a term in psychoanalytic theory referring to the process in therapy by which unconscious material is made conscious. The model sketched above was certainly not fully spelled out before the discussion of the experimental results. The model and the experimental results were clarified together, and the failure of the prediction led to a deeper elaboration of the assumptions behind the work.

Finally, if one views a defense mechanism as an attempt by the mind to avoid the tension associated with being conscious of two or more contradictory statements at the same time, then the connection with scientific research becomes even clearer. And in this context, one may delineate a hierarchy, in which denial is the most primitive method, displacement is slightly more clever and roundabout, and rationalization is the most sophisticated (of these three). Why is rationalization the most sophisticated?

Because it allows the contradictory statements to remain in the consciousness, and deals with the tension by making up new, reconciling, statements. Now in this spectrum, the defense mechanism of sublimation may tentatively be identified with "revolutionary" science (Kuhn, 1970). Sublimation is the creative resolution of psychic tensions on a higher level of being—the usual examples being the activity of science, art, or philosophy—as sublimations of sexual energies. But so-called revolutionary science involves precisely the ability to accept seeming contradictions, and to find a new framework in which they appear as harmonious expressions of a hitherto unidentified reality.

These ideas are preliminary, but they seem well suited to being developed to the point where a computer can take part in the process of hypothesis generation during anomaly resolution.

9. Conclusion

In summary, we have examined reasoning strategies used in a molecular biology laboratory: strategies for hypothesis formation; strategies for designing an experimental system; and strategies for debugging a model in the face of an anomaly. These strategies are abstraction-instantiation, the systematic scan, and modular anomaly resolution. An original abstract hypothesis was further specified in an abstract skeletal model that underwent several elaborations. Reasoning about this abstract model involved a scan of possible values of variables. Several were actually instantiated in detailed plans for experimental systems and experiments were run in the laboratory. For the one instantiation discussed here, the predicted effect was not found. Then, the modules of the abstract model were systematically formulated and manipulated to form alternative hypotheses to remove the failure. The experiments to choose among the alternative modifications to the model are still on-going. The problem with working at the forefront of science, rather than with its history, is that you do not know how the story will come out.

Note

[1]Lindley Darden's visit at Rockefeller University was supported by a grant from the Andrew W. Mellon Foundation. She thanks Joshua Lederberg for making this opportunity available and for stimulating discussions during the visit. She also thanks others in the lab who were so friendly and helpful: Michael Cook, David Thaler, Sri Sastry, Greg Tombline, Raphael Stimphil, Ken Zahn, Mick Noordewier, Mary Jane Zimmermann and Joice Johnson. Michael Cook's work was supported by a grant from the Defense Advanced Research Projects Agency, ARPA Order No. 8145, No. MDA972-91-J-1008. They both thank Joshua Lederberg, David Thaler, Raphael Stimphil, Sri Sastry, Nancy Hall (of the Committee on the History and Philosophy of Science at the University of Maryland, College Park) and William Wolfe (of the Mathematics Department at the University of Colorado, Denver) for inspiring comments or specific comments on earlier drafts of this paper.

References

Bechtel, W. and Richardson, R.C. (1993), *Discovering Complexity: Decomposition and Localization as Strategies in Scientific Research.* Princeton: Princeton University Press.

Brock, T.D. (1990), *The Emergence of Bacterial Genetics.* Cold Spring Harbor: Cold Spring Harbor Laboratory Press.

Cupples, C. and Miller, J.H. (1989), "A Set of *lacZ* Mutations in *Escherichia coli* That Allow Rapid Detection of Each of Six Base Substitutions," *Proc. Natl. Acad. Sci.* USA 86:5345-5349.

Cupples, C., Cabera, M., Cruz, C. and Miller, J.H. (1990), "A Set of *lacZ* Mutations in *Escherichia coli* That Allow Rapid Detection of Specific Frameshift Mutations," *Genetics* 125:275-280.

Darden, L. (1987), "Viewing the History of Science as Compiled Hindsight," *AI Magazine* 8(2):33-41.

______. (1990), "Diagnosing and Fixing Faults in Theories," in J. Shrager and P. Langley (eds.), *Computational Models of Scientific Discovery and Theory Formation.* San Mateo, California: Morgan Kaufmann, pp. 319-346.

______. (1991), *Theory Change in Science: Strategies from Mendelian Genetics.* New York: Oxford University Press.

______. (1992) "Strategies for Anomaly Resolution," in R. Giere (ed.), *Cognitive Models of Science*, Minnesota Studies in the Philosophy of Science, Vol. 15. Minneapolis: University of Minnesota Press, pp. 251-273.

______. (forthcoming) "Exemplars, Abstractions, and Anomalies: Representations and Theory Change in Mendelian and Molecular Genetics," in James G. Lennox and Gereon Wolters (eds.), *Philosophy of Biology.* Konstanz, Germany: University of Konstanz Press and Pittsburgh, PA: University of Pittsburgh Press, pp. 137-158.

Darden, L, and Cain, J.A. (1989), "Selection Type Theories," *Philosophy of Science* 56:106-129.

Davis, B.D. (1989), "Transcriptional Bias: A Non-Lamarckian Mechanism for Substrate-Induced Mutations," *Proc. Natl. Acad. Sci.* USA 86:5005-5009.

Foster, P.L. (1993), "Adaptive Mutation: The Uses of Adversity," *Annual Reviews of Microbiology* 47:467-504.

Froehlich, W.D., Smith, G., Draguns, J.G. and Hentschel, H. (eds.) (1984), *Psychological Processes in Cognition and Personality.* Washington: Hemisphere Publishing Corp.

Genesereth, M.R. and Nilsson, N.J. (1987), *Logical Foundations of Artificial Intelligence.* San Mateo, California: Morgan Kaufmann.

Jacob, F. and Monod, J. (1961), "Genetic Regulatory Mechanisms in the Synthesis of Proteins," *Journal of Molecular Biology* 3:318-356.

Judson, H.F. (1980), *Search for Solutions.* New York: Holt, Rinehart and Winston.

Karp, P. (1990), "Hypothesis Formation as Design," in J. Shrager and P. Langley (eds.), *Computational Models of Scientific Discovery and Theory Formation.* San Mateo, California: Morgan Kaufmann, pp. 275-317.

Keller, E.F. (1992), "Between Language and Science: The Question of Directed Mutation in Molecular Genetics," *Perspectives in Biology and Medicine* 35:292-306.

Kitcher, P. (1993), T*he Advancement of Science: Science without Legend, Objectivity without Illusions.* New York: Oxford University Press.

Kuhn, T. (1970), *The Structure of Scientific Revolutions.* 2nd Edition. Chicago: The University of Chicago Press.

Lakatos, I. (1970), "Falsification and the Methodology of Scientific Research Programmes," in I. Lakatos and Alan Musgrave (eds.), *Criticism and the Growth of Knowledge.* Cambridge, England: Cambridge University Press, pp. 91-195.

Lederberg, J. (1965), "Signs of Life: Criterion-System of Exobiology," *Nature* 207:9-13.

Lindsay, R.K., Buchanan, B.G., Feigenbaum, E.A. and Lederberg, J. (1980), *Applications of Artificial Intelligence for Organic Chemistry: The DENDRAL Project.* New York: McGraw Hill.

__________________________________. (1993), "DENDRAL: A Case Study of the First Expert System for Scientific Hypothesis Formation," *Artificial Intelligence* 61:209-261.

Rheinberger, H-J. (1992a), "Experiment, Difference, and Writing: I. Tracing Protein Synthesis," *Studies in the History and Philosophy of Science* 23:305-331.

__________. (1992b), "Experiment, Difference, and Writing: II. The Laboratory Production of Transfer RNA," *Studies in the History and Philosophy of Science* 23:389-422.

Sarkar, S. (1991), "Lamarck *Contre* Darwin, Reduction *Versus* Statistics: Conceptual Issues in the Controversy Over Directed Mutagenesis in Bacteria," in Alfred I. Tauber (ed.), *Organism and the Origins of Self,*" The Netherlands: Kluwer, pp. 235-271.

Schaffner, K. (1993), *Discovery and Explanation in Biology and Medicine.* Chicago: University of Chicago Press.

Suppes, P. and Warren, H. (1975), "On the Generation and Classification of Defense Mechanisms," *International Journal of Psychoanalysis* 56: Part IV, pp. 405-414.

Thaler, D.S. (1994), "The Evolution of Genetic Intelligence," *Science* 264:224-225.

Zwicky, F. (1967), "The Morphological Approach to Discovery, Invention, Research and Construction," in Fritz Zwicky and A. G. Wilson (eds.), *New Methods of Thought and Procedure.* New York: Springer-Verlag.

Interactions Among Theory, Experiment, and Technology in Molecular Biology[1]

Kenneth F. Schaffner

George Washington University

1. Introduction

In this paper, I revisit a problem in immunology and molecular genetics that I had first tried to understand some philosophical implications of over twenty years ago. At that time, some immunologists such as Mel Cohn at the Salk Institute, referred to it as the GOD problem, which was the acronym for *G*enerator *O*f *D*iversity (also see Cohn's more recent discussion in his 1994, 41-48). In the early 1970s there were three or four different theories that had been proposed to account for the way in which antibody diversity is generated and considerable argument among the proponents of the different approaches to the problem (see Cohn, 1994). In 1971-72 I attempted to assess the strengths and weaknesses of the competing theories of antibody diversity from the perspective of a "logic of comparative theory evaluation" that had seemed to work reasonably well in physics (Schaffner, 1970), and I drafted an essay that ultimately sided with one of those theories (somatic mutation). Though that essay was circulated to some biologists and immunologists, I felt it was based on far-too-limited laboratory data to publish it, and I set it aside until recently.[2]

In the mid through late 1970s this problem was significantly clarified (some might even say "solved")[3] by utilizing many of the powerful new techniques of molecular biology virtually as soon as they became available. The sophisticated techniques applied to the generator of antibody diversity problem included (1) nucleic acid hybridization to determine the number of copies of a specific gene, (2) the use of restriction enzymes to break up the long eucaryotic mouse genome, (3) electrophoretic separation of the DNA fragments to detect somatic rearrangement (a somewhat cumbersome technique that was soon replaced by, (4) the use of Southern blot analysis), and (5) the then emerging — and at that time quite ethically controversial — recombinant DNA technology, used in this case to clone the antibody genes being investigated.

This paper is concerned with outlining the early stages of how the "solution" to an important biomedical problem emerged, and how this required driving the level at which both theorizing and experimentation occurred down to the molecular sequence degree of resolution. This experimental thrust utilized and assisted in the development of a very powerful set of technologies that has several philosophically important implications. The rapidly evolving technology of molecular biology provided multiple instances of that extraordinarily strong form of evidence working scientists call "direct evidence" in the antibody diversity area. This concept requires some explication which I will provide toward the end of the paper, where I will argue for a middle posi-

PSA 1994, Volume 2, pp. 192-205

tion between the realist-sounding claims of the biologists and the anti-realist social constructivist interpretations of experimentation (Latour and Woolgar, 1979/1986; Latour, 1987; Knorr-Cetina, 1981). I will also argue what may seem to be a paradoxical thesis given that the inquiry took place at the sequence level: That this episode in the history of the biomedical sciences constitutes an instance of *partial* reduction in biology at the same time it satisfies, better than most biological examples, a fairly simple theory reduction model. In this symposium, it is also of special interest to determine whether there are any useful heuristics or strategies — rough guidelines for experimental planning (see Bechtel and Richardson, 1993 and Darden, 1991) — that can be identified in this case area. This is a case that richly amalgamates theory, experiment, and then-novel technology; thus it promises to yield heuristics that can be extrapolated to other historical and contemporary problem areas. I shall mention some of the strategies pursued by the molecular biologists, but will do so largely in general ways, since I think an in-depth discussion would require more literature analysis, and reports on interviews with the principal actors in this episode, than space permits. I will first begin by summarizing the state of the problem as it existed in the early 1970s, before the powerful molecular techniques that are the focus of this article were developed and used in this area, and then turn to the work of the molecular biologists.

2. The Historical Background

A. *Antibody Structure.* It is, I think, accepted by virtually all those who have looked at or participated in the events that I will be describing that "theory" played several critical roles in identifying the problem and in sketching several alternative solutions. The research programs I discuss all occur within the general framework of the clonal selection theory. These programs were directed at achieving an experimental choice among several subtheories — subtheories that are sometimes termed hypotheses, and also less frequently "models" — all of which are consistent with the general tenets of the clonal selection theory.[4] The clonal selection theory not only is the framework theory in terms of which the episode discussed in the present paper develops; it also continues to exercise a powerful background influence in current immunology.

The clonal selection theory emerged at a time during which a "template" or "instructive" theory still held sway in immunology. Template theories, which flourished from about 1930 until 1965, envisioned some type of mechanism by which antibodies are molded on the surface of the antigen. With the work of Landsteiner in the 1930's on the variety and specificity of antigen-antibody reactions (1945[1933]), the belief that some key structural information was contributed by the antigen to the antibody became irresistible to immunologists. (Landsteiner discovered that a large number of different synthetic determinants (termed haptens) could be coupled to proteins and could elicit the formation of antibodies specifically directed against the haptens, and it was thought extremely unlikely that an organism could have information stored within its cells to enable it to make antibody to thousands of synthetic haptens it would not have normally encountered; for details see Schaffner, 1992 or Silverstein, 1989.) Suffice it to say that by the late 1960s, the instructive theories were replaced by "selective" theories advanced in the mid- to late- fifties (Jerne, 1955; Burnet, 1957; Talmage, 1957; Lederberg, 1959), the most generally recognized one of these being Burnet's clonal selection theory. (Ehrlich's side chain theory of 1900 is also a selective type of theory but was formulated in a very different historical context.)

In his (1968) Burnet sketched what he characterized as the '*essence*' of his theory in terms of what can be considered five axioms. This formulation does articulate in a somewhat more explicit, modern, and concise manner what was asserted earlier in 1957, but it is better in this paper to begin with a concise account of the theory, as long as does not mislead historically. Burnet introduced the fundamental assumptions as follows:

(1) Antibody is produced by cells, to a pattern which is laid down by the genetic mechanism in the nucleus of the cell.

(2) Antigen has only one function, to stimulate cells capable of producing the kind of antibody which will react with it, to proliferate and liberate their characteristic antibody.

(3) Except under quite abnormal conditions one cell produces only one type of antibody.

(4) All descendants of an antibody-producing cell produce the same type of antibody.

(5) There is a genetic mechanism [Burnet preferred somatic mutation] capable of generating in random fashion a wide but not infinite range of patterns, so that there will be at least some cells that can react with any foreign material which enters the body. (1968, p. 213)

By the early 1970s, after the clonal selection theory had become the accepted theory, a number of facts had become known about antibodies and their structure, but the "genetic mechanism" named in assumption 5 above was still to be elucidated. The role of antibodies in the immune response was fairly well understood, and the structure of antibodies was being pursued down to the molecular level. Antibodies, also termed immunoglobulins, were known to be proteins and to possess a general common four chain structure (see Leder, 1994 for a current view of the structure that is not dissimilar to what was known by about 1970). There are essentially five different classes of immunoglobulins, though one of them IgG, usually written as γG and spoken of as gamma globulin, is a good prototype. The structure can be roughly visualized as a bifurcated letter "Y" with an additional line parallel to each of the top lines [`Y´]. The bifurcated Y proper consists of the two identical heavy chains of approximately 440 amino acids (in the case of IgG). The shorter lines parallel to the top of the Y are the two identical light chains of approximately 214 amino acids. These four chains are held together by chemical linkages known as disulfide or S-S bonds. Both the heavy and the light chains are analyzable into two regions, one known as a constant region (C region) and the other as a variable region (V region). In γG1 light chains, the V region is about 108 amino acids in length. The common functions of antibody molecules, e.g. complement fixation, are controlled by the constant region, whereas the *specificity* or the ability to discriminantly recognize antigens resides in the variable regions.

By 1970, a small number of amino acid sequences of the light chains of immunoglobulin molecules had been determined by various investigators (see Weigart et al, 1970). These light chains were obtained from certain types of cancerous tumors of mice and humans known as myelomas. Since normal immunoglobulins are too heterogeneous in structure to enable careful sequence work on the successive positions of amino acids to be done, most data on immunoglobin sequences at this time, and this primarily on light chains of the molecule, was based on the myeloma globulins.

The determination of a number of sequences of amino acids in such light chains constituted a major part of the *empirical* base of various competing theories of antibody diversity. A number of sequences were at that time in the early 1970s compared and were postulated to fall *into* what are known as "types" and subgroups." The light chains in humans, mice, and most mammals fall into two serologically and chemically distinguishable main types known as kappa (κ) and lambda (λ). Most antibodies in the frequently used mouse model appeared to be of the κ type (about 95%). Work which commenced in the mid-1970s brought molecular methods of gene counting, and then gene cloning, to bear on the questions how many antibody genes there were in the inherited genome, and how the apparently huge repertoire of different types of antibody might be generated.

B. *The Genetic Source of Antibody Diversity.* Since antibody molecules are proteins, and since it was then well known that genes (DNA) synthesize proteins via a rather elaborate collection of cellular machinery, the question as to the source of antibody diversity was thought to be best approached by examining various possible *genetic* mechanisms or theories of diversity.

There are essentially two major types of genetic theories which had been proposed by 1970 to account for antibody diversity, as well as several subvariants. The two major classes of theories — classes which Kindt and Capra (1984) refer to as polar opposites — were (1) the pure germline theory (sometimes referred to as the multigene theory) and (2) the somatic mutation theory (occasionally termed the paucigene theory since it assumed only about 50 antibody-producing genes in contrast to some 20,000 required by the pure germline theory). The germline theory also had a variant which reduced somewhat the number of genes required. The somatic mutation theory itself was often further subdivided into (i) a somatic hypermutation theory and (ii) somatic mutation theories with (either "positive" or "negative") selection (Brenner and Milstein, 1966; Cohn, 1970; Jerne, 1971). Further, there were several other paucigene theories, and one developed by Edelman and Gally (1967; 1970), and termed the recombination theory, actually seems to come closest to the main mechanism for diversity generation that emerged from the molecular investigations. In the following paragraphs I sketch three of these alternative theories of diversity.

(1) *The germline theory.* This theory was first proposed by Szilard in 1960 and later variants of it were developed by Dreyer and Bennett (1965), Hood and Talmage (1970), and others. In its simplest form it proposes that each heavy chain and each light chain possesses germline genes in which thousands of paired V and C genes lie adjacent to each other. This theory requires the largest number of different genes. The precise number of different genes required was not known, but if one assumes 10^8 different antibody types, as its proponents did, then even assuming that the genes coding for the variable regions of both light chains (V_L) and the heavy chains (V_H) can combine with each other in an unrestricted fashion, 2 x 10^4 different "V" genes, or genes coding for the variable region, would be required (10^4 V_L x 10^4 $V_H = 10^8$).

One problem much discussed by immunologists during the 1960s and into the 1970s related to the common character of the C genes in antibodies: the C gene acted as if it were one gene (it behaved in a simple Mendelian manner) whereas there appeared to be many different V genes (whether these were believed to be in the germline or in somatically mutated cells). This "paradox" was noted by Dreyer and Bennett in their (1965) paper, who proposed the then very radical hypothesis that either a single light or a heavy chain is based on genetic information provided by two different (and separated) genes, one for the constant region of the chain and the other for the variable region. This hypothesis was in sharp conflict with the "one gene — one polypeptide" chain dogma of the time, and was also one for which no precedent mechanism was then known. As we shall see below, tests of this paradoxical hypothesis served to motivate many of the molecular investigations in the mid- to late-1970s. In spite of its paradoxical character, the Dreyer-Bennett hypothesis was incorporated into several variants of both the germline theory and somatic mutation theories by several immunologists.

The flavor of this modified germline theory incorporating the Dreyer-Bennett hypothesis can be obtained from the following quotation from two immunologists writing in 1970:

> ...each organism has one variable gene in its germ line for each unique antibody polypeptide chain it can synthesize and...a separate gene encodes each type of common [or constant] region. During somatic differentiation of the immunocyte, a single variable gene or its product is joined to the common gene or its product at some stage of protein synthesis, and the resulting differentiated immunocyte synthesizes one type of light chain and, presumably by a similar mechanism, one type of heavy chain. According to this theory, the variable genes arise by the normal process of chemical evolution, that is, gene duplication followed by mutation and selection. (Hood and Talmage, 1970)

(2) *The somatic mutation theory.* This theory in its most general form proposed that the source of antibody diversity was somatic mutations in the V gene regions, only a

few copies (40—50) of which needed to occur in the organism's germline. This was the mechanism favored by proponents of the selective theories of the late 1950's, such as Burnet and Lederberg. Such a theory was often termed a "hypermutational" theory because of the need for very frequent mutations to generate the 10^6 to 10^8 different antibody types. In response to the widely voiced criticism that such a theory was unlikely because it could not account for the restriction of mutational diversity to the V regions only, Brenner and Milstein (1966) proposed a plausible mechanism that would accomplish such a restriction.

Two other variants of this approach were also proposed in the late 1960s and early 1970s. Eschewing a hypermutational mechanism, both Cohn (1970) and Jerne (1971) suggested that normal mutational rates plus *strong selection* pressures could account for antibody diversity. Jerne differed from Cohn in that he proposed a more standard type of "negative selection" mechanism whereas Cohn seemed to prefer what he termed a "positive mechanism of selection for diversity." Both Jerne's and Cohn's theories of antibody diversity are also part of their more general accounts of the immune system which touched on mechanisms for the self-nonself distinction and the ontogeny of the immune response.

(3) *The somatic recombination theory*. This theory was first proposed in an early form by Smithies(1963) but was most forcefully championed in the late 1960s and early 1970s by Edelman and Gally (1967; 1970). It assumed fewer germline genes than did the theory characterized above, and generated the requisite genetic diversity by postulating a joint process of genetic translocation plus recombination. As noted, most of the theories of antibody diversity accepted the need for some Dreyer-Bennett mechanism which would translocate the V gene next to the C gene prior to transcription and translation of the joined V-C genetic region. A theory that utilizes a mechanism of translocation for recombination, and thus diversity, would account for two well known processes by one mechanism. Gally and Edelman characterized the essence of their theory as follows:

> The theory assumes that vertebrate genomes contain several tandemly arranged V genes which arose by gene duplication and have acquired their diversity by the accumulation of point mutations, but they are capable of intrachromosomal somatic recombination to generate new nucleotide sequences. (Gally and Edelman, 1970)

This recombination, it is suggested, *might* be generated by a gene translocation process that is similar to the formation of episomes in lysogenic bacteriophage. The somatic recombination theory, though it does not require one V gene per light chain or heavy chain (~20,000 germline genes), still required between 10 and 100 genes per subgroup, averaging out to approximately 500 or so germline genes.

In the years 1970-1975 little resolution of the problem as to which theory was correct occurred, though there continued to be extensive debates on the issue (see Cohn, 1994 and also Kindt and Capra, 1984, for details). Steps toward a choice between the contrasting theories fell to the molecular biologists to accomplish, and it is to this part of the story that I now turn.

3. Molecular Methodologies

A. *Gene Counting*. In the early 1970s several groups turned their attention toward using molecular biology to obtain a more finely structured picture of how antibodies were synthesized. I will concentrate on two of those research groups who continued their investigations throughout the 1970s (see Kindt and Capra, 1984, for additional groups' contributions). Both groups, one associated with Susumu Tonegawa at the Basel Institute in Switzerland, and the other with Philip Leder at the NIH, began by attempting to count the number of genes responsible for antibody production by using recently developed molecular methods of RNA-DNA hybridization. Leder in his (1982, 4) writes that "in 1971 I set to work with my colleague David C. Swan ... to test the Dreyer-Bennet hypothesis." Tonegawa in his Nobel Prize essay writes that :

> In the early seventies the technology for purifying a specific eucaryotic mRNA was just becoming available. Furthermore a method to determine the number of copies of a specific gene by kinetic analysis of nucleic acid hybridization had already been established [here there are references to the work of Britten and his colleagues on RNA-DNA hybridization studies in the mouse and to Bishopís hybridization work on bacteria and phage]. These technical developments led some scientists, including myself to think that one can experimentally determine the number of immunoglobulin genes contained in the germline genome and thereby decide which of the two major theories of antibody diversity is correct. (1988, p. 254)

Tonegawa's initial experiments were focused on mouse κ light chain and heavy chain genes (see Tonegawa et al, 1974) and supported a paucigene theory, but he suggests that they were not very satisfactory (he terms them ìambiguous"). "The difficulty," he states, "was primarily due to the uncertainty about the purity of the mRNA used as the hybridization probe as well as a lack of knowledge on the extent to which a probe will hybridize with the related but not identical genes [recall he was looking for similarity and diversity] and the precise effect of sequence differences on hybridization kinetics" (1988, 254). Leder's group focused on the Dreyer-Bennet hypothesis and confirmed that there were only two or three C region genes, but could not rule out, with the techniques then available, the presence of perhaps "thousands of variable region sequences" (Leder et al., 1974).

However a later series of experiments by Tonegawa, published in 1976, that examined the gene coding for the mouse λ light chains, was successful. Using some mRNA that was at least 95% pure, Tonegawa showed that the mouse λ light chain gene was present at most two to three times, and possibly only once. In 1970 Weigert, Cohn, and their associates (Weigert et al., 1970), had laboriously, given the techniques available at that time, identified at least eight different V_λ sequences in mouse myelomas, sequences that were strongly homologous with each other, and which thus should crosshybridize if they existed in the germline. A statistical analysis provided strong evidence that this type of mouse has the capacity to synthesize many more than eight different V_λ sequences. Tonegawa adds that "On the basis of these results, I was convinced that a somatic diversification occurs in this gene system" (1988, 254).

This work thus represents the beginnings — but only the beginnings — of an *empirical* solution to the choice between the various theories of diversity discussed above. The molecular hybridization techniques that were the basis of this work continued to be controversial. Kindt and Capra (1984, 174-180) review the vigorous methodological debate revolving around hybridization techniques, and note that even at the 1977 meeting at Cold Spring Harbor, a paper presented by Smith (1977) asserted these results constituted "only rather weak evidence against the germline theory." Kindt and Capra add that these reservations were shared by "many immunologists" (1984, p. 179).

B. *Gene Rearrangement and the Use of Restriction Enzymes*. Hybridization techniques were also used by Tonegawa and Hozumi (1976) in a somewhat different way to test the Dreyer-Bennett hypothesis by comparing DNA from a mouse embryo with the DNA from a (mature mouse) plasmacytoma. In this case Tonegawa believed that the hybridization of probes would best follow the use of restriction enzymes to cut the long mouse genome into many smaller fragments. These fragments could then be electrophoretically separated and examined using the refined hybridization technique. Both mouse embryos and mouse myelomas were examined by Tonegawa, who found that the DNA from the two sources were "drastically different." This was, moreover, consistent with the Dreyer-Bennett hypothesis, suggesting DNA rejoining of the V and C regions, i.e., gene shuffling had occurred. These results were reported at the

1976 Cold Spring Harbor Symposium (and also in the October number of the PNAS that year) (See Tonegawa, 1988, p. 255; Tonegawa et al., 1976; Hozumi and Tonegawa, 1976). This inquiry was then later reconfirmed by using the now more standard Southern blot technique.

C. *Joining of Gene Segments and Recombinant DNA Techniques and Cloning of the Immunoglobulin Gene*. Our final chapter in this much longer inquiry involves clarifying how the gene rearrangement occurs, and ultimately, what this says concerning a germline or somatic theory for antibody diversity. Tonegawa understood that more details regarding the production of antibodies were necessary, and, as did Leder, looked to the new — and then quite controversial — technology of recombinant DNA. (Leder wrote concerning this cloning technology that "In 1973 ... the first successful application of new recombinant DNA techniques to insert foreign DNA into a bacterium or a bacterial virus [occurred, permitting one to]... clone a single gene in quantity. It was immediately clear that those of us working with more cumbersome genetic techniques that gene cloning would enable us to isolate antibody genes and determine their structure in a direct way" (Leder, 1982, p. 6).)

Believing that it would be wisest to begin with "the simplest of all chain types studied," as well as with that type with which he had previously had gotten clear results, Tonegawa started with the mouse λ light chain system. His goal was "to clone the V_λ and C_λ "genes" in the germline state from embryonic cells, as well as the rearranged V plus C "genes" from a λ myeloma and to determine the relationship between the relationship between these genomic DNA clones by electromicroscopy and DNA sequencing" (1988, 255). Leder's group meanwhile pursued work on what they believed to be the more representative system (recall that in the mouse about 95% of the light chains are of the κ type).

Tonegawa adds that "no precedent existed at that time for cloning "unique" eucaryotic genes" and that therefore they first had to "devise a few tricks" to accomplish their goal. The "tricks" involved further purification of the mRNA probes then still in use to avoid background noise — cDNA probes which are much more specific were not yet available. Tonegawa also needed to obtain a cloning vehicle, a phage λ which came from Lederís laboratory (see Leder, 1982, p. 6). Working with Christine Brack (his electromicroscopist), Tonegawa obtained evidence that they had cloned a V_λ(gene to which no C gene was contiguously attached (Tonegawa et al., 1977). This was then subsequently confirmed using the new rapid DNA sequencing technique developed by Maxam and Gilbert (see Tonegawa et al., 1978, an article that Kindt and Capra say reported what is "probably the key experiment in the modern era of molecular immunology" (1984, 200)). In the December 1977 PNAS article by Brack and Tonegawa, a surprise was reported. The long title of the article stated the result: "Variable and constant parts of the immunoglobulin light chain gene of a mouse myeloma are 1250 nontranslated bases apart" (Brack and Tonegawa, 1977, p. 5652). Tonegawa wrote in 1988 that this was among "the first demonstrations of an intron in eucaryotic genes (1988, 255).

There was also another surprise that emerged from this cloning work. The V gene identified in the germline genome turned out to be about 13 codons shorter than in the mature genome. The missing 13 codons were located in an unsuspected region many thousands of bases away from the "incomplete" V gene sequence and a few kilobases upstream of the C gene. This was interpreted as evidence for a new J or "joining" gene, and was, according to Tonegawa, "completely unexpected." However, he adds:

As soon as this discovery was made its implications for the somatic generation of antibody diversity was obvious. If the germline genome carries multiple copies of different V and J gene segments, the number of complete V "genes" that can be generated by random joinings between these two types of gene segments would be much greater than the total number of inherited gene segments. Thus contrary to the Dreyer and Bennett original concept [which favored a germline theory], DNA rearrangement can provide a major means for the somatic diversification of antibody molecules. (Tonegawa, 1988, pp. 255-256)

This concept was further confirmed with work on the mouse κ gene segment in both Tonegawa's and Leder's laboratory, and constituted the basis for extensive additional work on this mechanism of diversity generation. In the next few years, research in Leder's, Hood's, Tonegawa's and other groups' labs disclosed the existence of another D (for diversity) gene in heavy chains (see Leder, 1982; Tonegawa, 1988; and Kindt and Capra, 1984, 195-198). Leder recently wrote that the existence of the V, C, J, and D genes allows an organism's genetic system, which probably contains only about 300 germ line genes, to generate some 18 billion different antibody possibilities by recombination (1994, 93).

Though it appears that a recombination mechanism is the principal generator of antibody diversity, somatic mutation has also been confirmed in antibody diversity generation, though this is not a topic I can pursue in the present paper (see Paul, 1993, ch. 23). In addition, we also have, in a sense, a multigenetic germline (but of only 300 genes) that serves as the basic source of antibody formation. Transformed and integrated, then, all three theories mentioned earlier, have been discovered to be involved in the complete picture of antibody diversity generation.

4. Generalizations and Philosophical Implications of this Case Study

This episode in the history of recent immunology has a number of interesting implications for philosophical analyses of the biological sciences. I provisionally divide the implications into two categories, reflecting the process and the outcome of the research programs on the generation of antibody diversity.

A. *Process-related Implications*. The molecular biologists mwho pursued a solution to the mystery of the generation of antibody diversity in the years 1971-1979 found themselves having to develop or fine-tune a set of developing technologies, and to struggle to achieve a stability of results that was broadly consistent with several investigational methodologies. These investigators thus confronted similar problems discussed in recent philosophy of science under the headings of the use of multiple experimental techniques or robustness (see Culp, 1994, for references). I quoted Tonegawa earlier concerning his view that the DNA-RNA hybridization experiments, which were the first approach the molecular biologists pursued, were "ambiguous" because of the lack of "purity" of the mRNA. In their account of the dispute over this technique, Kindt and Capra (1984, 174-180) re-present graphical data using "Cot" curves that indicate the significant effect of the purity of the samples tested on the interpretation of the results. ("Cot" curves plot percent hybridization against the logarithm of the product of the DNA concentration (Co) and the time (t).) In his initial use of restriction endonucleases and electrophoretic separation, Tonegawa found he had to improvise with great difficulty a technology that later became standardized through the Southern blot technique. Weigert et al.'s laborious (1970) amino acid sequencing of the (light chains was eventually replaced by rapid sequencing of DNA, developed in 1977 by Maxam and Gilbert and also by Sanger et al. (see Schaffner, 1993, 455-456 for details), that has now become a standard part of the toolkit of every molecular biologist. Similar problems were encountered in developing and applying cloning methods to the antibody diversity problem as indicated in the text earlier.

The evolution of these combined technological-experimental methods suggest three theses:

(1) Pursuing a higher degree of experimental resolution of the principal entities occurring in an incomplete biological theory can clarify and not (fully) replace the assumptions of the theory.

(2) The experimental techniques will frequently require the adoption of technologies developed in closely related fields, and will often foreshadow the development of a stable set of technologies available to the area being investigated. These technologies may then become what Latour (1967, 131) calls a black box, but only after a period of critical scrutiny.[5]

(3) The set of developed technologies will be applied to similar systems (in our example it was the κ and λ light chains, and then the heavy chains) to yield a set of overlapping results that both secure the foundations of the theory and bolster the trust of the scientific community in the associated technologies.

The set of developed technologies that emerged from what I referred to in the historical review as "recombinant DNA methods" has become an extraordinarily powerful "technology" (see Alberts at al., 1994). This set of methods provided in a number of cases what investigators such as Tonegawa called "direct evidence" for a speculative hypothesis such as the Dreyer-Bennett proposal, or for new types of genes (the J and D genes). Since the work of Pierre Duhem (1914) almost a century ago, philosophers have been sensitive to the fact that experiments do not really provide direct or unmediated observation, and more recently sociologists of science such as Latour and Woolgar (1979/1986) have employed the complexity of experimental observations in the service of a constructivist view of scientific "reality."

I see the situation as presented in the episode presented above from a middle position. Whether an experiment can be classified as yielding direct or indirect evidence for an ontology would seem to depend on such factors as (1) the degree of scientists' confidence in the auxiliary hypotheses (including control of the initial conditions) used in obtaining the observable implication and (2) the existence (or nonexistence) of proposed plausible competing hypotheses, with an inconsistent ontology, accounting for the same observations. The issue of the "directness" of evidence has been the subject of several inquiries into experiments and sophisticated examples of "observation" in the past ten years, including the work of Shapere (1982) and Galison (1987), and though most of this philosophical discussion has focused on examples from the physical sciences, the analyses have relevance for biology and medicine.

This view I prefer (see my 1993, 156-165 and 194-200 for details) seems to be in general agreement with Galison's (1987) discussion of the *directness* of measurements, and what he terms the *stability* of experimental results — an account that also appears to involve *comparative* concepts. I see this type of analysis as supporting a kind of provisional or "conditionalized" realism, where the provisos depend on the availability of plausible competitor hypotheses asserting inconsistent alternative ontologies that can account for a diverse aggregate of experimental "observations." In the absence of viable challengers to the explanatory ontology, scientists (and philosophers) accept the ontology of the prevailing theory, and use the term "direct evidence" for an experiment that measures a core property of that theory's ontology that cannot be accounted for by a competing theory with a different ontology.

What we encounter, then, in the evolution of the antibody diversity story is the ever-growing and thickening web of experimentation and generalizable, robust technologies that make it extraordinarily difficult to find plausible alternative accounts for the principal way by which antibody diversity is generated. This stability and increasing stubbornness of the evidence develops along with the consolidation of the biological technologies, that in turn have found application in very diverse areas of basic research as well as economically important fields of practical applications, such as agriculture and medicine.

B. *Outcome-related Implications*. The relationship between more traditional biology (and medicine) and molecular biology (and molecular medicine) has occasionally been a fractious one. This fractiousness also extends to philosophical analyses of the relation between the more biological and the more chemical approaches in the life sciences. There is an extensive literature on this topic, much of it involving discussions of "reduction," but in recent years some writers (Kitcher, 1984; Culp and Kitcher, 1989; Bechtel and Richardson, 1993, 242-243) have urged that we change our vocabulary for referring to biochemical explanations of nonchemical biological knowledge. Culp and Kitcher (1989, 479) write "the intertheoretic relationships that philosophers have often tried to describe in terms of reduction are best reconceived in terms of the embedding of the problem-solving schemata of one field of science in those of another," a process they call an "explanatory extension." Part of the discomfort these authors feel with the term "reduction" arises from the fact that the traditional model of reduction appeals to "laws" and axiomatized theories which seem foreign to most of biology (Nagel, 1961). Another aspect of the argument suggests that biology is too specific even to consider developing the *bridge laws*, connecting the biological with the chemical in precise ways, required by the Nagel model.

In the episode discussed in the present paper, we have a plausible test in which a molecular explanation of antibody diversity is developed. A reasonable question thus poses itself: is the mechanism proposed and elaborated by Tonegawa, Leder and others in any sense a "bridge law" that connects the biological theory of clonal selection (as proposed by Burnet in 1959) with molecular biology?

I think that characterizing the relations between theories formulated at different levels of aggregation requires a much more complex set of categories than most of the debate in this area has considered. I provided some suggestions in my (1993, 487-500) for beginning to treat the varying ways we can analyze these relations, some of which do fit a modified form of the Nagel model of reduction. Frequently, however, and especially for still changing biological theories, the fit is not an easy one. Part of the problem arises from the pervasive interlevel character of biological theories, and part of the problem arises from the variation of biological systems and their resistance to capture in any simple generalizations with broad scope. In cases in which partial reductions involving interlevel theories are involved, even when the reduced theory can be axiomatized, the reticulate or weblike character of the *reducing* science will make any listing of explanatory generalizations and exceptions a Herculean (but not impossible) task. (If it was impossible, we would not have fine textbooks such as Alberts et al., 1994, nor adequately comprehensive collections of major review papers like Paul's 1993.)

Oddly, the story concerning the explanation of antibody diversity fits a Nagel-like model better than most biological examples. The clonal selection theory can be, and was, axiomatized. Burnet introduced, in effect, the five axioms of the theory in the quote from him earlier (second and third page of this manuscript) on the essential elements of the theory, and the axiomatization can be further elaborated as a more explicitly interlevel theory (see my 1992 and 1993, p. 222-223). In the historical story related in the present paper, Burnet's 5th axiom is explained (but in a modified and partially replaced form) as a consequence of a complex recombinational (largely non-somatic mutation) mechanism that provides the requisite diversity. But an explanatory mechanism, such as this, was never intended to be part of a "bridge law"; rather the mechanism (or more accurately theory) was articulated to *explain* the chemically characterized diversity as a causal consequence. The bridge law (I will use that terminology though it is misleading ; "connectability assumptions" is a better term) in this case is *an identification* — an (implicit) elaboration of the *biological* notion of immunological diversity — in terms of the enormous *chemical repertoire* of antibody molecule types. For reasons already mentioned, however, we have no easy recourse to an axiomatization of molecular biology, or even molecular immunology, though as biology continues to increase in complexity, we may find it necessary to formulate this knowledge base in a computer program language, and this would be tantamount to such an axiomatization (for recent approaches to a computational molecular biology see the papers in Hunter, 1993).

Though the antibody diversity story receives some clarification in terms of quasi-formal reduction models — the model points to where the identifications occur, and also to what more is needed to make an explanation explicit — the story at the present time is necessarily incomplete. In such circumstances it is also appropriate to characterize the outcome as a "partial reduction" — in which the amplification and causal explanation of one of the hypotheses of the clonal selection theory in sophisticated molecular terms occurs (Schaffner, 1993, 498). The evolved and amplified theory in such an account continues to remain interlevel, since not all aspects of the cells constituting the immune system have yet been able to be characterized in purely molecular terms. This approach may be what Culp and Kitcher were urging in recommending we think of reductions better as "explanatory extensions," than as "reductions," though I think Kitcher's (1989) interpretation of this notion within his unification model has limits (see my 1993, 312-313 and 500). It may just be a matter of semantics whether we characterize this episode as an "explanatory extension" or as a "partial theory reduction," but I am not confident that Culp and Kitcher would agree with this view, and suspect that we have not yet seen the end of wrangling about philosophical terminology in this (still fractious) area.

Notes

[1]I would like to express my gratitude to Drs. Philip Leder and Susumu Tonegawa for providing copies of their reprints. Partially supported by the National Science Foundation's Studies in Science, Technology, and Society Program. This paper is a short version of a much more detailed chapter in an in-progress book on theory structure and research strategies in molecular biology. Due to stringent space considerations, historical references have had to be kept to an absolute minimum, but a full bibliography is available from the author on request.

[2]I will describe what I mean by "far-too-limited laboratory data" later in this article. One of the most positive responses I had to that unpublished essay, entitled "Criteria of Theory Evaluation in Immunology" was a five page handwritten letter from Dick Levins, who at the time was a colleague of mine at the University of Chicago. That critically constructive letter stimulated many questions, and continued reflection on them yielded themes that found their way into later articles of mine.

[3]In his 1982 article Leder suggests that "the solution of the puzzle [how antibody diversity is generated] is now emerging" (1982, 2), and in the 1994 updated version of this essay he refers to the work in 1974-1984 as providing the "answer" (p. 83). I also use the expression "significantly clarified," rather than "solved" here, however, because though we now know an extraordinary amount about how antibody diversity is generated, immunologists still seem to feel that not all aspects of the regulatory mechanisms have been fully understood. In their Preface to their extensively detailed account of the history of antibody diversity, Kindt and Capra (1984) write that they believed it was not then possible to call their book *The Solution to the Question of Antibody Diversity*, and settled instead on titling it *The Antibody Enigma* (p. x). (I thank Sylvia Culp for bringing this book to my attention.) A review of some very recent summary articles on this topic, e.g., in Paul's (1993) collection, esp. chs. 10 and 23, continues to confirm this sense that the understanding of antibody diversity generators is still evolving.

[4]The clonal selection theory is examined from several perspectives in my (1993, chs. 2, 3, and 5); also see Silverstein (1989) and Mazumdar (1994) for the more general historical backdrop, as well as Tauber's (1994) very recent account of The Clonal Selection Theory.

[5]Rheinberger (1992, 311) argues that this scrutiny *never* realy ends, and reexamination of the fundamental processes is always available, and thus prefers his own term of "technological object " for a standardized experimental routine.

References

Alberts, B. et al. (1994), *Molecular Biology of the Cell.* 3rd edit. New York: Garland.

Bechtel, W. and Richardson, R. (1993), *Discovering Complexity: Decomposition and Localization as Strategies in Scientific Research.* Princeton: Princeton University Press.

Brack, C. and Tonegawa, S. (1976), "Variable and Constant Parts of the Immunoglobulin Light Chain Gene of a Mouse Myeloma are 1250 Nontranslated Bases Apart," *Proceedings of the National Academy of Sciences* USA, 73: 5652-5656.

Brenner, S. and Milstein, C. (1966), "Origin of Antibody Variation", *Nature* 211: 242-243.

Burnet, F.M. (1957), "A Modification of Jerne's Theory of Antibody Production Using the Concept of Clonal Selection", *The Australian Journal of Science* 20: 67-69.

______. (1959), *The Clonal Selection Theory of Acquired Immunity.* Nashville: Vanderbilt University Press.

______. (1968), *Changing Patterns.* Melbourne: William Heinemann.

Cohn, M. (1970), "Selection under a Somatic Model", *Cellular Immunology* 1: 461-467.

_____. (1994), "The Wisdom of Hindsight", *Annual Review of Immunology* 12: 1-62.

Culp, S. (1994) "Defending Robustness: the Bacterial Mesosome as a Test Case," in D. Hull, M. Forbes, and R. M. Burian *PSA 1994* vol 1. East Lansing: Philosophy of Science Association. Pp. 46-57.

Culp, S. and Kitcher, P. (1989), "Theory Structure and Theory Change in Contemporary Molecular Biology," *British Journal for the Philosophy of Science* 40: 459-483.

Darden, L. (1991), *Theory Change:in Science: Strategies from Mendelian Genetics.* New York: Oxford University Press.

Dreyer, W.J. and Bennett, J.C. (1965), "The Molecular Basis of Antibody Formation: A Paradox", *Proceedings of the National Academy of Sciences* USA 54: 864-869.

Duhem, P. (1914), *Aim and Structure of Physical Theory.* 2d ed. Translated by P. P. Wiener. New York: Atheneum Publishers.

Edelman, G.M. and Gally, J.A. (1967), "Somatic Recombination of Duplicated Genes: An Hypothesis on the Origin of Antibody Diversity", *Proceedings of the National Academy of Sciences* USA 57: 353-358.

Galison, P. (1987), *How Experiments End.* Chicago: University of Chicago Press.

Gally, J.A. and Edelman, G.M. (1970), "Somatic Translocation of Antibody Genes", *Nature* 227: 341.

Honjo, T.; Packman, S.; Swan, D.; Nau, M.; and Leder, P. (1974), "Organization of Immunoglobulin Genes: Reiteration Frequency of Mouse k Chain Constant Region", *Proceedings of the National Academy of Sciences* USA 71: 3659-3663.

Hood, L. and Talmage, D. (1970), "Mechanisms of Antibody Diversity: Germ Line Basis for Variability", *Science* 168: 325-334.

Hozumi, N. and Tonegawa, S. (1976), "Evidence for Somatic Rearrangement of Immunoglobulin Genes Coding for Variable and Constant Regions," *Proceedings of the National Academy of Sciences* USA 73: 3628-3632.

Hunter, L. (ed.) (1993), *Artificial Intelligence and Molecular Biology*. Menlo Park, CA and Cambridge, MA: AAAI and MIT Press.

Jerne, N.K. (1955), "The Natural-Selection Theory of Antibody Formation", *Proceedings of the National Academy of Sciences* USA 41: 849-857.

______. (1971), "The Somatic Generation of Immune Recognition", *European Journal of Immunology* 1: 1-9.

Kindt, T.J. and Capra, J. D. (1984), *The Antibody Enigma*. New York: Plenum Press.

Kitcher, P. (1989), "Explanatory Unification and the Causal Structure of the World," in P. Kitcher and W. Salmon (eds.) *Scientific Explanation*. Minneapolis: University of Minnesota Press, pp. 410-505.

Knorr-Cetina, K. (1981), *The Manufacture of Knowledge*. Oxford: Pergamon Press.

Landsteiner, K. (1945 [1933]), *The Specificity of Serological Reactions*. Rev. ed. Cambridge: Harvard University Press.

Latour, B. (1987), *Science in Action*.Cambridge: Harvard University Press.

Latour, B. and Woolgar, S. (1979/1986), *Laboratory Life: The Construction of Scientific Facts*. Princeton: Princeton University Press (2nd edit. publ. 1986).

Leder, P.; Honjo, T.; Packman, S.; and Swan, D. (1974), "The Organization and Diversity of Immunoglobulin Genes", *Proceedings of the National Academy of Sciences* USA 71: 5109-5115.

Leder, P. (1982), "The Genetics of Antibody Diversity", *Scientific American* 246: 102-115. (Page references are to the reprint.)

_____. (1994), "The Genetic Basis of Antibody Diversity," in P. Leder, D. Clayton, and E. Rubenstein (eds.) *Scientific American Introduction to Molecular Medicine*. New York: Scientific American, Inc., pp. 83-102.

Lederberg, J. (1959), "Genes and Antibodies", *Science* 129: 1649-1653.

Mazumdar, P.M. (1994), *Species and Specificity*. New York: Cambridge University Press.

Nagel, E. (1961), *The Structure of Science*. New York: Harcourt, Brace & Co.

Paul, W.E. (ed.) (1993), *Fundamental Immunology*. 3rd edit. New York: Raven Press.

Rheinberger, H-J. (1992), "Experiment, Difference and Writing: I.: Tracing Protein Synthesis; II.: The Laboratory Production of Transfer RNA," *Studies in History and Philosophy of Science*, 23: 305-333 and 389-422.

Schaffner, K.F. (1970), "Outlines of a Logic of Comparative Theory Evaluation with Special Attention to Pre-and Post-Relativistic Electrodynamics", in R. Stuewer, (ed.) *Historical and Philosophical Perspectives of Science.*

Minnesota Studies in the Philosophy of Science, vol. 5. Minneapolis: University of Minnesota Press, pp. 311-364.

________. (1992), "Theory Change in Immunology: The Clonal Selection Theory -- Part I: Theory Change and Scientific Progress; Part II: The Clonal Selection Theory" *Theoretical Medicine*, 13, No. 2 (June): 191-216.

________. (1993), *Discovery and Explanation in Biology and Medicine*. Chicago: University of Chicago Press.

Shapere, D. (1982), "The Concept of Observation in Science and Philosophy," *Philosophy of Science* 49: 485-525.

Silverstein, A.M. (1989), *A History of Immunology*. San Diego: Academic Press.

Smith, G.P. (1977), "The Signficance of Hybridization Kinetic Experiments for Theories of Antibody Diversity", *Cold Spring Harbor Symposia on Quantitative Biology* 41: 863-875.

Smithies, O. (1963), "Gamma-Globulin Variability: A Genetic Hypothesis", *Nature* 199: 1231-1236.

Talmage, D.W. (1957), "Allergy and Immunology", *Annual Review of Medicine* 8: 239-256.

________. (1972), "Immunological Factors", *Report in Nature* 236: 203-204.

Tauber, A.I. (1994), *The Immune Self: Theory or Metaphor?* Cambridge, UK: Cambridge University Press.

Tonegawa, S.; Steinberg, C.; Dube, S.; and Bernardini, A. (1974), "Evidence for Somatic Generation of Antibody Diversity", *Proceedings of the National Academy of Sciences* USA 71: 4027-4031.

Tonegawa, S.; Hozumi, N.; Matthyssens, G.; and Schuller, R. (1976), "Somatic Changes in the Content and Context of Immunoglobulin Genes", *Cold Spring Harbor Symposia on Quantitative Biology* 41: 877-889.

Tonegawa, S.; Brack, C. Hozumi, N. and Schuller, R. (1977), "Cloning of an Immunoglobulin Variable Region Gene from Mouse Embryo," *Proceedings of the National Academy of Sciences* USA 74: 3518-3522.

Tonegawa, S.; Maxam, A.M.; Tizard, R.; Bernard, O.; and Gilbert, W. (1978), "Sequence of a Mouse Germ-Line Gene for a Variable Region of an Immunoglobulin Light Chain", *Proceedings of the National Academy of Sciences* USA 75: 1485-1489.

Weigert, M., Cesari, I,, Yonkovich, S. and Cohn, M. (1970), “Variability in the Lambda Light Chain Sequences of Mouse Antibody.” *Nature* 228: 1045-1047.

Part VII

FOUNDATIONAL PROJECTS IN MATHEMATICS AT THE BEGINNING OF THE 20TH CENTURY IN THEIR SYSTEMATIC AND HISTORICAL CONTEXTS

The Contemporary Interest of an old Doctrine[1]

William Demopoulos

The University of Western Ontario

My purpose in this talk is to give an overview of the rediscovery of Frege's theorem together with certain of the issues that this rediscovery has raised concerning the evaluation of Frege's logicism—the 'old doctrine' of my title.

1. Frege's theorem

The contextual definition of the cardinality operator, suggested in §63 of *Grundlagen*—what, after George Boolos, has come to be known as Hume's principle[2]—asserts

The number of Fs = the number of Gs if, and only if, $F \approx G$,

where $F \approx G$ (the Fs and the Gs are in one-to-one correspondence) has its usual, second-order, explicit definition. The importance of this principle for the derivation of Peano's second postulate ('Every natural number has a successor') was emphasized by Crispin Wright (1983, §xix) who presented an extended argument showing that, in the context of the system of second-order logic of Frege's *Begriffsschrift*, Peano's second postulate is derivable from Hume's principle. And in a review of Wright's book, John Burgess (1984) proved Wright's conjecture that Hume's principle is consistent.

The significance of Wright's proof, as he himself observed, is that the argument proceeds without any appeal to a theory of sets; in particular it does not rely on the inconsistent theory of extensions of concepts implicit in *Grundlagen*.[3] Boolos (1987) later showed in detail how, in *Grundlagen* §§68 - 83, Frege had already established Wright's result, and proposed that we call Frege's discovery that, in the context of second-order logic, Hume's principle implies the infinity of the natural numbers, *Frege's theorem.*

In *Grundgesetze* concepts are treated as a special type of function (after the proposal of Frege's lecture, *Function and concept*), and what in *Grundlagen* is called the extension of a concept is, in *Grundgesetze*, represented by the notion of the value range of the function corresponding to the concept. Basic Law V, explicitly formulated in *Grundgesetze* I, §20, implies that the extension of the concept F = the extension of the concept G if, and only if, everything falling under F falls under G, and conversely, everything falling under G falls under F. Richard Heck (1993) has recently investigated how, in *Grundgesetze*, Hume's principle may be deployed in the proof of Frege's theorem without the use of Basic Law V.

PSA 1994, Volume 2, pp. 209-216

There can be no question that the rediscovery of Frege's theorem is of the greatest importance for our appreciation of Frege's mathematical achievement. It nevertheless remains unclear whether the theorem can be marshalled in support of a possibly revised formulation of his logicism. The difficulties with such a development of Frege's view have clustered around three questions: (i) To what extent does Hume's principle yield an *analysis* of number? (ii) How securely does the principle fix the reference of numerical singular terms? And finally, (iii) with what justification can we say that our knowledge of the truth of Hume's principle is 'independent of experience or intuition'?

2. The analysis of statements of number and the context principle

Frege's belief that Hume's principle expresses the preanalytic meaning of assertions of numerical identity is based on his conviction that the equivalence relation $\approx$ is 'conceptually prior' to any notion of number. His argument to this effect is indirect, being first presented[4] in connection with the notion of the direction of a line. Frege claims that we attain the concept of direction only when we have grasped the relation of parallelism: although the direction of l = the direction of m if, and only if, l is parallel to m, our understanding of direction depends on our grasp of parallelism, rather than the other way round, and this is what accounts for the fact that direction can be given an analysis in terms of parallelism. It is clear that Frege intends to extend this consideration to the analysis of 'the number of Fs = the number of Gs' in terms of the existence of a one-to-one correspondence, and that he regards the two cases as analogous in all relevant respects.[5] Indeed, since in the projective geometric tradition of the 19th century, a tradition with which Frege was certainly familiar, 'the direction of l' meant *the point at infinity associated with l*, the analogy with numbers appears more perfect than we might otherwise have imagined.[6] Frege, however, chooses not to pursue this connection, and asks instead whether 'we distinguish in our intuition between [a] straight line and something else, its direction?';[7] although we may perhaps take his remark that while contextual definition '... seems to be a very odd kind of definition, to which logicians have not paid enough attention, ... it is not altogether unheard of ...'(63) as an allusion to the geometrical use of this notion. In any case, if one grants the correctness of Frege's analysis of 'the number of Fs = the number of Gs,' then Hume's principle acquires the status of a condition of adequacy, a characterization of the principle that comports well with Frege's practice: Once the explicit definition of a cardinal number as a class of equinumerous concepts has been shown to imply Hume's principle, the explicit definition is no longer appealed to, and the entire account of the arithmetic of natural numbers, given in *Grundlagen*, is developed from this principle.

Frege's proof of Peano's second postulate from Hume's principle proceeds by establishing the existence of an appropriate family of 'representative' concepts: With the exception of the first, each representative concept is characterized as holding of precisely the cardinal numbers less than its number. If we pass to the sequence of extensions of such concepts, we have a clear anticipation of the construction of the finite von Neumann ordinals. Judged from the standpoint of their centrality to the key mathematical argument of *Grundlagen*, it could be argued that this family of extensions (rather than the family of equivalence classes of equinumerous concepts) form the true Frege finite cardinals.

Hume's principle, the contextual definition of number, or more exactly, the contextual definition of the cardinality operator, 'specifies' a second level concept which establishes a many-one correspondence between first level concepts and certain objects, namely, the cardinal numbers. It follows that if the contextual definition restricts the reference of the cardinality operator to a particular mapping from first level concepts to objects, then, assuming that the reference of the relevant concept-expression has been fixed, the reference of a wide class of numerical singular terms will also have been settled. This is why the equivocation between 'contextual definition of number' and 'contextual definition of the cardinality operator' is not so important as it might at first appear: To the extent that the contextual definition successfully picks out the cardinality operator, it must also determine the cardinal numbers.

The context principle was first formulated in the Introduction to *Grundlagen* as one of three 'fundamental principles' guiding the enquiry: '... never ... ask for the meaning of a word in isolation, but only in the context of a proposition.' The relation between this principle and contextual definition is by no means a simple matter, but when the context principle is interpreted as a principle governing reference, it suggests that reference to abstract objects can be achieved once we have established the truth of the propositions into which they enter. The relevant contrast is with a naive Platonism which would suppose that we can refer to numbers independently of our knowledge of such truths. On such a view, knowledge of reference precedes knowledge of truth. In §62 of *Grundlagen*, Frege makes it clear that he sees his use of the context principle as an inversion of this traditional ordering of truth and reference. So understood, the context principle is still very much a part of *Grundgesetze;* if in *Grundlagen* the point of the principle is that truth takes precedence over reference, then in the later work, its point is that *reference to truth* (to the True) takes precedence over reference to other objects.[8]

For Frege the propositions that are accorded a special role in settling questions of reference are what he calls 'recognition statements'; in the case of number words (and other singular terms) recognition statements involve the relation of identity, so that for this case, recognition statements are said to provide a 'criterion of identity,' or 'standard of equality,' for numbers. Hume's principle is an example of such a recognition statement. The 19th century added to the idea of a criterion of identity given by an equivalence relation the practice of passing to the quotient structure of equivalence classes determined by the relation—what has come to be known as definition by abstraction. Frege combines his use of the context principle in *Grundlagen* with definition by abstraction. Having determined what are the recognition statements appropriate to a particular class of numerical expressions, he proceeds to infer from the truth of such statements to the referential character of the expressions of this class. This inference is then supplemented by an appeal to the theory of definition by abstraction, with the equivalence classes providing the referents of the numerical singular terms. By contrast with Frege, one might proceed *without* resorting to definition by abstraction. But it should be clear that on either approach the context principle is vindicated as a heuristic or guiding principle in the philosophy of arithmetic if the contextual definition succeeds in 'specifying' the cardinal numbers. It is in this connection that 'the Julius Caesar problem' has come to be regarded as an issue of central importance for the contextual definition of number.

3. Hume's principle and the Julius Caesar problem

In *Grundlagen* §56 Frege considers an inductive definition of the numbers based on the conclusion reached in §46—what, in *Grundgesetze* (p. ix), Frege describes as 'the most fundamental' of his results—that a statement of number makes an assertion about a concept. The problem Frege raises —what I am calling the Julius Caesar problem—is, to a first approximation, that the definition does not determine what objects the numbers *are*:

> ...we can never—to take a crude example—decide by means of our definitions whether any concept has the number Julius Caesar belonging to it, or whether that conqueror of Gaul is a number or is not.

The context in which Frege places his discussion of criteria of identity (in §62) suggests that by supplementing the definition of §56 with Hume's principle it might be possible to resolve this difficulty. It is therefore natural to ask whether the Julius Caesar problem can be 'iterated,' to ask, in other words, whether the problem it poses for the inductive definition isn't also a problem for Hume's principle. And indeed, in *Grundlagen* §66 Frege raises a similar difficulty for his proposed criterion of identity for *the direction of l*—a criterion of identity which, as we noted earlier, he takes to be exactly analogous to Hume's principle. He resolves this difficulty, and by analogy, the difficulty with the criterion of identity for numbers, by the introduction of extensions of concepts.

It is evidently a presupposition of Frege's objection (a presupposition of the Julius Caesar problem) that numbers are objects. Frege's main support for this assumption is the theorem, which occupies the mathematical core of *Grundlagen*, that Hume's principle, when understood to incorporate the assumption that numbers are objects, implies the infinity of the natural numbers. *Grundlagen*, taken as a whole, both justifies Frege's assumption, and clarifies its sense, by showing that its key implication is that numbers are possible arguments to first level concepts. This, it should be noted, is the central difference between Frege's conception of numbers as objects and the conception of the cardinal numbers that emerges from Russell and Whitehead. If, working within the framework of the simple theory of types, we suppose that a cardinal number is the extension of a concept of second level, the type restrictions preclude a number from falling under a concept of first level; and the extensional character of all concepts (including those that are numbers) means that to guarantee the infinity of the numbers, we will require an axiom of infinity governing the number of *non*-logical objects.[9] That Frege is able to avoid such an axiom is one respect in which the rediscovery of Frege's theorem can be cited in support of his logicism.

Returning to our discussion of the Julius Caesar problem, it seems reasonable to demand of an account of Frege's presentation of the problem, in connection with Hume's principle, that it explain how the introduction of extensions overcomes the difficulty, which the Julius Caesar problem posed for numbers, while not itself succumbing to a similar objection. In short, the Julius Caesar problem must not iterate to extensions. This requirement may not seem especially pressing for an account of *Grundlagen*, where extensions are simply assumed; but it certainly needs to be addressed in connection with *Grundgesetze*, where extensions are introduced (I, §§3, 9 and 20) in a manner that is formally exactly analogous to the contextual definition of number. Any interpretation which fails to satisfy this demand implies not only that Frege's mature theory of number is ungrounded, but that Frege must have known this; clearly, an interpretation which avoids such an implication is to be preferred.

The difficulty is that once we take the Julius Caesar problem to show that the contextual definition fails to specify the referents of numerical expressions, we seem committed to interpreting *Grundgesetze* I, §10 as raising precisely the same problem for extensions of concepts. In this section Frege complains that he has so far provided only a means of recognizing an extension if it is 'given to us' as an extension, i.e. if it is referred to as the referent of an extension-expression; if an object is not referred to by such an expression, we cannot simply say, on the basis of the stipulations presented so far, whether or not the object is an extension. But when Frege comes to resolve this issue, he does not (as this section might lead one to expect) address the question of how extensions and other 'logical objects,' such as the truth values, are to be singled out from non-logical objects. Instead, he begins his discussion with the observation that, as we might put it, the reference of extension-expressions is fixed only up to arbitrary permutations of the domain of any 'model' of *Grundgesetze*. He then shows how an elaboration of this argument (an elaboration that has come to be known as the permutation argument) establishes that the truth-values (the only 'primitive' logical objects which are not 'given to us' as extensions), can be consistently identified with their own unit classes. This eliminates any problem of distinguishing, from among the logical objects, those which are not extensions, since it makes extensions of *all* the primitive logical objects. It would, however, be highly artificial to try to extend this solution to the case of non-logical objects. Moreover, the long footnote of §10 shows that the key idea of the section—the possibility of replacing the truth values with their unit classes—cannot be extended to the case of every extension which is not given to us *as* an extension (as the reference of an extension-expression) without conflicting with Frege's earlier stipulations regarding extension-expressions, i.e., essentially, without conflicting with Basic Law V. Clearly, neither the observation that the truth values may be taken to be extensions, nor the observation that any 'model' of the system of *Grundgesetze* is determined only 'up to permutations,' settles the question whether an arbitrary extension is, or is not, identical with Julius Caesar.

The analogy between *Grundlagen*'s discussion of the Julius Caesar problem and the discussion in *Grundgesetze* I, §10 thus runs as follows. Both in the case of the numbers and in the case of extensions, Frege finds that the truth value of certain identity statements has been left indefinite by a statement having the form of a contextual definition, Hume's principle or Basic Law V, as the case may be. And in both cases he proposes to remedy the deficiency by a stipulation: the explicit definition of the cardinal numbers as classes, in the first case, and the identification of the truth values with their unit classes, in the second. He then has the problem of showing that his stipulations are compatible with what has gone before. In *Grundlagen* this is established by the proof that Hume's principle is a logical consequence of the explicit definition of a cardinal number as a class of concepts, a procedure that would be unexceptionable as a proof of consistency were it not for the fact that the explicit definition rests on Frege's inconsistent theory of concepts and extensions. In the case of *Grundgesetze*, the proof of consistency is the point of the permutation argument, and modulo the inconsistency of *Grundgesetze*, the permutation argument *does* show that it is consistent to stipulate that the True and the False are extensions, thus enabling Frege to 'resolve' the question, whether either of these objects is a class, by the adoption of a convention. The interpretive difficulty arises from the fact that the question whether an extension is identical with Julius Caesar is one that could be posed for any expansion of the language of *Grundgesetze* which included names for non-logical objects and the fact that Frege's discussion, of what appears to be an obvious analogue of the Julius Caesar problem for extensions, fails even to address this issue.

4. The role of extensions of concepts

Of Frege's derivation of Peano's second postulate from Hume's principle, we can say that it requires that numbers be objects. But if the derivation of Peano's second postulate from Hume's principle is to support Frege's logicism, numbers must not only be *objects*, they must be *logical* objects; i.e., they must not only be possible arguments to first level functions, but our knowledge of them must be capable of being shown to be independent of the principles of any 'special science.' In particular, our knowledge of the numbers cannot depend on geometry or kinematics without renouncing the claim that it is free of intuition. This suggests an interpretation of Frege's use of the Julius Caesar problem which allows for a certain asymmetry between Basic Law V and Hume's principle. In order to see this, it is necessary to distinguish two accounts of the role of extensions: one holding them to be necessary to complete the argument that our knowledge of the numbers has the requisite autonomy and independence, and that Hume's principle is a logical principle; the other holding that even if the notion of an extension is not necessary to insure the logical character of the numbers or of Hume's principle, it, or something like it, *is* needed to fix the reference of numerical singular terms.

To begin with, notice that, as interpretations of Frege's methodology, both accounts need to explain why Frege believed himself justified in holding that our knowledge of extensions is independent of experience or intuition, the former, in order that his appeal to extensions might *justify* his logicism, the latter, in order that his use of extensions should be *compatible* with his logicism. But on the latter view Frege required more than a characterization of the numbers that would show our knowledge of them to be independent of the principles of any special science; he also required a characterization that would enable us to settle in a unitary way—i.e., by a single stipulation, general enough to cover all cases—the truth of every identity involving numerical singular terms. To this extent, the introduction of extensions of concepts formed part of a general explanation of our ability to refer to the natural numbers. A central difficulty, according to this view, is that Frege's identification of numbers with extensions is simply insufficient to settle all such questions of identity. For example, even if we know that the number of all objects (the number of the concept *is self-identical*) is the extension of a (second level) concept, it is still not determined by Frege's principles whether this number is identical with or distinct from the first infinite cardinal.

But even if Hume's principle fails to settle whether (say) Julius Caesar is identical with the number of the planets, the ordinary notion of number is surely just as unequivocal as any notion of extension in deciding this identity. If neither the number-theoretic nor the ordinary notion of number seems capable of resolving whether or not our knowledge of the numbers—in particular our knowledge of the fact that they form an infinite series—depends on experience or intuition, perhaps Frege's point, in introducing extensions, was to vindicate the *logical* character of the numbers and of Hume's principle. On the surface, this interpretation seems to be excluded by Frege's formulation of the question which opens §62: 'How, then, are numbers to be given to us, if we cannot have any ideas or intuitions of them?' The formulation suggests that Frege takes himself to have established—before Hume's principle has even been stated—that our knowledge of the numbers is not based on intuition. If this were right, it would have been quite unnecessary for Frege to have introduced extensions for the purpose of showing that arithmetic, in general, and Hume's principle, in particular, owe nothing to intuition.

Certainly, in the sections preceding §62, Frege has succeeded in refuting a variety of accounts of number which depend on some notion of intuition. By and large, the accounts targeted for criticism in these early, polemical, sections of *Grundlagen*—even the position attributed to Kant in §5—have an obviously psychologistic ring to them. At this point in the argument of the book, all Frege may justifiably claim to have established is that arithmetic exhibits the generality we associate with logic and that our knowledge of the numbers is not intuitive in the sense of one or another of the psychologistic accounts he has reviewed. But this review of accounts of number based on intuition is hardly exhaustive—presumably the notion of intuition Frege thinks relevant to geometry is not tainted with psychologism, and so is not among those canvassed. In *Grundgesetze* (I, p. vii) Frege makes essentially this point:

> Of course the pronouncement is often made that arithmetic is merely a more highly developed logic: yet that remains disputable so long as transitions are made in proofs that are not made according to acknowledged laws of logic, but seem rather to be based upon something known by intuition.

It therefore remains to be shown that our knowledge of arithmetic is not, in *any* sense, based on intuition, and that arithmetic is, in fact, an autonomous science. That this is what the introduction of extensions was supposed to achieve is suggested by Frege's own final evaluation of his project. If in *Grundlagen* Frege expressed a certain indifference toward extensions of concepts, by the time of *Grundgesetze* he had come to regard their use as essential:

> … I myself was long reluctant to recognize ranges of values and hence classes; but I saw no other possibility of placing arithmetic on a logical foundation. But the question is, How do we apprehend logical objects? And I found no other answer to it than this, We apprehend them as extensions of concepts … . I have always been aware that there are difficulties connected with them: but what other way is there?[8]

If extensions are self-evidently logical objects, the contextual definition's inability to decide the logical character of the numbers does not 'iterate' to the case of extensions and Basic Law V, and our interpretive problem is solved. We are, however, left with the task of showing that there is an explanation of the notion of the extension of a concept which serves the purposes of Frege's logicism, while not depending on the principles of any special science. It is the apparent intractability of this problem that has recommended the development of Frege's theory of the natural numbers without recourse to the notion of the extension of a concept. And it is in this connection, rather than for its value as an interpretation, that the view of the Julius Caesar problem as primarily a problem of reference acquires its main support and its chief relevance to current work.

Let us distinguish between two closely related, but distinct goals which the elimination of appeals to intuition might establish. I have suggested that Frege's first objective was to show that arithmetic is autonomous from geometry and kinematics; this objective is what we normally think of as the refutation of Kant. Another objective—one that is perhaps of greater interest to us—was to solve the problem of reference to abstract objects without resorting to a naive 'Platonist' picture, according to which abstract objects are 'ostended in intuition,' where intuition may (but need not) be tied to the Kantian tradition and the issue of the autonomy of arithmetic. The difficulty which the paradoxes presented for Frege's notion of the extension of a concept was an obstacle in the way of his refutation of Kant because it showed his justification of the *logical* character of Hume's principle to be unsound; and the chief effect of this failure was to throw into doubt the logical character of his demonstration of the natural number concept. But what of the second objective, that of avoiding naive Platonism?

For Frege, the basis for introducing abstract terms is the determination of truth conditions for the identity statements into which they enter; Frege believed that he could fix the truth conditions of such identity statements while (as we might put it) simultaneously specifying the domain of quantification of the first-order quantifiers. A mathematical theory like arithmetic or set theory is distinguished from one like Euclidian geometry by the fact that, in the latter case, we are content to speak only of truth in the appropriate class of structures; by contrast, arithmetic, at least, is generally thought to be true *simpliciter*. Frege seems to have been exclusively concerned with problems of reference for mathematical theories which, like arithmetic, are 'absolutely' true.[10] He sought an account of the notions of truth and reference radically different from one modelled on our notion of truth-in-a-structure, different, that is, from an account which begins by giving a characterization of the domain, a characterization that is external to the theoretical assumptions of the theory, and then proceeds to specify reference and truth with respect to this domain. If we were to follow this model for our account of the reference of the terms of arithmetic, then, since the truth of any proposition of the theory—including any recognition statement—would depend upon the reference of its constituent terms having first been given, we could hardly turn round and propose to account for reference by an appeal to the context principle and the truth of the appropriate class of recognition statements. Indeed, it would be possible to employ this model for our account of the truth of recognition statements even if we had not progressed beyond a naive Platonist explanation of how the objects of arithmetic are, in Frege's phrase, 'given to us.' This is why the truth of Hume's principle is insufficient for Frege's purposes so long as this is understood to depend on our having *first* specified the referents of its constituent expressions: this would defeat the whole point of an account of the reference of numerical expressions by a subsequent appeal to the context principle. Had Frege succeeded in establishing the truth of Hume's principle independently of such a procedure, he would have given a complete answer to our concerns regarding reference to the numbers. Had he achieved this goal by the derivation of Hume's principle from logic, he would have succeeded in answering both Kantians and Platonists.

Notes

[1]Support from the Social Sciences and Humanities Research Council of Canada is gratefully acknowledged.

[2]So called because Frege introduces it with a quote from the *Treatise*, I, III, 1, para. 5. See e.g., (Boolos 1987), reprinted in (Demopoulos 1995). My talk is based on my editor's introduction to this collection.

[2]This observation and the appreciation of its significance can already be found in (Parsons 1964,§VI).

[3]In *Grundlagen* §§64 - 67.

[4]See, for example, the first footnote to §65 of *Grundlagen*.

[5]See (Wilson 1993).

[6]*Grundlagen* §64. Quotations from *Grundlagen* are in the translation of J. L. Austin.

[7]The proposal that the context principle is concerned with the relative priority of the semantic categories of truth and reference should be contrasted with Wright's suggestion that the context principle asserts 'the priority of syntactic over ontological categories'; this is evidently a different (though not necessarily incompatible) claim. See (Wright 1983, p. 51.).

[8]Although Russell and Whitehead do not postulate a *Dedekind*-infinity of non-logical objects; rather, the Dedekind infinity of the finite cardinal numbers is shown to follow—without the Axiom of Choice—from the assumption that the set of individuals is 'non-inductive.' See (Boolos 1994).

[10]Letter to Russell of 28.vii.1902, in (McGuinness 1980, pp. 140 - 41).

[11]Of Course, Frege held that Euclidian geometry is also true *simpliciter*.

References

Boolos, G. (1987), 'The consistency of Frege's *Foundations of arithmetic*,' in Judith Jarvis Thomson, ed., *On being and saying: Essays for Richard Cartwright*, Cambridge: M. I. T. Press, pp. 3 - 20, reprinted in (Demopoulos 1995).

______. (1994) 'The advantages of honest toil over theft,' in Alexander George, ed., *Mathematics and mind*, Oxford: Oxford University Press, 1994, pp. 27 - 44.

Burgess, J. (1984), *The philosophical review*, 93 638-40.

Demopoulos, W. (ed.) (1995), *Frege's philosophy of mathematics*, Cambridge: Harvard University Press.

Heck, R. Jr., (1993) 'The development of arithmetic in Frege's *Grundgesetze der Arithmetik*,' *Journal of symbolic logic* 58 579 - 601.

McGuinness, B. (ed.) (1980), Gottlob Frege: *Philosophical and mathematical correspondence*, Hans Kaal, tr., Chicago: University of Chicago Press, 1980.

Parsons, C. (1964) 'Frege's theory of number,' in Max Black ed., *Philosophy in America*, Ithaca: Cornell University Press, 1964; reprinted with its 'Postscript' in (Demopoulos 1995)

Wilson, M. (1992),'Frege: the royal road from geometry,' *Noûs* 26 149 - 80, reprinted in (Demopoulos 1995).

Wright, C. (1983), *Frege's conception of numbers as objects*, Aberdeen: Aberdeen University Press.

Poincaré on Mathematics, Intuition and the Foundations of Science[1]

Janet Folina

Macalester College

In his first philosophy book, *Science and Hypothesis*, Poincaré gives us a picture which relates the different sciences to different kinds of hypotheses. In fact, as Michael Friedman has pointed out (Friedman 1995), Poincaré arranges this book—chapter by chapter—in terms of a hierarchy of sciences. Arithmetic is the most general of all the sciences because it is presupposed by all the others. Next comes mathematical magnitude, or the analysis of the continuum, which presupposes arithmetic; then geometry which presupposes magnitude; the principles of mechanics which presuppose geometry; and finally experimental physics which presupposes mechanics. Poincaré's basic view was that experiment in science depends on fixing other concepts first. In particular he believed at the time that our concept of space had to be fixed before we could discover truths about the objects in space. This is in general how his arguments for the conventionality of metric geometry are understood. What is less well known about his view is, interestingly, he argues that a great deal of the concepts underlying science, including most involved in our conception of space, are fixed for us—by the nature of our minds. Though known as a conventionalist about geometry there are actually only a couple of places where choice really plays a role in his hierarchy: as it turns out, these are the stages where measure is imposed.

Today this hierarchy of sciences may seem less quaint than simply wrong, as with general relativity (physical) geometry, mechanics and experimental physics might more accurately be viewed as a package deal. Nevertheless the mathematical portion of the hierarchy is still an interesting question. The purpose of this paper is to clarify the steps in the hierarchy from arithmetic to geometry.

To understand Poincaré's hierarchy it is important to note that the different levels of mathematical sciences carry with them different concepts which are *a priori* fixed. It is well known that Poincaré saw himself as a defender of the Kantian tradition, and in particular a theory of *a priori* intuition for number-theoretic mathematics. Yet he disagreed with most of Kant's claims about Euclidean geometry, regarding the choice of a metric geometry to be both conventional and influenced by experience. Euclidean space is not an *a priori* intuition. It is thus important to bear in mind how different Poincaré's claims about mathematical intuition are from Kant's. The discovery of non-Euclidean geometries necessitated a re-examination of the Kantian categories of the synthetic *a priori*. So in order to retain the spirit of Kant's philosophy, which Poincaré seemed to want to do, geometry in particular and its relation to science had to be reconceived.[2]

PSA 1994, Volume 2, pp. 217-226

1. Arithmetic

The intuition at the foundation of arithmetic is for Poincaré indefinite iteration. The scope of this intuition is completely general: it is everything thinkable. So it is as general as logic. Iteration is a form of experience, intuited *a priori* as the power of the mind to understand the indefinite repetition of an act when the act is once possible. This form of experience is foundational for systematic thinking. On the Poincaré view, then, the base intuition for arithmetic is also foundational for logic. We must appeal to the indefinite repetition of an act in order to understand even the setting up of a formal system (as in the definition of "well formed formula"), and in order to understand any rule of inference in general. Furthermore the formal investigation of set theory or logic requires induction as both Hilbert and Poincaré stressed. But for the latter induction is only knowable because of the "power of the mind", given by intuition, to understand indefinite iterations. It is in this way that Poincaré's critiques of logicism should be understood. His charge of circularity is that of an epistemological, or foundational, circle—not a logical circle. Simply put: logicism cannot show that arithmetic has no need of intuition if intuition is needed for logic.[3]

2. Analysis

I will argue that there is an intuition of continuity at the base of analysis for Poincaré. This is not obvious from his philosophical writings. References to an intuition of continuity occur in very different forms throughout his work[4], but Poincaré never explicitly relies upon an intuition of continuity to explain the mathematics of the real numbers. Nevertheless I think that an intuition of continuity—on which he relies to explain analysis situs, or topology—provides a way to escape from certain dilemmas in which he eventually found himself. Though on the whole he approved of the arithmetization of analysis, it became clear that this approach to the continuum required impredicative definitions which he rejects in his discussion of the set theoretic paradoxes. Indeed he also objects to the impredicativity inherent in the standard proofs of Cantor's result of the uncountability of the real numbers. So he does back himself into a corner.

Yet hypothesizing an intuition of continuity was not simply a way out of his dilemma (especially since he never explicitly connects this intuition with the real numbers). Even before he was worried about the impredicativity of analysis, Poincaré was unhappy about the tensions he saw in analysis between rigor and intuition. Though he approved of the introduction into analysis of rigorous definitions, he always balanced this approval by reminding the reader that rigor is not everything in mathematics, however essential it is. He argues more than once that reliance on an intuition of continuity is necessary both to create and to apply mathematics. For one thing it provides a link between the symbols and physical objects.

But intuition as providing a connection between pure and applied mathematics is very different from intuition which has a role within pure mathematics, as in indefinite iteration. Thus at this time the "intuition of continuity" is not a *mathematical* intuition. Instead, in *Science and Hypothesis*, Poincaré claims that we construct the mathematical continuum in order to make sense of experiences which would otherwise seem inconsistent. I am referring to his well-known discussions of Fechner's experiments:

> It has been observed, for example, that a weight A of 10 grams and a weight B of 11 grams produce identical sensations, that the weight B is just as indistinguishable from a weight C of 12 grams, but that the weight A is easily distinguished from the weight C. Thus the raw results of experience may be expressed by the following relations:
>
> $$A=B, \quad B=C, \quad A<C,$$
>
> which may be regarded as the formula of the physical continuum.

> But here is an intolerable discord with the principle of contradiction, and the need of stopping this has compelled us to invent the mathematical continuum. We are, therefore, forced to conclude that this notion has been created entirely by the mind, but that experience has given the occasion.... (Poincaré 1913a, 46-7)

We are forced to postulate increments in magnitudes which we cannot measure in order to account for apparent inconsistencies in sense experience. Indefinitely iterating this process, he says, gives us an idea of a one-dimensional continuum. Once we have the idea of magnitudes in order we impose an additive operation (which he regarded as conventional) to obtain a theory of measurable magnitude. That the continuum constructed in this way presupposes arithmetic is seen by the fact that iteration is involved in the interpolation of elements. It is also presupposed by addition.

Of course, as Poincaré well knew, the "continuum" obtained in this way by iterated additions of interpolated elements is not the "classical" continuum of real numbers. It gives us, only, the dense set of rationals. To explain the introduction of the irrationals Poincaré appeals to our intuitive understanding of a geometric line.

> ...two lines which cross have a point in common, and this truth seems intuitive. But it would imply contradiction if lines were conceived as ... only points having for coordinates rational numbers... (1913a, 48-9)

Poincaré then goes on to say that our general understanding of a real number comes from the understanding of all the places at which to cut or divide a line in two. (1913a, 49)

It seems therefore that Poincaré has a mixed theory of the continuum in this book. On the one hand he endorses the standard view that in mathematics the mind is free to create new objects and that the mathematical continuum "is only a particular system of symbols." (1913a, 49) Yet his view is non-standard in its reliance on what we might call geometric intuition. He was explicit that the mathematical continuum must not only be defined or constructed consistently, "but neither is it in contradiction with various propositions called intuitive, which are derived from empirical notions more or less elaborated." (1913a, 49)

The addition of particular irrationals is motivated by the empirical truth that when two lines cross they appear to have a point in common. Thus certain intuitive geometric truths are seen by Poincaré as derived from empirical notions. He says of the pure geometer that he

> makes a further effort; without entirely renouncing the aid of the senses, he tries to reach the concept of the line without breadth, of the point without extension. This he can only attain to by regarding the line as the limit toward which tends an ever narrowing band, and the point as the limit toward which tends an ever lessening area. (1913a, 48)

Here, then, it seems that by intuition of geometric truths Poincaré means something like abstraction from experience.

As we know, however, Poincaré did not regard geometry as truths based (at least not directly) on abstractions from experience. More problematically, it seems we are caught here in a circle. Poincaré seems to be appealing to the intuition of geometric truths to explain the epistemology of analysis. But geometry is the next level up from analysis in the scientific hierarchy. The concepts of analysis are supposed to be fixed *before* the truths of geometry can be established. So any intuition appealed to here must be independent of the truths of geometry. Before I return to this question, however, I will turn to the next level in the hierarchy of sciences: geometry. An examination of the epistemology of geometry will help to clarify what role the intermediary science of analysis plays in Poincaré's philosophy of mathematics.

3. Geometry

To understand Poincaré's theory of geometry it is essential first to distinguish between physical and pure geometry. Poincaré is famous for being a conventionalist about geometry. But his conventionalism extends only to certain choices regarding physical geometry, and even these choices are not completely free. First, the choice of a physical geometry (a geometry to describe the space of our best physical theory) is limited by the possibilities given by pure geometry. For Poincaré pure geometry is the study of certain groups: the groups of continuous free motions of solid bodies which he held is guided by "geometric intuition". (1913b, 26) So in order to understand the nature of this intuition—is it *a priori* or empirical, or a mixture of both?—we must understand the three concepts at the foundation of pure geometry: group, continuity (continuous free motion), and rigid body. Putting these three ideas together yields the concept of Lie group which leaves open three possible systems of geometry for three-dimensional space: that of constant positive curvature (one of the Riemannian systems), that of zero curvature (Euclidean geometry), and that of constant negative curvature (Lobatchevsky-Bolyai geometry). Which of these three then chosen for physical geometry is a conventional matter, but the choice is influenced by experience via the heuristic of overall theoretical simplicity. (Interestingly, Poincaré does not consider geometries of variable curvature to be real possibilities. Instead he regarded them as "merely analytic". This is a consequence of his view that the homogeneity of space is given *a priori* as part of our form of sensibility.)

What is required is to understand why Poincaré thought certain concepts were given *a priori*, either exhibited in intuition or existing as a form of the understanding. The concept of rigid body is an idealization which seems accessible by abstraction from experience. Indeed this was Poincaré's view. (1913a, 64) Although he knew that there were no real rigid bodies, he also knew the idea was not *a priori* imposed. So we have only to examine the concepts of group and continuity.

Continuity is the only part of the epistemological foundation for geometry which Poincaré explicitly identifies as an *a priori* intuition (in addition to the intuition of iteration). The concept of group is also *a priori* imposed on Poincaré's view. But it is imposed as a form of the understanding, not a form of sensibility; and Poincaré's several claims to this effect are not supported by any obvious argument. Certainly the group concept clusters several basic operations which recur in various places in mathematics. It is thus an important and fruitful concept. But why did Poincaré regard it as a form of the understanding? (1913a, 79)

3a. Group

Groups are sets closed under a certain operation, *, s.t. the following three properties hold:

(1) For any a, b, c in the set: a*(b*c) = (a*b)*c.
(2) There is a neutral element, **e**, such that for all a in the set a*e = e*a = a.
(3) For all a in the set there is an inverse a' s.t. a*a' = a'*a = e.

The neutral element and the inverses depend on the set and the operation. For example for the set of positive and negative integers with addition as the operation, 0 is the neutral element and the negative of a number is its inverse. For the set of non-zero reals with multiplication as the operation, 1 is the neutral element and the real number calculated by dividing any number into 1 is the inverse of that number. This is familiar arithmetic but what is its epistemological significance?

Calling the group concept a form of the understanding is an obvious allusion to Kant's categories—the concepts which are *a priori*. Poincaré here applies what he did to the theory of intuition now to the understanding, endorsing a semi-Kantian view that there are some basic concepts which are fixed and by which our understanding organizes and conceptualizes our intuitions. These are structural concepts by which we interpret experience.

Indeed, groups are mathematical structures. The concept of group codifies a certain structure which has many different realizations or models, one of which is the movement of relatively rigid bodies, like our own, in space. Because movement of physical bodies through space is possible we can distinguish between change of position and change of state. A change of position, Poincaré points out, can always be "corrected" by the movement of some body through space so that a return to the neutral place or original perspective is possible. We can either move ourselves to view the object from different perspectives or we can move the object to try to return it to the original perspective, and so to its original position. This is not the case with change of state. (Poincaré 1913a, 70-1) One conclusion Poincaré draws is that immobile beings would not have our conception of space. So there is an empirical condition underlying our conception of space: the movability of rigid bodies.

Poincaré is insisting here that there is also an *a priori* condition underlying our conception of space. In trying to determine whether an object has changed position or changed state we presuppose several things in the case of a change of position. First that there is an original or neutral position; second that it does not matter how we get back there (and that there are various ways of doing so); and third that we can always get back to the neutral place (there is always an inverse) no matter where the object is. These three presuppositions roughly correxpond to the three conditions which define groups. The group concept might codify the way we conceptualize motion or change of position—especially that of our own bodies through space. Furthermore if it is foundational for understanding change of position, the group concept might play a role in some inchoate theory of identity of physical objects. Certainly the distinction between change of position and change of state is essential to the way we understand and conceptualize experience of objects. For example we may distinguish an object from its background via some such understanding of possible "corrections" (its movability independent of the background visual field). It is perhaps along these lines that Poincaré characterized the group concept as a form of understanding. It is highly abstract and structural, yet might play such a regulatory role, as sketched above, in enabling us to have a concept of enduring object—a concept which is surely necessary for the way we understand experience.

3b. Continuity

We seem to have three choices for continuity. Is it a form of sensibility, like the intuition of iteration; or is it a form of understanding like the concept of group; or is it, as Poincaré first seemed to imply, an abstraction from experience like that of the rigid body? Poincaré's thoughts on this are notoriously difficult, partly, I think, because he changes his mind several times about just where continuity fits into his mental schema.

It is clear that in the end the intuition of continuity is a form of sensibility for Poincaré—not a form of understanding, and not empirical. Two quotes are particularly revealing. One is originally from *The Value of Science* (1905):

> I believe, therefore, that if by space is understood a mathematical continuum of three dimensions, were it otherwise amorphous, it is the mind which constructs it, but it does not construct it out of nothing; it needs materials and models. These materials, like these models, preexist within it. But there is not a single model which is imposed upon it; it has choice;... (Poincaré 1913a, 276)

Now we know that Poincaré refers to the Lie groups as the different possible models or types from which we choose a metric geometry. (See 1913a, 91 and 337.) We also know that the general concept of group is a form of the understanding. So the form of understanding provides certain possible models. I therefore think that talk of materials here should be understood as a reference to the form of sensibility. And what other material would go to make up space except the n-dimensional amorphous continuum, which he has speculated elsewhere is a form of sensibility?

That the intuition of continuity ought to be so understood is further reinforced by the following quote from a paper written in Poincaré's last year.

> I shall conclude that there is in all of us an intuitive notion of the continuum of any number of dimensions whatever because we possess the capacity to construct a physical and mathematical continuum; and that this capacity exists in us before any experience because, without it, experience properly speaking would be impossible and would be reduced to brute sensations, unsuitable for any organization; and because this intuition is merely the awareness that we possess this faculty. (Poincaré 1913b, 44)

The intuition of an n-dimensional continuum is that which makes brute sensations into conceptualizable experiences. This seems to capture exactly the spirit of Kant's notion of form of sensibility.

4. The Intuition of Continuity and Analysis

So much for Poincaré's use of the intuition of continuity in topology, or pure geometry broadly construed. We must now return to the question of the role of this intuition in analysis. Rather than appealing to the intuition of geometric truths, if Poincaré appealed merely to the intuition of the n-dimensional continuum he could avoid the appearance of a circle in *Science and Hypothesis*. The question is, does this solve Poincaré's real dilemma?

In Poincaré's philosophy there is a problem more serious than the apparent epistemological circle in *Science and Hypothesis*. We might call this problem the "dilemma of analysis". The dilemma of analysis arises out of Poincaré's quest for rigor in mathematics combined with the rejection of impredicative definitions and with the desire to do classical analysis as a mathematician. The dilemma of continuity poses, as Weyl claims, a "conceptual problem". For both Weyl and Poincaré there is a tension between the ideal of mathematical rigor on the one hand and certain other mathematical virtues—applicability, beauty, understanding—on the other. There is a *prima facie* gap between the mathematical continuum as it was understood at the turn of the century and the physical continuum, the elements of which Poincaré says are "hazy" or "overlapping" (1913a, 241; 1913b, 30). In fact Poincaré is explicit that the mathematical continuum, because it is rigorous, is different from that of the physicist and the metaphysician (1913a, 29 and 44; 1913b, 30).

> The mathematical continuum is a collection of 0-dimensional points, or individuals ranged in a certain order, infinite in number, it is true, but exterior to one another. This is not the ordinary conception, wherein is supposed between the elements of the continuum a sort of intimate bond which makes of them a whole, where the point does not exist before the line, but the line before the point. Of the celebrated formula 'the continuum is unity in multiplicity,' only the multiplicity remains, the unity has disappeared. The analysts are none the less right in defining their continuum as they do, for [reasons of] rigor. But this is enough to apprise us that the [veritable] mathematical continuum is a very different thing from that of the physicists and that of the metaphysicians. (Poincaré 1913a, 43-44)

The "arithmetized continuum" proposes to analyze the continuum in terms of points or Dedekind cuts. What is missing, according to Poincaré is an understanding of the unity of the elements, or their order, once constructed—how they can be put together into a single whole. He argues as follows. If we try to put them together by enumerating them in some order, then what we get is the eternal "disruptability" of the continuum. This is what we learn from Cantor's proof of the uncountability of the reals: that the order type of the continuum is different from that of any countable set. But how are we to understand this different order type? If we appeal to the physical continuum for such an understanding then we *contradict* analysis, since the physical continuum has overlapping elements. If, on the other hand, we appeal to the intuitive geometric continuum then we are *inexact*, because the geometric continuum relies on visual imagination or abstraction from experience (when two lines cross they appear to have a point in common).

Now, the question is whether the *a priori* intuition of continuity to which Poincaré appeals for the epistemology of topology solves the dilemma of analysis. Is the gap between mathematial analysis and the physical continuum, noted by the early Poincaré, effectively bridged by this intuition?

In *The Continuum* (1918) Weyl argues that the answer would have to be "no". Weyl took up Poincaré's campaign for predicative definitions in mathematics. He agreed with Poincaré that there is an intuition of iteration, that this intuition is capable of precise mathematical analysis, that it is identifiable with the structure of the natural numbers, and that it is presupposed for other areas of formal inquiry (like set theory). He also agreed with Poincaré that we possess an intuition of the continuum, which is an intuition of something other than the predicative continuum constructed "from below". But for Weyl this intuitive continuum is not determinate enough for mathematical analysis. A theory of the continuum is required to apply analysis to physics. But appeal to the intuitive notion of continuity does not help for it is too nebulous (Weyl 1918, 92). Furthermore, any attempt to try to make it exact is bound to fail, for the inexactness, is inherent in the intuitive conception (1918, 49). Yet, despite the inexactness it is unsatisfactory to replace the intuitive continuum with the exact concept of real number. (1918, 93) The predicative continuum seems to fall short of the intuitive conception. Yet classical impredicative analysis is unacceptable, for it is halfway between exact mathematics and an inexact representation of reality. (1918, 96) Either way, we are left with a conceptual gap which we can only bridge via pragmatics. (1918, 93) In other words, for Weyl of *The Continuum*, a wholly satisfactory theory of the continuum is impossible.

The question here is whether we can justify regarding the Poincaréan intuition of continuity as something distinct enough to be capable of mathematical analysis? How is his intuition of continuity different from Weyl's?

If by the "intuition" of the continuum Poincaré meant just visual imagination or appeal to intuitive images then I think he cannot escape Weyl's dilemma. And indeed through *The Value of Science* (1905) into *Science and Method* (1908) his remarks continue to lead to the existence of a gap between the intuitive and the mathematical continua. Through most of his work he asserted that there is only one pure mathematical intuition—that of indefinite iterability. So the intuition of continuity is something else—not a pure mathematical intuition. However, by 1912 he decided that "analysis situs" depends essentially on an intuition of continuity. The intuition proposed, that of an n-dimensional continuum, is no longer confused with an appeal to visual images for we have no visual images of n-dimensional objects. Furthermore, Poincaré claims that the continua of analysis situs are mathematical continua. Each point is indivisible and individual, in contrast (again) with the continua of the senses which overlap. Therefore, when Poincaré claims that the intuition of the continuum guides analysis situs, what he is referring to here ought to be seen as a pure, mathematical intuition.

Like the intuition of iteration that of continuity is now seen as playing a role in enabling the possiblity of systematic thinking about experience. For Poincaré claims in the same (1912) paper (reprinted in Poincaré 1913b, ch3) that this intuition is required for coherent sense experience as opposed to unorganized brute sensations. What is pure about this intuition, to meet one of Weyl's objections, is that it is concerned primarily with the imposition of order and organization on elements which would otherwise be disordered and therefore incapable of being conceptualized or codified. (See Poincaré 1913a, 425; 1913b 29 for the role of the intuition of continuity in ordering, and giving purpose to, an "assemblage".) This goes for the real numbers just as for brute sensations. What Poincaré objects to in Hilbert's list of axioms for geometry is the axioms of order. (Poincaré 1913b, 42-3) These he thinks are not mere conventions, but express a deeper set of intuitive truths—truths about geometric intuition, the true domain of which is analysis situs. It is its ability to contribute an understanding of order—an order which transcends our understanding of enumerations—which makes the intuition of continuity indispensable for both conceptualizable experience and for an understanding of the classical set of real numbers. And it is because the intuition of continuity is primarily concerned with order type or structure, and not with the visual images Poincaré writes about in his early work, that it is pure and so capable of rigorous mathematical analysis.

The intuition of continuity, then, can perhaps bridge for Poincaré the gap between rigor and practice which seemed unbridgeable to Weyl. If so, Poincaré not only avoids his and Weyl's dilemma concerning ineliminable impredicative definitions in classical analysis. (As an intuition rather than a set theoretic object there is no need to construct the continuum "from below".) He also addresses the problem of applied analysis. As a form of sensibility, the intuition of continuity is mathematically represented in analysis and topology; and it is phenomenologically experienced in motion, for example. Analysis can be applied to experience since experience has as part of its form the subject matter of analysis. This also goes some way towards explaining how mathematics can be both rigorous and informed by reasoning by analogy with the senses and by an aesthetic sense of beauty. Mathematical beauty is as Poincaré says what is most natural to the intellect. (1913a, 367) It therefore makes sense that it helps the mathematician create, given that what is most natural to the intellect provides the subject matter for what is mathematically true.

5. Conclusion

To conclude, I claimed that in *Science and Hypothesis* Poincaré envisions a hierarchy of sciences, with each level up in the hierarchy presupposing the ones below. I also said that his view of the nature of continuity changes, from that of a quasi-empirical visual intuition to a pure mathematical intuition. This change, however, does not undermine the hierarchy-picture; it supports it for it avoids the appearance of an epistemological circle in the hierarchy.

Arithmetic, the most general of all the sciences, requires an intuition of indefinite iterability which is foundational for any systematic thinking. *Analysis* adds to this an intuition of continuity which is also (eventually) a pure mathematical intuition which has its own role to play in making experience coherent and conceptualizable.[5] At the next level is *pure geometry* where two things are added: the concept of group, which is a form of the understanding, and the concept of a rigid body which is an idealization from experience. Also, the number of dimensions is generalized. Next, for *physical geometry*, experience guides us in our choice of a number of dimensions; and then, once dimensionality is fixed, experience also guides us in our choice of a metric from which there are now only three possibilities supposing we chose three dimensions. The *principles of mechanics* "partake of the conventional character of the geometric postulates" (1913a, 29), though they are more directly based on experience. It is only when one gets to *experimental physics* that one has *bona fide* empirical, falsifiable hypotheses.

Thus, in *Science and Hypothesis* Poincaré appears more Kantian than even I thought he was before I wrote this paper. This early vision of the hierarchy of sciences makes a great deal of science seem *a priori* fixed, in fact *a priori* synthetic.

Since he was prior to general relativity, he was able to make a case for this very Kantian picture of science by reconceiving Kant's categories to accord with the discovery of non-Euclidean geometries. That he was so entrenched in this picture perhaps explains the vigor with which he attack programs like logicism. But it was not a mere picture for him. Great mathematician that he was he experienced mathematical intuition. To his credit he tried to philosophically justify these intuitions, by explaining the role that they play, not only in our knowledge of mathematics and science, but in making experience coherent and conceptualizable. A more complete analysis of the extent to which this "honest toil" is successful is still needed.

Notes

[1]I would like to thank David Stump and especially Peter Clark for helpful discussion, Henry West for editing suggestions, and Alan Richardson for all his work.

[2]I am thankful to Michael Detlefsen for this perspective.

[3]Please see Folina 1994 or 1995 for a more extended treatment of Poincaré on arithmetic.

[4]The difficulty is that "the continuum" and "continuity" are terms which mean several different things, each of which Poincaré called "intuitive", but for different reasons. There is the mathematical continuum of analysis, the physical continuum that we perceive, the continuum of physics, and the n-dimensional continuum as it figures in analysis situs (topology) and geometry. By the same token there is the intuition of continuity which guides science (it is a heuristic by which we choose between theories, preferring hypotheses expressible by continuous functions), the intuition of continuity which provides a link between analysis and mathematical physics (and which facilitates the application of mathematics as well as mathematical creation and understanding), and the intuition of continuity which Poincaré says guides the practitioner of analysis situs (i.e., himself).

[5]And as I argue elsewhere (Folina 1995) in making thinking about abstract objects systematic.

References

Folina, J. (1994), "Poincaré's Conception of the Objectivity of Mathematics", *Philosophia Mathematica*, Series 3, vol. 2., pp. 202-227.

______. (1995), "Logic and Intuition in Poincaré's Philosophy of Mathematics", to appear in first book of European Forum of Science (new collection, forthcoming 1995), edited by Akademie Verlag (Berlin) and A. Blanchard (Paris).

Friedman, M. (1995) "Poincaré's Conventionalism and the Logical Positivists", European Forum of Science, edited by Akademie Verlag (Berlin) and A. Blanchard (Paris).

Poincaré, H. (1902), *Science and Hypothesis*, W.J. Greenstreet transl., Paris: Flammarion (New York: Dover, 1952).

________. (1905), *The Value of Science*, G.B. Halsted transl., Paris: Flammarion (New York: Dover, 1958).

________. (1908), *Science and Method*, Francis Maitland transl., Paris: Flammarion (New York: Dover, 1952).

________. (1913a), *The Foundations of Science*, authorized translation of Poincaré 1902, 1905, 1908; G.B. Halsted, transl., Washington D.C.: The Science Press; references to 1982 edition by University Press of America.

________. (1913b), *Mathematics and Science: Last Essays*, J. Bolduc transl., Paris: Flammarion (New York: Dover, 1963).

Weyl, H. (1918) *The Continuum*, S. Pollard and T. Bole transls., Kirksville, MO: Thomas Jefferson University Press, 1987.

Poincaré, Richard's Paradox and Indefinite Extensibility

Peter Clark

University of St. Andrews

Sometimes themes exist only in the eye of the beholder and emerge from the history of mathematics only with the benefit (or otherwise) of hindsight. There is however at least one issue (no doubt there are others) which was clearly present throughout the foundational debates of the early Twentieth century. It formed the core component of one of the major traditions that grew up as responses to the paradoxes, though the intuition behind it has never been fully articulated nor has it been possible to give a fully fledged mathematical articulation to that intuition. Essentially the central idea is that of 'indefinite extensibility' generated by an appropriate form of diagonalisation and it has its fundamental source in Richard's paradox[1] and in particular in Poincaré's response to that paradox.

Of the four great epistemological concerns around which much of the work in the foundations of mathematics this century has concentrated *viz.* the notions of demonstrability, definability, set or class and computability only the latter clearly falls outside the scope of the Richard type reasoning.[2] Furthermore the Richard paradox is at the centre of the constructive understanding of the continuum and the interpretation of Cantor's theorem. Recently the notion of 'indefinite extensibility' has been revived by Michael Dummett as the real lesson of the paradoxes. This is in sharp contrast to the standard classical response which is based ultimately on Zermelo's axiomatisation of the notion of set and the iterative concept of set which provides the epistemologically most plausible underpinning of that (perhaps only partial) characterisation of the notion.[3]

In the final chapter of his study of Frege's philosophy of mathematics[4] Dummett attributes the failure of the logicist programme in the foundations of arithmetic, that is the infamous contradiction derivable from Basic Law (V) of Frege's *Grundgesetze* to a failure to grasp the consequences of the existence of indefinitely extensible concepts. He argues that[5]:

> It is clear that Frege's error did not lie in considering the notion of the extension of a concept to be a logical one, for that it plainly is. Nor did it lie in his supposing every definite concept to have an extension, since it must be allowed that every concept defined over a definite totality determines a definite subtotality. We may say that his mistake lay in supposing there to be a totality containing the extension of every concept defined over it; more generally, it lay in his not having the glimmer of a suspicion of the existence of indefinitely extensible concepts.

PSA 1994, Volume 2, pp. 227-235

This Dummett asserts is the lesson of the set-theoretic paradoxes in contrast to Cantor's idea of 'inconsistent multiplicities', he says[6]:

> What the paradoxes reveal [is] not the existence of concepts with inconsistent extensions, but of what may be called indefinitely extensible concepts.

The point would seem to be this. There is a very well known argument,due to Zermelo, which shows that for any set x, the set $x \cup \{\{y \in x: \neg (y \in y)\}\}$ is always a proper superset of the set x, so there can be no universal set on pain of the Zermelo-Russell contradiction. Similarly the Von Neumann construction of the ordinals yields that for any set x, $\bigcup x \cup \{\bigcup x\}$ is always a larger ordinal than any ordinal in the set x, so the collection of all ordinals cannot itself be an ordinal, though it is transitive and well-ordered. Now Dummett argues, the Zermelo-Russell paradox shows that the extension of the concept $(\exists F)(x = \text{ext } F \;\&\; \neg Fx)$ can never belong to the domain, can never be one of the objects in the domain, over which the first-order variables run. He claims that it is precisely the introduction of the second order quantifier which forces an extension of the domain to include the extension of the Russell concept. Once the second order quantifiers are added, which they must be in order that class membership can be defined in the formal system of the *Grundgesetze* , no domain can have as members all the extensions of concepts defined over that domain.[7]

Thus the argument goes, each domain generates a more encompassing one, whose members are all the extensions of concepts defined over the original domain. An indefinitely extensible concept, so understood, has nothing that can be called an extension corresponding to it. What corresponds to such a concept is a sequence of objects, a sequence of extensions, that sequence being of indeterminate ordinal length. So what the paradoxes do *not* reveal, he claims, is that some properties have no corresponding extension *simpliciter*, or that there is not an intimate *logical* connection between concept and extension, but rather that there exist indefinitely extensible concepts. That is, there are concepts such that any attempt to regard a collection of objects falling under those concepts, as containing *all* the objects satisfying those concepts, always produces a 'new' object falling under the concept but not in that collection.

The issue immediately arises as to how such concepts could, as such, be responsible for the set-theoretic paradoxes, for it is certainly not true according to Dummett that every indefinitely extensible concept generates a contradiction when it is supposed that a set or extension corresponds to it. So for example he takes the concept of 'natural number' to be a clear instance of indefinite extensibility under the generating principle 'successor of' but of course there is no contradiction in supposing that there is a definite collection of all natural numbers.[8] The argument which generates, say, the Burali-Forti paradox, cannot be applied here for the obvious reason that the collection of natural numbers is not itself a natural number, while the collection of all ordinals being itself transitive and well-ordered ought to be an ordinal and consequently not a member of itself.

Rather it is when indefinitely extensible concepts serve to characterise a fundamental mathematical domain that a contradiction will arise from the supposition that a definite extension exists corresponding to the concept, as with, it is claimed, set or ordinal. Contradiction will arise because given that such an extension exists quantification over it can always be assumed classically to give rise to statements with definite truth conditions. But when there is no such domain, Dummett argues, quantification cannot be understood classically. It is his contention that the logic appropriate for such domains is intuitionistic logic and that the core insights of logicism that is, to keep mathematics uncontaminated by empirical notions, to present it as a science, that is, a body of truths and to solve the problem of the application of mathematics, can be saved once constructive reasoning is accepted. I shall not take up these latter claims here[9], rather I shall argue that Dummett hasn't made an adequate case that the paradoxes of set-theory are of the same sort as those which might be called paradoxes of indefinite extensibility (concerning definability and demonstrability) and further that there isn't an adequate independent case, that is a case independent of already having accepted a constructivist thesis about the foundations of mathematics, that establishes that the paradoxes of set-theory force the conclusion that the universe of sets is an indefinitely extensible domain.

Now it is evident that Dummett is reviving, in an interesting way, an old argument, one which provided a systematic theme in discussions of the paradoxes and the nature of the continuum at the turn of the century. An example of this is Russell, in his post *Principles* view[10]. In 1906 in a paper on the theory of types, he wrote[11]

> the contradictions result from the fact that, according to current logical assumptions, there are what we may call self-reproductive processes and classes. That is, there are some properties such that, given any class of terms all having such a property, we can always define a new term also having the property in question. Hence we can never collect all the terms having the said property into a whole; because when we hope to have them all, the collection we have immediately proceeds to generate a new term also having the said property.

He made a very similar claim in formulating the vicious circle principle. In 1908 he argued[12]

> All our contradictions have in common the assumption of a totality such that, if it were legitimate, it would at once be enlarged by new members defined in terms of itself.

This diagnosis of the source of the paradoxes as 'self-reproducibility' was accepted by Russell after reading Poincaré's paper of 1906 (Poincaré (1906)). It is with Poincaré and his diagnosis of the error which leads to Richard's paradox that the conception of indefinite extensibility has its real source. To substantiate this claim we need to have a brief look at the evolution of Poincaré's ideas on the foundations of analysis. Essentially his views centre around four theses. They are

1) the thesis of the priority of arithmetic over logic;
2) the thesis that our knowledge of the continuum is grounded in spatial intuition;
3) the vicious circle principle and the requirement of predicativity; and
4) certain key concepts in mathematics do not have determinate, fixed content.

As Poincaré's philosophical views matured from 1893 through to 1912, the role played by thesis (2) gradually declined as he elaborated a view of logic and the content of concepts very much opposed to that of Frege. The evolution of Poincaré's ideas on the continuum can be understood as the gradual elimination of any appeal to spatial intuition and its replacement by a doctrine about the content of concepts and what logic is.

In his 1893 paper he proposed a two stage, psychogenetic theory (as Goldfarb has called it)[13] of the 'creation' of the continuum. The idea is that the continuum is a double extension of the system of natural numbers, so that in the extension field, a contradiction which arises when we try to apply just the natural number sequence to experience is avoided. Thus he asserts that it is possible to have three integer assignments of weight such that it is simply a fact of experience that the weight assigned to A is the weight assigned to B and the weight assigned to B is the weight assigned to C, but it nevertheless be a fact that the weight assigned to A be less than the weight assigned to C. This contradiction with the transitivity of identity with respect to assigned or felt weight, when only the natural numbers are available for measuring weight, can be resolved he argues by extending the integers to the ordered field of the rationals. This he calls a continuum of the first kind. However if we want to apply this continuum to geometry and to guarantee that any two lines which intersect always have a point in common, which he takes to be a truth of geometric intuition then we will again obtain a contradiction, for it is not the case that this obtains for the rationals. Now we can avoid this contradiction by extending the rationals to the complete ordered field of all real numbers by, in effect, regarding a point as the 'common frontier' as he puts it 'of two classes of rational numbers'. The line or set of all such points is what he calls a continuum of the second order.

What we are given here is a familiar mathematical story, think of the theory of extension of fields through the surd field to that of the complex numbers so that we guarantee as a general truth that every polynominal equation of degree n has at least one root. This time the guiding principle is not just that we should remain consistent and always have a root but that we remain consistent and faithful to geometric intuition.

Importantly however, Poincaré insists that the authority of intuition can be overthrown. In discussing the notion of line and curve in the same essay he says that the theory of the continuum of the second kind entails the existence of among other things objects which have no intuitive representation, for example, the existence of a curve without a tangent at any point. He simply remarks that in the case of this 'contradiction' with intuition, intuition can go to the wall. Now if, geometric or spatial intuition can be transcended in this way and yet the objectivity and correctness of the theorems of analysis still be preserved without intuition playing a role, it immediately invites the question as to what role intuition can have had in even the elementary part of analysis. If existence and the correctness of proof in analysis relies not at all upon intuition in cases like the Peano space-filling curve, why it is relied upon in the elementary parts of analysis?[14] This thought clearly invites the answer that intuition after all plays no role in the foundations of analysis.

It is essentially this argument which accounts for the transition away from intuition in Poincaré's later writing and its replacement by the general claim that the objects of mathematics, to be legitimate, must be definable. This doctrine he calls 'pragmatism': 'the pragmatists admit only objects which can be defined in a finite number of words; the possible definitions, which can be expressed in sentences, can always be numbered with ordinary numbers from one to infinity.'[15] But as Poincaré well knew any attempt to delineate the mathematical universe in this way involves a contradiction just as much as does that of Frege or Cantor, in which a constraint of definability is entirely alien. What suggests that the definability constraint is contradictory is Richard's paradox. Consider the set E of all real numbers expressed in decimal rotation that can be defined in a finite number of words. E is manifestly enumerable, since we should be able to effectively list the definable numbers. Now Poincaré argues as follows:[16]

> Suppose the enumeration of E be effected, let us define a number N in the following manner. If the nth decimal of the nth number of the aggregate E is
>
> 0, 1, 2, 3, ... or 9
>
> then the nth decimal of N is 1, 2, 3, ... or 0. As we see, N is not equal to any number of E and so N does not belong to E, but N should belong to this aggregate, since we have defined it in a finite number of worlds.

To anyone who holds to the definability constraint the Richard paradox is a very serious difficulty indeed. Poincaré's response, which essentially forms the core contant of the vicious circle principle (a set x can be said to exist only if all of its potential members can be specified in a way which does not make reference, direct or indirect to the set x) is the indefinite extensibility of the concept 'definable in a finite number of words'. He says: 'we have defined N by a finite number of words, it is true, but only with the help of the notion of the aggregate E, and that is the reason why N does not form a part of E.'[17] There are two points to be made about this, the first concerns the role of the aggregate E in defining N and the second concerns the content of the concept of definability.

It is not just that in defining N, we have to refer to E, rather we have to refer to the specific members of E. Which new member N we get depends crucially on the form E takes. As it does of course for the constructively acceptable part of Cantor's diagonal argument for the uncountability of the reals. In either case, the new number formed by the diagonalisation depends on the initial enumeration. Now, as Goldfarb has argued, this is not true of the Burali-Forti paradox, for all that depends upon is that Ord is the collection of all ordinals, and so is well-ordered and transitive and the theorem that no ordinal is self-membered.[18] We certainly don't, unlike in the Richard paradox and the informal Cantor argument, get different 'new' members depending upon how we characterise, the collection of all ordinals. This is an important structural dissimilarity between the two types of reasoning and one sufficient to undermine the claim that the Burali-Forti paradox is a case of indefinite extensibility.[19]

The second point again hinges upon the way in which the new member N depends upon the specific enumeration E. In the Richard paradox we can think of specific different enumerations E, as different formalisations of the concept[20] 'definable in a finite number of words' and what the paradox shows is that each such attempt to exhaust the content of the concept is in fact inadequate to it. That is that the content of the concept 'definable in a finite number of words' is not determinate or fixed – it is 'indefinitely extensible'. What determines its successive extensions Poincaré argued was in fact nothing more than mathematical practice. It is this which explains the profound opposition Poincaré felt towards the idea that logic could constrain or be a foundation for mathematics in the way that Frege envisaged. That is because basic mathematical concepts cannot have the determinacy of content they must have if Frege's programme were to succeed. But the arguments here depend upon us already having accepted that what is fundamental to mathematics is the concept of definability or some more precise constructive interpretation of that informal notion, for there is nothing, as Gödel pointed out in his famous criticism of the VCP (Gödel (1944)) in the indefinite extensibility of definability or demonstrability which forces a constructive interpretation of mathematical existence on us.

Notes

[1] Richard (1905).

[2]In his (1946) Gödel remarks that the manner in which the epistemological notion of computability avoids 'diagonalisation' is 'a kind of miracle'. In his introductory note to Gödel's paper Parsons puts the reason for the 'miracle' clearly. 'But, since a function enumerating the recursive functions is not recursive and there is no reason to think it computable, the diagonal function it gives rise to is simply non-recursive, rather than "recursive at the next level". One can of course effectively enumerate computing procedures (partial recursive functions), but then the diagonal procedure simply leads to partial recursive functions that must be undefined for certain arguments (and to the undecidability of the question whether an arbitrary partial recursive function is defined for a given argument,' (Parsons (1990), pp.145). The Richard type reasoning and the possibility of transfinite iterations of the notion of definable in a formal language was clearly an important heuristic analogue for Gödel's programme of adding to the axioms of set theory, stronger and stronger axioms of infinity.

[3]For the iterative conception of set see Boolos (1971),(1989)and Parsons (1977).

[4]Dummett (1991), pp.308-321.

[5]Op.cit., p.317. A radically different account of the origin of the contradiction is given in Boolos (1993).

[6]Op.cit., p.316. Cantor's distinction between 'inconsistent' and 'consistent' multiplicities rests on the idea that consistent multiplicities alone can be consistently considered as *one* object. Cantor (1899), p.114.

[7]Indeed Frege's use of second order quantification in the *Grundgesetze* is directly connected with his deployment of value-ranges. As Dummett says (Dummett (1991), p.217): 'it was only by means of it that he could define his application operator $\cap$, a $\cap$ g being the value for the argument a of the function whose value-range is g; when g is a class, a $\cap$ g is the truth-value of 'a is a member of g'. In effect we can think of the application operator as defined explicitly by a $\cap$ g $\equiv (\exists F)(g = [x]Fx \; \& \; Fa)$ (where [x] Fx stands for the value range (or extension) of F). One can then think of the class theoretic notion of membership as defined by $x \in y. \equiv. (\exists F)(y = [x]Fx \; \& \; Fx)$. This makes it absolutely clear that second-order quantification is not only needed for the efficient statement of various crucial notions, but is intrinsic to the operation with value ranges.

[8]Dummett (1993), p.443. A similar point could be made concerning the set of all real numbers, for as Dedekind's theorem on the completeness of the system of cuts shows, reiterating the operation of taking all cuts over the reals, generates no new real numbers. See Boolos (1994), pp.44-47. Dummett rightly makes the point that the notion of proof or demonstrability is an indefinitely extensible concept, but it is not clear that that fact renders any conception of 'absolute' demonstrability inconsistent.(Gödel (1972a)) The indefinite extensibility of the concept 'finite number' arises from the fact that if we have obtained an initial sequence of natural numbers up to n, then the appropriate concept with which to obtain the successor of n is "a natural number ancestrally preceding n or is equal to n"; that is to the finite set of n and its predecessors.Of course none of the above characterisations of successor make any appeal to the entire collection N.

[9]The argument for these claims has been discussed in Velleman (1993).

[10]In the *Principles* he argued that the contradiction derivable from Basic Law (V) showed that not every property determines a class *simpliciter*. He wrote: 'The reason that a contradiction emerges here is that we have taken it as an axiom that any propositional function containing only one variable is equivalent to asserting membership of a class defined by the propositional function. Either this axiom, or the principle that every class can be taken as one term, is plainly false, and there is no fundamental objection to dropping either. But having dropped the former, the question arises: Which propositional functions define classes which are single terms as well as many, and which do not?' (Russell (1903), pp.102-3).

[11]Russell (1906), pp.144.

[12]Russell(1908), p.63.

[13]Poincaré (1893). Goldfarb gives an account of the evolution of Poincaré's views in his excellent (1988). A very good source on Poincaré's concept of intuition is Folina (1992).

[14]The Peano curve is not an object of visual representation at all. It was originally defined purely arithmetically by Peano, using tenary numbers and was only later given a geometric interpretation by Hilbert. Of course what can be represented are the initial stages of a 'construction' of the curve, not the curve itself which is a limit object. (Cf. Young and Young (1906), pp.168-9). The role of visualisability in analysis has been very thoroughly investigated by M. Giaquinto in his (1994).

[15]Poincaré (1912a), p.68.

[16]Poincaré (1906), pp.189-90.

[17]Ibid.

[18]Goldfarb (1988).

[19]Hallett in his (1994) has argued that there is a close conceptual connection between the set-theoretic concept of absoluteness, the Skolem paradox and the VCP. Certainly Poincaré thought that Zermelo's 1908 axiomatisation of the notion of set would not succeed in entirely eliminating the problem which generates the Richard paradox. Referring to Zermelo's notion of a definite property used in the separation schema he wrote: 'The author believed he was avoiding the paradox of the largest cardinal by denying himself any speculation beyond the limits of a closed *Menge*. He believed he was avoiding Richard's paradox by asking only questions which are *definite*, and this, according to the meaning which he attached to the expression, excludes all consideration of objects which can be defined in a finite number of words. But even though he has closed his sheepfold carefully I am not sure that he has not set the wolf to mind the sheep.' (Poincaré (1912b), p.60).

[20]The connection between Richard's paradox and the notion of definability is a complex one as was pointed out by Tarski (Tarski (1948)). However that the notion of definability for sets of natural numbers in arithmetic, is not itself definable in arithmetic is the content of Addison's theorem (Cf. Boolos and Jeffrey (1988), pp.207-18).

References

Boolos, G. (1971), 'The Iterative Conception of Set',reprinted in Paul Benacerraf & H. Putnam (eds.), *Philosophy of Mathematics, Selected Readings*, Cambridge University Press, 1985, pp.486-502.

_ _ _ _ _ . (1989), 'Iteration Again',*Philosophical Topics*,17,pp.5-21.

_ _ _ _ _ . (1993), 'Whence the Contradiction',*Proceedings of the Aristotelian Society*,Supplementary Vol.LXVII,pp.213-249.

_ _ _ _ _ . (1994), '1879?' in P. Clark & R. Hale (eds.), *Reading Putnam*, Blackwell, Oxford, 1993, pp.31-48.

_ _ _ _ _ . & *Computability and Logic* (Third Edition), Jeffrey, R.C. (1988), Cambridge, Cambridge University Press, 1988.

Cantor, G. (1899), 'Letter Dedekind', in Van Heijenoort (ed.): *From Frege to Gödel, a source book in mathematical logic*, pp.113-117.

Dummett, M. (1991). *Frege philosophy of mathematics*, London, Duckworth, 1991.

_ _ _ _ _ _ _ . (1993), 'What is Mathematics About?' in M. Dummett, *The Seas of Language*, Oxford, Oxford University Press, 1993,, pp.429-445.

Folina, J. (1992), *Poincaré and the Philosophy of Mathematics*, Macmillan Studies in Contemporary Philosophy, 1992.

Giaquinto, M. (1994), 'Epistemology of Visual Thinking in Elementary Real Analysis', *British Journal for the Philosophy of Science*, Vol.45, pp.789-813.

Gödel, K. (1944), 'Russell's mathematical logic',in Feferman,*et.al. (eds.): Kurt Gödel, Collected Works*, Vol.II, pp.119-141.

_ _ _ _ _. (1946), 'Remarks before the Princeton bicentennial conference on problems in mathematics', in Feferman, *et.al. (eds.): Kurt Gödel, Collected Works*, Vol.II, pp.150-53.

_ _ _ _ _. (1972a), 'Some remarks on the undecidability results'in Feferman, *et.al. (eds.): Kurt Gödel, Collected Works*, Vol.II,pp.305-6.

Goldfarb, W. (1988), 'Poincaré Against the Logicists', in Aspray W. and P. Kitcher (eds.), *History and Philosophy of Modern Mathematics, pp.61-81.*

Hallett, M. (1994), 'Putnam and the Skolem Paradox', in P. Clark and R. Hale (eds.) *Reading Putnam*, Blackwell, 1994, pp.66-97.

Parsons, C. (1977), 'What is the iterative concept of set?' reprinted in P. Benacerraf and H. Putnam (eds.): *Philosophy of Mathematics Selected Readings*, CUP.1985, pp.503-25.

Parsons, C. (1990), 'Introductory note to Gödel (1946)',in Feferman,*et.al. (eds.): Kurt Gödel, Collected Works*, Vol.II,pp.144-50.

Poincaré,H. (1893), 'Le continue mathematique' *Revue de Metaphysique et de morale*,1,pp.26-34.

_ _ _ _ _ _. (1906), ' Les Mathematique et la logique',*Revue de Metaphysique et de morale* ,14,pp.294-3 17.(Reprinted in *Science and Method,* New York, Dover Publications).

_ _ _ _ _ _. (1912a), 'Mathematics and Logic',reprinted in H. Poincaré *Mathematics and Science:Last Essays*, New York, Dover Publications) pp.65-74.

_ _ _ _ _ _. (1912b), 'The Logic of Infinity',reprinted in H.Poincaré *Mathematics and Science:Last Essays*, New York, Dover Publications) pp.45-64.

Richard, J. (1905), 'Les principes des mathematique et le probleme des ensembles', *Revue generale des sciences pures et appliquées*,16,p.541. Translated and reprinted in Van Heijenoort(ed.), *From Frege to Gödel, a source book in mathematical logic*, pp.142-44.

Russell,B. (1903), *Principles of Mathematics*, Cambridge Cambridge University Press,1903.

_ _ _ _ _. (1906), 'On Some Difficulties in the Theory of Transfinite Numbers and Order Types', reprinted in *Bertrand Russell Essays in Analysis*, edited by D.Lackey,1973 pp.135-64.

_ _ _ _ _. (1908), 'Mathematical Logic as based on the theory of Types', reprinted in *Logic and Knowledge* edited by R.C. Marsh,1956, pp.135-64.

Tarski,A. (1948), 'A problem concerning the notion of definability', *Journal of Symbolic Logic*, 13, pp.107-11.

Velleman, D (1993), 'Constructivism Liberalised', *Philosophical Review*, 102, pp.59-84.

Young, W.H.& Young, G.Chisholm (1906): T*he Theory of Sets of Points*, Cambridge, Cambridge University Press,1906.

Part VIII

SCIENCE AND PHILOSOPHY IN THE CLASSIC TEXTS

Putting Philosophy of Science to the Test: the Case of Aristotle's Biology[1]

James G. Lennox

University of Pittsburgh

Aristotle's *De Partibus Animalium* (*PA*) is, if there ever was one, a classic. It consists, at the broadest level, of four books. The first is devoted to articulating (I'm quoting its introduction) "...standards, by reference to which one will judge the manner of the demonstrations <of natural inquiry>, apart from the question of how the truth has it, whether thus or otherwise." (639a12-15). Books II-IV, on the other hand, are introduced as attempts to provide causal explanations for the facts regarding the parts that belong to the various kinds of animals, facts systematically organized in the *Historia Animalium* (646a8-12). This means that Aristotle's *De Partibus* consists of an introductory book on the *philosophy of* biological science, and three books *of* biological science.

Such an arrangement provides the student of this great work an opportunity to explore one of the perennial issues in the history and philosophy of science: the connection between a scientist's theory of science, and his actual scientific practice. This issue has been a center of controversy regarding (among others) Galileo, Newton, Lyell, Darwin, and Einstein. So has it been with Aristotle.

II. The Issue in its Aristotelian Context

Aristotle was the first Greek thinker to articulate self-consciously a taxonomy of intellectual pursuits. At the widest level, he distinguishes theoretical, practical and productive areas of knowledge, based on their fundamental aims and subject matter. Theoretical knowledge (ἐπιστήμη) is sub-divided into mathematics, second philosophy (the study of natural objects) and first philosophy (the study of being *qua* being). In addition the four books of *Analytics* present a theory of scientific knowledge, a remarkably rigorous and systematic account of what a body of propositions must be like in order to count as a theoretical science.

That theory, notoriously, seems to put insuperable barriers in the way of there being a natural science that could live up to its ideals. At best, it appears to be enigmatic on how its prescriptions would apply to a natural science (as opposed to mathematics)—it never mentions a distinction between matter and form (and therefore never raises the question of whether a proper definition of a natural object or its parts should include reference to its material nature), and never mentions conditional necessity, even in the brief discussion of natural processes occuring both for an end and of necessity (*APo*. II 11, 94b27-95a9). Yet many of the examples in the *Posterior Analytics* (*APo)* are drawn from natural science (especially, meteorology, botany and zoology), and are discussed side by side with

PSA 1994, Volume 2, pp. 239-247

mathematical examples—as if a rigorously formal demonstrative science of nature posed no special problems. Aristotle's biological practice, on the other hand, presents us with a relentlessly theoretical explanation of why animals have the parts they have, and develop and behave as they do. Yet, according to some, it looks nothing like the prescriptions for proper theoretical science in the *Analytics*. Where are the axioms, definitions, theorems, and proofs, they say? Why does it not look like Euclid's *Elements*? To quote one proponent of this view, G. E. R. Lloyd:

> It is not just that actual explanations set out in syllogistic form are difficult to find: the whole discourse of the practising natural scientist resists, one might say, being recast in the mould of the ideal formal language that the Organon desiderates. (Lloyd 1991, 394)

The existence of *PA* I offers an obvious approach to this issue. Suppose it does, as the *Posterior Analytics* does not, detail what a theoretical science of natural objects should be, but does so in a way that *specifies* and *builds on* the *Analytics* ideal, rather than abandoning it? There would be a philosophy of biology based on the *Analytics* philosophy of science. We may then ask whether the explanations of *PA* II-IV mirror the philosophy of biology provided in *PA* I.

The work I have done over the last six years has convinced me that *PA* I was intentionally written to answer the question of how the *Analytics* model of science is to apply to Aristotle's paradigm natural substances, animals; and that *PA* II-IV carries out the program of *PA* I (cf. Lennox 1987, 1991). In the sections that follow I will provide an outline of the arguments of *PA* I 1-5 viewed from this perspective, and provide a single, extended example of zoological explanation from *PA* III that shows Aristotle practicing what he preaches.

III. Aristotle's Philosophy of Biology: *Parts of Animals* I.

I begin with a brief outline of *PA* I's five chapters.

Chapter 1. Biology's Explanatory Principles. Chapter one begins with a series of questions, all but the first of which being answered as they are raised. There is a gradual transition to a statement of principles and methods based on the results achieved by answering the initial questions. The following is an analytical outline of chapter 1:

> [i] **639a16-b5.** At what level of generality should our investigation be organized, i.e. should we study the nature of each species independently, or should we focus first on general attributes and then more specific ones as necessary?
>
> [ii] **639b5-10.** Should the biologist follow the lead of astronomy, first establishing the facts of the domain, and only then studying the reason why and the causes of these facts?
>
> [iii] **639b10-21.** Since natural processes are subject to both motive causation and goal causation, which should take priority in our study?
>
> [iv] **639b22-640a9.** Do we find both unqualified and conditional necessity governing natural processes, and if so, what is the nature of conditional necessity, and of the demonstrations appealing to it?
>
> [v] **640a 11-33.** Since animals come to be, should we attempt to understand the fully developed animal by reference to processes leading up to it (as most of our predecessors have), or vice versa?
>
> [vi] **640a33-641a14.** Should we study only the material constituents of animal bodies, or their parts and especially the functional capacities specific to each of their parts?

[vii] **641a14-641b10.** Since studying an animal functionally is in effect to study the soul, should biologists study all aspects of the soul, or should reason be excluded?

[viii] **641b10-642a1.** Biologists cannot study their subject in abstraction from matter, since nature always acts for the sake of an end, which involves studying the relation of what is potentially something to its full realization.

At this point, a gathering up of the results is clearly apparent.

[ix] **642a1-24.** There are two sorts of causation, teleological and necessitarian, and they are related through the concept of conditional necessity. This is part of what prior natural philosophers lacked in their investigation of nature.

[x] **642a24-31.** The other thing they lacked was a clear notion of essence and definition. Socrates provided this, but in a moral and political context rather than in the study of nature.

[xi] **642a31-b4.** Finally, a closing passage provides a sketch demonstration explaining breathing, in which both sorts of necessity are operative.

The entire chapter shows an over-arching concern with the issue of how to integrate the account of natural substance in terms of matter and form, and teleology and necessity, with the ideals of a demonstrative science laid out in the *Posterior Analytics*.

For example, listen to the text referred to in [ii] above:

> ...<should> the natural scientist first study the appearances regarding animals and their parts, and only then state the reason why and the causes, just as the mathematicians demonstrate the astronomical appearances, or should he proceed in some other way? (639b5-10)

The question here is methodological: whether investigation should first establish the explananda of a domain—the 'appearances'—before articulating their causal explanation. It is answered in the affirmative at 640a13-15 (and see *HA* I 6 491a7-14, *PA* II 1 646a8-12, *IA* 1 704b6-11 for the principle stated in biological practice). Aristotle here claims mathematical astronomy as his model for this methodology. Elsewhere, in the *Prior Analytics*, we find a detailed articulation of this position.

> Thus the principles are provided by experience in each case. I mean, for example, astronomical experience provides the principles of astronomical knowledge; for when the appearances had been grasped sufficiently, astronomical demonstrations were easily discovered. *And it is likewise with any other art and science.* So that if the predicates about each thing have been grasped, we will be well-prepared to exhibit their demonstrations. (46a20-24)

The *Posterior Analytics* adds that a demonstration involves knowing the cause(s) of the fact, and using that knowledge to construct proofs in which the cause is identified by the middle term of the proof, the term which is subject of one premise and predicate of the other (cf. 89b24-31, 90a5-7).

But only once, and only briefly, does the *Analytics* acknowledge that natural objects come to be both for the sake of something and from necessity (94b27-95a9), and it doesn't respond at all to the obvious question: what would a demonstration look like in that case? Again, in *PA* I Aristotle faces this question directly, and forcefully.

> But the mode of demonstration and of necessity in the natural sciences is different from that in the other theoretical sciences. This has been discussed elsewhere. In the other sciences, the starting point is what is, in the natural sciences what is to

> be; for <one would say> 'since health or man is such and such, this must be or come to be', rather than 'since this is or has come to be, that from necessity is or will be'. (640a1-6)

The 'other discussion' referred to here is almost certainly *Physics* II. 9, in which such demonstrations are shown to be formally analogous to those in mathematics, but in content different in just the way sketched above (cf. Gotthelf 1987, 197-198).

PA I 1 and *Physics* II 8-9 refine both the concepts of 'that for the sake of which' and of 'necessity' so that they become, through the notion of *conditional* (or hypothetical) necessity, intimately related explanatory tools for organic investigation. It seems clear from *APo* II 11 (94b26-95a9) that Aristotle had not yet formulated, in the *Analytics*, the concept of conditional necessity—perhaps because the matter/form analysis, upon which it depends, was also not yet clearly formulated. The concept of conditional necessity is, however, highlighted in the outline of proper explanation provided in *PA* I 1. In two central passages (639b21-640a9, 642a1-17), the existence of certain materials and processes is said to be necessary *given that* certain goals are to be—given that there is to be an eagle, certain materials and processes *cannot not be*.

Chapters 2-3: The reform of division. The *Prior* and *Posterior Analytics* are both critical of the use made of logical division by Plato and other Academics, and yet give division an important place in the scientific enterprise (cf. *APr* I 31, *APo* II 5, 13). The second and third chapters of *PA* I develop a systematic reform of division which avoids a set of problems arising from the Platonic method (for a detailed account of the reforms, cf. Balme 1987, 71-80). It would take a paper in itself to go through the entire package of reforms, but it is generally acknowledged that there are three principal ones that imply the others:

> [i] Division must not be restricted to dichotomy, if its aim is to aid in grasping the real natures of things. (642b5-20)
>
> [ii] There must be a method of pursuing many different divisions simultaneously with respect to the same kind. (643b10-13, 644a3-10)
>
> [iii] The products of a division must be determinate forms of the general differentiae, to avoid 'accidental' division; e.g. if the general feature being divided is wing, the products of the division must be forms of wing.

Here again, we see Aristotle adopting both the criticisms of Platonic division presented in *APr* I 31 and *APo* II 5-6, 13, and, as there, insisting that, *properly revised*, it has an important place in science. But the *Analytics* once more gives little guidance as to how a suitably revised divisional method would work in the complex world of organisms. *De Partibus Animalium* I 2-3 provides the application, but only after further revising the method.

Chapter 4. Finding the Appropriate Kinds. Chapter four provides an answer to a question growing out of the revised method of division: Since the starting point of proper division is a multiply-differentiated general kind, how are we to establish the appropriate kinds initially? Aristotle argues that one looks for a signficant number of 'species' that are similar in overall bodily configuration, and have parts, habits and modes of activity the perceptible features of which differ only in degree on the same scale. If these criteria are met, as they are in the case of bird and fish, you have identified a natural kind. Aristotle ends up identifying seven or eight others that, it seems, were not so recognized prior to his work.

Chapter 5a. Exhortation to Biology. Perhaps the best known passage in the *Parts of Animals*, and certainly the most elegant, constitutes the first 48 lines of chapter five (in the Bekker text). The passage is a plea to put aside the natural distaste for dissection, in the interests of philosophy. To whom is Aristotle addressing this wonderful little bit of rhetoric?

The answer, it seems clear, is to someone who wonders whether it is possible to have scientific knowledge of non-eternal composites of matter and form. He begins by dividing natural substances into those that are eternal and those that come to be and pass away, arguing that, while the former are more noble, the latter are more knowable, since 'the perishable plants and animals live all around us'. (644b22-645a4) He goes on to stress that the study of living things provides great pleasure 'to those by nature philosophical and able to know the causes of things' (645a9-10). More than anywhere else, the good for the sake of which things exists is clear in the living world (645a23-26).

Finally, if you aren't yet convinced to cut open the next fetal pig, Aristotle reminds you that you too are flesh and blood, and if that fetal pig's guts offend you, you must find yourself offensive. (645a26-30) He concludes by pointing out that this study must involve matter, since an end for the sake of which implies something which comes to be and exist for the sake of that end (645a30-36).

Chapter 5b. The integration of division and teleological explanation. The rest of the chapter distinguishes division of the attributes to be explained and division of the causes relative to those divisions, making rich use of the ideas on division of kinds in chapters 3 and 4, while integrating these lessons with two from chapter 1: the principle 'first grasp and organize the appearances, then study the causes', here becomes 'first apply division to the proper attributes, then attempt to divide off their causes'; but in order to apply this principle to biology, given the method of conditional necessity, there must be parallel divisions of parts and of functional activities, since the former are for the sake of the latter. (645b18-646a4)

Aristotle's aim throughout is the application and development of a general model of scientific explanation set forth in the *Analytics* to matter/form composites, with their matter causally dependent on (and conditionally necessary for) their functionally defined form. It is a *tour de force* in the philosophy of biology. One can understand how, after reading it, Charles Darwin wrote (in one of his last letters) to its 19th century translator, Dr. Wm. Ogle, that it established that Linnaeus and Cuvier were 'mere school boys' to old Aristotle. Since he mentions only having read a third of Ogle's volume, it is primarily *PA* I to which he was referring, and he is dead right. Neither of those 18th century geniuses provided anything quite so systematic and powerful in the philosophy of biology as this, and indeed on division and teleology both had learned their lessons from Aristotle.

IV. Lessons about Method from Practice

Suppose, then, that *PA* I provides a philosophy of biology that is an application of the *Analytics* model of science to the study of matter/form composites governed both by material and teleological principles. This does not guarantee that Aristotle's biological practice *conforms* to the ideal. Furthermore, *PA* I has not resolved one question regarding this 'application'—how will multi-causal demonstration conform to the demonstrative ideal? To deal fully with these issues, one would need to look in detail at the entire biological enterprise, since not only do specific explanations have to take a certain form, but so does the entire research program. I cannot begin to make the general case today, but the explanatory example I have chosen will at least hint at the overall structure of the *Parts of Animals*.

V. The Chemical Mechanics of Fat and Blood

Aristotle concludes his discussion of blood and fat (in *PA* II 3-5) by declaring that he has stated "what each of these is and on account of which causes" (651b18-19). Later, in *PA* III, the possession of fat by the kidneys offers us an example of Aristotle's infamous 'dual explanations', in which he argues that a part belongs to the animals that possess it *both* from necessity *and* for the sake of something. By looking at each of these explanations, one begins to get a picture of the demonstrative structure of the *PA* as a whole, since the latter account is demonstratively dependent on the explanations in II 5 we are about to examine.

Soft and hard fat, or lard and suet (πιμελὴ, στέαρ) are both produced by concoction of excess blood, the excess being present because an animal is well nourished—not a bad theory, actually. The overarching explanatory goal of the chapter is why there is lard in certain blooded animals, but suet in others. Nevertheless, since both are products of excessive blood, Aristotle is able quickly to note that "because none of the bloodless animals have blood, none of them have soft or hard fat" (651a26-27). That is:

p1: Being Blooded belongs of necessity to no Bloodless animal.
p2: Having lard and suet belongs of necessity to all that are Blooded.
c: Having lard and suet belongs of necessity to no Bloodless animal.

Not surprisingly, since he opens the discussion by noting that the two fats differ in accordance with the differentiation of blood, he proves that those animals with fibrous blood have suet and those with non-fibrous blood have lard. Thus, in accord with the recommendations of *PA* I 5, there is an explanatory dependence of the division of the fats upon a causally more basic division of blood-types. The form of explanation is in line with the *Analytics*, but the content is very much determined by the composite nature of the substances in question.

These explanations depend, in their turn, on a detailed theory of the differential effects of heating and cooling materials of different elemental constitutions. This theory is borrowed from *Meteor*. IV, to which we are twice referred for a justification of premises in *PA* II (646a16, 649a32-33). Thus to understand fully the demonstrations regarding fat and its formation, we need to see how firmly established are Aristotle's views about the effects of hot and cold on various sorts of earth/water compounds.

VI. PA III. 7-9: Kidneys and their Fat

In the discussion of suet and lard in general, the natural scientist is focused almost entirely on understanding their *material* differences. The fat around the kidneys, on the other hand, is another matter, and introduces the problem of multi-causal demonstration.

PA I 1 640a33-b2 divides explanations in biology into those that establish the conditional necessity that a part belong to a certain kind of animal, and those that establish that a part, though not strictly necessary, is good for the life of the animal in question. The explanation for kidneys provides us with an example of the latter sort of explanation.

> The kidneys belong to animals that have them, not out of necessity, but for the sake of what is good and fine. For, in accord with their distinctive nature, they are present for the sake of the collection of residue in the bladder, in those animals in which such deposits are large, so that the bladder may better perform its function. (*PA* III 7 670b23-28)

That is, animals with excessive fluid residues could survive without kidneys—they have kidneys because that is better for them than the mere possession of a bladder.

The kidneys themselves are not present of necessity, then; but they *are* the fattest of viscera both of necessity *and* for the sake of an end. Kidney fat results from the process by which kidneys filter blood as it moves from the blood vessels surrounding the kidneys, through the kidney walls, to their hollow core, from which it flows into the ureters and bladder. As a result, a residue of blood, well-prepared for concoction, forms on the outside of the kidneys. The nature of that residue is either lard-like or suet-like, depending on the nature of the filtered blood. This explanation explicitly refers back to the explanation of the production of suet and lard (cf. III 9 672a12-13). Though it is thus a necessary by-product of this 'filtering' process, kidney fat also forms for the sake of an end.

> On the one hand lard arises of necessity—on account of the cause just given, that is, as a consequence of what happens of necessity in animals with kidneys. On

> the other hand, it comes to be for the sake of preservation, i.e. for the sake of preserving the hot nature of the kidneys. (III 9 672a13-16)

As we saw earlier, the *Posterior Analytics* acknowledges such explanations in natural science, but provides no answer to the question of how to integrate this idea with his views about the causes as the middle terms in demonstrations. *PA* I suggests a priority ranking of the causes, and briefly sketches the form a teleological explanation (with conditional necessity) will take, but still leaves the reader with many questions about the structure of dual explanations. By looking to his actual biological practice, we find answers to our questions.

There is, in this case, a *single fact* requiring explanation: In animals with kidneys, kidneys are the fattest of viscera. The explanation of this single fact, however, is complex. We are given both antecedent material conditions and processes which, being present, must produce one of two kinds of fat around the kidneys; and we are told that kidney fat arises for the sake of the contribution it makes to preserving the (hot) nature of the kidneys. This makes it crystal clear that goals are causes, and that in explanation they take priority.

The explanation offered in this chapter involves reference to (at least) two causes. And since the middle term in a demonstration identifies the cause of the predication to be explained, the questions raised at the beginning of this paper arise in a particularly compelling way here. What will a mutli-causal demonstration look like in practice?

Very briefly, the explanation by reference to necessary consequences has the following demonstrative form.

> p1: Being well-concocted residue of blood belongs of necessity to the product of kidney filtering.
> p2: The product of kidney filtering belongs of necessity to all kidneys.
> c1: Well-concocted residue of blood belongs of necessity to all kidneys.
> p3: Being lard and suet belongs of necessity to well-concocted residue of blood. [*PA* II 5]
> p4: Well-concocted residue of blood belongs of necessity to kidneys. [c1]
> c2: Lard and suet belong of necessity to kidneys.

I have fully spelled this out as two syllogisms, though the reader can see that the second simply identifies lard and suet with well-concocted blood residue. Making this step explicit has the virtue of showing how this explanation borrows premises from previous results about [a] the nature of fat and [b] the product of kidney filtration.

What of the teleological explanation, and its integration with necessity? The logic can be construed in a variety of ways (one of which is offered below), but the essential points seem clear: all the viscera require heat to function; flesh protects the heat of the viscera around the heart; but kidneys, being located at the loins, lack this sort of protection, and fat is provided for this purpose instead.

It seems clear, however, that even if kidneys didn't need fat around them (imagine them located in a fleshy part of the body), fat would nevertheless arise by the necessary process described. It is an empirical question for Aristotle whether 'residues' produced by such a process also come to be for a function—bile arises in essentially the same manner, but serves no function for the organism (cf. IV 2 677a12-30). As he puts it:

> Sometimes the <formal> nature makes use even of residues for the benefit <of the organism>; nevertheless it is not for this reason necessary to seek 'for the sake of what end?' in every case—but when some things are such and such, others often result from necessity because of these. (677a16-18)

Thus, it is necessary that fat appear as a necessary by-product of the proper function of the kidneys; whether the nature of the organism uses such by-products for an end is not.

In the case of bile, Aristotle notes that it only arises as the by-product of *impure* blood, and thus has a universally negative effect on the animals that have it (677a19-29). Having determined this, he concludes, "[t]herefore it is apparent that bile is not for the sake of something, but dross, off-scouring." (677a29-30)

Fats derive from a similar process; but they derive from a pure blood ripe for being 'well-concocted'. Nothing precludes them serving a useful function then; furthermore, the presence of fat around the kidneys is necessary for their proper function.

To fully capture the structure of this 'dual explanation' for kidney fat, then, a minimum of three modal syllogisms would be required. Furthermore, the same fact is explained via two distinct sets of syllogistic inferences. By looking at the formal structure of these explanations, we learn a good deal about Aristotle's biological science.

VII. Philosophy of Science, Philosophy of Biology and Biology

Contemporary philosophy of biology was defined by the fact that logical positivism and logical empiricism focused almost exclusively on physics—whether one looks at Woodger, Sommerhoff, Nagel, Beckner, Schaffner, Ruse or Hull, the central questions were defined by that legacy. From the beginning, philosophically inclined biologists such as George Simpson and Ernst Mayr protested the importation of inappropriate philosophical standards from physics, and the philosophy of biology eventually listened.

For Aristotle, on the other hand, the paradigm natural substances were not the common material constituents of the universe, but the most active, complex and organized of bodies, the living ones. He might, one would then suppose, have been free to develop a philosophy of science with biology as its paradigm case.

But it was not to be. The *Posterior Analytics* shows a Platonic influence in at least one crucial respect—the paradigm case of scientific knowledge in that first great treatise of philosophy of science is mathematics. Thus Aristotle faced problems analogous to those of contemporary philosophy of biology. Most generally, those problems can be summed up in the question: to what extent can a general philosophy of science, initially defined by reference to mathematics, be applicable to a world of teleologically organized, complex living systems? This, I have argued, is the central question of *Parts of Animals* I, the first great treatise in the philosophy of biology. Aristotle's biological practice, I have additionally suggested, is a valuable source of insight into Aristotle's answer to that question.

Notes

[1]It is a pleasure to thank the Division of Research Programs of the National Endowment for the Humanities for their support during work on the translation and commentary of Aristotle's *De Partibus Animalium* (to be published by Oxford University Press). It was Professor Finocchiaro's wonderful idea to invite Daniel Jones of that Division, to chair the Symposium in which this paper was presented, and I would like to thank him for agreeing to take part. Finally, I would like to thank Maurice Finocchiaro for organizing the Symposium, and Ernan McMullin for his perceptive comments on my paper.

References

Balme, D.M. (1987), "Aristotle's Use of Division and Differentia" in Gotthelf and Lennox eds. 1987, 69-89.

Bekker, I. ed. (1831), *Aristotelis Opera*, Vol. 1. Berlin, Prussian Academy.

Bowen, A.C. ed. (1991), *Science and Philosophy in Classical Greece*. New York: Garland Publishing.

Gotthelf, A. (1987), "First Principles in Aristotle's *Parts of Animals*'" in Gotthelf and Lennox eds. 1987, 167-198.

Gotthelf, A. and Lennox, J.G., eds. (1987), *Philosophical Issues in Aristotle's Biology*. Cambridge: Cambridge University Press.

Lennox, J. G. (1987), "Divide and Explain: the *Posterior Analytics* in Practice" in Gotthelf and Lennox eds. 1987, 90-119.

_ _ _ _ _ _ _ _ . (1991), "Between Data and Demonstration: the *Analytics* and the *Historia Animalium*", chapter 12 of Bowen ed. 1991.

Lloyd, G.E.R. (1991), *Methods and Problems in Greek Science*. Cambridge: Cambridge University Press.

Methodological Judgment and Critical Reasoning in Galileo' s *Dialogue*[1]

Maurice A. Finocchiaro

University of Nevada, Las Vegas

The aim of this paper is to suggest that Galileo's *Dialogue* may be fruitfully interpreted and evaluated from the viewpoints of methodological judgment and critical reasoning. This approach has significant historical precedents in the readings of Thomas Salusbury and the Port-Royal logicians. This focus on the book's philosophical dimension is not meant to exclude its scientific, historical, rhetorical, and aesthetic dimensions; indeed, such anti-reductionism is suggested by methodological judgment applied at the metalevel; the latter also suggests a criticism of the excessively rhetorical readings prevalent today, as well as viable ways for resolving the problems of hermeneutical pluralism, interpretation versus evaluation, and theory versus practice. Finally, the book's methodological judgment and critical reasoning can be shown to correspond to Galileo's intentions and self-reflections.

1. Methodological Judgment

The full original title of the book Galileo published in 1632 may be translated as follows:

> Dialogue by Galileo Galilei, Lincean Academician, Extraordinary Mathematician at the University of Pisa, and Philosopher and Chief Mathematician to the Most Serene Grand Duke of Tuscany; where in meetings over the course of four days one discusses the two chief world systems, Ptolemaic and Copernican, proposing indeterminately the philosophical and natural reasons for the one as well as for the other side. (Galilei 1632)

This title could have been abbreviated by focusing on its last clause rather than on its first word, and then this Galilean work would have been known by the title "Philosophical and Natural Reasons for the Ptolemaic and for the Copernican World Systems." Such an abbreviated title would advertise more explicitly both the book's real subject matter (namely, the arguments for and against the earth's motion) and the impartiality of the book's discussion (or at least its intended impartiality). Of course, even as it stands the full title does suggest (intended) impartiality when it asserts that the arguments of both sides are presented and that they are presented "indeterminately." However, this word conveys a somewhat oblique suggestion rather than an explicit implication, partly because it is more vague than the term "impartially," and partly because it is somewhat ambiguous and can also mean "inconclusively."

PSA 1994, Volume 2, pp. 248-257

One reader who was struck by the book's impartiality was Thomas Salusbury, the author of the first published English translation of Galileo's *Dialogue* in 1661. In fact, he translated the Italian term which I have transliterated "indeterminately" as "impartially and indefinitely" (Salusbury 1661). Here Salusbury seems to be making explicit in his translation what he felt was implicit in the Italian text. This was not a mere slip of the pen on his part for in his translator's foreword he explicitly formulates the corresponding interpretation. There, in the context of advancing his interpretation of the Inquisition trial occasioned by the *Dialogue*, Salusbury (1661, unpaginated preface to "Reader") says that the book has "been with all veneration valued, read, and applauded by the judicious."

I want to capitalize on Salusbury's talk of impartiality and judiciousness and claim him as the first to have advanced an approach to the reading of the *Dialogue* which I find fruitful and in my own way have been elaborating for at least fifteen years. The key notion may be called judgment, judiciousness, or impartiality; it may be defined as the avoidance of one-sidedness and extremes. The book's title refers to judiciousness in regard to a substantive issue of physical theory, namely the Ptolemaic versus the Copernican systems. I apply the idea more widely to methodological issues; in methodology the various sides become such ideal types[2] as deductivism, inductivism, hypothetico-deductivism, apriorism, empiricism, positivism, retroductivism, and mathematicism; they can also be such historical traditions as Platonism, Aristotelianism, Archimedeanism, and the tradition of "mixed sciences." But a number of clarifications are needed.

When I say that Salusbury's suggestion is fruitful for the *critical reading* of the *Dialogue*, I am referring to both the interpretation and the evaluation of what he says and does in that text. There is no presumption that Galileo was perfectly or completely judicious and impartial on any one issue (e.g., earth's motion versus rest), let alone all issues, methodological and theoretical. To take the point of view of judgment means simply that one examines whether and if so to what extent the text displays judiciousness on various occasions. To uncritically attribute judiciousness to Galileo would betray on the part of the reader or scholar at the metalevel precisely the kind of injudiciousness we are talking about.

2. Critical Reasoning

There is a second interpretive viewpoint I find extremely useful and which happens to have classical antecedents. This is the viewpoint of what I label critical reasoning. By critical reasoning I mean reasoning aimed at the analysis, evaluation, and/or self-reflective formulation of arguments. Here analysis means identifying, distinguishing, and interrelating various elements (basically, propositions) for the purpose of understanding the reasoning. Evaluation means determining whether the reasoning is valid or invalid, strong or weak, cogent or fallacious, and so on. By self-reflective formulation of arguments I mean arguments which exhibit an appropriate degree of self-analysis and self-evaluation. For the cases of analysis and evaluation, critical reasoning simply consists of reasoning about reasoning or arguments about arguments, namely arguments which support conclusions about other arguments. For the case of self-reflective reasoning, critical reasoning is simply the presentation of an argument supporting a conclusion about some entity other than an argument (usually some physical phenomenon), as long as the presentation is carried with adequate attention to and awareness of what the structure and strength of the presented argument are.

Like all reasoning, critical reasoning is not always correct; some is correct and some is incorrect. Thus, to say, as I would, that the *Dialogue* is full of critical reasoning and that critical reasoning is its essential and most fundamental feature is merely an analytical interpretation, not an evaluation of the book. In this regard, critical reasoning may be contrasted with methodological judiciousness, which is primarily an evaluative notion; but, as we saw, judiciousness was given an analytical interpretive import in a derivative manner by means of the notion of *attempting* to avoid one-sidedness and extremes. At any rate, I would also argue that the critical reasoning in the *Dialogue* is usually correct and cogent, but such an evaluation would have to be supported in a different way than the textual interpretation.

One of the earliest examples of this kind of reading of the *Dialogue* is found in the *Port-Royal Logic*, first published in 1662 (Arnauld and Nicole 1965, 243). The *Port-Royal Logic* tried to do in the seventeenth century something analogous to what present-day scholars in the fields of informal logic and critical thinking are aiming at. Thus, it is not surprising that it contains a good illustration of my present point. This occurs in Part III, chapter 19, entitled "Sophisms: the different ways of reasoning incorrectly." The second of nine sophisms discussed is the fallacy of begging the question. This is defined in a standard manner, namely assuming as true the conclusion you are trying to prove, and a reference is made to Aristotle as the originator of this definition. Then several illustrations are given. The first one of these involves a passage from the First Day of the *Dialogue* (Galilei 1632, 59-61). The passage contains Galileo's criticism that Aristotle's empirical argument for geocentrism begs the question. The fallacious argument in question is the following: the natural motion of heavy bodies is straight toward the center of the universe since their natural motion is opposite to that of light bodies, and the natural motion of light bodies is toward the circumference of the universe; but the natural motion of heavy bodies is also straight toward the center of the earth; therefore, the center of the earth coincides with the center of the universe. The *Port-Royal Logic* approvingly summarizes Galileo's criticism that the first step in this argument assumes that the opposite of a direction "toward the circumference of the universe" is a direction "toward the center of the universe"; that this assumption holds only if the phrase "toward the circumference of the universe" is understood to mean "in a direction which intersects the circumference of the universe at right angles"; and that, when so understood, we can know that light bodies move naturally in that direction (the corresponding premise of the argument) only if we know that the earth is at the center of the universe (the argument's conclusion). Now, I am inclined to concur with the *Port-Royal Logic*ians and Galileo that the featured argument begs the question. I am not saying that Galileo's interpretation of the relevant Aristotelian text is correct; nor am I sure that the Port-Royal interpretation of Galileo's interpretation and of his evaluation is correct. All I want to claim is that such a reference involves an approach to the *Dialogue* from the point of view of critical reasoning.

3. Judgment Calls

I want to continue in the indirect and allusive style by applying my idea of methodological judgment at a metalevel in such a way as to address a number of issues which the reading of the *Dialogue* presents. In fact, like many other classics, the *Dialogue* is a multidimensional work. In the present instance the various relevant dimensions are science, history, philosophy, rhetoric, and literature. These are just the major viewpoints from which the book may be approached, and each of them in turn subsumes several more specific viewpoints. For example, a scientific reading of the book may focus either on physics, astronomy, cosmology, or mathematics. A historical reading may take the book as a document of such developments as the Galileo Affair and the Copernican Revolution. The most common philosophical reading involves methodology or epistemology; it may also involve applied logic or informal logic or critical reasoning. The rhetorical reading focuses on persuasion, verbal communication, emotional appeal, linguistic composition, dramatic structure and interaction, and the like. Finally, the book may be studied as literature, namely as a work of art; this is an aesthetic reading and focuses on such things as the eloquence, beauty, and cleverness of the linguistic expression, and the vividness of the images.

All five major dimensions are legitimate; each has its place and is appropriate in some context. I would object only to a one-sided approach which would focus excessively on just one of these viewpoints or try to reduce all other dimensions to it. In recent years, I believe most abuses in this regard have been committed by the rhetorical reading (e.g., Feyerabend 1975). However, to say that these five readings are individually legitimate is not the same as saying that they are equally legitimate or important. For example, it seems obvious that the aesthetic approach is less important than the other four. However, to determine the relative importance of the other four dimensions would be more difficult. Their relative importance would in part depend on their mutual interrelationships. Thus, let me hasten to add that, although it is useful to distinguish these five major dimensions, it would not be proper to treat them as separate. Instead, I would argue that they are interrelated and that the distinction should not be turned into a separation; nor should the interrelation become a conflation and lead to a confusion among the various dimensions. In short, the proper approach is to distinguish without separating and to interrelate without conflating. Finally, I do not wish to give the impression that there is anything special about the number five. I have already suggested that each dimension subsumes several aspects; thus, depending on how these subdimensions are defined and interrelated, we could end up with a different number of major dimensions. Nevertheless, I believe it is important to retain the notion of a dimension because it is important to distinguish this problem of multidimensionality (or multisciplinarity) from three other problems: the problem of hermeneutical pluralism or variety, the problem of interpretation versus evaluation, and the problem of theory versus practice.

In fact, the notion of judgment also helps us to solve the problem that, like many other classics, the *Dialogue* is susceptible of many different interpretations and evaluations. The differences I have in mind are substantive differences within the same disciplinary category or hermeneutical dimension; for example, from the methodological point of view Galileo has been interpreted as an apriorist, empiricist, positivist, mathematicist, deductivist, inductivist, and hypothetico-deductivist, and in other ways lacking a handy label (e.g., Pitt 1992). The notion of methodological judgment enables us to capitalize on such hermeneutical variety, to make a virtue out of the necessity, and to describe the situation positively and constructively. The initial point to stress here is that there are certainly conflicting *tendencies* in the *Dialogue*, namely instances of conflicting methodological *principles*. Second, he never undertook to articulate a theoretical systematization of methodological problems. Therefore, I believe there is no justification for a philosopher or historian to construct a systematization of Galileo's work in terms of any single methodological theory or principle. This can only be done by being one-sided in regard to the distinct methodological problems he faced or by exaggerating the generality of particular solutions he gave; this would happen to the detriment of the other distinct methodological problems and of the opposite solutions useful on other occasions. In short, the philosopher or historian would be lapsing into injudiciousness.

Next, the problem of interpretation versus evaluation is that these two activities need to be, but often are not, judiciously distinguished and interrelated. The corresponding fact about the classics is that it is necessary and desirable to both interpret and evaluate them. In some contexts things are clear and the problem does not arise. However, in other contexts the situation is not so clear. In particular, I believe that, once again, rhetorical readings of the *Dialogue* suffer from a damaging equivocation between interpretation and evaluation. It seems that almost everybody expresses a favorable evaluation of Galilean rhetoric, but does so without explicit justification; what we find is documentation for some rhetorical interpretation, but then his rhetorical procedures are uncritically declared effective, brilliant, and proper without adequate justification (e.g., Moss 1993). My approach to the book's rhetorical dimension is that at the level of interpretation I find it interesting to elaborate this rhetoric, but I would judge that more often than not his rhetoric is ineffective.

The ineffective rhetoric begins in the title, in regard to the alternative title originally chosen by Galileo, namely "Dialogue on the Tides." The actual title seems to me a rhetorically foolish one in the light of the anti-Copernican decree of 1616 and the other ecclesiastic restrictions under which he was operating, for it calls attention directly to the fact that the book discusses the dangerous and semi-forbidden topic, and so it invites scrutiny from that point of view. Another strikingly bad piece of rhetoric is found in his preface to the reader, which I find incoherent insofar as it claims both that the geokinetic arguments are better than the geostatic ones, and that the Church is justified in requiring Catholics to believe the geostatic thesis. A third rhetorical weakness involves the ineffectual rhetoric of strict demonstration trying to convey the impression that the book provides a strict demonstration of the earth's motion; this is undermined by a much more considerable amount of rhetoric to the contrary as well as by the clearly evident fact that his pro-Copernican arguments, while strong, are inconclusive.[3] Finally, there is the self-defeating way Galileo presented the pope's favorite objection at the end of the book; the self-contradictory rhetoric of anti-rhetoric, namely a series of remarks to the effect that rhetoric has no place in science, which is belied at almost every turn by his own practice in the text; and the rhetorical excesses in which the book frequently lapses, involving criticism, insults, and sarcasm about his opponents. In regard to the latter, it should be noted that it is possible, interesting, and even valuable to be able to understand and appreciate such alienating excesses; but doing so involves moving to the aesthetic plane and leaving the rhetorical dimension behind, and so my point about the rhetorical situation remains valid. My criticism would be purely rhetorical and not scientific, methodological, or logical. What I am saying is that the book seems to reveal mostly ineptness in the art of persuasion and verbal communication and the handling of human emotions, rather than the brilliant polemicist and master rhetorician we hear so much about. I believe this hermeneutic problem stems from a failure to properly distinguish and interrelate interpretation and evaluation.

One last distinction crying out for judicious exercise is that between words and deeds, theory and practice, or concrete scientific work and methodological reflection. Here the most widespread tendency is to attribute to Galileo a divergence between his scientific practice and his methodological reflection (e.g., Duhem 1969, 113; Feyerabend 1975). Thus it may be useful to sketch an account which would not only interpret the *Dialogue* primarily in terms of critical reasoning and methodological judgment, but also show that Galileo was reflectively aware that this is what he was doing and what he should be doing.

4. Integrating Theory and Practice

To sketch my own interpretation, I would begin by showing that the *Dialogue* is an argument designed to support the conclusion that the pro-Copernican arguments are stronger than the anti-Copernican ones. This means that the Copernican theory is preferable to the geostatic view, or that Copernicanism is more probable or more likely to be true than geocentrism; the conclusion does *not* mean that Copernicanism is either clearly true, or certainly true, or absolutely true, or demonstrably true; nor does it mean that there are no reasons for believing the earth to stand still; nor that the geostatic arguments are worthless. The point is that the book's key thesis is one about the relative merits of the arguments on each side, that this thesis is substantiated and not merely asserted, and that the substantiation proceeds by the reasoned and self-reflective presentation, analysis, and evaluation of the respective arguments. In short, critical reasoning is a key part of the book's content as well as of the book's approach.[4]

The book's methodological judiciousness is shown (Finocchiaro 1980, 103-41 and 157-64; and forthcoming) by the fact that in the course of his main argument Galileo elaborates methodological ideas which may be described as follows: a critical empiricism which may be equated with critical apriorism, but such that it rejects both naive empiricism and dogmatic apriorism; a penchant for the mathematical approach, but combined with an awareness of the difficulties in applying mathematical truths to physical reality; epistemological modesty which avoids both skepticism and facile dogmatism; independent-mindedness which advocates neither total rejection of authority nor total submission to it; a realistic rational-mindedness which avoids both simple minded rationalism and despairing misologism; a judicious attitude toward the principle of simplicity which judges simplicity considerations to be neither worthless nor binding, but rather probable and plausible; a belief that many human concepts (e.g., size) are subjective and relative in several ways but not anthropocentric or teleological; a willingness to admit that the stellar parallax objection to Copernicanism cannot be refuted, and that all one can do is to outline a research program designed to test its existence.

After this account of the book's content and structure, the rest of our story would be an account of various Galilean reflections corresponding to it, in the sense that these reflections provide the theory of which the book is the practice. These reflections involve Galileo's response to three things: Bellarmine's epistemological objections, the biblical argument against the earth's motion, and the official restrictions by Church authorities.

Galileo's response to Bellarmine is found in his "Considerations on the Copernican Opinion," written in 1615. Galileo explicitly mentions prudence, which is intimately related to judiciousness; he stresses that the key problem is one of a critical comparison between the two world views; and he explicitly uses probabilistic and fallibilist language. Finally, his critical-reasoning program emerges clearly when he asserts that "those who hold the false side cannot have in their favor any valid reason or experiment, whereas it is necessary that all things agree and correspond with the true side" (Finocchiaro 1989, 85).

Next, there is Galileo's position in regard to the key religious objection, the biblical argument, elaborated in 1615 in the "Letter to the Grand Duchess." To shorten another long story (cf. Finocchiaro 1986), the key claim is a principle attributed by Galileo to Cardinal Baronio, stating that "the intention of the Holy Spirit is to teach us how one goes to heaven and not how heaven goes" (Finocchiaro 1989, 96). This memorable formulation is the one directly applicable in the context of the "Letter," namely in the criticism of the biblical objection; in fact, this objection argued that the earth must be standing still because it is so stated or implied in the Bible; and Baronio's principle directly invalidates the inferential soundness of this argument. The "Letter" also criticizes the truth of argument's premise, but that need not concern us here.

More important for now is a corollary of this principle formulating a norm corresponding more directly to Galileo's procedure in the *Dialogue*. The corollary is that biblical assertions about physical reality ought to be disregarded in natural science, or that scientists are free to investigate physical theories that contradict biblical assertions. In the words of the Inquisition Sentence which in 1633 found that procedure to be heretical, the corollary is "that one may hold and defend as probable an opinion ... contrary to the Holy Scripture" (Finocchiaro 1989, 291). I am here concurring with the Inquisitors' *interpretation*, although I would respectfully dissent from their *evaluation*.

However, the "Letter" could not have just assumed Baronio's principle, and so one of its central purposes is to justify it. Now, it is interesting and important that Galileo attempts what might be called an orthodox justification, namely one based on orthodox ideas. These stem primarily from St. Augustine. Galileo accepts Augustine's stress on "prudence"; this is intimately related to judiciousness, and should come as no surprise in the light of our earlier analysis. At the substantive level, the key premise of Galileo's argument is Augustine's traditional principle that if a biblical assertion contradicts a physical claim which has been conclusively proved, the latter is to be given priority and the biblical assertion set aside or reinterpreted. The crucial step in the argument is to ask for the rationale for this traditional practice: what is the reason why conclusively proved physical truths are (traditionally and uncontroversially) given precedence over conflicting biblical assertions? Baronio's principle gives the answer and provides the rationale. That is, Baronio's principle explains why Augustine's principle is correct, and this explanation in turn justifies the former's plausibility.

Next, once one accepts Baronio's principle, one can apply it to give an answer to another question, yielding another corollary. What should one do when biblical assertions contradict physical claims which have not yet been conclusively proved, but are capable of such a proof? The answer is that the scientist should be free to examine such claims and search for a proof. This corollary must be regarded to be as well grounded as the traditional Augustinian principle; the same reasons that justify the latter, will justify the former. Now, if Galileo were in possession of a conclusive proof of Copernicanism, then he would not have had to write this "Letter," or to answer criticism; he could have simply produced his proof, and the application of the traditional Augustinian principle would have easily and quickly resolved the problem. Thus the mere writing of the "Letter" is an indication that he felt Copernicanism was capable of conclusive proof, though not yet so proved. From this point of view, the *Dialogue* may be described as aiming to establish that the earth's motion is susceptible of conclusive proof (as distinct from establishing that this phenomenon is indeed conclusively proved).

Finally, one may also ask what to do in regard to physical claims which, besides lacking a conclusive proof, are not even capable of being conclusively proved. For this class of propositions, Galileo sees no difficulty in conceding to accept the Bible's word.

A third important element of the methodological background of the *Dialogue* involves the various ecclesiastical restrictions under which he was operating. To make another long story short, the net effect of these restrictions was to push Galileo away from the Aristotelian ideal of demonstration (which is the legacy he inherited) and toward a fallibilist, retroductive, hypothetico-deductive conception of science. One important restriction involved the proceedings of 1616, especially Cardinal Bellarmine's private warning to Galileo and the anti-Copernican Decree of the Index; these are briefly, clearly, and authoritatively summarized in Bellarmine's Certificate. This document states that Galileo was not supposed to hold, support, or defend the earth's motion (Finocchiaro 1989, 153). The other main relevant restriction was Pope Urban VIII's views on Copernicanism, which Galileo was able to directly glimpse at in the audiences of 1624, at which time he started writing the *Dialogue*; there is no simple or clear documentary record here, but we can find hints and references in a number of places, including the book's preface and ending. The restriction may be summarized by saying that only a hypothetical discussion of Copernicanism was legitimate.

Thus, the relevant prescriptions were: no holding, no supporting, no defending, only hypothetical discussion. Beginning with the latter, although the pope had an instrumentalist conception of hypothesis, Galileo seems to have been inclined to construe a hypothesis primarily as a proposition which describes physical reality, which is potentially true or false, whose truth value is not yet known with certainty, and whose status is in the process of being investigated. In regard to the prohibition to hold the proposition that the earth moves, Galileo seems to have interpreted it as meaning that he was not supposed to believe or accept that this proposition is true; however, this was not the same as believing that the proposition is probable. Thus, these two restrictions reinforced each other in suggesting to him that he adopt a probabilist, fallibilist stance. Now, in regard to supporting and defending, these activities may be viewed as correlative of one another in the sense that to support is to argue positively by providing favorable evidence and arguments, while to defend is is to argue negatively by answering, refuting, or criticizing objections and counterevidence. Thus, the question of supporting and defending is intimately related to the question of impartiality. Rather than supporting or defending the earth's motion, Galileo decided to simply discuss the arguments. What kind of discussion of the arguments? He must have felt that there could be nothing wrong with stating, analyzing, and evaluating the arguments on both sides.

This was a plausible, realistic, and viable program for operating within the restrictions. There were only two ways of violating them: (1) by presenting the argument(s) for Copernicanism as completely conclusive, which would entitle one to hold, believe, or accept it as true; and (2) by failing to be impartial. Now, it seems to me he could plausibly claim that his book was committing neither of these two violations.

To see this, I would argue that one must first disentangle the key thesis of the earth's motion from other parts of the Copernican system; the ecclesiastic restrictions applied only to this thesis; with respect to other subsidiary theses, there was no difficulty for the book to exhibit belief in their truth and to advance conclusive arguments; such was the case for the propositions that the lunar surface is rough, that the sunspots are part of the solar body, and that the planets (Mercury, Venus, Mars, Jupiter, and Saturn) revolve in heliocentric orbits. Second, once the focus becomes the earth's motion, it is entirely appropriate to omit explicit discussion of the Tychonic system since it shares the geostatic thesis with the Ptolemaic system; as long as the relevant issues were discussed, impartiality could be preserved; and the book did discuss the relevant issues; for example, Galileo is quite clear that the heliocentrism of the five agreed-upon planets is no conclusive evidence for the earth's annual motion, since part of the crucial issue is whether or not the earth is a planet (Galilei 1632, 354). Third, the book did not hide the fact that there was one important piece of evidence against Copernicanism which remained unrefuted, the absence of stellar parallax; the Third Day goes to great lengths in clarifying this objection and admitting its cogency; it also sketches a research program to test its existence, and expresses confidence that the result will favor the geokinetic hypothesis; but Galileo is perfectly aware that the test could yield negative results (Galilei 1632, 385-416). Finally, the book is very explicit about the hypothetical, explanatory, and causal form and structure of the two best pro-Copernican arguments, based on sunspot motion and on the tides; for the argument from sunspot motion, Galileo himself sketches an alternative geostatic explanation, and so there is no question that he realizes that, while the argument strongly favors the earth's motion, it is nevertheless inconclusive. For the tidal argument, he felt it was even stronger, and was unwilling or unable to seriously consider any alternative explanations; but even here he stated a general objection detracting from its absolute conclusiveness; this was the divine-omnipotence objection favored by Pope Urban VIII, which he was ordered to include in the book; but in a sense this is a theological version of the epistemological problem of induction and of the logical invalidity of the argument form of affirming the consequent, and so the objection can easily stated in a way which makes it valid; thus, the presumption must be that he realized and understood this (Finocchiaro 1980, 8-12); moreover, there is indirect evidence to that effect because Urban's objection also corresponds to an idea advanced by Galileo in the *Assayer* and greatly appreciated by the pope in that context; this is the idea that nature is bountiful and can produce a given effect by means of many different causes, a point illustrated by the story of a man searching the cause of sound and ending up killing a cicada in the process (cf. Biagioli 1993, 301-11).

Notes

[1]This research was supported by a grant (no. RH-20980-91) from the National Endowment for the Humanities and a sabbatical leave (Fall 1994) from the University of Nevada, Las Vegas.

[2]Although I mean the notion of "ideal type" in the general sense originating from Max Weber, I am adapting the application of this notion to methodology from McMullin (1990, 29-32). I believe McMullin's account of "Conceptions of Science in the Scientific Revolution" may be viewed as a comparison and contrast of the conceptions of Descartes, Bacon, Boyle, Kepler, Galileo, Newton, and Locke with the abstractly defined ideal types of deductivism, inductivism, hypothetico-deductivism, and retroductivism. If this interpretation of McMullin (1990) is correct, then I believe it sheds considerable light on his earlier account of "The Conception of Science in Galileo's Work" (McMullin 1978), which may then be seen as a similar analysis focused on Galileo; however, in the latter case I would want to emphasize that we have at least four strands because, as McMullin argues, the Aristotelian ideal of demonstration inherited by Galileo constituted "an ambiguous heritage" (McMullin 1978, 211) in which demonstra-

tion meant two distinct activities, namely intelligible explanation as well as conclusive proof; further, the conception of science toward which Galileo was groping can be shown to contain at least two distinct procedures, retroduction from effects to causes and acausal hypothetical reasoning. Parts of McMullin (1967) may be read in the same vein.

[3]What I am here labeling "rhetoric of strict demonstration" would perhaps be interpreted by other scholars from a historical point of view as important evidence of Galileo's Aristotelian roots, and from a methodological point of view as indicative of the nature of his methodology. I do not mean to deny these Aristotelian influences, which I would now judge as established beyond any reasonable doubt by Wallace (1984; 1992a; 1992b). Nor do I mean to deny the "Aristotelian" component of Galileo's methodology; however, this Aristotelian component is ambiguous in itself and only one of several, as suggested for example by McMullin (1967). Moreover, once we distinguish the rhetorical from the methodological dimensions and allow the legitimacy of both, I believe that both McMullin and Wallace admit and argue for the rhetorical ineffectiveness of these Galilean demonstrative claims.

[4]Further details and documentation are beyond the scope of this paper, but may be found in Finocchiaro (1980; and forthcoming); I believe that this critical interpretation also corresponds to the one earlier advanced by McMullin (1967, 35-42), although the context of his inquiry is different and he emphasizes the notion of a "reduction argument," namely one which "reduces the number of motions in a system" (p. 37). In fact, he is very clear that "most scientists among Galileo's readers were persuaded that the Copernican view had been adequately validated by the arguments of the *Dialogo*, but it is doubtful that they were any more impressed by their strictly *demonstrative* character than the theologians were" (McMullin 1967, 35); that "a reduction argument ... is, in fact, a dynamic argument of a particularly cogent sort" (p. 37); that, for example, Galileo's argument for terrestrial rotation at the beginning of the Second Day "is cogent, and suffices to 'prove' the diurnal motion of the earth in the only sense of 'prove' appropriate to the context" (p. 38); and that with such reduction arguments even "Tycho's own model ... could easily be attacked" (p. 40), though they would apply less easily against a semi-Tychonic system in which the earth has diurnal rotation but remains at the center. I now believe our main difference is not about the actual accomplishment of the *Dialogue*, but about Galileo's methodological self-conception; I take the latter to correspond to the accomplishment, whereas McMullin (1967) takes it to diverge from it and conform to the demonstrative ideal. This difference misled me in my earlier writings and made me neglect the points we share.

References

Arnauld, A. and Nicole, P. (1965), *La Logique ou l'Art de Penser*. Critical edition by P. Clair and F. Girbal. Paris: Presses Universitaires de France.

Biagioli, M. (1993), *Galileo Courtier*. Chicago: University of Chicago Press.

Duhem, P. (1969), *To Save the Phenomena*. Trans. by E. Doland and C. Maschler. Chicago: University of Chicago Press.

Feyerabend, P.K. (1975), *Against Method*. London: Verso.

Finocchiaro, M.A. (1980), *Galileo and the Art of Reasoning*. Dordrecht: Reidel.

___________. (1986), "The Methodological Background to Galileo's Trial", in W.A. Wallace (ed.), *Reinterpreting Galileo*. Washington: Catholic University of America Press, pp. 241-72.

__________. (ed. and trans.) (1989), *The Galileo Affair: A Documentary History*. Berkeley: University of California Press.

__________. (ed. and trans.) (forthcoming), *Galileo on the World Systems*. Berkeley: University of California Press.

Galilei, G. (1632), *Dialogo sopra i due massimi sistemi* ..., in *Le opere di Galileo Galilei*, vol. 7, National Edition by A. Favaro et al. Florence: Barbera, 1890-1909.

McMullin, E. (1967), "Introduction: Galileo, Man of Science", in E. McMullin (ed.), Galileo, *Man of Science*. New York: Basic Books, pp. 3-51.

_______. (1978), "The Conception of Science in Galileo's Work", in R.E. Butts and J.C. Pitt (eds.), *New Perspectives on Galileo*. Dordrecht: Reidel, pp. 209-57.

_______. (1990), "Conceptions of Science in the Scientific Revolution", in D.C. Lindberg and R. S. Westman (eds.), *Reappraisals of the Scientific Revolution*. Cambridge: Cambridge University Press, pp. 27-92.

Moss, J.D. (1993), *Novelties in the Heavens*. Chicago: University of Chicago Press.

Pitt, J.C. (1992), *Galileo, Human Knowledge, and the Book of Nature*. Dordrecht: Kluwer.

Salusbury, T. (ed. and trans.) (1661), *Mathematical Collections and Translations*, Tome 1, part 1. London.

Wallace, W.A. (1984), *Galileo and His Sources*. Princeton: Princeton University Press.

_______. (1992a), *Galileo's Logical Treatises*. Dordrecht: Kluwer.

_______. (1992b), *Galileo's Logic of Discovery and Proof*. Dordrecht: Kluwer.

Newton's *Opticks* as Classic: On Teaching the Texture of Science

Dennis L. Sepper

University of Dallas

The opening paragraphs of Thomas Kuhn's *Structure of Scientific Revolutions* noted that different kinds of scientific writings have peculiar roles (Kuhn 1962). A textbook written for pedagogical purposes in a well-established scientific field gives a view of the field quite different from the actual history—an actual history that for the most part has to be reconstructed from the writings that originated the field. The originating writings correspond to the period of founding, to revolutionary science, whereas conventionalized textbooks belong to normal science.

This is almost too well known to be rehearsed again. Certain works found a science, like Newton's *Opticks* or Watson and Crick's original papers on the double-helical structure of DNA; others come in their wake, not just textbooks used for beginners but all the future texts that contribute to the paradigm project embodied in the originals. Even within the paradigm the originals are gradually displaced by the evolution of understanding through ongoing research; and when the paradigm is swallowed up by the next revolution, the originals are further displaced, even eclipsed and forgotten.

The transience or volatility of scientific writings, even of founding ones, may simply be a reminder that science is a practice whose primary aim is to produce knowledge and further practice in accordance with that knowledge rather than texts. Texts are temporary vehicles for reports on the current state of experimental and theoretical practice. The transcription of procedures, results, theories, and the like is important, but such transcription does not produce works that are strict analogues of humanistic *works of art.* One might then expect that the category of 'classicity' should not be used of scientific writing as it is in the humanities. Scientific works, even the best, have a transient effect, whereas a classic in the humanities represents a more durable achievement. Yet scarcely anyone would contest that Isaac Newton's *Opticks* is a classic of the physical sciences just as much as Shakespeare's *King Lear* is a classic of English literature.

1. Classics in Science

What do we have in mind when we make classic claims? A useful jumping off point for clarifying the question is Hans-Georg Gadamer's discussion of classicity in *Truth and Method,* in the section titled "The Example of the Classical" (Gadamer 1989, 285-290). Gadamer begins by distinguishing an original, though also special, use of 'classic' with normative implications from the more general use of the term to designate an outstanding example of a cultural or artistic style. Gadamer interprets the

---

PSA 1994, Volume 2, pp. 258-265

special, normative sense as "a notable mode of being historical: the historical process of preservation that, through constantly proving itself, allows something true to come into being....The classical is something that resists historical criticism because its historical dominion, the binding power of the validity that is preserved and handed down, precedes all historical reflection and continues in it" (287). He notes that "when we call something classical, there is a consciousness of something enduring, of a significance that cannot be lost and that is independent of all the circumstances of time—a kind of timeless present that is contemporaneous with every other present" (288).

Gadamer has a specific understanding of what this timelessness amounts to. "What gives birth to the classical norm is an awareness of decline and distance." In particular, in he Renaissance the artistic and political examples of the ancient Greeks and Romans were seen as a challenge to greatness after a long period of decline. The achievements of antiquity thus became classic in the normative sense. The more general, stylistic sense of 'classic' arose by analogy, through a mode of judgment that extended the term to any works of culture that represent the culmination of a genre or style. Thus, according to Gadamer, although 'classic' used loosely can designate any work that is an outstanding example of a cultural movement, style, or moment, this usage is rooted in a historically older one, the recognition of the achievements of a privileged moment in time that continues to make an appeal to subsequent ages because it is still a part of a living tradition. I will henceforth refer to the difference between the two kinds of classic by calling the first a stylistic(-historiographic) classic and the second kind a classic of tradition.

Is this decidedly humanistic account relevant to works of science? Gadamer does not answer this question directly. *Truth and Method* is of course aimed at shaking the hold that the ideal of progressive research had asserted over the humanities in the nineteenth century, precisely in imitation of the natural sciences. As much implicitly as explicitly the book distinguishes truth in the humanities from the methodical truth of the sciences; without argument it concedes to the natural sciences a kind of unremitting progressivity that subsequent historians and philosophers of science have debunked (*Truth and Method* was first published in German in 1960, before the new historiography and philosophy of science had had its revolutionary effect). Gadamer's account therefore suggests but does not attempt to prove that science and the humanities are too different for 'classic' to mean the same for both.

Kuhn, on the other hand, hoped to show that the sciences were very much like the arts and humanities in having a history of styles (read *paradigms*). We acknowledge the existence of classics of scientific style whenever we give an account of a science that identifies its paradigmatic works, even if in view of later developments the works appear to be relics. Although there is no doubt of Kepler's importance in the history of several modern sciences, his books on astronomy and optics seem distinctly odd, far more distant from us than Newton's. In the history of method Francis Bacon's *New Organon* is a stylistic-historiographic classic but is no longer a normative one. Whether there are normative classics for Kuhn is doubtful, since the incommensurability problem makes it difficult to see how a work can withstand the ravages of revolutions and changes of world-view.

Even setting Gadamer and Kuhn aside, we must note a dilemma about the applicability of "classic" to science: insofar as science expands progressively it actively embodies in the present moment the best of the past, and thus it in effect displaces the founding works as obsolescent; insofar as science changes in a revolutionary way it puts any candidate for classic status at the even greater distance of irrelevance. The "classic" is simply more problematic in the sciences than it is in the humanities.

Are there scientific works that are classic in the normative sense, classics of tradition? One of the ironies in the wake of the so-called "canon wars" of the past few years is that a committee of academics could probably come closer to agreeing on a canon of scientific works than on a canon of art or literature; even more important, many of the canonical works of science (which would certainly include Euclid's *Elements* and some of Newton's writings) would display a living hold on us—not in terms of entertainment value, of course, but as representing a still living tradition and practice.

Whether or not someone is gripped by a work depends not just on the person but also on the work's character. Perhaps any work has the power to grip, or at least to appeal to, an appropriately prepared audience. Newton's *Opticks* has a special ability to take hold of its readers, however. It is, to begin with, a stylistic-historiographic classic, given its founding status in modern optics and theory of color. Yet it is also a classic of tradition, and in a sense even deeper than many literary classics. Unlike optical works of Kepler and Descartes it has a freshness and directness that engages us in its activity, even if we follow along only in imagination. Very much like works of literature the *Opticks* creates its own ethos and world by engaging even the naive reader in its viewing and practice. It introduces the reader into—if I may coin a term—the texture of science.

'Texture' as I use it here is first of all a play on 'text.' A text in the first instance appears linear because of the linearity of first reading. Texts nevertheless also have depth, expansiveness, density, pattern—in a word, texture. The texture is less a matter of writing style than of the subtlety and scope of the work's manner of engagement with a subject matter and the care with which themes are interwoven. This texture of the text has a nontrivial relationship to another texture, that of the scientific activity from which it arises. Ordinarily we can expect the texture of scientific activity to be richer than the texture of the corresponding text (contemporary scientific journal articles and textbooks no more than suggest the complexity and depth of the activity and community out of which they are produced). These two different textures, and in addition the differences between the scientific activity that gives rise to a text and the larger scientific field and community of which it is a part, suggest a further coinage, *contexture,* to indicate the texture of supporting activities or surrounds in relationship to the texture of a text and also to mark the texture of activities in the larger scientific community in relation to the texture of a particularized area of activity within it.

2. The Texture of the *Opticks*

An obvious difference between scientific literature and literature in general is their intentional object. What Shakespeare's intended object was in *The Tempest* is not easy to state, and when we try to state it we are involved in a complicated hermeneutic gambit. Scientists, on the other hand, intend to characterize, isolate, control, and explain things and phenomena that arise from nature. This intentionality does not at all exclude a socio-psychological construction of science or a complicated hermeneutics, but it does provide a determinate arena and a fundamental directedness within which constructive, interpretive, and even arbitrary and willful activities can take place. What this means, of course, is that scientific classics have an avenue of maintaining their power to grip the intelligence and imagination of readers that is largely closed to other literature, in that it can involve the reader in an excursion into nature (or at least into the interface between free nature and the laboratory). A literary work can open a world of meaning, but the insight it gives into the lived world is indirect; a scientific work, especially one that skillfully presents the practice of scientific investigation along with theory, can bring one nearer to natural things and their ways of appearing.

This is not simply to say that a scientific work must be phenomenal and experimental to have the power of a classic of tradition. Robert Boyle's historically important but largely forgotten *Experiments and Considerations Touching Colours* is more plentiful than Newton's work in its array of phenomena and experiments, but its aim rarely goes beyond presenting the phenomena for the sake of an articulate natural history of color. Newton, by contrast, introduces no experiment or phenomenon unmotivated. He intends his work to be theoretically productive even more than to be experimentally productive. He describes his experiments with prisms not, like Boyle, to familiarize his readers with the variety of remarkable refraction and color phenomena out to show that the differential refraction of a beam of white light yields results that confound prevailing conceptions (see Hall 1993 and Sepper 1994). Newton weaves a narrative and a corresponding experimental sequence that constantly challenge and expand the current state of explanation. This holds true even of his own explanations. Although we must sometimes make generous allowance for special pleading, he expects (and often shows) that further experimentation will either confirm his original theories or force their extension or revision.

Newton did these things so resolutely and so succesfully that he managed to transform the chief genres of scientific communication from modes of curiosity- and hypothesis-mongering into vehicles driving progressive research. Others, like Descartes and Robert Hooke, had used experiments for the theoretical purpose of motivating their speculations about light's nature and what happens when it encounters matter. But there is more than a hint of inertia in their hypotheses, as though once you have a motivated hypothesis the work of knowledge is basically done. Newton reoriented natural philosophy to the task of constant evidencing and reevidencing, construction and reconstruction, as new combinations of optical devices and the emergence of new categories of phenomena (like thin-film colors and diffraction) not only induce theoretical and experimental refinements but also force substantial changes in conception (for example, thin-film colors led him to devise a theory of fits of easy transmission and reflection of rays; see Shapiro 1993) and strike bridges to other subject areas (as in the Queries of Book 3, which among other things broach issues of physiology, psychology, chemistry, and general matter theory).

The forward impetus of the *Opticks* is driven by Newton's desire to convince his readers of the truth of the differential refrangibility of rays according to color and at least the probability of the theory of fits of easy reflection and transmission. Yet the basic architecture of the work comes less from theory than it does from an articulation of light phenomena into basic classes. This articulation is suggested by the opening sentence of the work: "My design in this book is not to explain the properties of light by hypotheses, but to propose and prove them by reason and experiments." In the first instance the aim is to present not so much hypotheses and experiments as the *properties* of light. The success of the theory, debates about the underlying conception of light, Newton's nearly incredible skill as experimenter, and the bold research program sketched out in the concluding Queries have made it easy to overlook this fact. The chief organizing principle of the work is not theories, experiments, or entities but properties: refraction, reflection, inflection (thin-film phenomena), and diffraction. Although these phenomena must reside in some substrate, and his conception of 'ray of light' tends to foster a corpuscular rather than an impulse or wave understanding, the chief strategy is to divide the appearances of light into classes and subclasses and to correlate these classes with one another. The fundamental phenomena of refraction show that there is a differential displacement of light according to color; this difference in light then reappears in the phenomena of reflection, inflection, and diffraction, a reappearance that makes it possible to extend the investigation in ever more sophisticated ways without losing sight of the fundamental principles of organization. The texture of the *Opticks* is thereby made ever more intricate, but the phenomenal and theoretical patterns stand out clearly.

Although the properties of light are each correlated with different varieties of experimental setup—refraction requires prisms, reflection mirror-like surfaces, inflection thin films of transparent substances, diffraction sharp edges—the experimental survey is in each case so ample that their relationship to natural phenomena (like the rainbow) is clarified, and Newton is able to show that differences detected in any one of these properties are relevant to differences in the other properties. Moreover, he establishes through his exposition of differential refraction a fundamental way of conceiving all the relevant phenomena as more or less complex cases of a simple event: the decomposition or differentiation of white light according to its components. If Newton no longer appeals to crucial experiments in the *Opticks,* he nonetheless identifies this as the crucial or basic phenomenon to which everything can be referred and on the basis of which everything can be reckoned.

I. B. Cohen's *Franklin and Newton* shows that eighteenth-century experimentalists took Newton's *Opticks* as a model of experimental efficiency and productivity; in particular, they aspired to reach the level that Newton had achieved in letting experiments speak for themselves, that is, in devising and deploying experiments so that their theoretical significance became as close to self-evident as possible (Cohen 1956). In Kuhnian terms, the *Opticks* became a paradigm for eighteenth-century experimental sciences. Of course we do not find it credible any longer that phenomena can speak for themselves, and our historical distance makes it easier to identify ways in which the *Opticks* is theory laden. Yet I believe the impression that the phenomena of light and color can clarify their own significance was precisely what attracted his eighteenth-century readers and what makes the work a genuine classic of normative tradition. If one is at all inclined to pick up a prism, play with it, and wonder why it works as it does, Newton's experimental evocation of the fundamental phenomenon of differential refraction and its clarifying force has a nearly irresistible appeal, one that is as strong today as it was nearly three hundred years ago. If in comparison most other scientific works fall short of this we thereby find confirmation of Gadamer's claim that the birth of the classical norm requires "an awareness of decline and distance."

It is by working with the phenomena in relatively simple ways that Newton draws the reader into the investigation; even if the reader is unsure about the technicalities of theory, he or she can follow the experiments. They are woven together to produce a fabric of mutually supporting strands. The weaving metaphor, implicit in the notion of texture, brings out this characteristic of deepening, broadening, and intensifying the experimental and theoretical relationships. The equipment used for experiments in one part is incorporated into later, more complicated ones; differential refraction becomes the leitmotif in preparing light for experimental use; experiments draw on multiple properties of light to show interconnections suggestive of light's nature; Newton uses analyzed light to probe microscopic properties of matter and the forces that make matter cohere (see Sepper 1994). There is also the texture of context, what I call 'contexture.' An attentive reader recognizes, and a historically informed one knows, that the *Opticks* takes a controversial stance in the history of light and color theory. Not least important in this regard is its running polemic against proponents of modificationist theories of color; the experimental and theoretical shadows of these proponents, people like Boyle, Hooke, Huygens, and Grimaldi, constantly flicker against the grain of the text.

I am not implying that only a work as complex and rich as the *Opticks* has texture and contexture. By their nature these terms should apply to any work of letters. But not every work deploys texture and contexture so as to directly grip scientific neophytes. Think for a moment of the 1953 papers of Watson and Crick in contrast with Watson's *Double Helix*. The pieces that appeared in *Nature* have the format of the modern journal article: an outline of the state of the problem, a discussion of relevant recent findings, the presentation of hypotheses and evidence for them, and a rather spare selection of possible implications (see Watson and Crick 1953a and 1953b; also Wilkins et al. 1953 and Franklin and Gosling 1953). One would hardly suspect from them the drama that is narrated in *The Double Helix* (Watson 1968). This tale of the discovery is a popularization, to be sure, even an overdramatization, but it probably reveals more truly the texture of the relevant scientific knowledge and activity. The original papers conventionalize and flatten texture into journal-article rhetoric. This serves the purposes of rapid communication to a small group of colleagues, but it also filters out many of the qualities of the work that give it depth and consistency. So Crick's predilection for attacking problems by taking a high-level theoretical point of view, Watson's liking for philosophical ideas and concrete models, the serendipitous acquisition of relevant information from neighboring fields (like the difference between the enol and keto forms of amino acids), the problems of using and mastering techniques of X-ray diffraction, the competition with Maurice Wilkins, Rosalind

Franklin, and Linus Pauling—these and many others contribute to the texture of the scientific activity. These are the strands that are woven together to make up the fabric of the science, a fabric that would show different patterns were the circumstances or personalities different, a fabric that depends on many vagaries of the historical path to scientific research and achievement.

3. Teaching the Texture of Science

I do not with these reflections intend to reintroduce the notion of what is internal and external to science; quite the opposite. The particulars and singularities of the situation do determine which strands figure prominently in the texture of scientific activity and the texture of the resultant text. The patterning and specific character of the context or background, on the other hand, depends far less immediately on singularities and more on the givens of the scientific field and the larger historical structurings that have shaped it.

To speak in Kuhnian terms for a moment, the paradigmatic quality comes not from interesting personalities and their social life but from the specific achievement produced by an unprecedented weaving together of theories, results, practices, equipment, and techniques. Some works are so innovative and well constructed that they create a new scientific field and practice, a new ethos. Such works must have either an extraordinarily rich texture—in that case they might even constitute the new ethos virtually by themselves—or, if they are texturally less rich, they must play off characteristics of the already-established scientific background, in which case the scientists know almost immediately how to situate the texture within its context. Self-constituting, ethos-creating works are rare in the history of the sciences, and rarer still in recent times, because in most cases scientific communications are tailored for an already constituted community. The richer the contexture of the scientific community, the less elaborate and dense, the less deeply textured, the communications need be. Scientific communications do not have to engage their intended readers with anything more than a relatively small part of the field and its practice, and only rarely do they have to lead readers into an intensive encounter with an ample range of phenomena and theory.

This problem of a disproportion between texts and their supporting activity is not unique to the modern sciences of nature. Philosophers of science, or for that matter philosophers in general, know that the journal article has been one of the most effective ways to communicate ongoing research to one's colleagues. An ample understanding of the state of the question usually has to be presupposed, a fact that is evident when one tries to use collections of articles to enlighten undergraduate or even sometimes graduate students. It is not mere accident, then, that classics maintain their role in philosophical education. They are works with a texture sufficiently deep and rich that they can engage the interest even of nonspecialists long after their original composition. If their execution is skillful and their texture deep, we are not in immediate need of amplifying the text by understanding context and contexture; they can grip a reader by a power they have and by the living tradition they carry with them.

The history of the sciences is rich in stylistic-historiographic classics but more impoverished in classics of tradition. As I have explained the difference, this is not a fault in science but is due to an organization of activity and communication that is necessary for rapid development. There is still a place for the classics of tradition in liberal education, of course, and for that matter even in the education of scientists. Here at the end I will take it as granted that a liberal education is desirable for everyone who undertakes higher studies and concentrate instead on how a classic of tradition serves such an end. As opposed to a conventionalized textbook account, the classic presents theory and practice in a living problem setting. What that problem setting was has to be reconstructed to some degree, but reconstruction helps make clear to the student that a problem is relative to a situation involving theories, hypotheses, practices, techniques, equipment, methods, and (not least important) controversies. The non-scientist picks up at least a smattering of science thereby; sciences students gain insights relevant to contemporary work. To return once more to the *Opticks,* both groups of students can be induced to grasp how a problem situation is set up by the questions and actions of predecessors and to imagine how hard it is to conceive, execute, and duplicate new experiments. They can worry about whether it matters where in the phenomenal and experimental realm one begins one's investigations and about the difficulties of weaving a narrative of history, theory, and phenomena. Both kinds of student will, not coincidentally, be introduced thereby to the pleasures and pitfalls of philosophizing and doing historical reconstruction.

My intention is not to create a new academic demand for (or supply of) philosophers and historians of science, nor simply to urge everyone to use the *Opticks* for these purposes (although the *Opticks* is virtually unique in the way it allows students with the most various backgrounds to get an accessible experience of both hands-on and minds-on science). Each teacher, whether philosopher, historian, or scientist, would want to use whatever materials make a layered engagement with science possible, including the kind of guided studies of scientific classics that have recently been supported by the National Endowment for the Humanities (for example, Corcos and Monaghan 1993 and Sepper 1994). Different audiences will require different expedients. The object with all audiences, however, should be to give some experience in depth and an expansive view of the horizons of the sciences.

Pedagogical success depends as much on us as on what there is to read, yet the foundation for that success is the classic works of science. Teaching texture and contexture is not just an ideal but a genuine possibility residing in the power of classic texts to engage simultaneously an aspect of the natural world and the cooperative activities of the reader. Thus works like the *Opticks* do more than introduce a reader to a world-view: they allow the person to participate, however briefly, in a way of acting and viewing that follows the many threads that make up texture. Just learning about science, its history, and its philosophy is no substitute. The difference is like that between taking up an ideology and actually thinking and living a set of ideas through. If we have an interest in continuing the tradition of science, especially in an age like ours, which, despite the world-political events of the past few years, is still shaped by ideologies and world-views that are tenuously connected to the many strands of nature and culture, then it is worth our effort to introduce the students we face and the readers we address to the life of the tradition's most vital works.

References

Boyle, R. (1664), *Experiments and Considerations Touching Colours.* London: H. Herringman.

Cohen, I.B. (1956), *Franklin and Newton: An inquiry into speculative Newtonian experimental science and Franklin's work in electricity as an example thereof:* Memoirs of the American Philosophical Society 43, Philadelphia: American Philosophical Society.

Corcos, A.F. and Monaghan, F.V. (1993), *Gregor Mendel's "Experiments on Plant Hybrids."* New Brunswick, N.J.: Rutgers University Press.

Franklin, R.E. and Gosling, R.G. (1953), "Molecular Configuration in Sodium Thymonucleate," *Nature* 171 (April 25): 740-741.

Gadamer, H.-G. (1989), *Truth and Method,* 2d ed. New York: Crossroad.

Hall, A.R. (1993), *All Was Light: An Introduction to Newton's Opticks.* Oxford: Clarendon Press.

Kuhn, T.S. (1962), *The Structure of Scientific Revolutions.* Chicago: University of Chicago Press.

Sepper, D.L. (1994), *Newton's Optical Writings: A Guided Study.* New Brunswick, N.J.: Rutgers University Press.

Shapiro, A.E. (1993), *Fits, Passions, and Paroxysms: Physics, Method, and Chemistry and Newton's Theories of Colored Bodies and Fits of Easy Reflection.* Cambridge: Cambridge University Press.

Watson, J.D. (1968), *The Double Helix: A Personal Account of the Discovery of the Structure of DNA.* New York: Atheneum.

Watson, J.D. and Crick, F.H.C. (1953a), "A Structure for Deoxyribose Nucleic Acid," *Nature* 171 (April 25): 737-738.

_ _ _ _ _ _ _ _ _ _ _ _ _ _ _ _ _ _ . (1953b), "Genetical Implications of the Structure of Deoxyribonucleic Acid," *Nature* 171 (May 30): 964-967.

Wilkins, M.H.F., Stokes, A.R. and Wilson, H.R. (1953), "Molecular Structure of Deoxypentose Nucleic Acids," *Nature* 171 (April 25): 738-740.

Scientific Classics and Their Fates

Ernan McMullin

University of Notre Dame

The term 'classic' runs a risk that all our terms of approbation face in these inflationary times, the risk, that is, of losing its ability to mark off singular works of human achievement. A "classic" today might be anything from a horse-race to a hair-style. But it was not always so. There is some debate about the origins of the term ("of the highest class"? "books for class use"?), but it long ago came to designate those works of Greek and Latin literature that for centuries shaped the education of young Western Europeans. These books were held up not only as models of literary accomplishment but also as sources of moral and social wisdom. Though they were composed in ages long past, their resonance was still felt in the present. And so the broader sense developed of a significant literary work of the past that still in one way or another speaks to us today. Thus Dante and Shakespeare and Racine could be added to the list that already contained Homer and Aeschylus and Horace.

1. Classics of science

Are there scientific "classics"? The term seems less often used in the context of scientific works. But why should it not apply to significant books in the history of science just as it does to chosen literary works? The problem is that major scientific works of the past do not seem to enjoy the sort of presence today that great works of literature do. They are rarely read, except by professional historians. They are in a real sense superseded, set aside, no longer consulted in the daily work of science. If someone today wants to explore the scientific issues that they once treated, that person would ordinarily consult the most up-to-date reference. Such works seem to fail the "resonance" test: people do not turn to them as they do to Homer or Dickens. (In that connection, however, I am tempted to recall that ancient definition of a classic as a book on everyone's shelves that hardly anyone reads!) Clearly, if we wish to speak of "classics" of science, then, we have to recognize that their relevance to the present is not of the sort that great works of literature might claim.

Inspired by Gadamer, Denis Sepper in our symposium distinguishes between two different usages of the term 'classic'. One is to designate, in a very general way, an outstanding example of a particular cultural movement or style. This he calls a stylistic-historiographical classic; its value to us is that it gives us an insight into the culture (style, mode of thinking) of which it is a representative. A subset of these qualifies, however, as classics in a more demanding sense: not only are they outstanding achievements in their own context, but they are part of a living tradition that endures

---

PSA 1994, Volume 2, pp. 266-274

to the present, hence the title: "classics of tradition". They "address us where we live"; they are "fecund even in the contemporary situation". Extending this distinction to science, and calling also on Kuhn, Sepper distinguishes between a general category of "paradigm-founding" works which can be classed as stylistic-historiographical classics even though they may be no more than "relics" in the contemporary scientific perspective, and classics of tradition which, like Euclid's *Elements*, can plausibly be held to retain a normative status in science even today.

Gadamer's terminology is cumbersome and the distinction he points to is far from sharp when applied to the history of science, as he himself would be the first to admit. There is a sense in which any scientific work of the past that would qualify in the first category would have *some* claim on the second category too. One does not have to subscribe to the old cumulative ideal of science, according to which progress consisted in laying brick on brick, with the old bricks retained intact, to note that major works of the past almost inevitably would find *some* echo in the science of today. The empirical regularities to which they point, for instance, might serve, under altered linguistic guise, as part of the evidential base of later theory. The difficulty of drawing the requisite distinction is brought out very well by the examples Sepper himself uses to illustrate it. As "relics" of only historical interest today he mentions Kepler's works on astronomy and Bacon's *Novum Organon*.. But Kepler's three "laws" of planetary motion and his insistence on a dynamical account of that motion did much to shape Newton's later achievement. And many of Bacon's prescriptions on method find an unmistakeable echo in our own century, in the work of Karl Popper, for example (Urbach 1982). The whole issue of *retention*, the extent to which later science typically incorporates earlier stages of inquiry has of course been the subject of sharp disagreement among philosophers of science in recent decades (see, for example, Feyerabend 1981 and McMullin 1984). In the circumstances, it seems wiser not to employ a distinction which relies for its force on the degree to which the classic in question remains "normative" at the present day.

The point of this discussion is not just a matter of word-usage. The quest is for those works of science that are most worthy of continuing study. The motives for such study would, of course, be various: historical (the effort to understand how a particular transition occurred, what the science involved conveyed about the world, what mode of evidence it appealed to); or philosophical (becoming clearer on how scientific inquiry has been carried on in the past, disentangling and evaluating specific arguments, testing contemporary theories of science against historical case-studies). Not every landmark in the past history of science is marked by a book, but when this *is* the case, such books offer an unrivaled resource for those who desire to understand the complex communal activity called "science". Let us agree, then to designate as "classics" those works that give us a special insight into the history and nature of science. Might one further require that they mark scientific *revolutions*, sharp shifts in research tradition, as Derek Gjertsen suggests (Gjertsen 1984)? This seems, at first sight, a plausible clarification. Ironically, however, none of the three works we have been studying in this symposium quite qualify under it. In the remainder of this brief commentary, I want to draw attention to some of the points made in the course of the symposium, and to reflect on how strange the fates were of each of the three works that were discussed.

2. Aristotle's De Partibus Animalium

Aristotle scholars have long struggled with what Jonathan Barnes calls "The problem of demonstration": "The method which Aristotle follows in his scientific and philosophical treatises and the method which he prescribes for scientific and philosophical activity in the *Posterior Analytics* seem not to coincide" (Barnes 1964). One possibility is that the model of demonstration described in *Post. An.* represents an early Platonic phase in Aristotle's thinking, and that the vast empirical research reported in his biological works belongs to a later and more mature phase (Jaeger 1934). Another is that the account of demonstration in *Post. An.* was put forward as an *ideal* of what knowledge itself should look like, not at all as an account of the procedures to be followed in actual inquiry (Randall 1960). Barnes' own solution is that *Post. An.* was intended as a model of how science should be *taught*, not how it should be acquired. William Wians, on the other hand, argues that dialectic (as outlined in the *Topics*), not demonstration, is Aristotle's chosen mode of teaching, that dialectic is a proper part of his theory of science and that this is the part exemplified by his biological treatises (Wians 1983). The great majority of recent commentators who have dealt with this issue (D.M. Balme, P. Moraux, G.E.R. Lloyd, are some others), though they disagree as to how to deal with the "problem of demonstration", agree at least that there *is* a problem.

But there have always been scholars who see no particular tension here. Indeed, this would have been the majority view among medieval commentators who assumed that even if explicit demonstrations are almost entirely lacking in Aristotle's works on natural philosophy, one could always, with a little ingenuity, convert his "proofs" to proper syllogistic form. A somewhat similar view is implicit in the work of several recent scholars (F. Solmsen and M. Grene, for example) who seem willing to allow many of the informal justifications given by Aristotle in his natural science to qualify as demonstration in a broad sense. However, James Lennox takes a bolder line in our symposium. Focusing on a single work, the *De Partibus Animalium*, he claims that *PA* I "was intentionally written to answer the question of how the *Analytics* model of science is to apply to Aristotle's paradigm natural substances, animals, and that *PA* II-IV carries out the program of *PA* I". Thus there *is* no "problem of demonstration" in the first place, for this work at least, and by extension, for the biological works generally.

The key to his argument is the notion of conditional (or hypothetical) necessity introduced in *PA* I, 1, where it is contrasted with the unqualified (or absolute) necessity which constitutes the ordinary meaning of the term for Aristotle. The notion is not a simple one. John Cooper sums up a detailed analysis of the relevant texts as follows:

> An organ or feature of a living thing is formed by hypothetical necessity if, given the essence of the thing (specified in terms of capacities and functions) and given the nature of the materials available to constitute it, the organ or feature in question is a necessary means to its constitution.... Explanation by appeal to hypothetical necessity is not an alternative to explanation by reference to goals. It is a *special case* of the latter kind of explanation, the case where the independently given nature of the materials available for use in realizing the goal makes precisely *one* possible means, or some narrowly circumscribed set of possible means, to the end in question mandatory (Cooper 1987, 256; see also Balme 1987).

Aristotle remarks that this sort of necessity is appropriate to explanations of "things generated" (PAI, 642a 7), where final cause is primary. It is plausible, then, so Lennox argues, to suppose that Aristotle is here showing how to adapt the strong *Post. An.* notion of demonstration to the sciences of nature: simply weaken the notion of necessity required. One can then retain the general framework of *Post. An.*, the emphasis on deduction from principles themselves seen, on the basis of experience, to hold with necessity. In this way we can formulate truths as mundane as that animal kidneys are necessarily fat-covered. The ways in which the parts of an animal serve the good of the whole organism, the functions each part plays in the larger whole, these are accessible to the student of living things in a way that the more abstract relation of essence to property, on which the *Post. An.* had focused, is not.

I think that Lennox makes a good case. Does it dissolve the "problem of demonstration"? Not entirely. A number of reservations suggest themselves. First, his thesis applies at best only to PA where conditional necessity is indeed important because of the stress on the relationship of part to function that runs through the book as a whole. But elsewhere in the works on natural science, even in the other biological works, this is much less evident. And even in PA, Aristotle stays for the most part at the descriptive level; passages like the one on the kidneys, where necessity is explicitly mentioned, are relatively rare. *Post. An.* specifies syllogistic form: there is not, I think , a single formal syllogism in all of PA. One can, of course, as Lennox does, convert various arguments there into syllogisms by supplying premises left implicit, adding the necessary quantifiers, and so forth. But this seems hardly enough to satisfy the *Post. An.* specifications, which would seem to require explicit syllogistic form.

Finally, a central concern in *Post. An.* is definition by genus and difference, and the kind of classification that this makes possible. Most of the examples given there are drawn from the living world. (See, for example, the application of the method of division to the highest genus, animal, in II, 13). One would have expected, then, a very different approach to the science of living things than is found in PA, where careful classification of this sort is notably lacking. Nor is it found in the other biological works either (Wians 1983). The linking of part and function by conditional necessity represents a significantly different approach. It seems plausible to suppose that when Aristotle began his researches into the living world he found that the necessary relations of essence and property were in practice not accessible to *epagoge* (insight based on experience) in the way that the schema of science announced in *Post. An.* presumed them to be, so he turned to a much more manageable alternative instead.

In his concluding paragraph, Lennox himself notes that the paradigm of science underlying *Post. An.* is mathematics, and he asks to what extent a model of science drawn from mathematics (more specifically, from axiomatic geometry) can be applied to a world of teleologically-organized living systems. Though he leaves the question unanswered, the answer to which the argument of his essay would seem to point is: hardly at all. And if this is the case, then his approach to the "problem of demonstration" cannot entirely satisfy. PA cannot be simply read, as he claims, as the application of the *Post. An.* model of science to the study of the living world. PA *does* propose an ingenious approach to at least one part of that study, but this approach, despite its reliance on a special kind of necessity, still marks a significant departure from the program of *Post. An.*.

Did PA leave behind a thriving research program? The answer is: no, and this poses a new problem. In a recent essay, Lennox notes that although the period after Aristotle's death saw unprecedented developments in such "special sciences" as mechanics, astronomy, and optics, the study of zoology to which so large a part of his writings is devoted, vanishes from sight until the late Middle Ages (Lennox, 1994). Why? He rejects two possible hypotheses: that Aristotle's biological works themselves fell out of sight, and second, that there were not people of the right talents available to continue on the tradition. Galen, for example, refers many times to Aristotle's biological works, but shows no interest in carrying on the research programs they embody. Lennox speculates that the sort of concern with the messy detail of the living world that the program called for would very likely not have been shared by many in the Hellenistic period, from what we know of the sensibilities of the time. It was not until the sixteenth and seventeenth centuries that others (like Cesalpino, Fabricius, Ray) were found who *did* share that concern and carry it further. Here, then, was a classic whose influence took two thousand years to show itself!

3. Galileo's Dialogue on Two Chief World Systems

There is nothing quite like Galileo's *Dialogo* in all the long history of Western science. It is constructed with consummate skill as an interlocking sequence of arguments directed to a single conclusion: the superiority of the Copernican over the Aristotelian and Ptolemaic world systems. It is intended for the general reading public, not for professionals, and hence for the most part avoids technicality without losing its logical force. It is a paragon of literary elegance, one of the seminal works that helped to form the Tuscan "canon" of the Italian language. Its publication set off a theological firestorm whose embers still occasionally flare.

In his *Galileo and the Art of Reasoning* (1980), Maurice Finocchiaro provided an extended analysis of the logic of the *Dialogo*, lauding it as a treasurehouse of argumentative strategies. Some of his conclusions he summarizes for us in his symposium paper. I will be concerned here only with what he has to say about the role played by the *Dialogo* in the "Galileo affair". Galileo was condemned by the Church authorities in 1633 because the *Dialogo* was held to violate the norms laid down by the Holy Office in 1616. This is the nub of the Galileo affair. But *did* Galileo in fact violate the restrictions laid on him? Finocchiaro believes that a "plausible claim" can be made that he did not. The *Dialogo* in his estimation is an "impartial" work, presenting the arguments on each side of the Copernican debate in a fair manner: "Rather than supporting or defending the earth's motion [outlawed by the mandate laid on him in 1616], Galileo decided to simply discuss the arguments.... He must have felt that there could be nothing wrong with stating, analyzing, and evaluating the arguments on both sides. This was a plausible, realistic and viable program for operating within the restrictions".

Though I can agree with much of the supporting argument Finocchiaro brings, I think that this conclusion is mistaken, and it is on a matter of great moment in any assessment of the trial of 1633. He is not merely claiming to show how Galileo could have *believed* himself to be operating within the norms laid on him, thus explaining why he pursued a strategy that in its outcome was so disastrous for him. He is claiming that a good case can be made for saying that *in fact* the *Dialogo* did not contravene those norms.

It would require much more space than I have at my disposal to deal adequately with the intricacies of this much controverted issue. Let me go back very briefly to the events of 1615-16, when the stage was set for what was to come. It was at that point that the Holy Office, the Roman Congregation concerned with matters of doctrine, made the fatal error. What happened later in 1633, when the author of the *Dialogo* was brought to trial, though far more dramatic than the events of the earlier time, was the sort of consequence that could have been predicted.

In 1615, as the storm clouds gathered in Rome around the Copernican doctrine, Galileo composed one of the most interesting theological documents of the century, the *Letter to the Grand Duchess Christina*. He asked: what is the Christian to do when there is an apparent conflict between a Biblical passage, taken in its literal sense, and some finding of natural science? The standard answer which had been formulated by St. Augustine a thousand years before (call it the A principle for short) was that the literal reading of the Bible should be maintained unless the scientific claim could be *demonstrated,* in which case an alternative reading of the Biblical passage should be sought. Galileo repeats this hermeneutic principle, with apparent approval. But he also proposes and argues effectively for a very different one, linking it with a *bon mot* attributed to Cardinal Baronio: the purpose of the Scriptures is to tell us how to go to heaven, not how the heavens go. The Bible, he concludes, carries no weight in matters of natural philosophy since its books were not written for that purpose. Thus, a conflict between the two cannot in principle arise, and objections to particular scientific doctrines cannot call on Scripture in their support (call this the B principle).

Finocchiaro makes two claims, each of which I would dispute. One is that B provides the rationale for A, thus Galileo in proposing B is showing, among other things, why the traditional principle holds. The second is that an immediate corollary of B, that a natural philosopher should be free to propose a doctrine at apparent odds with Scripture even where he cannot demonstrate the doctrine, can be justified by the same arguments as would justify A. Thus anyone who accepts A ought to accept this corollary, the one that Galileo so badly needed to defend his procedure in the *Dialogo*.

First, B does *not* provide a rationale for A. If B were correct, the natural philosopher would *not* be obliged to provide a demonstration to sustain his side when apparent conflict threatens. Second, the rationale given for A by Augustine and later theologians in no way would warrant B or the corollary drawn from it. B is a much broader principle, and in the context of the debates then raging between Catholics and Reformers, a far more dangerous-sounding one. What follows from all this is relatively simple: if Galileo is ruled by A, the principle that his theological critics will hold him to, he has to produce a *demonstration* of the earth's motion in the *Dialogo* in order to gain a hearing. If, on the other hand, he goes by B, a plausible case for the earth's motion will suffice, but his critics are not in the least likely to accept the principle that would permit this. What made matters even more complicated for Galileo were the restrictions that Bellarmine communicated to him in the aftermath of the 1616 decree, i.e. explicit orders not to "hold or defend" the Copernican doctrine. These instructions implicitly contradicted the B principle, so that Galileo could not call on it to justify his planned defense of the Copernican system. But if he were to follow the A principle, he would have to produce a *demonstration* of the earth's motion. He was not at all sure, I suspect, that he *had* a demonstration: good grounds, yes, but a strict demonstration, hardly. Worse: he had been forbidden even to *defend* the condemned view, so how could he produce a demonstration, even if he had one? It seemed a hopeless tangle.

When the new Pope, his friend Urban VIII, encouraged him in 1624 to proceed with his plans to write about the Copernican controversy, he thought he saw a way through the tangle. He was authorized by Urban (so it would seem) to treat Copernicanism as an "hypothesis". But therein lay an ambiguity that proved disastrous in its consequences. What Urban would most likely have meant was that the Copernican formalism could be used merely for calculational purposes, the standard sense of the term 'hypothesis' in the context of mathematical astronomy for many centuries before. Whereas what Galileo evidently took away from his meetings with the Pope was that he could offer evidence in support of the truth of the Copernican world system, so long as he did not lay claim to *demonstrate* it. (This, in effect would be our modern understanding of the term, 'hypothesis'.) Sly attempt to circumvent the restrictions laid on him in 1616? Wishful thinking? Genuine misunderstanding? It is impossible to say. But it was his own sense of what constituted hypothesis, not Urban's, that guided the construction of the *Dialogo* (McMullin, 1978b).

Now, to Finocchiaro's principal claim: that the *Dialogo* did not violate the prescription against holding or defending the suspect doctrine. The importance of this issue is, of course, that it was on the opposite claim that the Holy Office case against Galileo primarily rested. Finocchiaro argues that the prescription would have been violated only if 1) the evidence for Copernicanism were presented as completely conclusive, or 2) that the case made on its behalf failed to be impartial. I would question both parts of this. Nothing was said in 1616 about impartiality. The prescription forbade Galileo to *defend* Copernicanism. But an impartial (that is, fair) presentation of the evidence could just as easily count as a defense as a partial one would. (I am not so sure, furthermore, that Galileo *did* make his case in an impartial way. Finocchiaro himself brings out how effectively loaded against the Aristotelian side was the rhetoric of sarcasm and insult that Galileo employed.) Nor was the prescription laid on Galileo in 1616 limited to forbidding claims to *demonstrate* the Copernican system. "Defending" is much weaker than that: to defend, it would be sufficient to present the evidence on one side as much stronger than on the other.

And (as Finocchiaro himself allows) Galileo certainly *did* do that. Over and over again, the arguments he advances in the *Dialogo* are said to favor the Copernican side, to "strengthen the Copernican hypothesis until it might seem that this must triumph absolutely" (Preface). In concluding the *Dialogo*, just before the argument he inserts in deference to Urban, he says: "In the conversations of these four days we have, then, strong evidences in favor of the Copernican system, among which three have been shown to be very convincing [the apparently irregular motions of the planets, the paths of the sunspots, the ebb and flow of the tides]". Speaking of the tidal argument in particular, Finocchiaro himself remarks that Galileo "was unwilling or unable to seriously consider any alternative explanations." In short, then, readers of the *Dialogo* would have been in no doubt that the author aimed to defend the merits of the Copernican over the Aristotelian alternative. And that, of itself, would have been sufficient to warrant the accusation that he had violated the prescriptions laid on him. His accusers at the trial made a point of this. (I am bracketing some famously disputed questions concerning the actual procedures followed at the trial.) What had been banned in 1616, they pointed out, was not just the claim to *demonstrate* the truth of the Copernican doctrine but even the attempt to show it to be well-supported, i.e. probable. This would be "a serious error since there is no way an opinion declared and defined to be contrary to Holy Scripture may be probable" (Trial sentence, Finocchiaro 1989,289.)

Neither Galileo nor his oppontents, Aristotelians all in matters of logic, knew how to deal with the awkward intermediate category of likelihood or probability, the category that, so obviously to our eyes, the Copernican debate called for. Nor could they know that the issue of realism (the reality in this case of the earth's motion dependent upon the explanatory force of the Copernican theories) would still be debated more then three centuries later. Given the conflicting constraints under which the *Dialogo* labored, it could never have achieved the primary goal its author had set for it. But it could and did play a significant part in a paradigm-shift more profound, perhaps, than any other in the history of science.

4. Newton's Opticks

Half a century later, Newton was still struggling with the issue of the admissibility of probable reasoning in science proper. Alan Shapiro in his masterly reconstructions of Newton's abundant optical writings has shown how this concern shaped the *Opticks* of 1704, (Shapiro 1989, 1993). By Newton's day, a number of natural philosophers, like Boyle and Huygens, had argued for the acceptability of hypothesis as a proper part of science, and had proposed criteria that such hypothesis would have to satisfy (McMullin 1990). But Newton's disposition was quite otherwise. In his first lectures at Cambridge (1668-69), he set out to treat optics as a part of mathematics: "Although colors may belong to physics, the science of them may be considered mathematical" (Shapiro 1993, 25). And when, shortly after, Hooke described Newton's explanation of the spectrum produced by the refraction of sunlight by a prism as a "hypothesis", Newton was incensed. As far as *he* was concerned, it was a straightforward "deduction from the phenomena", with no shadow of the hypothetical or the probable about it. Others could, if they wished, call on "mechanical hypothesis" to give an account of how the colors themselves are caused, but in Newton's view this was "foreign to the purpose" of science. A few years later, he relented, under pressure to make his mathematical treatment of light "more intelligible", and developed a highly speculative theory of an ethereal medium compounded of a variety of active "spirits" whose action might explain not only the phenomena of the spectrum but also, perhaps, those of electrical attraction and even muscular movement (McMullin, 1990, 68-71).

When in 1687, with the *Principia* completed, Newton started to assemble his earlier writings on light and color with a view to a second major treatise, he determined to return to his original idea of a science of light that would have nothing of the hypothetical about it. It would be broadly deductive in logical form, deploying as the starting-point of deduction the various experiments on light he had so brilliantly devised in the 1670's, in addition to some new work on thick plates that offered new insight. The opening lines of the *Opticks* sixteen years later recall this goal but give no hint of the difficulties to which it led: "My design in this book is not to explain the properties of light by hypotheses, but to propose and prove them by reasoning and experiments". Shapiro has followed the working and reworking of the materials that occupied so much of Newton's time in the intervening years. No matter how hard he tried to avoid them, causal hypotheses linking the evident periodicity of the color phenomena to some sort of vibrations in the medium or elsewhere seemed to be the only way in which the observational results could be drawn into unity.

Finally, he hit on the notion of "fits of easy reflection and easy transmission", an abstract set of mathematically-describable dispositions, that would (he hoped) prescind from the awkward question of what mechanisms were causally responsible. But it was not enough. After the introduction of the "fits", the *Opticks* contains a long section in which dozens of new observations of assorted color phenomena are set forth. The text then breaks off abruptly ("I was suddenly interrupted....") leaving this mass of observational material unanalyzed. It is difficult to avoid the conclusion that he was unable to carry further his aim of constructing a non-hypothetical science of directly describable properties. Instead, he ends the work with the famous series of "Queries" in which all sorts of causal hypotheses are introduced without embarrassment, but where his conviction that they are merely heuristic devices intended only to aid in the formulation of mathematical propositions that make no physical or causal statement, remains unchanged.

What Sepper calls the "texture" of the *Opticks* is determined in large part, then, by this effort to separate the task of the natural philosopher into two, one mathematical and conclusive, the other "physical" and speculative and of heuristic value only. This strategy had worked reasonably well for him in the *Principia*, though critics like Leibniz would have none of it (McMullin 1978, chap. 4). But it led him astray in dealing with the far greater variety of optical phenomena. A more tolerant approach to hypothesis and probable reasoning would have led to an *Opticks* of a very different texture, one whose legacy to later generations of scientists might have been a more effective one.

For, it must be said, the *Opticks* was not a classic in the fullest sense. It did not initiate a successful research program nor a fundamental paradigm shift. Despite the extraordinary brilliance of the experimental designs it unveiled, despite the wealth of invention displayed in the suggestive mechanisms of the Queries, it gave mixed signals to those who attempted to follow its lead. The theory of fits found few supporters in the century that followed, and had little influence on the later development of wave theory. Supporters of Huygens' wave theory were opposed by Newtonians who defended the corpuscular emission theory implicit in the light-ray model employed in the formalism of the *Opticks*. Following a Newtonian lead, some tried unsuccessfully to use the concept of force to describe the interaction between light-ray and medium.

In Newton's defense it could be said that in the light of what we now know, speculation about the causal mechanisms underlying the phenomena of light was indeed premature. The irreducibly dual wave and particle aspects of light could not have been harmonized in the language of Newton's mechanics; a different mechanics would be needed, one that would not be tied to the inductivist ordinary-language presuppositions of the *Principia*. It could be argued, then, that nothing that conceivably lay within Newton's reach could have established a successful paradigm for optics at that time.

But the main negative effect of the *Opticks* lay elsewhere, in the attitude of distrust towards explanatory hypothesis that it encouraged. Such hypotheses were not entirely proscribed, but they were to be regarded as heuristic devices, dispensable aids to be laid aside once the desired mathematical description of the properties of the phenomena under investigation was reached. The "physical" side of natural philosophy, with its appeal to hypothetical underlying causal mechanisms, was to be subordinated to the "mathematical". The philosopher, Thomas Reid, constructed a tightly empiricist philosophy of science around these and similar Newtonian dicta, one that would still carry weight a century later when J.S. Mill was writing his *System of Logic*. But in the later eighteenth century, the reliance on fluids and ethers of all sorts in the theories of heat, electricity, and especially optics, posed a severe challenge for any philosophy of science that would call on this side of the divided Newtonian heritage. Perhaps the best that can be said for the *Opticks* in this regard is that it displays, to a quite striking degree, an ambivalence that philosophy of science has not yet quite overcome.

References

Balme, D.M. (1987), "Teleology and Necessity", in Gotthelf and Lennox (eds.), pp. 275-290.

Barnes, J. (1964), "Aristotle's Theory of Demonstration", *Phronesis* 19: 123-152.

Cooper, J.M. (1987), "Hypothetical Necessity and Natural Teleology", in Gotthelf and Lennox (eds.), pp. 243-274.

Feyerabend, P. (1981), *Philosophical Papers*, Cambridge: Cambridge University Press, 2 vols.

Finocchiaro, M. (1980), *Galileo and the Art of Reasoning*, Dordrecht: Reidel.

________. (1989), *The Galileo Affair,* Berkeley: University of California Press.

Gjertsen, D. (1984), "Are There Classics of Science?" in his *The Classics of Science*, New York: Lilian Barber, pp. 1-10.

Gotthelf, A. and Lennox, J.G. (eds.) (1987), *Philosophical Issues in Aristotle's Biology,* Cambridge: Cambridge University Press.

Jaeger, W. (1934), *Aristotle: Fundamentals of the History of His Development*, Oxford: Clarendon.

Lennox, J.G. (1994), "The Disappearance of Aristotle's Biology: A Hellenistic Mystery", *Apeiron, 24: 7-24.*

McMullin, E. (1978a), "Newton on Matter and Activity", Notre Dame: University of Notre Dame Press.

McMullin, E. (1978b), "The Conception of Science in Galileo's Work", in Butts, R.E. and Pitt, J.C. (eds.), *New Perspectives on Galileo*, Dordrecht: Reidel, pp. 209-257.

________. (1984), "Stability and Change in Science", *New Ideas in Psychology* 2: 9-19.

________. (1990), "Conceptions of Science in the Scientific Revolution", in Lindberg, D. and Westman, R. (eds.), *Reappraisals of the Scientific Revolution*, Cambridge: Cambridge University Press, pp. 27-92.

Randall, J.H. (1960), *Aristotle,* New York: Columbia University Press.

Shapiro, A.E. (1989), "Huygens' *Traité de la Lumière* and Newton's *Opticks*: Pursuing and Eschewing Hypotheses", *Notes and Records of the Royal Society of London,* 43: 223-246.

Shapiro, A.E. (1993), *Fits, Passions, and Paroxysms,* Cambridge: Cambridge University Press.

Urbach, P. (1982), "Francis Bacon as a Precursor of Popper", *British Journal for the Philosophy of Science* 33: 113-132.

Wians, W. (1983), *Aristotle's Method in Biology,* Ann Arbor: Ann Arbor Microfilms, Ph.D. dissertation.

Part IX

INTEGRATING COGNITIVE AND SOCIAL MODELS OF SCIENCE

Psychological, Social, and Epistemic Factors in the Theory of Science

Alvin I. Goldman

University of Arizona

1. Introduction

Traditional philosophy of science concentrated on logic and methodology, dismissing psychology and sociology as irrelevant (except for the context of discovery). Recent movements to 'naturalize' philosophy of science have reinstated psychological and social factors repudiated by the tradition, but these two types of factors have mostly been addressed independently and by different authors. Most cognitive approaches (e.g., Thagard 1989a, 1992; Churchland 1989) pursue the microcognition of science in abstraction from the social, and most sociologists of science ignore, postpone, or reject cognitive explanations of science (Latour and Woolgar 1986, 280). More recently, however, several philosophers of science have urged a blending of the cognitive and the social (Thagard 1993, in press, Solomon 1992, 1994a, 1994b, Kitcher 1993, Giere 1988), and this paper has a similar thrust. I shall not endorse a reduction of the social to the psychological, but a substantial overlap or intermingling of the two. Psychological and social approaches to science often seek to replace the epistemic, but another theme of this paper is the compatibility of a unified psychosocial picture of science with an epistemic picture.

The theory of science, in my view, has two tasks: the first explanatory and the second normative. The explanatory task is to explain what happens in science, why, for example, a scientific hypothesis grows or wanes in popularity at a given juncture. The normative task is to identify the features of scientific practice that generally promote or impede the institutional goal(s) of science, and to recommend therapies where appropriate. Admittedly, it is controversial whether science has a unique set of goals, but I believe in such a set and so I'll take the normative mission on board.

Let me begin with terminological matters. Although our symposium's title is "Integrating *Cognitive* and Social Models of Science," I prefer the term 'psychological' to 'cognitive,' because 'cognitive' often means 'epistemic' and this confusion should be avoided. So I shall speak of 'psychological' factors. By this I mean two things: first, psychological *states* of individual agents, and second, psychological *operations* or *processes*, i.e., causal transactions that take psychological states as inputs, outputs, or both. Psychological states include doxastic attitudes, such as believing or accepting a theory, and motivational states, such as desiring professional recognition. Psychological processes include perception, hypothesis formation, theoretical reasoning, practical reasoning, and so forth. My use of the term 'social' will be very inclu-

---

PSA 1994, Volume 2, pp. 277-286

sive. It applies, first, to any causal interactions between two or more agents. When opinions or behavior of certain scientists influence the opinions or behavior of others, this qualifies as a social transaction. Second, the term 'social' applies to a single agent's psychological state if the state's propositional content refers to the actions or attitudes (actual or prospective) of other agents. A scientist's belief about the beliefs of other scientists, for example, is a social belief, i.e., a belief with a social content. Similarly, a desire to persuade other scientists that one has made a significant contribution is a social desire. In this usage there is obviously no incompatibility between psychological and social factors, since many states turn out to be both psychological and social. A third use of 'social' pertains to institutional rules, such as codes of professional conduct or guidelines for awarding a prize. A fourth sense of 'social' refers to global properties of a community, e.g., the distribution of beliefs in a population at a given time, whether or not there is causal interaction or intentional interrelations among its members. My use of the term 'social' is obviously more liberal than that of writers who restrict it to those factors that are 'external' rather than 'internal' to science, but I believe that this liberal usage is likely to be more fruitful in the end.

2. The Explanatory Mission

The shape of my explanatory program for the theory of science is roughly indicated by Figure 1 on the next page. The right side of the figure presents some major categories of psychological states and actions of a typical scientific agent. This catalogue of states and actions is obviously not exhaustive,and leaves it open whether every scientist has states in each category, or what the specific contents and strengths of the states may be. The left side of the figure depicts the agent's natural and social environment, including the scientific community, which is composed of numerous other agents with similar characteristics. The figure also depicts some selected paths of causal influence, represented by arrows: (I) from the environment to internal states of the agent, (II) from internal states to other internal states, (III) from internal states to actions, and (IV) from actions of the agent to the natural and social environment. To keep the figure perspicuous, many causal paths are omitted. The figure assumes that there are 'natural' psychological operations, not explicitly labeled, that govern the transitions along the intra–agent causal pathways. These operations may be supplemented by culturally acquired inference rules or methodologies, which also influence the transition from prior beliefs to new beliefs. One interesting topic for the cognitive science of science is the relation between biologically given inferential processes and learned principles. However, I shall concentrate on a single kind of process that vividly illustrates the intermingling of the psychological and the social, viz., the process of *interpersonal persuasion*.

The dominant approach to persuasion in the social studies of science is what I shall call the *political approach*. This approach claims, roughly, that all argumentation in science is "just politics"; it is not oriented toward epistemic ends or rational merit. This approach is not only dominant in the social studies of science, but perhaps expresses the essence of what is there meant by 'social'. By my own reckoning, however, there is a rival approach to interpersonal persuasion that equally counts as social: the *epistemic approach*. This claims that scientists are persuaded by what they regard as the best evidence or argument, the evidence most indicative of the truth by their lights. The epistemic approach does not claim that scientists are persuaded by what is in fact good evidence or good argument, only by what they *take* to be such; so it leaves room for misguided methods or just plain irrationality. Each approach is a psychosocial approach to persuasion. A third position would hold that political and epistemic factors each play a partial role, at least some of the time, and this middle position is the one I shall ultimately endorse, though with a strong tilt toward epistemic factors. Initially, however, the discussion will focus on the two pure views.

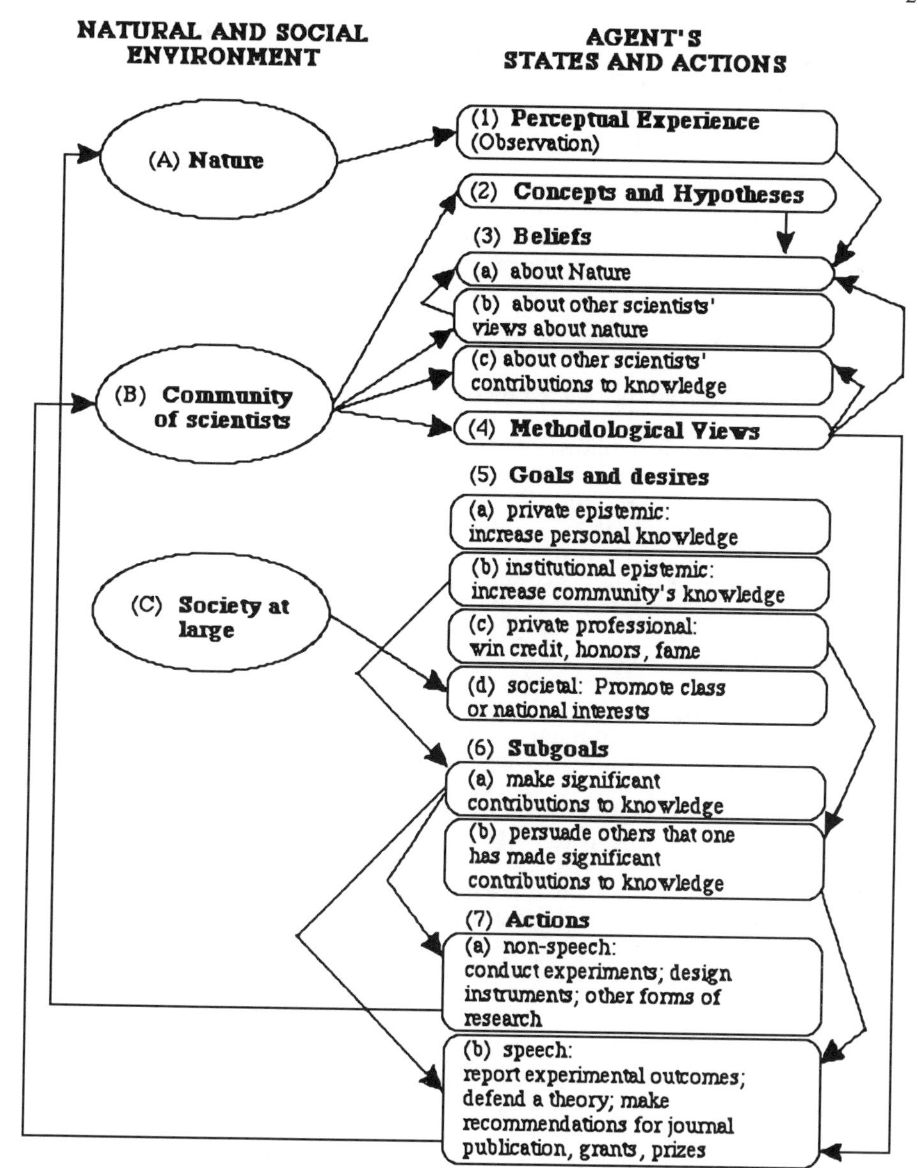

Table 1

One statement of the political approach is given by Shapin and Schaffer:

> The contest among alternative forms of life and their characteristic forms of intellectual product depends upon the political success of the various candidates in insinuating themselves into the activities of other institutions and other interest groups. He who has the most, and the most powerful, allies wins. (1985, 342)

This political approach is elaborated by Latour (1987), who claims that persuasion is a function of the greater force of numbers behind an article or study. Scientists win the battle for persuasion, according to Latour, by constructing alliances with other researchers.

> Mr. Anybody's opinion can be easily brushed aside.... The situation is suddenly reversed when Mr. Anybody supports his claim with a new set of allies: a journal, *Nature*; a Nobel Prize author; six co–authors; the granting agencies.... Mr. Anybody is to be taken seriously since he is not alone any more: a group, so to speak, accompanies him. Mr. Anybody has become Mr. Manybodies!... (1987, 31)

> We understand now that going from the outer layers of the articles to the inner parts is not going from the argument of authority to Nature as it is going from authorities to more authorities, from numbers of allies and resources to still *greater numbers* (1987, 49; italics in original).

Slightly simplifying Latour's theory, we might formulate it as PT_1:

> PT_1: Scientists are persuaded by the force or weight of greater numbers.

There are two obvious difficulties with PT_1. First, not every random person who supports a scientific view will help sway the opinions of scientists. Utter novices, however numerous, exert no persuasive force, so the weight of sheer numbers cannot be the right story. Second, PT_1 cannot explain how a small group of minority dissenters could ever convince others to switch theoretical commitments, let alone persist in holding a minority view, or how dissent could ever arise in a previously uniform community; but these things sometimes happen.[1] Let us waive these two points despite their seriousness. We come then to my main point, which is the availability of a rival epistemic theory. Even if greater numbers always win, there might be a deeper epistemic explanation of this phenomenon. Scientists might believe that the most reliable indicator of truth is the opinion of the greatest number, and this *evidential* consideration, rather than sheer force of popular opinion, could be the factor that psychically commands assent, There is clearly a difference between the claim that a scientist's opinion is dictated by the 'vector sum' of the voices on each side, and a theory saying that a scientist's opinion is determined by her assessment of the evidence, which is gauged by the numbers. Let us formulate the latter as ET_1:

> ET_1: To the extent that scientists are persuaded by greater numbers, what promotes conviction is their judgment that majority opinion is reliable evidence of truth.

Even if Latour were right that numbers usually win in science, this would not vindicate PT_1 in preference to ET_1.

An analogous point holds if we revise PT_1 to accommodate varying levels of expertise or authority. Such a revision would yield PT_2, which is intimated by many of Latour's passages.

> PT_2: What persuades scientists is the power or influence of superior scientific authorities.

This 'authority' version of the political approach also has a corresponding epistemic rival. A plausible definition of 'authority' is someone whose opinion within the relevant domain is likely to be right, or true (Goldman 1991). So if scientists are persuaded by authority, this need not mean they are cowed by the power of authorities, or driven by interest considerations to agree with them, as PT_2 suggests. Rather, they might believe that authorities are the most reliable indicators of truth, and apparent truth is what commands their assent. This would be an epistemic theory (exemplified, for example, by Kitcher 1993, chap. 8), which we may formulate as follows:

> ET_2: To the extent that scientists are persuaded by authority, what promotes conviction is (primarily) the judged credibility of an authority, i.e., the hearer's judgment of the likelihood that the authority is right.

The political approach to authority is dominant in the social studies of science. Unfortunately, its popularity may be largely traced to sheer neglect of the rival epistemic approach. The political approach cannot be sustained, however, unless it can be shown that it accounts for the behavior and internal states of scientists better than the epistemic approach. I suggest, to the contrary, that current evidence favors ET_2 over PT_2. For one thing, ET_2 allows that authority is not the only persuasive factor, and this fits existing evidence. As Cole (1992, 51) points out, Watson and Crick's model of DNA was quickly accepted by others despite the fact that when their brief paper was published in *Nature* they were young scientists without any significant reputation. Furthermore, a study by Cole supports the conclusion that evaluations of scientific grant applications are not strongly influenced by 'political' characteristics of the applicant such as personal prestige or departmental rank but seem to reflect the judged quality of the proposal itself (Cole 1992, chap. 6).

Second, to the extent that authority does play a role, studies of persuasive communication suggest that credibility, i.e., judged truth–conduciveness, is a critical factor. I draw here on a wide survey of research on persuasion by O'Keefe (1990). Although this research did not use scientists as subjects, it is reasonable to assume that if even ordinary subjects are driven by epistemic considerations, the same is true of scientists. One portion of O'Keefe's survey makes use of an influential model of persuasion developed by Petty and Cacioppo (1986a, 1986b), called the elaboration likelihood model. This model contrasts 'central' versus 'peripheral' routes to persuasion. A central route to persuasion involves the hearer in a high level of elaboration, or mental exploration, of the speaker's message. It typically features issue–relevant thinking, e.g., scrutinizing the arguments contained in the message, recalling related arguments from memory, and/or devising additional arguments oneself. A peripheral route to persuasion, by contrast, involves the hearer in a relatively low level of elaboration. It uses simple decision rules for assessing the credibility of the message, e.g., the likability of the speaker or his general credibility. Insofar as subjects use high elaboration some of the time, this undercuts PT_2, since PT_2 says that persuasion relies *wholly* on authority. The elaboration likelihood model implies that simple reliance on authority occurs only some of the time. Furthermore, as O'Keefe explains the credibility heuristic, it is clear that even this low–elaboration procedure is a pretty epistemic affair. A speaker's credibility is judged by two dimensions, competence and trustworthiness, where competence is the degree to which the communicator is in a position to know the truth, and trustworthiness is the likelihood that a communicator is inclined to tell the truth as he or she sees it (O'Keefe 1990, 132). A hearer's acceptance of a communicator's message is heavily influenced by his/her assessment of the communicator's competence and trustworthiness. Moreover, even ordinary subjects use moderately subtle evidential considerations, for example, judging a communicator who argues for a position opposed to his own apparent self–interest as comparatively believable. If even non–scientific hearers reflect on telltale signs of trustworthiness or untrustworthiness, in conformity with ET_2, it is likely that scientific agents do so as well.

Perhaps neither PT_1 nor PT_2, however, does full justice to the political approach. So let us consider a third variant of that approach, PT_3:

> PT_3: What causes a hearer to believe or disbelieve a speaker's claim are the hearer's political or professional interests.

For example, a hearer may be inclined to believe a speaker's claim if it fits a certain political ideology that advances the hearer's interests. Similarly, a hearer who wants a certain scientific view to be true because he/she is identified with that view may resist a speaker's claim that cuts against that view. Third, graduate students, laboratory assistants, and young scientists have professional interests in agreeing, respectively, with their professors, laboratory directors, and prominent figures in their field who can advance their careers. According to PT_3, scientific persuasion will only be produced by these sorts of interests. A pure form of the epistemic theory would presumably deny that these kinds of political/professional motives ever play a role in influencing scientific beliefs. I shall not endorse this extreme epistemic theory, but rather a middle position that recognizes a limited role for political/professional motives in the production of scientific belief. I wish to emphasize, however, that there are firm limits on the causal efficacy of these factors, limits that are specifically epistemic in nature.

Purely anecdotal evidence suffices to refute PT_3 as stated. There are many cases of scientists who abandon or change their scientific positions although it contravenes their professional interests. For example, Galison comments on a team of particle physicists who were forced by the evidence to relinquish their view that there are no 'neutral currents', although they had a great deal riding on this claim:

> [I]t is stunning to reread Cline's memorandum ... that began with the simple statement, "At present I do not see how to make this effect go away." With those words, Cline gave up his career–long commitment to the nonexistence of neutral currents. "Interest" had to bow to the linked assemblage of ideas and empirical results that rendered the old beliefs untenable .... (1987, 258)

Valuable though such evidence is, we cannot fully identify the extent and limits of the impact of professional and political interests without a theoretical model of interest–driven, or motivated, reasoning. Indeed, one might even question whether motives or desires can causally affect beliefs at all. When we read bad news in the morning paper, for example, we certainly lack the power to disbelieve it simply because we wish it hadn't occurred. Although desires guide voluntary behavior, can they guide belief as well?

A recent analysis by Kunda (1990) provides ample evidence for the existence of motivated, or interest–driven, belief causation. At the same time, it convincingly indicates the epistemic limits of such causal factors. Following Kruglanski (1980), Kunda points out that two kinds of motives can drive reasoning: (A) to arrive at an accurate conclusion, whatever it may be, and (B) to arrive at a particular, directional conclusion (a preferred conclusion). Concerning type (B) cases, Kunda reviews evidence showing that when subjects have a particular desired conclusion, they search memory for beliefs and rules that could support this conclusion. They do not realize that the process is biased by their goals, that they are accessing only a subset of their relevant knowledge, and that they would probably access different beliefs and rules in the presence of different directional goals. She stresses, though, that they draw a desired conclusion only if they can muster up the evidence necessary to support it; often they will be forced to acknowledge and accept undesirable conclusions when confronted with strong arguments. For example, Sanitioso, Kunda and Fong (1990) preselected subjects who were extraverts or intraverts and induced them to theorize that a given trait (extraversion or introversion) was beneficial to academic success. Both groups viewed themselves as more extraverted when induced to believe that extraversion was beneficial than when induced to believe that introversion was beneficial. But in all conditions the extraverts still viewed themselves as considerably more extraverted than the introverts viewed themselves. In other words, the effects of the manipulation on self–concepts were constrained by prior self–knowledge.

Similar studies concern the assessment of science. Lord, Ross, and Lepper (1979) preselected subjects who were for or against capital punishment and exposed them to two studies with different methodologies, one supporting and one opposing the conclusion that capital punishment deterred crime. Subjects were more critical of the research methods used in the study that disconfirmed their initial beliefs than they were of methods used in the study that confirmed their initial beliefs. Similarly, Kunda (1987) had subjects read an article claiming that caffeine was risky for women. Women who were heavy caffeine consumers were less convinced by the article than low–caffeine–consuming women. No such effects were found for men; and even women showed this pattern only when the health risks were said to be serious. The principal moral of Kunda's treatment is that interest–oriented biasing occurs through the mechanisms of search and construction, but only when an acceptable rationale is located; one cannot believe a desired conclusion simply by an act of will. Thus, the causal impact of interests is constrained by epistemic factors.[2]

3. The Normative Mission

I turn now to the normative branch of science theory, beginning with the axiology or goal–structure of science. Science as an institution has several goals, but these are all heavily focused, in my opinion, on the community's acquisition of knowledge (true belief). Being a scientific realist, I hold that one institutional aim is to increase true belief in *theoretical* propositions. For present purposes, however, I offer the empiricist option of restricting the knowledge sought to empirical, i.e., observable, propositions, especially conditional observational propositions ("If you do X and look in direction Y, you will see Z"). This view still takes true belief as the aim, but the desired truths are restricted to observables. Returning to the preferred realist position, I should add that not all theoretical truths are equally valued. Truths having greater simplicity, wider scope, greater explanatory strength, and so forth are preferred in science. Science also has technological goals: promote greater social wealth, improve the environment, provide immunity from diseases, and so forth. Technological goals, however, are not totally separate from veritistic (truth–oriented) ones. Given technological goals, it becomes a sub–goal for science to acquire belief in relevant technological truths, e.g., 'Technique X will clean up oil spills,' 'Vaccine Y will immunize against disease D,' etc.

Institutional aims of science must be distinguished from personal goals of scientists. I assume that most scientists have an interest in advancing personal and community knowledge, but they also have personal career goals, including credit, honor, and fame. Although sociologists of science tend to emphasize career goals, these are compatible with simultaneous possession of epistemic aims. The two types of goals may of course conflict, but that is another matter.

The task of normative science theory is to examine the factors involved in scientific practice and to identify those that advance or impede *institutional* goals, particularly the knowledge (or truth) goal. Emphasis on the truth goal contrasts with the typical approach in the social studies of science, where 'facts' or 'truths' are claimed to be mere social constructions, not independently existing entities to which beliefs might correspond or fail to correspond. Arguments for these claims, however, are far from compelling. First, there seems to be a confusion between real facts (or truth–makers) and taken–to–be facts, i.e., agreed–upon beliefs or inscriptions. When agreed–upon beliefs are shown to result from social disputation, negotiation, and argumentation, sociologists of science commonly infer that the facts themselves have been constructed. This betrays a confusion between real facts and taken–to–be facts.

Perhaps there is no confusion here, however, merely a metaphysical theory that seeks to reduce all reality and 'out–there–ness' to consensus beliefs, eliminating any putative reality independent of consensus belief. Thus, Latour and Woolgar say: "reality is formed as a consequence of [the resolution of a controversy].... Our point is that 'out–there–ness' is the *consequence* of scientific work rather than its cause" (1986, 180–182). This is a kind of new–age idealism, and the argument for it is extremely thin. As I reconstruct it, the argument says that because we can explain all consensual belief in terms of social negotiation, there is no reason to posit any extra–social reality. This is no more convincing than the following position in legal theory (perhaps represented by Critical Legal Studies). Since all consensual opinions by juries (i.e., verdicts) can be explained in terms of disputation and negotiation among attorneys and/or jurors, we might as well reduce all 'facts' of the litigated affairs to the verdicts arrived at. In the case of criminal trials, the agreed–upon judgment, the verdict, will *comprise* or *constitute* the criminal facts. This is unacceptable for at least two reasons. First, on this view it makes no sense to say that a verdict conflicts with the real facts of the case, because the verdict *constitutes* the facts. But surely it does make sense to speak of a discrepancy between verdict and fact. It is axiomatic that human judgment is fallible, and given this fallibility, reality can never be equated with the beliefs of any specific individual or group. Second, although an interesting partial explanation of the verdict may be generated by disputations and negotiations among attorneys and juries, no full explanation should entirely omit reference to the evidence introduced at trial. Furthermore, a complete explanation of the evidence would normally go back to the actual crime: the perpetrator's identity, the time of the act, the means employed, the positions of the eye–witnesses, and so on. This calls out for recognition of facts (or events) that are (logically) independent of the jury's verdict. So it is wrong, in both trial and science cases, to say that full explanation of consensus (or dissensus) requires no reference to an extra–social reality, or to facts involved in that reality (see Goldman, forthcoming.)

Return now to the normative mission of assessing scientific factors in terms of their tendency to promote or impede the institutional, knowledge–seeking goal of science. Traditional philosophy of science focused on methodology, especially on rules or criteria for accepting theories (or assigning probabilities to them). I cheerfully accept this as part of the normative task of science theory; clearly, different methodological practices may have dramatically different impact on the knowledge–attaining properties of science. But methodological practice is not the only factor that influences scientific outcomes for good or ill, nor the only one that deserves attention and possibly 'therapeutic' intervention. Consider the reward system of science, and imagine that scientists' salaries are set directly by their citation index. Would this reward system have beneficial or deleterious consequences, on balance, for the knowledge–seeking goal? While the answer is not obvious, at least one worry is that citations often result from mere provocativeness. A reward system based on citations alone might bolster incentives for research that is more sensational than sound.

Let us next consider a type of factor discussed earlier that might bode ill for the knowledge–increasing aim of science, viz., the existence of political/professional (PP) motives. Although we saw that there are limits to the extent that motives can influence *belief*, there are no comparable constraints on the capacity of motives to influence *action*. Thus, if PP motives are more prevalent than epistemic motives, or stronger than the latter, this might threaten veritistic goals. Scientists might choose modes of research and argumentation that advance their own careers more than the community's knowledge. Several recent analyses, however, offer grounds for greater optimism. Hull (1988, 357) holds that by means of a 'hidden hand', self–interest in science promotes the greater good. Kitcher (1990, 1993, chap. 8) and Solomon (1992, 1994a, 1994b) are more qualified but also fairly optimistic. Similarly, Goldman and Shaked (1992) have shown that there are certain cases in which even a purely credit–motivated scientist can advance the goal of truth–acquisition.

Consider the Goldman and Shaked model in more detail. This model assumes that the only thing motivating scientists is the prospect of receiving credit from their peers. How is credit assigned? The model assumes that when S makes a contribution, e.g., performs and interprets an experiment, K credits S in proportion to the magnitude of K's subjective–probability change that is prompted by the contribution. If S's experiment leads K to change his mind a lot (on the topic at hand), then K gives S a lot of credit. The model further assumes that scientists use Bayesian methods to update their probabilities. Since contributors are assumed to be motivated by credit alone, their subgoal will be to change their peers' opinions as much as possible, whether or not in the direction of truth. Can this subgoal still have a truth–enhancing tendency? Where a contributor is choosing between two experiments, for example, will this subgoal lead her to select the more informative or the less informative experiment (given knowledge of the crediting practices and the Bayesian reasoning practices of her peers)? As is proved in Goldman and Shaked (1992), when the scientists'subjective likelihoods match the objective likelihoods, the contributor's choice will *usually* be the more informative choice, i.e., the experiment with the greater (objectively) expected increase in truth–possession for the community. Not always, however. The credit–motivated scientist will sometimes make less informative experimental choices than the purely epistemically–motivated scientist, but the discrepancy is pretty small.

How, one might ask, could PP–motivation fail to have a deleterious or at best random tendency toward truth–production? The answer lies mainly in the 'consumers' of scientific research. If consumers employ certain reasoning methods, credit–assignment practices, and accurate likelihoods, then the contributors' best prospect for maximizing credit is to conduct and present research that coincidentally has truth–conducive properties. We see, then, that certain combinations of psychological, social, and methodological practices can be assessed and compared to other practices in veritistic terms. Moreover, given certain crediting practices, reasoning practices, and accurate likelihoods, credit motivation need not have bad veritistic consequences at all, though purely epistemic motivation would have even better consequences. Thus, in terms of the institutional goals of science, purely epistemic goals are preferable to PP goals, but the latter are by no means disastrous.[3]

Notes

[1]Thanks to Joel Pust for this point, and for other extremely helpful comments on many aspects of the paper.

[2]For similar application of Kunda's research, see Thagard (1989b).

[3]This is only a tentative conclusion based on the Goldman–Shaked model.

References

Churchland, P.M. (1989), *A Neurocomputational Perspective*. Cambridge: MIT Press.

Cole, S. (1992), *Making Science: Between Nature and Society*. Cambridge: Harvard University Press.

Galison, P. (1987), *How Experiments End*. Chicago: University of Chicago Press.

Giere, R.N. (1988), *Explaining Science*. Chicago: University of Chicago Press.

Goldman, A.I. (1991), "Epistemic Paternalism: Communication Control in Law and Society," *Journal of Philosophy* 88: 113–131. Reprinted in Goldman (1992).

________. (1992), *Liaisons: Philosophy Meets the Cognitive and Social Sciences*. Cambridge: MIT Press.

________. (forthcoming), "Social Epistemology, Interests, and Truth," *Philosophical Topics*.

Goldman, A.I. and Shaked, M. (1992), "An Economic Model of Scientific Activity and Truth Acquisition," in Goldman (1992).

Hull, D. (1988), *Science as a Process*. Chicago: University of Chicago Press.

Kitcher, P. (1990), "The Division of Cognitive Labor," *Journal of Philosophy* 87: 5–22.

______. (1993), *The Advancement of Science*. Oxford: Oxford University Press.

Kruglanski, A.W. (1980), "Lay Epistemology: Process and Contents," *Psychological Review* 87: 70–87.

Kunda, Z. (1987), "Motivation and Inference: Self–Serving Generation and Evaluation of Evidence," *Journal of Personality and Social Psychology* 53: 636–647.

_ _ _ _ _. (1990), "The Case for Motivated Reasoning," *Psychological Bulletin* 108: 480–498.

Latour, B. (1987), *Science in Action*. Cambridge: Harvard University Press.

Latour, B. and Woolgar, S. (1986), *Laboratory Life*. 2d ed. Princeton: Princeton University Press.

Lord, C.G., Ross, L., and Lepper, M.R. (1979), "Biased Assimilation and Attitude Polarization: The Effects of Prior Theories on Subsequently Considered Evidence," *Journal of Personality and Social Psychology* 37: 2098–2109.

O'Keefe, D.J. (1990), *Persuasion: Theory and Research*. Newbury Park,: Sage Publications.

Petty, R.E. and Cacioppo, J.T. (1986a), *Communication and Persuasion: Central and Peripheral Routes to Attitude Change*. New York: Springer–Verlag.

_ _ _ _ _ _ _ _ _ _ _ _ _ _ _ _ _ _. (1986b), "The elaboration likelihood model of persuasion," in L. Berkowitz (ed.), *Advances in Experimental Social Psychology*, vol. 19. New York: Academic Press, pp. 123–205.

Sanitioso, R., Kunda, Z., and Fong, G.T. (1990), "Motivated Recruitment of Autobiographical Memory," *Journal of Personality and Social Psychology* 59: 229–241.

Shapin, S. and Schaffer, S. (1985), *Leviathan and the Air Pump*. Princeton: Princeton University Press.

Solomon, M. (1992), "Scientific Rationality and Human Reasoning," *Philosophy of Science* 59: 439–455.

_ _ _ _ _ _ _. (1994a), "Social Empiricism," *Nous* 28: 325–343.

_ _ _ _ _ _ _. (1994b) "A More Social Epistemology," in F. Schmitt, ed., *Socializing Epistemology.* Lanham, MD.: Rowman and Littlefield.

Thagard, P.R. (1989a), "Explanatory Coherence," *Behavioral and Brain Sciences* 12: 435–502.

_ _ _ _ _ _ _. (1989b), "Scientific Cognition: Hot or Cold?", in S. Fuller et al, eds., *The Cognitive Turn*. Dordrecht: Kluwer.

_ _ _ _ _ _ _. (1992), *Conceptual Revolutions*. Princeton: Princeton University Press.

_ _ _ _ _ _ _. (1993), "Societies of Minds: Science as Distributed Computing," *Studies in History and Philosophy of Science* 24: 49–67.

_ _ _ _ _ _ _. (in press), "Mind, Society, and the Growth of Knowledge," *Philosophy of Science*.

Multivariate Models of Scientific Change

Miriam Solomon

Temple University and The Dibner Institute

1. Introduction: Integrating Cognitive and Social Models of Scientific Change

Philosophers are particularly susceptible to the temptation to produce what Donna Haraway calls a "TOE (=a Theory of Everything)" (Haraway 1994). Many of us like to integrate the methods and results of different disciplines, discern underlying unity in bifurcations and thereby—so we think—get closer to a single, true, representation of the universe. Proposals to integrate cognitive and social models of scientific change have come from philosophers—and not from historians, sociologists, feminist critics, anthropologists, rhetoricians or semioticians of science. The proposals are also responses to the growing influence of sociologists of science (e.g. Collins, Latour, Shapin, Woolgar) who have taken stands on epistemological matters, formerly the province of philosophers. It is common among sociologists of science to reject all proposals to integrate cognitive and social accounts, as well as to reject all cognitive accounts[2]: Bruno Latour's famous moratorium on cognitive studies of science (Latour 1987, 247) is one example of this.

I have begun this paper by describing disciplinary differences over proposed integration of cognitive and social models because I think that metaphysical views indigenous to these disciplines have influenced the *content* of the debate in important ways. Philosophers tend to think of scientific change in terms of a few independent social and cognitive processes which may be individually assessed for their rationality. The metaphysics of such accounts has a structure that is analogous to the paradigmatic examples of causation in Newtonian mechanics. Sociologists of science, on the other hand, are likely to privilege the factors salient to them—various kinds of social factors—and draw normative conclusions from these one–sided descriptions which they embed in plausible–sounding narrative accounts. I will begin the paper by summarizing some things we already know about scientific change, which show that existing models of integration are inadequate. As a philosopher, I shall indulge my own temptation to defend an integrated model of scientific change—but I will choose an approach—multivariate analysis—that I hope sociologists of science, and others working in science studies, will be unable to resist. Multivariate analyses yield results that require careful interpretation, especially for epistemological purposes, and the paper will conclude with a discussion of this.

2. Some Features of Scientific Change

Some causes of scientific change, at the individual and social level, are: peer pressure, influence of authority, logical reasoning, financial incentives, birth order, salient experimental and technological successes, analogical reasoning, religiosity, ideology,

PSA 1994, Volume 2, pp. 287-297

influence of friends, gender, rhetorical styles, reasoning styles, national agendas, institutional agendas, desires for personal credit, age, education, relationship with parents, social class and prior beliefs. These are just some of the relevant variables, and I have listed them in random order, without dividing into categories such as "social," "institutional," "cognitive" or "psychological". Frank Sulloway (1995) has investigated the role of *forty* variables in theory choice, and he has only looked at *some* "hot cognitive," social and institutional factors (he has left the "cold cognitive," logical and some motivational and social factors out of his analysis). Any account of scientific change needs to be able to handle this complexity.

It turns out, not surprisingly, that some of these variables are more important than others, because they have a comparatively large influence on scientific change. Any account of scientific change needs to assign *magnitudes* to the variables affecting scientific thinking. These magnitudes can be obtained only from empirical studies, with the data either historical or contemporary. I have found, for example (Solomon 1992), that cognitive salience and availability of data from the Southern Hemisphere accounts for a large portion of the decisions to accept or reject the hypothesis of continental drift before the 1960s. Sulloway (1995) finds that birth order is, in many scientific controversies, the most important variable predicting theory choice.

It is also the case that some of these variables interact with one another to produce effects, and do not simply sum additively. Thus, for example, Sulloway (1995, 206) has found that there is an interaction between gender and birth order, such that when siblings are both female, the usual birth order effects on personality and thereby theory choice are inverted. There is also an interaction between birth order, social class and parental loss, such that in middle and upper class families with parental loss, birth order differences in radicalism are decreased, and in working class families with parental loss, birth order differences in radicalism are increased (Sulloway 1995, 162).

Variables operate differently—with different magnitudes and different effects—in different scientific situations. For example, international competition between France and the USA was an important variable influencing choice of direction of research during the early history of genetics (see Sapp 1987) but international competition was much less important—although it did play some role—during the history of development of plate tectonics (see Solomon 1992). Even birth order, which Sulloway has shown to be a widely important variable, has minimal effect in controversies where there is little ideological import. So a model of scientific change cannot assign constant values to the magnitudes of the variables.

Classification of the variables influencing scientific change into categories such as the pervasive dichotomy of "social" versus "cognitive" is inadequate. For instance, analogical reasoning is pervasive in scientific theorizing and uses cognitive mechanisms[3], yet the actual analogies and metaphors which guide the reasoning are often drawn from the social and political context. The pervasive nineteenth century understanding of natural selection, metaphorically, as a design– governed selection of species by nature (see Young 1985) is an example of an important cause of theory acceptance that is not categorizable as either "social" or "cognitive" alone.

Finally, descriptive accounts of scientific change do not straightforwardly map onto normative judgments. The same reasoning process can be effective in one domain or social setting, and ineffective in another. For example, as Bechtel and Richardson (1992) have argued, the strategies of decomposition and localization are each successful for different problems in the life sciences. Or, for example, reasoning based on the representativeness heuristic varies in effectiveness, depending on other reasoning processes (e.g. memory) used together with it. And, for example, as I have argued (Solomon 1992, 1994a, 1994b), so–called "biasing" factors such as salience, wish fulfillment, belief perseverance, can be effective if the biases are well– distributed across the scientific community. Effectiveness of reasoning can thus be assessed as a property of a research community, instead of the traditional assessment as a property of an individual scientist. Effectiveness of reasoning can also be assessed relative to a particular domain of inquiry, instead of making traditional, more general, assessments of processes. Thus reasoning processes do not themselves have intrinsic properties such as "rational" and "irrational". Whether or not a process is counted as "rational" is relative to the social context and the intellectual context. This kind of relativism is not to be confused with the relativist and constructivist views of sociologists of science: it is a *relational*, rather than a skeptical, account of rationality.

Current accounts of integration overlook one or more of the above features of scientific change and, for this reason, are seriously incomplete or inadequate. I give a few examples of this—this is not the place for a full criticism of these accounts.[4]

Kitcher (1993, Chapter 8) considers the effect of only a few variables—principally individual scientists' desires for credit, scientists' reliance on authority and some cognitive variation—in an abstract mathematical model. The calculations do not show how scientific change actually occurs in particular situations, only how it might occur in a situation with far less complexity than actual cases. Empirical investigation of the variables influencing scientific change, and their magnitudes, is needed. Without this, it is impossible to know whether or not Kitcher's abstract mathematical models tell us anything about scientific practice. The historical case studies he sets out earlier in the book are not analyzed in terms of the variables used in the abstract mathematical models.

Thagard (1994) models the effect of many variables as separable, non–interacting causes, rather like a Newtonian diagram of addition of forces. Kitcher (1993) does consider interaction effects between a few variables, but his investigation is only of possible, and not actual, interaction effects. As mentioned above, Sulloway (1995) has shown that interaction effects can be significant.

Giere (1988, Chapter 8) makes use of a dichotomy between social and cognitive factors, often talking of relative weights of "epistemic" and "non–epistemic" values in the choices of individual scientists. The epistemic values are scientific interests (specifically, the interest in being right) which activate logical and cognitive abilities; the non–epistemic values are "personal, professional and social interests". Such a dichotomy conflates "cognitive" with "epistemic". It leads to Giere's misleading suggestion that the plate tectonics revolution was more scientific because—according to him—the "cognitive" factors play a greater role than in other revolutions. Cognitive factors can generate as much "bias" as social factors, as I have argued in Solomon 1992.

Goldman (1992) evaluates the effects of thinking processes one by one—for example he considers perceptual processes for their accuracy in representation (166–169) and the practice of epistemic paternalism for its contribution to true beliefs in a community (Chapter 11). He evaluates the processes alone, not together with other concurrent, interacting cognitive or social processes, despite an official acknowledgement that this is necessary (in Chapter 7). Furthermore, he assumes more general applicability of his findings than is supported by the data. The efficacy of the practice of epistemic paternalism, for example, is not established for the case of peer review in scientific communities, although he extends his claims to that case.[5]

All the accounts of scientific change tend to evaluate *individual* decision making primarily and social decision making only secondarily and derivatively, especially at consensus. They investigate social processes only insofar as they contribute, ultimately, to good individual decision making (Kitcher 1993 and Goldman 1992, especially, do this). This tends to constrain both descriptive and normative investigations: much more will be said about this below.

3. Why Integrate Cognitive and Social Accounts?

Two reasons for integration are relevant here. First, a *descriptive* account of scientific change that is powerful enough to be useful for prediction and explanation of change needs to include all that influences scientific change—psychological ("hot" and "cold" cognitive), social, political, ideological etc. Whatever the differences between these influences, they are not operating in causally independent domains. Second, social epistemologists have shown that it is not enough to have normative assessments and recommendations of cognitive processes: *all* causes of scientific change need to be assessed for their conduciveness to scientific progress. Since there are complex causes that operate at the same time, and often interact, normative assessment must be of the dynamics of an episode of scientific change as a whole, and not of single causes or processes. Hence, normative assessments depend on good descriptive accounts.

To say that normative assessments are dependent on descriptive accounts is not to say that they may be read *straightforwardly* off descriptive accounts. Naturalized epistemology neither collapses the normative to the descriptive (Quine's remarks in "Epistemology Naturalized" notwithstanding) nor makes the normative obviously inferable from descriptive accounts. A normative account is one that *evaluates* episodes and processes of scientific change; to get a normative account from a descriptive account, one must first settle the standards of evaluation. This means deciding the goals of the enterprise (truth, or problem solving success, or predictive success, or experimental success etc) and the units to be evaluated for attainment of the goals (individual scientists, groups of scientists, scientific institutions, scientific instruments etc).

There have been confusions when moving from descriptive to normative accounts, in multivariate approaches as much as in philosophers' approaches. Thus I will proceed in stages here, first discussing multivariate analysis and then showing how normative questions arise and are addressed for multivariate models of scientific change.

4. Multivariate Models

Multivariate analyses are now the standard methodology for investigating complex phenomena in epidemiology, economics and the social sciences. These analyses employ statistical methods to discern correlations between several variables and a phenomenon under investigation which is dependent on them. Also, interaction effects between the variables can be detected and measured. The analysis is quantitative. When multivariate analysis is supplemented with causal hypotheses which account for the discovered correlations, the result is a complete dynamical account of scientific change. Causal hypotheses can come from qualitative studies in which likely causes are identified in particular case studies, or they can come from interventions and observations in which the values of variables are changed so that their relations of dependence and independence are likely to show.

Multivariate models of scientific change have rarely been offered in the science studies literature. Philosophers of science generally discuss only a few of the variables, historians of science tell narratives of scientific change which are qualitative accounts featuring a few variables and sociologists of science have generally (especially recently) eschewed quantitative methods in favor of qualitative ethnographic and narrative accounts. The most substantial exception is the recent work of Frank Sulloway (1995) which investigates the correlation of birth order and other variables with theory choice, and also examines these variables for interaction effects. My multivariate analysis of so–called "biasing" factors in the history of genetics and the recent revolution in geology (Solomon manuscript) is a simpler, although still multivariate, analysis— an improper linear model—which, despite its simplicity, shows some important aggregate effects of the "biasing" factors that Sulloway does not consider. It is worth summarizing these examples of multivariate analysis here.

Frank Sulloway has amassed data bases for around 30 scientific controversies which contain measures of over 40 psychological and social variables for the scientists involved. Sulloway's claim is that birth order is the most important variable, because it is the best predictor of attitudes towards radical theories; this conclusion emerges from a multivariate analysis of variables which also include variables such as age, religious and political attitudes, parental loss and age at parental loss, sex, years of education, conflict with parents and professional contacts. Using data on all these variables combined, the multivariate model can predict an individual's attitude towards a theory with an accuracy of, typically, well over 80%. The correlation coefficient for each variable, and predictability of choice when all variables are known, depends on the characteristics of the controversy. For example, the more ideological the controversy, and, in particular, the closer the connections to religious ideology, the higher the correlation of attitude with birth order (radical choice is correlated with being raised as a later–born), and the more predictable an individual scientist's choice.

Sulloway supplements this quantitative work with an explanation for the effect of birth order and the interaction of birth order with some other variables. His earlier explanation (Sulloway 1990) was in terms of psychodynamic causes alone; his current explanation (1995) adds a Darwinian explanation of the psychodynamic mechanisms. It is not important to evaluate this explanation here: I mention it to show that Sulloway combines a quantitative model which measures correlations with a qualitative account that supplies causal mechanisms and causal relations. Such combination of quantitative and qualitative work is typical of recent research in sociology (although not in sociology of science).

Sulloway's multivariate analysis considers many variables acting and interacting and generating scientists' choices. The variables considered are for the most part social and motivational, but include a few with significant cognitive characteristics (e.g. years of education). Other variables, especially those traditionally labelled "cognitive" (such as reasoning based on salience, availability, or analogies), could be included, although Sulloway does not himself do so. His view is that social and motivational variables—in particular birth order and the variables which interact with it—account for about 36% of the variance—a very high figure in social psychology—in scientists' preferences. (I am not fully in agreement with this, and will discuss my objections below.)

In my own historical studies, I have used a simple multivariate model—much simpler than Sulloway's—to investigate effects of so–called "biasing factors" (such as interests, salience of particular data, ideology) on theory choice. The purpose of this is not prediction of individual scientists' choices (although it could be used for that) but assessment of the *aggregate* effect of these individual choices in particular episodes of scientific change. It is popular, especially among philosophers of science and scientists themselves, to assume that the aggregate effect is an effective distribution of cognitive labor (see Goldman and Shaked 1992, Hull 1988, 357, Kitcher 1993 Chapter 8, and even Sulloway manuscript 1994, 473–474). Elsewhere (Solomon, manuscript), I have called this an "invisible hand" assumption— the assumption is that the so–called "biasing factors", appearances to the contrary, work for the benefit of science because, through distributing labor, they maximize the search for a successful theory.

I used an improper linear model to tally the variables generally regarded as "biasing" in two scientific controversies—the plate tectonics revolution and the development of genetics. An improper linear model simply counts the variables and weights them equally. So it is a multivariate model, although a simple one. As Robyn Dawes (1988, Chapter 10) has shown, it is superior to informal (sometimes called global) assessments—and thus superior to the usual assessments made by historians, scientists and philosophers. For example, Dawes has shown that improper linear models outperform the "experts," who make global (or intuitive) judgments, in three cases: diagnosis of neurosis versus psychosis from scores on the MMPI, prediction of grade point averages from 10 variables assessing academic aptitude and personality, and prediction of graduate student performance based on GRE, undergraduate GPA and the selectivity of their undergraduate institutions.

Using an improper linear model, I have found that the "biasing factors" were responsible for equitable distribution of effort in the plate tectonics revolution, but resulted in inequitable distribution of effort during the development of genetics[6]. For example, those who worked on Southern Hemisphere materials were biased in favor of drift; but this was counterbalanced by the belief perseverance of those working on Northern Hemisphere materials. Throughout the plate tectonics revolution, mobilists and stabilists had an approximately equal number of biasing factors responsible for their decisions (see Table 1, and also Solomon 1992 and 1994a for the full case study). The development of genetics, on the other hand, proceeded with unequal distribution of biases and thereby inequitable distribution of effort. Mendelism was especially favored in the early part of the century, but this was not because it, exclusively, was successful: social, political and cognitive factors together caused a skewed distribution of research effort. The aggregate result of individual decisions was less good for the development of genetics than it might have been: the genetics community was slow to accept important results about non–nuclear inheritance and cellular differentiation and is still dominated by a misleading "master molecule" view of the role of DNA (see Table 2, and also Solomon 1994b and Solomon manuscript for the full case study).

Biasing Factors in the Plat Tectonics Revolution

+ increased support
- decreased support

Stabilism
Belief perseverance +
Peer pressure + and -
Influence of authority +
Cognitive biases
(salience/availability of Northern Hemisphere data)+

Drift
Peer pressure + and -
Influence of authority +
Cognitive biases
(salience/availability of Southern hemisphere data, orogeny, climatology, paleomagnetism) +

Table 1

Thus, multivariate models can be used to describe both individual decisions and aggregate outcomes. It may not be apparent from these two examples that *any* variables may be chosen for the multivariate analyses. In fact, all that is necessary is that the variables be measurable (presence/absence, or quantity). So, for example, observance of the law of non–contradiction could be a variable scored in terms of presence and absence. There is not, however, any motivation for coding this variable here because observance or non–observance of this law has not (yet?) been found to correlate with the various choices *among those theories we regard as genuine competitors*, and it is such correlations between variable factors and choice that I have been interested in discovering. Furthermore, I have been especially interested to investigate the epistemic role of those factors that philosophers have typically regarded as "biasing".

Although multivariate analysis is a *general* approach to modelling scientific change, which can be used for modelling all scientific decision making, the *findings* are not general. Different variables have different strength in different scientific revolutions. Sulloway has found a variable that has fairly general effects, at least in historical cases, viz. birth order, but even here there are significant and explainable differences in its effects in different controversies. The less ideological the controversy, the less influence birth order has. I would add to this that the less influence birth order has, the more influence (comparatively speaking) that other biasing factors—especially cognitive biases—have. The evidence so far suggests that there will not be a general model of scientific change that specifies constant magnitudes for the varibles influencing scientific change. Any general model will carry less information han one developed specifically for a particular domain.

Biasing Factors in the Development of Genetics

+	increased support
-	decreased support

Mendelism and "Master Molecule" Theory
Institutional support in the U.S. +
Morgan's political effectiveness +
Support for eugenics realized in Mendelism +
Hierarchical ideology realized in Mendelism +
Plant and animal breeders could use results; gave funding +
Vitalists and teleologists -
Lack of institutional support in Europe -
Cognitive biases + (early confirming results, salience of microorganisms used)

Non-Mendelian Inheritance
Competition with USA in France +
German intellectual traditions +
Institutional support in Europe and USA -
Lysenko and Cold War -
Antisemitism -
Sexism -
Cognitive biases + (some confirming results, embryologists, early evolutionary biologists)

Table 2

Multivariate analysis *ought* to appeal to sociologists of science. It is, after all, nethodology that is currently widespread in the social sciences. I am not defending his kind of integrated model of scientific change on philosophical grounds. I am preenting a strategy for integration that is already widespread and empirically successful n sociology, economics and medicine and I am appealing on intradisciplinary rounds that it be taken seriously.

. Normative Implications

Two kinds of normative enterprise are of particular interest: first, *evaluation* of pisodes of scientific change and, second, *recommendations* for improvement of scintific decision making. Notice that I am not talking of evaluation of *scientist's decisions* or recommendations for *scientist's choices*, individually speaking: since the goal ere is scientific progress, the interest is in evaluating the aggregate effort towards hat goal. It is in this sense, above all, that I am a social epistemologist.

The two examples of multivariate analysis given in the previous section each looked t the effects of *some* variables and not others. Sulloway, for the most part, detects the hot" cognitive (motivational) processes that social psychologists investigate. The improper linear model I used examines the effect of many processes generally regarded as biasing": these processes include both "hot" and "cold" cognitive processes, as well as ocial and political influences. What I did not examine, and Sulloway does not examne either, is the effect of reasoning according to the guidelines of logic, probability thery and confirmation theory. This may give the impression that a multivariate account an only measure "external" or "non– scientific" (sometimes, misleadingly, called non–cognitive") influences on theory choice. As I said in the above section, this is alse. When use of logic, probability theory and confirmation theory can be detected (say, by the kinds of inference made and the kind of mistakes made) the methods can also be modelled in a multivariate account. The reason that they were not modelled is twofold. First, we have selected disputes in which choice was not determined by "scientific" factors ("scientific" factors may of course have been involved in judgments tha the theories under consideration were worthwhile). Thus, modelling "scientific" factors is of less epistemic interest. Second, Sulloway and I both have a specific *normative agenda*: to assess the effects of influences other than traditional scientific method.

There are a number of inappropriate ways in which multivariate models have been used to evaluate the influence of so–called "biasing factors". Some sociologists of science (e.g. Stewart 1990, Rodeghier 1993) who also develop multivariate models[7] adop the same dichotomy between "cognitive" and "social" that I objected to above: they assume that social and motivational factors are non–scientific whereas ("cold") cognitive factors are scientific (i.e. rational). Therefore, just like some philosophers (Giere 1988 Chapter 8—mentioned above, Thagard 1993 and forthcoming), they take a measure of the percentage of cognitive factors to be a measure of the amount of scientific rationality. In this kind of normative assessment, "scientific" causes of change are modelled as the *residue* of causes of change after a multivariate model has modelled all "non–scientific" influences. This is the inverse of Laudan's well–known view that we should only bring in "external" factors to explain choice only when rational reconstructions fail! As I have already mentioned above, work in social epistemology investigating the epistemic worth of social processes, as well as the discovery that not all that is cognitive is conducive to scientific progress, tells against this normative view.

Another widespread and mistaken normative assumption is that "biasing" (or "external") factors cancel out, balance out, or combine in ways that are beneficial for scientific progress. Typically, a claim is made that the "baises" are well distributed, and result in a division of cognitive labor that maximizes the search for a good theory. Elsewhere (Solomon manuscript) I call this the "invisible hand" view. It is present, to varying extent, in the work of many, including Giere (1988), Goldman (1992, Chap 12), Hull (1988, p. 357), Kitcher (1993, Chapter 8), Kornblith (1993), Sulloway (1995) and Thagard (1992). A couple of quotations will serve as illustrations:

> ...particular kinds of social arrangements make good epistemic use of the grubbiest motives...Flawed people, working in complex social environments, moved by all kinds of interests, have collectively achieved a vision of parts of nature that is broadly progressive and that rests on arguments meeting standards that have been refined and improved over centuries... (Kitcher 1993, 305, 390)

> Depending upon the specific stage in the long "life cycle" of theories, conceptual biases play changing roles. Like a great river, these subjective influences meander together, gradually absorbing different tributaries of empirical support, until they finally reach the great ocean of 'truth'... (Sulloway 1995, 474)

These are optimistic fantasies. The fantasies are built on selective attention to the historical data: attention to particularly successful cases of scientific change, and attention to the role of "biases" in controversy and not in other aspects of scientific change Sometimes "biases" create controversy where there should be none (e.g. the creationism dispute, work in parapsychology) and sometimes they produce inappropriate consensus by causing a productive avenue of research to be dismissed (e.g. the early consensus on Mendelian genetics, which interfered with work on cytoplasmic inheritance). So–called "biased" thinking is also involved in coming to consensus, and in conceptual development (creativity): there are many stages of scientific change where normative evaluation is possible and appropriate.

Although "invisible hand" views are over–optimistic, they are, in my view, correct to take a social perspective for evaluation of scientific change: while individual scientists' decisions are biased, the aggregate effect (i.e. the effect judged from a social perspective) can *sometimes* be beneficial for science. I take the same social perspective for evaluation (Solomon 1994a, Solomon 1994b) but, since we have only just begun to make the evaluations, conclusions about progressiveness of scientific change are premature. Note that while a full *descriptive* model of scientific change will discuss both individual and aggregate processes, I am proposing that a normative model need assess individual reasoning only derivatively from the social, aggregate outcome.

Normative recommendations exceed normative evaluations not only in suggesting specific ways in which an episode of scientific change might have gone better, but also in giving strategies for implementing normative improvements. In order to do this, a multivariate model which gives *correlations* between variables and outcome is not sufficient: adequate knowledge of causes is also needed. Often, some knowledge of causes precedes and suggests measurement of correlations. Yet, appreciation of the multivariate context in which causes operate can only improve normative recommendations. Whoever is giving the practical advice—graduate student advisor, principal investigator, department head, dean of research or grant administrator—can proceed with a more accurate assessment of the likely outcome of various policies, strategies or funding decisions.

Notes

[1]I am grateful to Alvin Goldman, Philip Kitcher, Alan Richardson and Frank Sulloway for comments on this paper.

[2]The Society for Social Studies of Science refused to cosponser the symposium "Integrating Cognitive and Social Models of Science" in which this paper was presented.

[3]Holyoak and Thagard (1994) give an artificial intelligence account of analogical reasoning.

[4]See Solomon (forthcoming) for some more detailed criticisms.

[5]Goldman asserts that editors and referees who "weed out inferior contributions" are practicing epistemic paternalism (1992, 224). But the practice of weeding out inferior contributions is not obviously a case of epistemic paternalism, which was described earlier in the chapter as the practice of withholding true but misleading information. See Solomon (forthcoming) for a full discussion of this.

[6]'Equitable distribution of effort' does not mean 'equal distribution of effort'; it means a fair distribution of effort, given the relative promise of competing theories. I am arguing that an *equal* distribution of *biases* helps attain the desired *equitable* distribution of *effort*.

[7]As was mentioned above, it is rare for sociologists of science to use multivariate models. Those that have done so do not have data and analysises as wide ranging as Sulloway's; thus I feature his work in the previous section.

References

Bechtel, W. and Richardson, R. (1993), *Discovering Complexity: Decomposition and Localization as Strategies in Scientific Research*. Princeton, NJ: Princeton University Press.

The Biology and Gender Study Group (1988), "The Importance of Feminist Critique for Contemporary Cell Biology," *Hypatia 3:1*. Reprinted in ed. Nancy Tuana,

Feminism and Science (1989). Bloomington and Indianapolis: Indiana University Press, 172–187.

Dawes, R. (1988), *Rational Choice in an Uncertain World*. Harcourt Brace Jovanovich.

Giere, R. (1988), *Explaining Science: A Cognitive Approach*. Chicago: University of Chicago Press.

Goldman, A. (1992),, *Liaisons: Philosophy Meets the Cognitive and Social Sciences*. Cambridge, MA: MIT Press.

_ _ _ _ _ _ _ _. and Shaked, M. (1992), "An Economic Model of Scientific Activity and Truth Acquisition". In Goldman (1992), 227–254.

Haraway, Donna (1994), "A Game of Cat's Cradle: Science Studies, Feminist Theory, Cultural Studies" *Configurations 1*, 59–71.

Holyoak, K. and Thagard, P. (1994), *Mental Leaps*. Cambridge, MA: MIT Press.

Hull, D. (1988), *Science as a Process*. Chicago: University of Chicago Press.

Keller, E. (1985), *Reflections on Gender and Science*. New York and London: Yale University Press.

Kitcher, P. (1993), *The Advancement of Science*. Oxford and New York: Oxford University Press.

Kornblith, H. (1993), *Inductive Inference and its Natural Ground*. Cambridge, MA: MIT Press.

Latour, B. (1987), *Science in Action*. Cambridge, MA: Harvard University Press

Quine, W.V. (1969), "Epistemology Naturalized". In *Ontological Relativity and Other Essays*. New York: Columbia University Press, 69–90.

Rodeghier, M. (1993), "Factors influencing attitudes toward controversial research: quantitatively disentangling the social from the scientific". Talk, Society for Social Studies of Science Meetings 1993, part of PhD dissertation.

Sapp, J. (1987), *Beyond the Gene: Cytoplasmic Inheritance and the Struggle for Authority in Genetics*. Oxford: Oxford University Press.

Solomon, M. (1992), "Scientific Rationality and Human Reasoning" *Philosophy of Science* 59:3, 439–455.

_ _ _ _ _ _ _ _. (1994a), "Social Empiricism". *Nous* 28:3, 325–343.

_ _ _ _ _ _ _ _. (1994b), "A More Social Epistemology". In ed. Fred Schmitt, *Socializing Epistemology*, 217–233. Rowman and Littlefield.

_ _ _ _ _ _ _ _. (forthcoming), "Naturalism and Generality", *Philosophical Psychology*.

_ _ _ _ _ _ _ _. (manuscript), "Is There An Invisible Hand of Reason?" Presented at a conference "Non–Formal Foundations of Reason," Newcastle, Australia, August 1993. Forthcoming with proceedings of the conference.

Stewart, J. (1990), *Drifting Continents and Colliding Paradigms*. Bloomington and Indianapolis: Indiana University Press

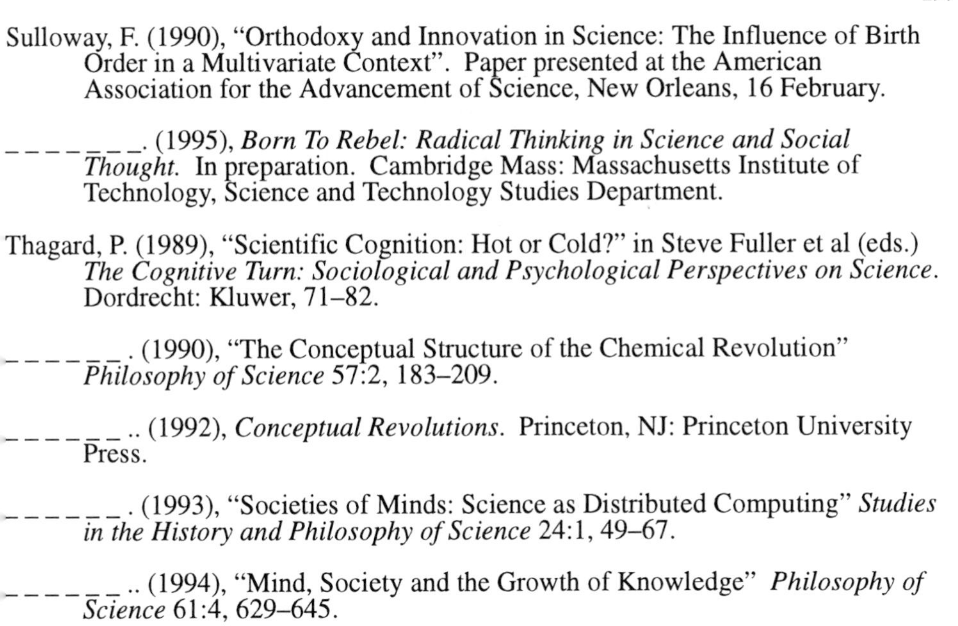

Sulloway, F. (1990), "Orthodoxy and Innovation in Science: The Influence of Birth Order in a Multivariate Context". Paper presented at the American Association for the Advancement of Science, New Orleans, 16 February.

________. (1995), *Born To Rebel: Radical Thinking in Science and Social Thought.* In preparation. Cambridge Mass: Massachusetts Institute of Technology, Science and Technology Studies Department.

Thagard, P. (1989), "Scientific Cognition: Hot or Cold?" in Steve Fuller et al (eds.) *The Cognitive Turn: Sociological and Psychological Perspectives on Science.* Dordrecht: Kluwer, 71–82.

_______. (1990), "The Conceptual Structure of the Chemical Revolution" *Philosophy of Science* 57:2, 183–209.

_______.. (1992), *Conceptual Revolutions.* Princeton, NJ: Princeton University Press.

_______. (1993), "Societies of Minds: Science as Distributed Computing" *Studies in the History and Philosophy of Science* 24:1, 49–67.

_______.. (1994), "Mind, Society and the Growth of Knowledge" *Philosophy of Science* 61:4, 629–645.

Young, R. (1985), *Darwin's Metaphor: Nature's Place in Victorian Culture.* Cambridge: Cambridge University Press.

Explaining Scientific Change: Integrating the Cognitive and the Social

Paul Thagard

University of Waterloo

1. Introduction

In 1979, Dr. J. Robin Warren of the Royal Perth Hospital in Australia discovered bacteria in the biopsies of stomach tissue taken from patients with digestive complaints. His colleague Dr. Barry Marshall followed up on Warren's work and found the bacteria in many patients with stomach inflammation and peptic ulcers (Marshall and Warren 1984). When Marshall claimed at a medical conference that bacteria are the principal cause of peptic ulcers, his remarks were rejected as preposterous. It was widely believed that the human stomach's caustic gastric juices made it too antiseptic for bacteria to survive for long. Moreover, alternative explanations of the principal cause of ulcers were available, focusing on excess acidity and emotional stress. Stung by rejection of his theory and failure of animal experiments, Marshall resorted in 1984 to drinking the bacteria himself, and underwent endoscopy and biopsy to show that his stomach had indeed become inflamed (Monmaney 1993).

Although Marshall's hypothesis that peptic ulcers are caused by bacterial infections seemed wildly implausible, it was easily tested, and evidence began to mount that the bacteria, eventually named Helicobacter pylori, were indeed prevalent in people with ulcers. They have also been implicated as a cause of stomach cancer. In February, 1994, a panel convened by the U.S. National Institutes of Health recommended that antibacterial agents be added to the conventional treatments for ulcers (Yamada 1994). In just a decade, the reception of Marshall's hypothesis has changed from derisive rejection to general (although not universal) acceptance (Graham & Go 1993).

Many aspects of this case cry out for explanation:

- Why were stomach bacteria noticed by Warren when they had not been noticed previously?
- How did Warren and Marshall come up with the hypothesis that bacteria produce ulcers?
- Why was this hypothesis rejected by most other researchers?
- Why did various researchers nevertheless set out to test the hypothesis?
- Why was the hypothesis that bacteria are implicated in stomach ulcers generally accepted?

In current science studies, there are three prevalent styles of explanation: logical, psychological, and sociological (Thagard 1994). Elsewhere I have argued at length

PSA 1994, Volume 2, pp. 298-303

that even in philosophy psychological explanations are more informative than logical ones (Thagard 1988, 1992). But what is the relation between cognitive and social explanations of scientific change? I maintain that cognitive and social explanations are complementary rather than competing, and will attempt in this paper to sketch how they can be integrated. The next section will depict a variety of ways in which social and psychological explanations can be viewed in relation to each other, and argue for an approach to explaining science that takes mind, society, and nature equally seriously. I will then use the ulcer case to illustrate in more detail the complex interrelations of causal factors needed to explain the development of scientific knowledge.

2. Mind, Society, Nature

Figure 1 schematizes six possible relations between psychological and social explanations of science. Schemas (a) and (b) express extreme views about the hegemony of a particular style of explanation. Psychological reductionism, (a), is the view that everything about science, including social aspects, can be understood in terms of the psychology of the individuals involved. An analog of this view may survive in the economic doctrine of methodological individualism which proclaims the reduction of macroeconomics to microeconomics, but I know of no one in science studies who holds this view. Sociological reductionism, (b), is the view that everything about science, including its psychological aspects, can be understood in terms of social factors. In their most rhetorical moments, some Marxists and social constructivists approximate to this view. A slightly more modest view is (d), which advocates social explanations of science but does not purport to explain the psychological. Similarly, (c) proposes to simply ignore the social while providing psychological explanations of science.

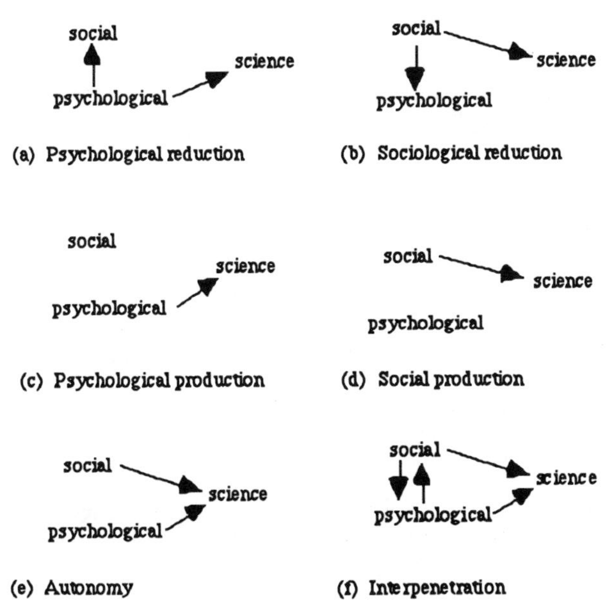

Figure 1. Six models of the relation of social and psychological explanations of science. The arrow signifies "explains".

The last two schemas present less dogmatic views of the relation of mind and society. Figure 1(e) eclectically proposes that social and psychological explanations of science can proceed in relative autonomy of science, perhaps explaining different aspects of science. Figure 1(f), however, presents a potentially richer and more dynamic view of science studies, in which the social and the psychological are mutually informed. The task before us is to specify these interactions in much more detail.

First, however, it is necessary to complicate the picture somewhat. The schemas in figure 1 seem to suppose that how science develops is merely a matter of mind and/or society. But bacteria are neither mental nor social creations. The story of the rise of the bacterial theory of ulcers has to include the role of physical entities such as bacteria, stomachs, and the instruments used to observe them. Of course, the use of instruments, observation, and experiment is not detached from the mental and social aspects of science, but it is not reducible to them either. A more adequate depiction of the influences on the development of scientific knowledge is shown in figure 2. If we want to understand the development of scientific knowledge, we need to understand not only the effects of mind, society, and nature on the growth of science, but also the mutual influences among the three kinds of factors. Figure 2, however, is more a logo than a theory, and to provide some content to the arrows requires looking in much more detail at particular cases in the history of science, such as the ulcer case.

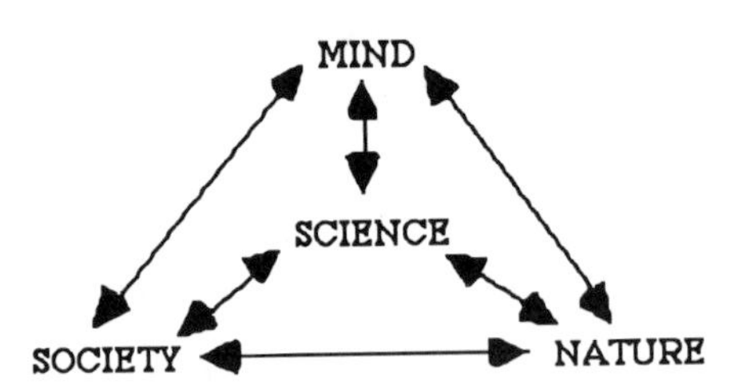

Figure 2. Science as a complex system. Arrows indicate mutual causal influences.

3. The Rise of the Bacterial Theory of Ulcers

I have only begun to investigate the details of the formation, development and acceptance of the bacterial theory of ulcers. But here is a list of the sorts of questions I am trying to answer on the basis of additional literature review and interviews:

Historical

1. When was the bacterial theory first proposed? What was the initial reception of the theory?
2. How did Marshall and his colleagues keep the idea alive?
3. When did researchers such as David Graham begin clinical tests?
4. When did these other researchers begin to be convinced?
5. How much resistance is there still?
6. How important was the availability of new instrumental techniques (e.g. endoscopy in which tubes with a tiny video camera and pincers are inserted down the throat) to the development of new ideas?

Psychological

1. What made Marshall and Warren first think that ulcers might have a bacterial cause?
2. Why was their proposal so roundly rejected by other researchers?
3. What made these researchers nevertheless decide to do the relevant studies?
4. What made them change their minds? Were there motivational factors as well as evidential ones?

5. What were the changes in conceptual structure that took place, for example in the concept of bacteria?

6. Can the discovery and acceptance of the bacterial theory be modelled computationally?

7. Did analogies play a role in the formation, development, acceptance, or communication of the theory?

Sociological

1. Was the spread of the bacterial theory affected by the social situations and status of the initial researchers?

2. By what social networks did the new theory begin to spread?

3. What role did collaboration play in the development of new ideas?

4. Were there competing research groups?

5. What were the journals and meetings through which the new studies were promulgated?

6. What role did pharmaceutical companies and government funding agencies play in assisting or retarding the development of new ideas?

Philosophical

1. Was there a rational basis for accepting the old theory of ulcers?

2. Was the initial rejection of the bacterial theory justified?

3. Was the eventual acceptance of the bacterial theory justified? If so, what kinds of reasoning provided the rational basis?

4. Were the social procedures by which the ideas spread effective?

5. How did the psychological and sociological factors interact?

Answering these questions will explain a lot about the development of the bacterial theory of ulcers. The psychological questions will reveal much about the mind-science links, the sociological questions will reveal much about the society-science links, and the historical questions concerning instruments will reveal much about the nature-science links. But these connections will not alone provide the integrated understanding that figure 2 suggests is needed. Here are some preliminary speculations about how the details of the theoretical integration might work.

Consider first the mind-nature connection. Discussion of the role of nature in the ulcer case will naturally focus on the kinds of instruments used to determine the existence of bacteria at ulcer sites: endoscopes and microscopes. Application of these instruments, however, is not blind, and presupposes various kinds of theoretical and practical intentions. We know that nature affects mind, since the experiments of taking stomach samples and looking for bacteria are highly reproducible and convinced even skeptics. But mind also affects dramatically what aspects of nature will be observed. Marshall's experiments that first found a link between ulcers and bacterial infections were not done randomly, but depended on knowledge concerning stomach disorders to which the bacteria might be relevant. The mental structures of members of the medical community certainly affected their interpretation of Marshall's experiments: most gastroenterologists were highly skeptical. Nevertheless, when the skeptics found that they could replicate Marshall's experiments despite their attempts to refute him, many gastroenterologists came over to Marshall's side.

Even more complex is the mind-society connection. I am identifying the most important individuals who contributed to the new views about ulcers, as well as the social groups that were most crucial in the formation and spread of the ideas. These groups include collaborative research teams, institutions such as hospitals and medical schools, and scholarly organizations such as associations of gastroenterologists who meet regularly. Mind affects society, since what individuals present to groups depends in part on what they have been thinking about the relevant problems. But society also affects mind, first because each individual's information is substantially affected by the flow of information from human and literary sources, and second because an individual's thinking is affected in many ways by social factors such as how the scientists wants to succeed and be viewed by peers.

Society-nature links are perhaps the hardest to describe, since they are typically mediated by mind. One connection is that what instruments are available for observing nature can be affected greatly by social factors such as granting agencies. Scientists who cannot afford to buy an instrument will never get access to the aspects of nature that it reveals. Instruments like electron microscopes, endoscopes with attached video cameras, and magnetic resonance imaging machines are very expensive, and their availability will depend on a scientist having funding or being member of a group that has funding. Another society-nature link is that some experiments are so complicated that they must be performed collaboratively.

The nature of all these pairwise effects will need to be spelled out in particular cases in the history of science. To make integrated analysis all the more complex, there is no reason to assume that all the effects will be pairwise. For simplicity I have not gone into ways in which nature and society together influence mind or other kinds of multiple causation. For systems as complex as society, the currently available vocabulary for describing causal influences seems all too limited.

4. Complex Causality

In medicine as in social science, causality is complex. Not everyone who is exposed to *Helicobacter pylori* gets stomach ulcers. Although the bacterial theory of ulcers has come to center stage in gastroenterology, the effects of stress may still be relevant. Perhaps stress does increase the likelihood of increasing ulcers by suppressing the immune system and making it less effective in dealing with the bacteria. One current textbook in medical microbiology hedges by saying that bacteria are "implicated" in gastric ulcers, while averring that bacteria "cause" gastritis (Murray et al., 1994). The nature of the causal interaction among factors such as stress and bacteria in ulcer formation is still unknown.

Similarly, we still have limited understanding of the causal interactions among mind, society, and nature in the development of scientific knowledge. We need many new studies that do not dogmatically restrict their focus to only one aspect of science. The situation in science studies is similar to that emerging in cognitive neuroscience. A decade ago, cognitive psychology and neuroscience were relatively independent fields, with the former performing behavioral experiments on humans and the latter performing neurological experiments on other animals. Development of new techniques such as magnetic resonance imagining has made possible a new collaboration between cognitive psychologists and neuroscientists (Kosslyn and Koenig 1992; Posner and Raichle 1994) . Cognitive psychologists have abandoned the presumption of autonomy from neural considerations, but they have certainly not leaped to the conclusion that psychology is to be reduced to neuroscience. Results of past psychological experiments are contributing to neurological experimentation as much as the reverse. The emerging relation between psychology and neuroscience is interpenetration rather than reduction or autonomy. Science studies should similarly encourage the integration of psychological and sociological explanations of the growth of knowledge.

References

Graham, D.Y., & Go, M.F. (1993), "Helicobacter Pylori: Current Status" *Gastroenterology,* 105: 279-282.

Kosslyn, S., & Koenig, O. (1992), *Wet mind: The New Cognitive Neuroscience*. New York: Free Press.

Marshall, B.J., and Warren, J.R. (1984), "Unidentified Curved Bacilli in the Stomach of Patients with Gastritis and Peptic Ulceration", *Lancet* 8390: 1311-1315.

Monmaney, T. (1993), "Marshall's Hunch", *New Yorker*, September 20, 64-72.

Murray, P.R., Kobayaki, G.S., Pfaller, M.A., and Rosenthal, K.S. (1994), *Medical Microbiology* (2nd ed.). St. Louis: Mosby.

Posner, M.I., and Raichle, M.E. (1994), *Images of Mind*. New York: Freeman.

Thagard, P. (1988), *Computational Philosophy of Science*. Cambridge: MIT Press.

______. (1992), Conceptual Revolutions. Princeton: Princeton University Press.

______. (1994), "Mind, Society, and the Growth of Knowledge", *Philosophy of Science* 61: 629-645.

Yamada, T., et al. (1994), *Helicobacter Pylori in Peptic Ulcer Disease.* Washington: National Institutes of Health.

Shifting Frames: From Divided to Distributed Psychologies of Scientific Agents

Peter J. Taylor

Cornell University

1. Framing

When reading the papers of Solomon, Thagard and Goldman, I observed their framing doing considerable explicit and implicit work. Framing, a visual metaphor, stimulated me to respond with images of one kind or another. These should allow readers to visualize more issues and propositions than an argumentive format could have pinned down in the limited space available.

Figure 1 conveys how the three papers seem to me to frame the issue of integrating the cognitive and social: Scientists' *beliefs* are the focal phenomena, within three nested boxes of *factors* surrounding them: thinking (reasoning etc.); cognition (information inpu and processing); and social (interaction among agents). (The other objects and lines will be explained in due course.) These factors are referred to as *influences*, something outside that gets into beliefs (1). The authors then argue about which set of influences is strongest or how to think about the factors "intermingling," "overlapping," "interacting."

Within this framing some obvious things are missing: *what the beliefs are about*, the *sources of change,* the *body or materiality of the scientist,* and *instructions for how we are to use this schema.* Let me fill these in, starting with the last. The authors aim to describe well the way the factors influence beliefs, that is, give descriptions faithful to actua scientific practice. If they can do so then scientists, at least those who take note of what they say, can adjust what they do individually or collectively so as to be more effective.

More effective, for these authors, would mean arriving at beliefs that correspond to some mind-independent, unmediated reality — that is *what the beliefs are ultimately about* (2). This reality could fit in the schema in two places: inside the beliefs box (r1) or outside all the boxes (r2). If placed outside, the nested boxes become not influences, but refracting lenses between reality and beliefs. The r1 position preserves the idea that the other boxes are *influences* , which can disturb any stable relationship between reality and beliefs, and this would allow for change, at least until th beliefs lock in on reality. Conceptually this inside position might work, but spatially it creates a problem. That is, beliefs and thinking go on inside a scientist's brain; cog nition lies inside the brain plus its attached sensory organs; and, if we follow Goldman, even social influences can, through memory, intentions and motivations, b brought back inside the brain. Spatially most of reality is not contained in these places. For now, let us diagram reality in both places, but remember the ambiguity.

PSA 1994, Volume 2, pp. 304-310

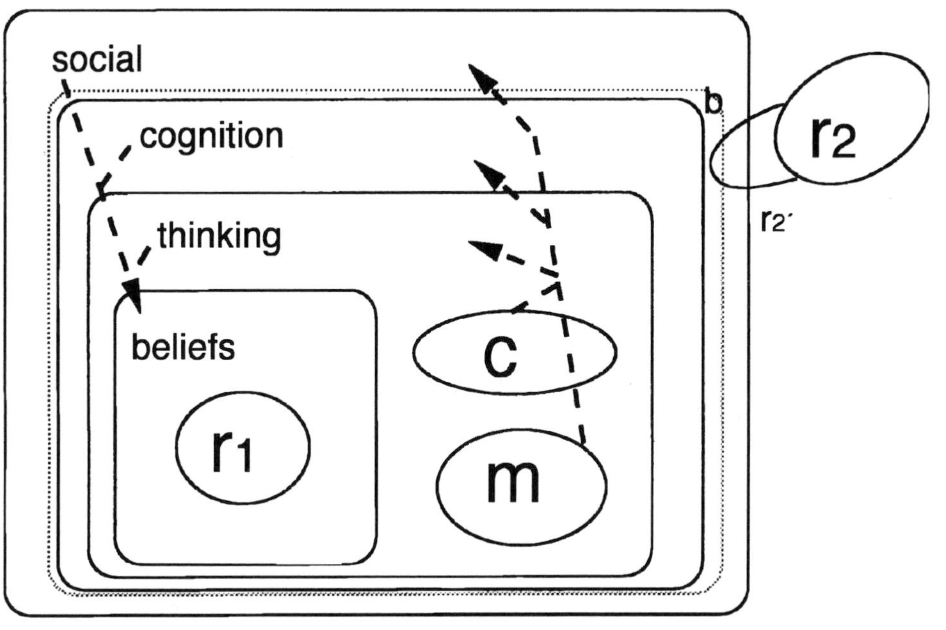

Figure 1. A schema of Solomon, Thagard and Goldman's accounts of social and psychological influences on scientific beliefs (see text for explanation of symbols).

What are the *sources of change*? One source is, as Goldman notes, the motivations scientists have, so let us add another set of factors (m). One of scientists' motivations is to improve the fit between beliefs and reality, and they will choose among hypotheses accordingly. But these papers do not make clear where these hypotheses come from in order to be chosen among (1); without this, acceptance/ rejection of hypotheses is no more than context of justification philosophy. To patch up the hole corresponding to the context of discovery there must be an implicit creativity circle (c). The picture is starting to get complicated, because motivations and creativity are outward influences, affecting the inward influencing factors. Moreover, they affect the very choice of phenomena to investigate in the first place.

But while we are adding an outward direction for influences, let us consider the *body*. I claimed it was missing, but actually it has been here as the container for the brain and its operations (dotted box b). But, of course, more substantial and noticeable bodies are needed if scientists are to build equipment, do experiments, move to where observations can be made, and sometimes even manufacture phenomena that exist nowhere else in the universe. And, having mentioned this, scientists' interest in manufactured reality means we now have to extend our outside reality circle into the social (r2'). I do not know what to do, however, with the other reality circle (r1) in this regard. The initial framing has, indeed, become very messy.

Complexification, however, is not my point; I want only to highlight the tensions among the images evoked by these papers. The image we started with was one of beliefs at the core and outside factors influencing them. Then we added reality. This could be located inside the core to allow influences to impinge on the dialog between relaity and beliefs — schematically neat, but spatially implausible. If, instead, reality is placed outside the nested boxes the factors become refractions occuring as reality penetrates through to beliefs. Then we added internal factors that influence how the outer factors, the body now included, move out to apprehend and draw reality in. We could tinker with these images and attempt to reconcile these tensions, but let me introduce a radically different framing, one which nevertheless addresses the integration of psychology, philosophy, and social studies of science.

2. Reframing

In an earlier paper (Taylor 1993; which led to me being asked to be this session's commentator) I argued that the psychology of individual agents has been an arena in which social studies of science (SSS) addresses social causality, that is, the effect of context on agents, and the re/production of structure/dness. Too often the agents privileged by SSS's theory and methods are people who can act almost without mental representations — a behaviorist image. Instead, I advocated that SSS should explore a *distributed* psychology. Let me sketch this idea here, starting from an image of scientists as agents who act in the world.

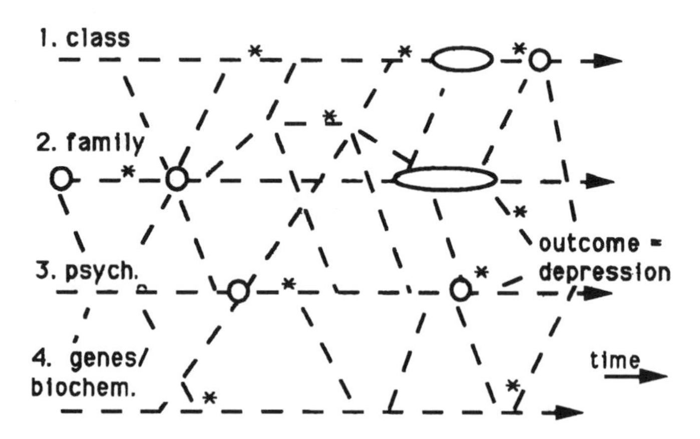

Figure 2. Intersecting strands in the development of severe depression (see Taylor 1995 for sources)

Admittedly, one part of acting is establishing support for a hypothesis or model, but scientists cannot avoid doing many other things as well—making observations, building equipment, securing funds, writing articles, addressing audiences, negotiating gender and racial dichotomies, suffering ill-health, watching children grow up, being treated with respect-for-authority, supervising others who work for them, reorienting or reframing work as the political winds or breezes shift, using language, and so on. The image I have of agents in general acting in the world is one of simultaneous different processes or strands operating at a range of scales or levels of generality. In Taylor (1995) I describe a generalized life course for working class women who have become clinically depressed. The strands involve class, family, and psychology (figure 2). Moreover, the processes intersect or are linked—what happens in the woman's family when she was a child, say, she loses a parent, conditions her susceptibility to psychological distress, to time in a custodial institution (the strand in-between 1 & 2), and to the hardships attendant on being working class. All of these, in turn, conditions her vulnerability to a severe crisis and onset of depression. The stars indicate a variety of points at which interventions could modify the processes and outcome. I then add a hypothetical genetic/biochemical strand (4.) to make the point that, if the goal is reduction in depression for working class women, the unchangeability of inherited genes says nothing about the most effective, economical, or otherwise socially desirable interventions to pursue.

Employing figure 2 very schematically now for the production of some *scientific* outcome, the kinds of strands might become 1. society as a broad audience and set of sources (and the in-between strand as immediate audiences and sources); 2. language, tools, and work organization (with models and representations as the intermediate node); 3. agents' creative processes; and 4. reality (starting from underlying unmediated reality and moving onto manufactured reality). (The placement of linkages is not meant to be important.) A scientist making science builds upon and links in a diversity of elements or resources. I call such linked processes *heterogeneous construction* (Taylor 1995). Science is much more than a matter of belief in hypotheses about the world; scientific change comes from many sources that have their effect only indirectly on belief. By analogy to the genes of the depression case, the fixity of some deep reality does not imply that it predominantly governs the actions of scientific agents (including how they establish some representation of this reality).

The framing has shifted to *science-in-the-making*; we no longer focus on what beliefs or knowledge *correspond to*. The earlier images of factors and influences or of refractions no longer make much sense (3); the tensions pointed to in section 1 disappear when we focus on a scientist as agent-in-the world. Let me summarize some of the directions this image of science as heterogeneously constructed can be taken (see Taylor 1993, 1995 for elaboration):

1. All outcomes are heterogeneously constructed =>

1.1 Construction is polyvalent, things involved in one construction process are implicated in many others =>

1.2 All describing has implications for explaining, and all explaining facilitates intervening.

2. All agents are imaginative, assessing the practical constraints and facilitations of possible actions ahead of their acting =>

2.1. Their psychology is thus not localizable inside them, but is *distributed* or *in circuit*; and

2.2 Agents are not innocent of 1.2.

3. Complexity is unruly = problematic boundaries and categories, levels and scales not clearly separable, structures subject to restructuring, and control or generalization difficult =>

3.1 To act, agents (usually) system-ize such complexity (see 1.2, 2).

Philosophers of science do not have many tools for addressing multiple causality, heterogeneous causes, and linked processes; many fascinating issues await those who join in conceptualizing heterogeneous construction. SSS by no means has the frameworks and methods available to be taken "off the shelf," but many SSS scholars have been making contributions in this direction. I recommend that the authors and other philosophers of science, as an item of methodology, abandon caricatures of SSS based on small samples (e.g., Latour, Wolgar, Shapin, Collins) and pay more attention to the range of things that actually go on in SSS. (Similarly, regarding what goes on in science.) Moreover, defences should be lowered long enough to understand the framings developed and employed by different practitioners, more or less on their own terms. Taking my own advice to heart, let me move back within the authors' own framing to make some specific comments.

3. Some less radical criticisms

In advocating multivariate analysis, Solomon claims that "sociologists of science have generally especially recently eschewed quantitative methods in favor of the ethnographic and narrative accounts". She overlooks the whole field of scientometrics, with its own methods of co-citation analysis, and so on, methods used even by Latour, one of the people she describes as qualitative. I suspect that she discounts (or perhaps has not even come across) such work because it addresses dimensions of science other than beliefs, that is, outside her framing. Yet, even on the terms of scientific change as change in beliefs (also the terms of Sulloway), multivariate analysis is a tool requiring more careful application.

Solomon's primary goal is explanation and she is clear that statistically significant *effects* need causal hypotheses before they provide insight into the causal processes—as statisticians have long warned, correlations do not equal causes. Yet few statisticians have avoided the sin of thinking about causes more or less in terms of the statistical effects they are able to discern. (The term "risk factors" in epidemiology exemplifies this occupational hazard.) Solomon talks about "interactions" between cognitive and social factors exposed by multivariate analysis as if they were causal interactions. At best, however, statistical effects are to use Alfred Lotka's term, "animated question marks," things to explain. At worst they are quite misleading. When I worked analyzing large data sets from international plant breeding trials, we always found the variety x environment interaction effects to be the largest source of variation in the raw analysis. However, after we used other multivariate techniques to group similar plant varieties and growing environments, we found that within *all* the groups interaction effects had become negligible. Nothing causal had changed—we were dealing with the same data—but different statistical effects came to prominence.

Multivariate analyses are sensitive in other ways that should also temper any quick translation from statistical effects to causal claims. Perhaps the most exploratory of all multivariate analysts are to be found in vegetation ecology (see the journal *Vegetatio*). Austin (1987) reviews the situations in which multivariate methods are good at exposing the underlying environmental gradients and biological interactions that caused vegetation patterns. This occurs precisely when the methods have been custom-made on the basis of models of causes that closely resemble the actual causes. Off-the-shelf methods based on linear and algebraic statistical models, which have no relationship to any known causal process, generate many artifacts. The general lesson is that we have to know the kinds of causes and their interactions being sought before we can design multivariate methods efficient at exposing effects related to such causes.

Thagard is also interested in multivariate models and integration of different kinds factors in science studies. In his paper he provides mostly lists of factors related to the peptic ulcer bacteria case (1) and notes that we have to develop appropriate vocabulary and methods for discerning interactions. He points to two analogous developments, from which we might take a lead: multivariate models of ulcer causation in medicine and the growing collaboration between cognitive psychology and neuroscience. Let me flag potential and revealing problems with both analogies. Cognitive psychology and neuroscience may be uniting in part because they share an important commonality, namely, an internal, brain-centered view of psychology. Integrating them would then be like a corporate merger, not a guarantee of disturbing the status quo. On the ulcer analogy, notice how conventional medical practice manages to separate different kinds of influence and treat the patient accordingly. Anti-bacterials may help treat ulcers. Afterwards the patient can be left, admittedly feeling physically better, to address (or not address) their stressful life. Conversely, not all people who have *Helicobacter pylori*get ulcers, but doctors do not have to worry about this. For them to deal with patients, a faithful integrated model of ulcer-causation is not needed.

Thagard's analogy provides a theme for addressing Goldman's paper. Doctors can act with some degrees of freedom relative to how the world works; the integrated nature of peptic ulcer causality does not dictate their actions. Now, as a young scientist I could not make sense of scientific method as it was presented, namely, a form of dialogue between reality and my models, hypotheses or theories; crucial places existed where decisions had to be made that were *not given by nature*. In contrast, Goldman, notwithstanding his talk about "psychological" (cognitive plus motivational) factors, wants to rehabilitate the traditional philosophy of science emphasis on method. The additional psychological factors and their institutionalization influence, but do not qualitatively change, the capacity of the community of users of scientific method to home in on true beliefs. I am not satisfied; figure 3 conveys my revision of the standard scheme, identifying six places where extra-natural decisions have to be made (see Taylor 1989 for elaboration).

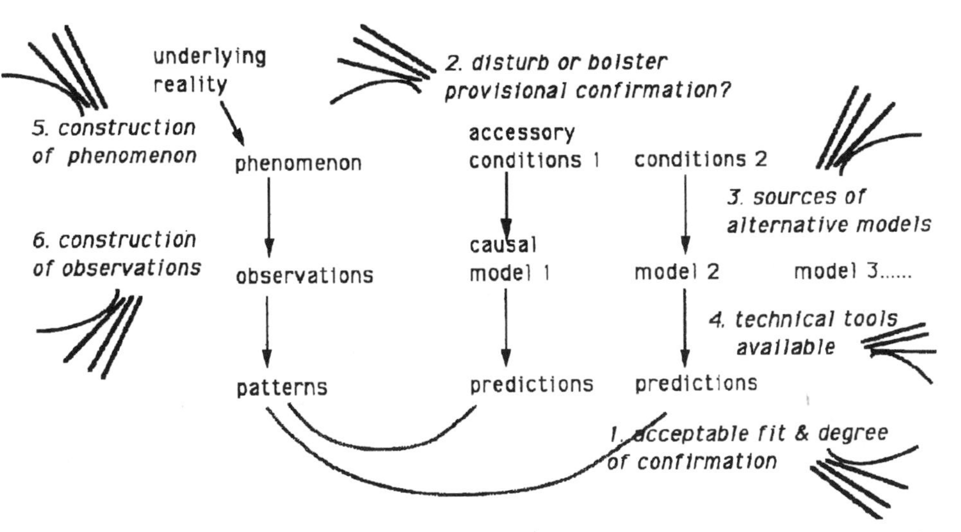

Figure 3. Sites of sociality superimposed on a schema of the confirmation of scientific models

4. Coda

In "Everyday metaphors of power " Timothy Mitchell identifies a master metaphor in social theory, the distinction between persuading and coercing, which corresponds to a distinction between mind and body. In science studies, an analogous deep split is apparent, that between believing and acting, representing and intervening. When Mitchell accounts for his master metaphor's persistence he might be read as providing an insight into the difficulties of integrating psychological and social models of science:

> One [reason for the persistence] stems from the fact that [the metaphor] is indissociable from our everyday conception of person[s]... as unique self-constituting consciousnesses living inside physically manufactured bodies. As something self-formed, this consciousness is the site of an original autonomy... [which] defies the way we think of coercion. It obliges us to imagine the exercise of power as an external process that can coerce the behavior of the body without necessarily penetrating and controlling the mind (Mitchell 1990, p. 545).

In this light, integrating psychological and social will probably require us to subvert this sense of our own self-formed consciousness, internal to our bodies. Instead, we need theories that extend the mind out of the brain, *embody* it and have that mind-body-person become, as s/he always is, an agent acting in a society.

Notes

[1]Thagard's spoken presentation deviated from this framing in presenting considerable detail of the science-in-the-making (see section 2).

[2]And scientific change is equated with belief change. Admittedly, Goldman refers to beliefs about other scientists' views and contributions and, during the discussion, Solomon related beliefs to anything that generates scientific practices. Nevertheless, without their having examined the conceptual implications of a broadened sense of belief, my construal remains apt.

[3]The arrows in Thagard's schemas fudge the question of process, but see note 1.

References

Austin, M.P. (1987), "Models for the analysis of species' response to environmental gradients", *Vegetatio*. 69: 35-45.

Mitchell, T. (1990), "Everyday metaphors of power", *Theory and Society*. 19: 545-577.

Taylor, P.J. (1989), "Revising Models and Generating Theory", *Oikos*. 54: 121-126.

_______. (1993),"What's (not) inside the heads of scientists? Implicit psychological models in the social studies of science," Society for Social Studies of Science, November.

_______. (1995), "Building on construction: An exploration of heterogeneous constructionism, using an analogy from psychology and a sketch from socio-economic modeling", *Perspectives on Science*. 3(1): in press.

Part X

POLICY ISSUES IN HUMAN GENETICS

Who's Afraid of the Human Genome Project?

Philip Kitcher

University of California at San Diego

1. Introduction

The Human Genome Project (henceforth HGP) arouses strong feelings. Enthusiasts view it as the culmination of the extraordinary progress of molecular biology during the past half century and as the beginnings of a revolutionized biology and medicine (Gilbert 1992, Caskey 1992). Detractors charge that it is wasteful, misguided, and pregnant with possibilities for social harm (Lewontin 1992, Hubbard and Wald 1993). In a short paper it is plainly impossible to explore all the sources of disagreement. My aim will be to consider the debate about the purely scientific merit of the HGP, to sketch the nature of the short-term issues which the project raises, and, finally, to identify what I take to be the deepest and most difficult questions.

2. The Scientific Payoff

The official goals of the HGP are to map and sequence the human genome, and the genomes of other organisms (so-called "model organisms"). Much of the criticism of the project focuses on the alleged uselessness of the full human sequence (Tauber and Sarkar 1992, Lewontin 1992, Rosenberg 1995). Little controversy surrounds the construction of detailed genetic maps in human beings and other organisms — and for good reason. Weekly, sometimes daily, discoveries of genes implicated in various human diseases and disorders testify to the power that new maps have brought. Outsiders frequently fail to recognize the success already exhibited by the strategy of positional cloning. Even though biomedical researchers may initially be entirely ignorant about the physiological processes that go awry in a particular disease, knowing how that disease is transmitted in a sufficiently large sample of families, they can sometimes isolate the locus that is responsible. The strategy is to find genetic markers (paradigmatically RFLPs) associated with the transmission of the disease, confine the locus to a particular chromosomal region (typically of the order of a megabase or two), pick out candidate genes, and, ultimately, clone and sequence the desired gene. Knowledge of the gene may then yield enough understanding of the protein to provide insight into the causal basis of the disease (as, for example, discovery of the gene whose mutations are implicated in cystic fibrosis suggested that the problem might have to do with transportation across cell membranes). Genetic maps, which assign markers to relative positions on chromosomes, are crucial to the initial stages of positional cloning; physical maps, which provide a collection of clones whose relative positions are known, are vital to the enterprise of hunting out the genes. Even with these aids, finding genes implicated in single-locus traits is not easy: it takes perse-

---

PSA 1994, Volume 2, pp. 313-321

verance, imagination, and a bit of luck to find the candidate genes and to settle on the right one. But without the maps, the entire enterprise would be impossible. (Perhaps improved maps will help positional cloning move to the next stage, the analysis of polygenic traits; for a lucid analysis of the problems currently bedevilling this area, see [Lander and Schork 1994]).

Currently, much of the work carried out under the auspices of the HGP is directed at producing better maps. The other major enterprises of the moment are those of trying to find ways of improving sequencing technology, and sequencing parts of the genomes of some model organisms (notably the yeast *Saccharomyces cerevisiae* and the nematode worm *Caenorhabditis elegans*). Contrary to what some people appear to believe, nobody is currently involved in trying to produce large chunks of contiguous human sequence. It is even quite possible that nobody will ever try to sequence an entire human chromosome. To understand the rationale for current practice, we need only consider the present difficulties of large-scale sequencing and the ways in which sequence information about human beings might be put to useful ends.

At present, standard gel electrophoretic methods can generate about 500 bases of sequence per lane, and large-scale genome centers with the appropriate machines to read the sequence run gels with 36 lanes. Typically, they manage one gel per day. So, you might think that it would be possible to produce, per center per day, 18,000 bases worth of sequence. However, to obtain "finished sequence" (i.e. sequence that can be held, with reasonable confidence, to be error-free), it is crucial to sequence the same DNA more than once — those involved often talk of "sevenfold redundancy". So the very best that a genome center is currently likely to be able to yield is between 2000 and 3000 bases of finished sequence a day. In conversations with directors of centers, I have usually been given the estimate of a megabase of finished sequence per year (projected for 1994-5, not yet achieved when the conversations took place in 1993-4); technicians who prepared the DNA and tended the machines were more conservative, foreseeing 600 or 700 kilobases of finished sequence per year. Even assuming the more optimistic rate, and supposing, charitably, that there will be thirty centers world-wide committed to the task, it would take about a century to produce the full 3 billion bases of the human genome sequence.

The genomes of some model organisms are much smaller. *S. cerevisiae* has a genome of around 15 megabases, *C. elegans* of around 100 megabases, *Drosophila* about 150 megabases. (The mouse, like other mammals, has about 3 billion bases). Even without significant improvements, we can expect the full sequence of the yeast genome to be available by the end of the decade; with predictable developments, the nematode genome should be sequenced by 2005, and the fruitfly genome may also be manageable. (Currently, the longest stretch of contiguous sequencing is 2.2 megabases from the nematode [Wilson *et.al.* 1994]; two yeast chromosomes have already been sequenced [Dujon *et.al.* 1994; Johnston *et.al.* 1994]). But to attack anything as massive as the human genome, significant refinements of current sequencing technology are required.

Some people believe that the improvements will come, that the current bottlenecks in automated sequencing (the preparation of the DNA and the analysis of the data) will be freed up . Indeed, genome researchers hope that the stimulus of the HGP will make large-scale sequencing a simple routine, so that a full human sequence could be achieved in one or two years at the very end of the official project, and so that the biologists of the next century would be able to commission sequence as easily as they now order glassware or strains of flies. However, even if the full human sequence never becomes manageable, it would be wrong to declare the HGP a failure. To appreciate this point, we need to turn to the issue of what exactly sequence data would do for us.

Complete sequencing is hailed as the most direct method of finding all the genes, where 'gene' is understood as picking out those parts of DNA that are transcribed. Genes are sparsely scattered in the genomes of complicated organisms (they occur at greater density in yeast, and in the soil amoeba *Dictyostelium discoideum*). Perhaps 5% of human DNA consists of coding regions. The most appropriate strategy for discovering the coding "islands" in the "ocean" of non-coding sequence, is to make use of what we already know about the sequences of genes (some human, the vast majority non-human). As the projects of sequencing yeast and the nematode have already shown, hitherto unsuspected genes can be discovered by searching for open reading frames (stretches of DNA that proceed for a long while without a stop codon), and investigating to see whether mRNAs corresponding to parts of these reading frames can be found. (In eukaryotes, mRNAs will only contain the sequences corresponding to exons.) As a database of gene sequences is found, one can then run computer programs to search for homologous sequences. *Human* genes are likely to be extracted from human sequence, by looking for parts of our DNA that are similar to the sequences of known genes.

This strategy of gene-hunting is biologically faithful. We share 40% of our genes with yeast (in our evolutionary history it wasn't necessary to reinvent the ways of carrying out the kinds of processes common to all cells), and it is probable that a very high percentage of our coding regions are very like coding regions in flies: the director of the genome center devoted to mapping and sequencing *Drosophila*, Gerald Rubin, has estimated, in conversation, that 99% of our coding regions are akin to some coding region in the *Drosophila* genome. In dealing with other organisms, we can carry out experimental manipulations that will reveal whether mutation at a putative locus exerts any phenotypic effect (although so-called "knockout" experiments may require refined abilities to pick out small phenotypic changes). Rounding up lots of genes in other species, we will have a basis for searching for homologues in stretches of human DNA sequence. So, *precisely because the HGP is not restricted to our own species*, we have a significant chance of parlaying human sequence data into the identification of human genes.

Can we go any further? Of course, given the genetic code, once you know the nucleotide sequence of a gene (and of its division into exons and introns), you can derive the amino-acid sequence of the protein it encodes. However, as critics of the HGP point out, there is currently no known way of moving from a linear sequence of amino acids to the three-dimensional structure of the protein: the protein-folding problem is presently unsolved. Plainly, a general solution (or even a bundle of partial solutions) to the protein-folding problem would be welcome. Lacking such resources, those who make use of future sequence data will have to emulate the strategy for finding human genes in their investigations of human proteins. Again, we have a database of proteins whose three-dimensional configurations are known — indeed, we often have knowledge not just of protein structure but also about the functional domains of the proteins and of the roles they play in intra-cellular interactions. Given a new sequence of amino acids, the appropriate technique is to seek out similar sequences among proteins whose structures (and possibly functions) are already known. Just this kind of research has already brought significant advances in our knowledge about the effects of genes implicated in disease: after cloning and sequencing a new gene, running the computer search exposes the protein it encodes as a cell-surface membrane protein or a DNA repair enzyme. To the extent that organisms play variations on a few simple themes, we can expect the sequence data to yield conclusions about human genes, about the structures and functions of human proteins, and *sometimes* about the kinds of interactions that underlie a particular physiological process.

So human sequence data would not necessarily be the jumble of gibberish detractors of the HGP often predict. Critics are quite right to point out that the route from a sequence of As, Cs, Gs, and Ts to biological understanding is by no means direct (Tauber and Sarkar 1992, Lewontin 1992, Rosenberg 1995), but err in supposing that there is no route at all. There are already promising signs that all sorts of genes common to a wide range of organisms can be identified and that the roles of corresponding proteins can be pinned down — through detailed investigation of model organisms. The real excitement of the HGP, at the moment and possibly throughout its whole history, consists in the development of maps, with their consequences for positional cloning, and in the sequencing of the small genomes of some model organisms. Quite probably, the political allies of the HGP would be appalled at the thought that the major triumph of the project may be the detailed understanding of the genomes of *S. cerevisiae*, *C.elegans*, and *D. melanogaster*, but the biological importance of these sequencing projects should not be underestimated. Knowledge of the yeast sequence will answer many basic questions about gene regulation in eukaryotes, as well as providing insight into the intra-cellular processes common to all organisms. Knowledge of the nematode sequence, coupled to the fate map for the nematode already constructed, will teach us just how different genes are switched on in the development of an organism with a "closed" developmental program. Knowledge of the fruitfly sequence, combined with the enormous understanding of early development in Drosophila achieved by Christiane Nüsslein-Vollhard and her co-workers (see Lawrence 1992 for an overview), will instruct us in the patterns of gene activation in development in an organism with a more open ontogeny. We can expect to be able to apply some of the new understanding of physiology and development to our own species.

I suggested earlier that the full human sequence might be difficult to obtain. Is the struggle to achieve it really necessary? Well, as noted earlier, improved sequencing technology would be a great boon to the biology of the twenty-first century, and, if we are out to get all the human genes, or as many as possible, then the most direct approach seems to be to sequence the entire human genome. However, if all else fails, there is an indirect strategy. Molecular biologists know tricks for extracting mRNAs from cells; rounding up human mRNAs, one can then use the enzyme reverse transcriptase to generate the corresponding cDNAs, using these to probe the genome to find coding regions. The *éminence noire* of the HGP, Craig Venter, is currently pursuing this approach, tagging pieces of human coding sequence, and inspiring much official ire with his efforts to patent them. Very probably, Venter will find a large number of human genes; it is very improbable that he will discover all of them, or even as many as could be garnered by grinding out the full sequence and running the appropriate computer programs. (If you start by extracting mRNAs from cells, you are unlikely to pick out all the mRNAs unless you have access to all cell types at all stages of development.) However, Venter's approach is a valuable fallback in case sequencing technology remains stuck near its present rates. A concerted program of hunting mRNAs, combined with the crucial information about the sequences of model organisms, could deliver the preponderance of the insights we might expect from the more problematic route of full human sequencing.

The moral of my story should be obvious. What is vital to the HGP is the enterprise of mapping and the sequencing of the genomes of the manageable model organisms. Truth in advertising would suggest that the HGP be renamed: calling it the "Genomes Project" would be more accurate. However, since the ghost of Senator Proxmire probably still haunts the halls in which Congressional funds are allotted, it is unlikely that representatives will hear testimonials to the importance of the nematode genome. We are probably stuck with a misleading name for a valuable enterprise.

3. Short-term Troubles

The great public appeal of the HGP stems from its expected medical payoffs. However, even in the cases of the diseases that have been most successfully explored with the new tools of molecular biology, much more is promised than is currently delivered. As the example of Huntington's disease makes apparent (and as the older example of sickle-cell anemia shows even more vividly), significant knowledge about the molecular basis of a disease is compatible with profound ignorance about how to cope with it. In the short-term, the medical applications of positional cloning and other work informed by the HGP will largely consist in the provision of tests. Genetic tests are becoming available on a broad scale. Some can be used to diagnose or to disambiguate the various forms of a disease. Others give us the power to make predictions, sometimes determinate, typically probabilistic, about the future phenotype of a person, about the characteristics of the person who would develop from a fetus, about the expected distribution of traits among offspring. The advantages of improved diagnostic tests tend to be underrated, but there are many diseases with ambiguous symptoms that can be more effectively treated if known therapies are introduced early: the extension of the median lifespan for Cystic Fibrosis patients stems, in part, from better diagnostic techniques. Similarly, patients can sometimes be spared useless or harmful treatments, or steered to the appropriate treatments, if the particular basis of their case of the disease is understood: dietary therapies are worthless for those people whose high cholesterol levels can be traced to a malfunctioning receptor protein in the liver.

The predictive tests have generated most discussion, both because enthusiasts have seen them as a great step forward in preventative medicine and because critics have recognized the possibilities for trouble. Francis Collins, current director of the HGP at the NIH, sometimes advertises the medical benefits by describing a future in which infants are routinely tested at birth and given a "genetic report card". The idea, of course, is that by knowing the kinds of diseases and disabilities that are likely to strike, we can take evasive action. That is a wonderful idea — to the extent that there is anything to be done to lower the chances, or to the extent that people can make better lives for themselves by knowing what will befall them.

The trouble is that, in the majority of instances, there is no *medical* benefit that comes from foreknowledge. If you find out that you have a cancer-predisposing allele, then your doctor may advise you to avoid fatty foods and pollutants, and to take exercise. That is good advice for anyone, and the only function of the genetic test is, perhaps, to stiffen your resolve. Recent celebrations of the identification of an allele implicated in early-onset breast and ovarian cancer (*BRCA1*) have tended to suggest that this will bring important benefits to all women, not just members of families "at risk". This, however, is a mistake. Mammograms are able to detect small tumors in the breasts of older women, only rarely in women in their twenties and thirties. If a young woman has the type of breast tissue that allows for mammogram reading, then, given the high incidence of breast cancer, she would be well-advised to have regular mammograms whether or not she carries a mutant *BRCA1* allele. The test may be worthwhile for women in afflicted families, but, given the limitations of current strategies of detection, it is unlikely to benefit the rest of the female population. By contrast, where there are effective monitoring techniques, as with colon cancer, recognition of increased risk will be valuable. Presently, such cases are a small minority.

Many who consider the likely spate of genetic tests draw inspiration from the practice of PKU testing. Here, at first sight, we seem to have an almost perfect example. The test enables doctors to divide the population into two subgroups, one of which would be harmed unless given a low phenylalanine, high tyrosine diet, the other of which would be equally damaged by the special diet. However, as Diane Paul has shown (Paul 1995), the history of PKU testing reveals significant problems. The unpleasantness of the diet, its cost, the initial lack of knowledge about how long it should be continued, the absence of any systematic program of following those originally diagnosed — all these factors make the medical solution far less effective than it might have been. Yet I don't think that the example confronts philosophers with any profound ethical problems. The morals of the history ought to be clear, and we should work to ensure that problems with medical solutions in principle do not fail us in practice because of a lack of social support. The real difficulties here are ones of practical politics rather than moral philosophy: it's abundantly obvious that people diagnosed with PKU need to be provided with far more than the initial evaluation; families may require economic assistance to buy the special food, continued counselling, and so forth; in other words, we can see what should be done, even though making sure that it is done is quite another matter.

In general, for reasons I detail elsewhere (Kitcher 1996), full-scale genetic testing is likely to be expensive, if it is done properly. The information already available about the effectiveness of genetic counselling is sobering, and recent studies have focused on the particular problems encountered by minority groups (Rapp 1994). Facing an immediate future in which the power to test will greatly outstrip the power to treat, it is important to resist the commercial pressures to introduce new tests without any attention to the benefits they might bring or the impact they might have on the lives of those tested. Without some independent body that will advise doctors of the exact nature of the information that a new test can yield, and of the extent to which test information can improve patients' lives, there is real danger that people will be swept into tests that they do not understand and given information that will prove harmful to them. Without serious attention to the problem of improving existing forms of genetic counselling, benefits that might be realized will not be achieved. (These points are made forcefully in Nelkin and Tancredi 1989 and Holtzman 1989).

The practice of widespread genetic testing can easily prove harmful in other ways. As genetic information about individuals is collected, various groups within society will clamor for that information. Insurers will want to know the genetic risks of those who apply for insurance; employers may demand the "genetic report card" as a condition of hiring. It is sometimes suggested that these problems should be solved by insisting on the privacy of genetic information, but this seems to me the wrong way to look at the situation. We feel it important that certain types of information about ourselves should be kept private, solely for the sake of privacy: we share with our intimates certain feelings or experiences that should not be broadcast " ...'twere profanation of our joyes/ to tell the laietie our love", as Donne puts it. But genetic information isn't like this. There is nothing intrinsically valuable in keeping secret the fact that I carry a particular sequences of As, Cs, Gs, and Ts at a certain chromosomal region. If I need to keep it private, it is because others might use the information to take advantage of me. The appropriate solution is thus not to engage in some (probably hopeless) attempt to dam up the flow of information, but to limit the kinds of things that can be done with genetic information.

In the large, it is fairly clear how to set the limits. There are straightforward arguments (Daniels 1994, Kitcher 1996) for denying health and disability insurance companies the right to use genetic information either in deciding eligibility or in setting premiums. General health risks are only occasionally relevant to a person's qualifications for a job, and the dangers that arise in specific workplace situations are best tackled by cleaning up the working environment (where that is feasible) or creating job opportunities for those with unlucky genotypes (see Draper 1991, Nelkin and Tancredi 1989, Kitcher 1996). Again, the issue is not one of balancing interests in a morally tricky situation, but rather of finding ways to implement the deliverances of relatively elementary lines of ethical argument.

Many of those most enthusiastic about the HGP recognize the need to address these short-term problems. They would rightly remind us that it would be myopic to be so overwhelmed by the gravity of the problems that we simply retreat from applying molecular genetics altogether. Not only do biomedical advances enable people to avoid bringing into the world children who would inevitably suffer, but they will also point to new forms of therapy for major diseases. Critics (for example, Lewontin 1992) retort that the promise is overblown. However, even though the future of molecular medicine is unpredictable, there are encouraging signs in newly developing treatments for Cystic Fibrosis, and in the first steps of gene replacement therapy (see Kitcher 1996 for an assessment of a rapidly changing situation).

From the very beginning of the HGP, funds were set aside to examine the ineptly-named "ELSI issues" ("ELSI" is an acronym for "ethical, social, and legal implications"). Many scientists involved in the project are inclined to say, in unguarded moments, that ELSI is an expensive piece of public relations, and many of them believe that their own perspective on the issues is as good as that of the publicly-funded "experts". That attitude is buttressed by the apparent lack of progress in coping with the short-term problems faced by the HGP: many genome scientists have attended conference after conference at which the same speakers introduce the same problems as topics that must be discussed during the next years. Ironically, the trouble isn't that the problems are hard to solve, but that the obvious general lines of solution—which scientists can see as clearly as professional medical ethicists, lawyers, or sociologists—call for policies that are unlikely to be popular with an electorate whose principal concern seems to be to cut the role of government. Add to this the fact that there is no ELSI body with any power to recommend legislative action, and the frustrating character of the current situation is patent. Scholars funded by ELSI can explore difficult questions about rare situations in which obtaining genetic information involves a conflict of rights (monozygotic twins at risk for Huntington's, exactly one of whom wants to be tested), or they can carry out ever more sophisticated studies of the current difficulties with genetic counselling. None of this will go anywhere until there is not only a vehicle for political action, but also a means of convincing the electorate that, without some rather obvious forms of governmental regulation, molecular medicine is likely to wreck a significant number of their children's lives.

4. The Deeper Issues

There are indeed deeper philosophical questions posed by the HGP, and exposing these questions enables us to understand some of the fiercer opposition to the project. One very obvious consequence of the HGP is that it will greatly enhance the power of prospective parents to know in advance the probabilities that the child who would result from a particular conception would have specific characteristics. On a quite unprecedented scale, our descendants may engage in the enterprise of choosing people.

Sometimes the scenarios are fantasies that outstrip any foreseeable reality. Exercises in imitating Frankenstein are surely remote: the difficulties of gene replacement therapy, wearyingly familiar to anyone who has read the literature—problems of sending the right DNA to the right cells, problems in regulating its expression—mean that our actual power to modify genes, now and in the next decades, is roughly equivalent in its precision to the crudest forms of electroconvulsive therapy. Gene replacement has so far been undertaken in desperate circumstances, when niceties of regulation are not an issue. Visions of the future in which prospective parents manipulate the genes of embryos produced by IVF can be discounted.

However, even if they cannot select *for*, our descendants will be able to select *against*. If the fetus has some combination of alleles that causes them concern, then they can choose to terminate the pregnancy. Waiving general worries about the use of abortion, there are surely some instances in which that choice appears warranted: fetuses can already be tested for genetic conditions that inevitably lead to neural degeneration and early death (Tay-Sachs disease) or that invariably cause severe retardation and acute behavioral problems (Lesch-Nyhan syndrome). The trouble is that we can readily conceive a future in which the practice of selection shades into something far less benign. Unlike some women in Northern Indian, it is unlikely that many American couples will use fetal testing to select against (female) sex. Whether they will abstain from using information about propensities for same-sex preference or obesity is another matter.

So a significant worry is that we are started on a course that will lead our successors to some dark venture in eugenics. Unlike some past chapters in the history of eugenics, the future is not likely to see some central body dictate the reproductive decisions of individuals (or of couples). Yet, even if we honor a principle of reproductive freedom, it is important that the practice of fetal selection be conducted in an informed and responsible fashion, that our descendants make their decisions in a context that allows them to attend to the morally relevant factors, not to be swept along (as, perhaps, women in Northern India are swept) by pervasive social prejudices.

Champions of the HGP are optimistic that the appropriate moral climate can be achieved. When their optimism is articulated, it rests, I believe, on a sense that responsible reproductive decisions are made by reflecting on the qualities of the lives that would be brought into being, and on the impact those lives would have on the qualities of other lives. There is no moral calculus that can be mechanically applied to yield an answer, but it is important to the moral status of the decision that the considerations of the qualities of live be paramount. So they envisage a world in which the overwhelming majority of genetic pre-natal tests are used responsibility, and in which the general tendency of the practice is to terminate pregnancies that would have led to unfortunate lives.

Critics are worried about this optimistic vision for a number of reasons. First, they recognize that the history of eugenics reveals how easy it is for a seemingly benign practice to decay into something morally repugnant. Second, they hold that much popular thinking is gripped by simple forms of genetic determinism, so that there will be a recurrent tendency to treat genes as doom. They expect this to be manifested in credulous acceptance of claims about the determination of behavioral traits. Third, they believe that the very social factors that currently make the short-term issues surrounding the HGP so hard to solve, in particular the reluctance to provide funds for social services, will make pre-natal testing an acceptable, cheap, way of eliminating people who could have lived productive lives, people with disabilities that can be overcome with social support. (Claims of these kinds, and supporting arguments, can be found in Lewontin 1992 and Hubbard and Wald 1993).

Those with direct experience of the tragedies of severe genetic afflictions are likely to view these responses as the resurgence of Luddism. Are we to foreswear an instrument that could do much good because we fear that it might be abused? Yet the critics' point cuts deeper. If the underlying rationale for a practice of pre-natal testing lies in the possibility of improving the quality of human lives, then we must recognize that the prevention of lives that would be damaged by unlucky alleles takes only a small step. There are far more children whose lives are smashed in their early years through social causes than who suffer from the ravages of defective proteins. So the critics confront the HGP with a serious question: why is public money expended on trying to prevent the birth of children with rare combinations of alleles, while social programs that could benefit many more go wanting?

This question sets the stage for a debate that has only been joined obliquely in the rhetorical furore around the HGP. The root criticism of the project should not be that it is scientifically worthless, or that the short-term problems are insoluble. Rather, the worry is that the ultimate rationale for the project is cast in terms of improvements to the quality of human lives, and it is inconsistent for a society that tolerates large social causes of reduced quality of life to offer any such rationale. The best case against the HGP would demand that it be accompanied by an equally serious commitment to attacking social problems that lower the quality of human lives.

I do not have space here to do more than indicate the main lines of argument in an important, and difficult, controversy. There is a pragmatic response to the critics' argument, that emphasizes the need to do the local good we can (develop the biomedical promise of the HGP) and not hold it hostage to grander social ventures with uncertain prospects (and here there is likely to be a recitation of the failures of past expensive programs). Pragmatists mix optimism with pessimism. For, on the one hand they are hopeful that future generations can pursue a practice of choosing people that is free and responsible, that social prejudices can be countered and the darker byways of eugenics avoided. At the same time, they doubt that attempts to remove the social causes of misery will succeed. The critics' position is a contrary mixture of fear and confidence. Concerned that the allegedly "free and responsible" reproductive decisions will not be sustained, they remain optimistic about the potential of social programs.

Plainly, these issues involve far more than the particularities of the HGP. They are deep and difficult, turning on fundamental questions in political and moral philosophy, as well as on details from both biology and social science. The HGP serves just as the occasion for re-examining them. So, if I am right, the philosophically important questions about the HGP have gone largely unnoticed in the numerous discussions about the project—which is not, of course to deny that some of the other questions raised here and in the contemporary literature are also significant. My aim has simply been to do what the HGP has so far done best, to wit, produce a clear map (for much more detailed exploration of the terrain, see Kitcher 1996).

References

Caskey, C.T. (1992), "DNA-Based Medicine: Prevention and Therapy" in D. Kevles and L. Hood (eds.) The Code of Codes. Cambridge: Harvard University Press, pp. 112-135.

Daniels, N. (1994), "The Genome Project, Individual Differences, and Just Health Care", in T. Murphy and M. Lappe (eds.) *Justice and the Human Genome Project* (Berkeley: University of California Press), pp. 110-132.

Draper, E. (1991), *Risky Business*. New York: Cambridge University Press.

Dujon, B. et.al. (1994), "Complete DNA sequence of yeast chromosome XI", *Nature* 369: 371-378.

Gilbert, W. (1992), "A Vision of the Grail", in D. Kevles and L. Hood (eds.) *The Code of Codes*. Cambridge MA.: Harvard University Press, pp. 83-97.

Holtzman, N.A. (1989), *Proceed With Caution*. Baltimore: Johns Hopkins.

Hubbard, R. and Wald, E. (1993), *Exploding the Gene Myth*. Boston: Beacon.

Johnston, M. *et.al.* (1994), "Complete Nucleotide Sequence of Saccharomyces cerevisiae Chromosome VIII", *Science* 265: 2077-2082.

Kitcher, P. (1996), *Choosing Genes, Changing Lives*. New York: Simon and Schuster.

Lander, E.S. and Schork, N.J. (1994), "Genetic Dissection of Complex Traits", *Science* 265: 2037-2048.

Lawrence, P. (1992), *The Making of a Fly*. Oxford: Blackwell.

Lewontin, R.C. (1992), "The Dream of the Human Genome", in R. Lewontin, *Biology as Ideology*. New York: Harper.

Nelkin, D. and Tancredi, L. (1989), *Dangerous Diagnostics*. New York: Basic Books.

Paul, D. (1995), [this volume]

Rapp, R. (1994), "Amniocentesis in Socio-cultural Perspective", *Journal of Genetic Conselling* (in press).

Rosenberg, A. (1995), [this volume]

Tauber, A. and Sarkar, S. (1992), "The Human Genome Project: Has Blind Reductionism Gone Too Far?", *Perspectives in Biology and Medicine* 35: 220-235.

Wilson, R. *et.al.* (1994), "2.2 Mb of contiguous nucleotide sequence from chromosome III of *C. elegans*", *Nature* 368: 32-38.

Toward a Realistic Assessment of PKU Screening[1]

Diane B. Paul

University of Massachusetts at Boston

Newborn screening for the genetic disease phenylketonuria (PKU) is generally considered the greatest success story of applied human genetics. Paradoxically, it is invoked both by those who stress the value and those who emphasize the limitations of genetic medicine.

PKU screening is often cited as a model for genetic medicine and as a precedent for those who favor the expansion of genetic tests (Azen 1991, 35; Scriver 1991; Bishop and Waldholz 1990, 18- 19). But even those skeptical of most screening programs tend to describe this program in sunny terms (Natowicz and Alper 1991, 387-89; Nelkin and Tancredi 1989, 160). The near-consensus on the success of PKU screening is explained by the variety of interests the example serves. Untreated phenylketonuria results in severe mental retardation and behavioral disorders. But if it is identified in the newborn, the disease is treatable through a special diet. Thus PKU screening seems to illustrate the good that screening may do. However, it also seems to demonstrate the falsity of the assumption that what is genetic is fixed. Although PKU is an inborn error of metabolism, a knowledge of its biochemistry enables us to supply the deficient metabolic products externally. During the 1970s, at the height of the controversy over the genetics of intelligence, PKU was frequently invoked to refute the view that biology is destiny. Thus both advocates of genetic medicine and critics of genetic determinism found PKU screening an attractive example. Despite—or perhaps because of—the strong and diverse interests served by the PKU case, there has been little interest in its realistic appraisal.

In fact, the reality is far more complicated than conventional stories suggest. Screening has indeed prevented mental retardation in tens of thousands of infants worldwide. That is a real achievement. But its significance is often exaggerated. PKU is a very rare disease, with an incidence in the US, Britain, and most of Western Europe of between 1 in 11,000 and 1 in 15,000 births. In the US, universal newborn screening identifies fewer than 400 cases each year. Claims that screening has eliminated PKU as an important cause of mental retardation are misleading since it was the cause of retardation in less than one percent of the institutionalized population (Edelson 1994). Moreover, PKU screening has been plagued with problems since its inception. While PKU is often portrayed as a disease cured by a simple change in diet, the change is neither simple nor fully effective in eliminating cognitive and behavioral deficits. Moreover, all the gains achieved by screening may be canceled by a problem that screening itself created. How did a program bedeviled by so many diffi-

PSA 1994, Volume 2, pp. 322-328

culties come to be viewed as the paradigm case of genetic testing? And what can we learn from its history?

1. History of PKU

Based on observations of patients with alcaptonuria, cystinuria, and albinism, the English physician/chemist Archibald Garrod suggested in 1908 that some congenital disorders resulted from a block in the conversion of an intermediary metabolite to another compound. On the basis of discussions with the geneticist William Bateson, he also concluded that these chemical abnormalities were transmitted according to a Mendelian pattern of inheritance. However, few geneticists at the time were impressed and Garrod himself did not emphasize the Mendelian aspects of the disease (Olby 1974, Moore 1985, Bearn 1993). Nor was his work of particular interest to physicians. Inborn errors were extremely rare and, at the time, Garrod's work had no practical significance.

In 1934, the Norwegian physician/biochemist Asbjørn Følling described for the first time another inborn error that he called "phenylpyruvic imbecility." By the mid-1950s, it was understood that the disease—now called phenylketonuria or simply PKU—was caused by a rare recessive gene responsible for a defect in the liver enzyme that catalyzes the conversion of phenylalanine (an essential amino acid found in most foods) to tyrosine. When the conversion is blocked, phenylalanine accumulates to disastrous levels in the blood. About 90% of those affected have IQs of less than 50 (Acuff and Faden 1991, 64).

However, PKU is treatable by a diet restricted to special phenylalanine-free foods, supplemented by a formula with extra tyrosine. The theoretical possibility of some form of therapy was first suggested by the British geneticist Lionel Penrose in his 1946 inaugural lecture as Galton Professor of Eugenics in University College. Notwithstanding his title, Penrose was hostile to eugenics. In "Phenylketonuria: A Problem in Eugenics" he invoked PKU to demonstrate the futility of eugenic selection and the need for a fundamentally new approach to human genetics.

Penrose noted the pointlessness of sterilizing affected individuals, since they rarely reproduce. Moreover, such a policy would have little effect on the incidence of the disorder since the responsible genes are maintained in the population almost entirely by the reproduction of symptomless heterozygotes. Even if one could identify the carriers, it would be necessary to sterilize one percent of the normal population in order to eradicate the gene. "Only a lunatic," he asserted, "would advocate such a procedure to prevent the occurrence of a handful of harmless imbeciles." Furthermore, he speculated that the effects of the disease might be alleviated "in a manner analogous to the way in which a child with club-feet may be helped to walk" (951).

Within a decade, a number of studies indicated that restricting dietary phenylalanine could prevent retardation if treatment began during the neonatal period. However, PKU could only be identified through a ferric chloride urine test, which was not very sensitive and could first be administered a few weeks after birth (Edelson, forthcoming). In 1961, Robert Guthrie announced a cheap and simple test utilizing a few drops of blood from the newborn's heel. The conjunction of the dietary therapy and Guthrie test strengthened an existing movement to screen newborns for the disease. In 1963, Massachusetts mandated screening for all newborns; other states quickly followed suit. Today, every American state screens newborns for PKU (and usually for other metabolic disorders as well [Andrews 1985, 1-2]).

In the 1960s, it was assumed that early dietary treatment would prevent complications in all the inborn errors of metabolism such as galactosemia, tyrosinemia, and glycogen storage disease. Bolstered by confidence in the efficacy of dietary treatment, screening initially appeared a more powerful tool in combating retardation than it turned out in practice to be.

In the early 1960s, laws mandating newborn screening were passed in spite of considerable opposition from the medical community. Both the AMA and the American Academy of Pediatrics opposed legislated screening. So did some scientists. While private practitioners feared state interference with the doctor-patient relationship and an increase in malpractice suits, researchers denied that enough was known about the prognosis and management of the disease to justify a mandatory program. However the professional organizations and scientists proved no match for PKU clinicians and lay organizations, especially the National Association for Retarded Children (NARC) and its allies in the Children's Bureau of the Department of Health, Education, and Welfare and state health departments (Acuff and Faden 1991, 64-65; National Research Council 1975, 44-87). Newspapers and magazines also promoted the cause, describing screening as a achievement with a potentially vast impact on mental retardation. The application of science to problems of retardation seems to have captured the imagination of the press and the public (Edelson 1994).

As a consequence, screening was instituted before anyone knew what proportion of infants with elevated phenylalanine levels were at risk for retardation, what level of blood phenylalanine was optimal, or whether the test for PKU was reliable. The early years of the program were marked by high false negative and extremely high false positive rates, as well as by unreliable laboratory work. For every PKU infant, 19 who did not have the disease received an initial positive screening test. As a result, some infants without the disease were treated for it, with disastrous results (Holtzman 1989, 5). (Treating unaffected newborns is as damaging as not treating the phenylketonurics).

Mandatory screening remained controversial for these reasons for at least a decade (Bessman and Swazey 1971; National Research Council 1975). The problems that plagued early screening programs were eventually resolved. However, all the initial assumptions about the ease and effectiveness of therapy turned out to be much too sanguine and serious new problems emerged. Indeed, assumptions about the efficacy of treatment in respect to all the inborn errors turned out to be over-optimistic. While nutritional therapy prevents retardation, a host of other cognitive and emotional problems usually remain. In fact, no one with an inborn error of metabolism "escapes some degree of adversity" despite therapy (Levy 1991; see also Segal 1992). But as problems have become increasingly visible to professionals, they have become increasingly invisible to the public.

2. Towards a More Realistic Account

In the 1960s, when screening was routinized, it was assumed that only the developing brain was vulnerable to damage and that the diet could be discontinued when the child was about five years old. However, studies in the following decades revealed that IQ scores declined after the diet was abandoned; as a consequence, dietary recommendations became progressively more conservative. Most treatment centers now recommend lifelong continuance, especially for females since, if women do not maintain the diet throughout pregnancy, the effects on their offspring are may becatastrophic. Children born to women with high levels of phenylalanine do not themselves have the disease. However, they are at very high risk for microencephaly and mental retardation among other disorders.

The PKU diet involves manufactured substitutes for most natural foods, including bread, cake, meat, fish, eggs, and dairy products (Medical Research Council 1993). Most phenylketonurics find these foods unpalatable and it is thus difficult to get them to follow the diet. It is even more difficult to convince adolescents and adults to resume it once they have stopped. Moreover, the adult women first need to be located. Most discontinued the diet during childhood and were not followed for many years. Before the advent of newborn screening, women with PKU bore few children. Thus screening has converted a rare occurrence into a major problem (Waisbren 1988). Indeed, all the benefits of screening may be neutralized by the birth of retarded children to women who have ended the diet (Azen 1991). (The problem of maternal PKU was recognized in the scientific literature long before any effort was made to address it (Mabry et al, 1963; Hsia 1966]).

Even when the diet is strictly followed, cognitive deficits and psychosocial problems are common. While treated phenylketonurics are not mentally retarded, they generally have lower IQs than would normally be expected and often experience reduced visual perception, visual-motor difficulties, and psychological disorders (Weglage et al. 1992; Levy 1993, Medical Research Council 1993). The dietary restrictions are a source of severe family stress and both the formula and special foods are expensive. There is a large literature on the scientific and medical aspects of PKU, on the psycho-social and cognitive effects of therapy, and on the impact of the dietary restrictions on family functioning. But of the more than 3,000 articles on PKU published since the mid-60s, only one concerns the economic impact on families. It reports that most patients who had health insurance or Medicaid coverage were unable to obtain reimbursement for the formula or special foods (Millner 1993).

While forty-three states had passed screening laws and 90% of all newborns were being tested by 1975, no state mandated treatment— or does so now. In the early years of the program, the cost of therapy was not an issue, apparently for two reasons. First, the states generally subsidized (and continue to subsidize) the formula for infants and children. Given the initial assumption that children could go off-diet at the age of about five, the cost of the formula and expensive special foods for adolescents and adults did not arise. Second, funds that initially supported therapy (such as lab fees or foundation grants) seem to have been gradually diverted to other uses. However, discussions in both the popular and academic literature assume an inevitable bridge between diagnosis and treatment.

Because PKU is such a rare disease (whose incidence also varies with ethnicity), some early screening programs identified few if any cases. Thus in the first three years of screening, the program in Washington, D.C. found no affected newborns and officials therefore reasoned that they had better things to do with their money and ended the program. Some states threatened to follow suit. The problems that emerged in the first years combined with the paucity of cases prompted a reappraisal of the value of screening programs (Paul Edelson, personal communication).

Advocates attempted to head this off by making the program appear more efficient. One method was to load other tests on the original. In the contemporary literature, motivations are bluntly stated: once you've pricked the heel and have the blood spot, you can test for other metabolic disorders and get more bang for the buck. For most of these disorders—unlike the case of PKU—there was no treatment available. Indeed, some were not disorders at all, but normal biochemical variants. The new tests were added "without careful assessment of the benefits and risks, often without the review of institutional review boards, and generally without concern for obtaining informed consent or even the opportunity for 'informed refusal'" (Andrews et al. 1994, 66). Some of the screens were in effect research programs which did not allow for consent on the part of the subjects' guardians.

There is a near-consensus in the policy literature that compulsion in genetic programs is inappropriate—a principle affirmed in numerous statements by professional associations and advisory committees. Moreover, federal law requires that when assistance is provided in establishment or operation of genetic services program, participation must be "wholly voluntary" (Faden et al. 1982a). Yet in most states, participation is mandatory either by law or regulation. Ethical guidelines issues by both public and private bodies rarely acknowledge the fact that few newborn screening programs are voluntary even in theory. In practice, there is little difference between states that allow for consent and those that do not. Parents have no practical opportunity to voice objections even where their consent is required. Indeed, most health care providers are unaware of regulations when they exist. Most of those who do know disapprove of them (Faden et al. 1982b).

PKU screening had originally been made mandatory in part out of concern that voluntary programs might cease to be cost-effective. In the early 1960s, advocates of screening stressed its financial benefits given the low expense of the test versus the large cost of institutionalizing children for lifetime care. For example, the head of the Children's Bureau calculated a savings of about $2,000,000 through the prevention of retardation in twenty-five infants identified through the urine test (which cost less than a penny [Science News Letter, July 15, 1961, 40]). But such figures seemed irrelevant to jurisdictions that bore all the associated costs of a testing program without identifying any cases. In part to address these concerns, screening was regionalized as well as expanded to include other conditions.

Cost-benefit arguments that compare the expense of the test and treatment to that of providing for lifetime institutional care are frequently invoked today in support of newborn screening (e.g. Scriver et al. 1989). Even this brief review of the history of PKU screening indicates some of the difficulties with these simple cost-benefit claims. They aggregate all costs, irrespective of whether they are assumed by individual families, insurers, or the state, although some costs may represent a large burden for one payer and a small burden for another. They thus ignore distributional questions. They do not take account of intangible harms, such as the anxiety produced by the approximate one percent of tests that are falsely positive or the stresses arising from the need to prepare and obtain compliance with an unpalatable diet. (Intangible benefits, such as reduction of suffering, are often cited). They do not take account of the problem of maternal PKU, a harm created by screening.

I do not mean to suggest that costs of screening outweigh the benefits. On the contrary, I expect that a broader assessment would show that the reverse is true. However, in PKU as in other screening programs, some kinds of harm have been systematically ignored, thus exaggerating the benefits and understating the harms (Russell 1994).

3. The Lessons

What does the history of PKU screening tell us about the likely path—and pitfalls—of other screening programs? It warns us that even highly controversial programs may be quickly routinized and, once routinized, easily expanded for other purposes, that the benefits of screening may be exaggerated and the problems minimized, and that these distortions may be amplified by reporting in newspapers and in popular magazines. It also warns us that cost-benefit analysis may drive program expansion, that even ostensibly voluntary programs may become mandatory in practice, and that identification of cases is readily confused with provision of services. Perhaps the most important lesson from the history of PKU screening is this: to evaluate success, we need to encompass the experience of clients "on the ground." What counts is not how programs should work in theory but how they function in practice. If they are to be realistic in appraising genetics programs, philosophers need to take that lesson to heart.

Note

[1]I am greatly indebted to Dr. Paul Edelson both for stimulating discussions and his generous sharing of unpublished work on the history of PKU screening.

References

Acuff, K.L. and Faden, R.R. (1991), "A History of Prenatal and Newborn Screening Programs: Lessons for the Future," in R. Faden et al., (eds.), *AIDS, Women, and the Next Generation*. New York: Oxford University Press, pp. 58-93.

Andrews, L.B (1985), *State Laws and Regulations Governing Newborn Screening*. Washington, D.C.: American Bar Association.

Andrews, L.B. et al., eds. (1994), *Assessing Genetic Risks: Implications for Health and Social Policy*. Committee on Assessing Genetic Risks. Division of Health Sciences Policy. Institute of Medicine. Washington: National Academy Press.

Azen, C.G. et al. (1991), "Intellectual Development in 12-Year-Old Children Treated for Phenylketonuria." *American Journal of Diseases of Children* 145: 35-39.

Bearn, A.G. (1993), *Archibald Garrod and the Individuality of Man*. Oxford: Oxford University Press.

Bessman, S.P. and Swazey, J.P. (1971), "Phenylketonuria: A Study of Biomedical Legislation," in E. Mendelsohn et al. (eds), *Human Aspects of Biomedical Innovation*. Cambridge, MA: Harvard University Press, pp. 49-76.

Bishop, J.B. and Waldholz, M. (1990), *Genome*. New York: Simon and Schuster.

Edelson, P.J. (1994), "History of Genetic Screening in the United States I: The Public Debate over Phenylketonuria (PKU) Testing." Paper presented at the Annual Meeting of the American Association for the History of Medicine, New York.

Edelson, P.J. (forthcoming), "Lessons from the History of Genetic Screening in the US: Policy Past, Present, and Future," in P. Boyle and K. Nolan, (eds), *Setting Priorities for Genetic Services*. Washington: Georgetown University Press.

Faden, R. (1991), "Autonomy, Choice, and the New Reproductive Technologies," in J. Rodin and A. Collins (eds), *Women and New Reproductive Technologies: Medical, Psychological, Legal, and Ethical Dilemnas*. Hillsdale, NJ: Lawrence Erlbaum, pp. 37-47.

Faden, R. et al. (1982a), "Parental Rights, Child Welfare, and Public Health: The Case of PKU Screening," *American Journal of Public Health*. 72: 1396-1400.

_ _ _ _ _ _ _ _ _. (1982b), "A Survey to Evaluate Parental Consent as Public Policy for Neonatal Screening," *American Journal of Public Health* 72: 1347-1351.

Holtzman, N.A. (1989), *Proceed with Caution: Predicting Genetic Risks in the Recombinant DNA Era*. Baltimore: Johns Hopkins University Press.

Hsia, D. Y.-Y. (1966), *Inborn Errors of Metabolism,* Part I: Clinical Aspects. 2nd ed. Chicago: Year Book Medical Publishers.

Levy, H.L. (1991), "Nutritional Therapy in Inborn Errors of Metabolism," in R.J. Desnick (ed), *Treatment of Genetic Diseases*. New York: Churchill Livingstone, pp. 1-21.

Mabry, C.C. et al. (1963), "Maternal Phenylketonuria," *New England Journal of Medicine*. 269: 1404.

Medical Research Council (1993), "Phenylketonuria due to Phenylalanine Hydroxylase Deficiency: an Unfolding Story," *British Medical Journal*. 306: 115-119.

Millner, B.N. (1993), "Insurance Coverage of Special Foods Needed in the Treatment of Phenylketonuria," *Public Health Reports*. 108: 60-65.

Moore, J.A. (1986), "Science as a Way of Knowing. III. Genetics," *American Zoologist*. 26: 583-747.

National Research Council. Committee for the Study of Inborn Errors of Metabolism (1975), *Genetic Screening: Programs, Principles, and Research*. Washington, D.C.: National Academy of Science.

Natowizc, M.R. and Alper, J.S. (1991), "Genetic Screening: Triumphs, Problems, and Controversies," *Journal of Public Health Policy* 12: 475-491.

Nelkin, D. and Tancredi, L. (1989), *Dangerous Diagnostics: The Social Power of Biological Information*. New York: Basic Books.

Olby, R. (1974), *The Path to the Double Helix*. Seattle: University of Washington Press.

Penrose, L.S. (1946), "Phenylketonuria: A Problem in Eugenics." *The Lancet*. (June 29): 949-953.

Russell, L.B. (1994), *Educated Guesses: Making Policy about Medical Screening Tests*. Berkeley: University of California Press, Berkeley.

Scriver, C.R. (1991), "Phenylketonuria—Genotypes and Phenotypes," *New England Journal of Medicine* (May 2), pp. 1280-1281.

Scriver, C. et. al. (1989), "The Hyperphenylalaninemias," in C. Scriver et al. (eds.) *The Metabolic Basis of Inherited Disease*. New York: McGraw-Hill.

Segal, S. (1992), "The Enigma of Galactosemia," *International Pediatrics*. 7: 75-82.

Waisbren, S. et al. (1988), "The New England Maternal PKU Project: Identification of At-Risk Women," *American Journal of Public Health*. 78: 789-792.

Weglage, J. et al. (1992), "Psychological and Social Findings in Adolescents with Phenylketonuria," *European Journal of Pediatrics*. 151: 533-525.

Subversive Reflections on the Human Genome Project

Alex Rosenberg

University of California, Riverside

In the Museum of Science and Technology in San Jose, California, there is a display dedicated to advances in biotechnology. Most prominent in the display is a double helix of telephone books stacked in two staggered spirals from the floor to the ceiling twenty five feet above. The books are said to present the current state of our knowledge of the eurcaryotic genome: the primary sequences of DNA polynucleotides for the gene products which have been discovered so far in the twenty years since cloning and sequencing the genome became possible.

In order to grasp what is problematical about the human genome project (HGP), I want you to hold on to this image of a stack of phone books, or rather two stacks, helictical in shape. Imagine that each of the phone books about the size of the Manhattan white pages, and that the two stacks of phone books reach up a mile and a half into the sky. Assume that the books are well glued together, and that there are no gusts of wind strong enough to blow the towers down. The next thing you are to imagine is that there are no names in these phone books, or on their covers. Only numbers. We do know that each phone number is seven digits long and we know the numbers have been assigned to names listed alphabetically, but without the names we cant tell to whom a number belongs. Moreover, the numbers are not printed in columns down the pages that will enable you to tell where one phone number ends and the next begins. Instead of being printed in columns down the page, the numbers begin at the top left and fill up the page like print without any punctuation between them. They are grouped within area codes, of course, and we can tell when one area code list stops and another begins, but we don't know the area codes, still less what geographical area they cover.

Sounds like a set of phone books that would be pretty difficult to use, doesn't it? Well, lets make them harder to use. Of course none of the individual phone books have names or any other identifying features on their covers. In fact, the books don't have covers, and what's more the binding of each directory was removed before the stack was constructed, and a random number of successive pages of adjacent phone books were rebound together. This rebinding maintains the order of pages, but it means that each volume begins and ends somewhere within each directory, and there is no indication of where these beginnings and endings are.

Can we make our mile and a half stack of phone books even harder to use? Sure. Imagine that somewhere between 90 and 95 % of all the phone numbers in all the phone books have been disconnected, or have never even been assigned to customers. And of course we don't know which ones they are. These unused numbers look just like se-

---

PSA 1994, Volume 2, pp. 329-335

quences of assigned phone numbers, and they even have area-code punctuation, though there is no geographic area assigned to these area codes. Remember, we can't tell which area codes represent a real area and which do not. We do know that between 5 and 10 % of the numbers are in area codes which have been assigned, and that within these assigned area codes there are long lists of phone numbers of real phone company customers.

Although we don't know which are the area codes that are real, nor where they are in the directories, we do know some interesting things about these area code phone number listings. First sometimes area codes and their phone numbers are repeated one or more times rather close together in a single volume, sometimes they are repeated in distant volumes in the stack: second, sometimes there are sequences of phone numbers which are very similar in digits to the numbers in a real area code, but their area codes are unassigned and all the phone numbers are unused. Even within almost all of the real area codes, the lists of assigned phone numbers are interrupt by long sequences of digits which when grouped into phone numbers are unassigned; sometimes within a real area code there are several of these sequences, longer than the sequences of assigned phone numbers within the area code.

Perhaps you are tiring of all the bizarre details of this idea of telephone numbers impossible to read. So, I will stop adding detail to our picture. But don't let go of the picture. Imagine that some one, a numerologist, say, now proposes to you that for 3 billion dollars of the US government's money, he will put together a team that will transcribe all the digits in the mile and a half double stack of phone books into a computer. It's not the phone numbers he offers to transcribe, just the digits—one after the other—unsegmented into the phone numbers. The numerologist promises to make the list of digits available to any one who asks for it, free. Assume further that 3 billion dollars is the cost of copying out the numbers with no hidden profit for the numerologist.

I suppose one's first reaction to such an proposal would be to thank the numerologist for his offer, but to decline it on the grounds that the list of digits is of no immediate use to anyone, even if we were going to have a very large party and wanted to invite everyone who had a phone number. But it is in our nature as philosophers to wonder, so we ask our numerologist, "what's in it for you, why would you do this transcription at cost, without any profit?"

Imagine our numerologist is candid and comes clean as follows: He is not really a numerologist, but rather represents a relatively large number of privately held direct-marketing companies, each of which has a potentially very useful product, which it can only sell over the telephone. The companies know that there are enough potential customers out there to go around so that each of their shareholders can become rich though the sale of the very useful product they can manufacture, if only they had the phone numbers of the customers. So, our numerologist direct-sales marketing representative says that if the companies he represents had all the digits, they could sell the products, make every customer better off, and become rich themselves.

There are two responses one should make to the numerologist's admission: the first is, why should the government pay for the phone lists, if you and the consumers are the ones to profit; more important, surely putting all those digits from all those books into a large computer file, without being able to tell the meaningless ones from the meaningful ones, just for starters, is not the best way to get in touch with potential customers.

Consider the first question, why should the government pay for the phone list? The answer given on behalf of the direct sales team is that their product is guaranteed to help people stay healthier and live longer But in that case, if they think putting all these phone numbers in a computer memory is so valuable, why don't they arrange to fund the project themselves, and reap the rewards by selling the product? The answer we get is that their capital is tied up in even more valuable investments, and besides, there is a free-rider problem. If any of them get together to fund the transcription, it will become available to others without the others paying. So, we might reply, what's it to us? Why should the government get you out of this predicament? If it does, will you cut in the government on your profits from using the phone numbers? Oh no, comes the reply. That would be a disincentive to developing new products to sell to people on the phone list.

But wait a minute, lets get back to the first question. What's the use of a transcription of all these digits. Aren't there far better ways to get the names of customers with telephones. In fact, is this any way of getting the names of customers at all? Well, comes the response, what if developing the technology to transcribe all these phone numbers, will also enable us to identify the real area codes, to segment the digits into meaningful phone numbers, and to begin to tell which ones are actually in use? That might justify some investment in transcribing the phone numbers. But unfortunately our numerologist can make no such assurance. At most he can promise that once we have the total list of real area codes, that 5 to 10 % of the list of digits will become valuable. Are there ways of identifying these area codes, we ask. Certainly, says our interlocutor. Well. what are you waiting for, go and find them. When you have done so, you may or may not have any use for the transcription of all the digits. But until then, you would be wasting your time, or someone else's, along with a lot of money, government or private, to transcribe all these digits, including the ones in the unassigned area codes and the numbers with no customers.

This allegory, I suggest, pretty well matches the biochemical facts about the human genome, the molecular structure of the nucleic acids that compose it, the prospective pay-off to sequencing the 3 billion base pairs of the human genome, and the policy advocated by the proponents of the HGP. Here is a brief explanation of my simile between the human genome and the mile high stack of phone books: the human genome contains 3 billion base pairs of purine and pyrimidine nucleic acids. These are the digits in our "phone numbers". Each phone number is composed of three digits—a codon of three nucleic acid bases. 90 to 95 % of these sequences code for DNA that has no role in gene transcription—this is the so-called junk DNA. They compose phone numbers that are not in use. Of the 5 to 10 % of the nucleotide sequences that do code for gene products, we know little that distinguishes it from the non-coding "junk". These sequences of codons that do code for gene product are the phone numbers in a real area codes. Unfortunately we can't tell them from area codes that contain only "phone numbers" not in use. In our story we didn't know how many area codes there are, where they are in the phone books, how often they are reprinted, and how many corrupt sequences of meaningless phone numbers they contain.

Similarly, we do not know whether there are 50,000 genes or 100,000. We don't know their nucleotide size, the number of their copies, their locations, the number of stretches of meaningless numbers—the introns within each of them. The DNA for gene products is disbursed throughout the non-coding part of the genome. Within regions that code for gene products, there are long stretches of polynucleotides that, like non-sense or junk DNA, code for nothing, and whose messenger RNA sequences are deleted before protein synthesis. Many if not most genes are repeated two or more times throughout the genome, on the same or different chromosomes, as are many stretches of junk-DNA. Sometimes the same strand of DNA can code for two different gene-products depending on codon-punctuation. Although we know what the start- and stop codons are, we don't know how to segment the sequence of bases to tell either where a gene for some product begins, or which of the possible triplets of successive bases is the reading frame for the product—we don't know which among the digits in a sequence is the first digit of a phone number, even though we know that each phone number is three digits—three nucleotides long.

Defenders of the HGP may react to the allegory with a denial that the HGP really contemplates sequencing 3 billion base pairs of mainly non-sense DNA as an integral part of its project. Such a reaction of course grants the aptness of the allegory, admits the pointlessness of the project of completing the sequence. If it were true that sequencing the entire genome is no part of the original or subsequent mission of the HGP its proponents would of course be guilty of seriously misleading the governments which support the project. But the fact is, sequencing the whole human genome has been and still is the goal of the HGP.

Writing in the fall of 1993 in *Gene* the original director of the National Center for Human Gnome Research, James Watson described the HGP as follows:

> Its mission was not only to make much higher resolution genetic maps but also to assemble all the human DNA as overlapping cloned fragments running the entire length of all the human chromosomes. In their turn, these DNA pieces were to be sequenced and their respective genes revealed. Upon completion of the Human Genome Project we would then know how many human genes exist and so whether the then estimated 100,00 number was either too low or too high. (Watson 1993, 310)

But making physical maps at varying scales of the human genome, and sequencing all the DNA will not answer these important questions about how many genes there are.

In October of 1993 Francis Collins, who replaced James Watson as director of the National Center for Human Genome Research, and David Galas associate director of the DOE Office of Health and Environmental Research, have written

> Although there is still debate about the need to sequence the entire genome, it is now more widely recognized that the DNA sequence will reveal a wealth of biological information that could not be obtained in other ways. The sequence so far obtained from model organisms has demonstrated the existence of a large number of genes not previously suspected...Comparative sequence analysis has also confirmed the high degree of homology between genes across species. It is clear that sequence information represents a rich source for future investigation. Thus the Human Genome Project must continue to pursue its original goal, namely, to obtain the complete human DNA sequence. (Collins and Galas 1993, 46.)

This passage is quite revealing for what it omits. It is certainly true that knowing the entire sequence would provide a wealth of information, though it would not be biological—where biological means functional. It would be physical information. Despite Collins' claim, the sequences so far obtained for simpler organisms do not demonstrate the existence of hitherto unsuspected genes, because sequence data cannot do this. Sequence data can only help **localize** genes whose existence has already been established by genetic techniques—i.e. breeding experiments. Establishing sequence homologies between known genes of model organisms and parts of the DNA of humans is of the highest biological importance. But first, it requires that we have identified the gene of the model system, then localized and sequenced it, and finally hybridize it with human genomic DNA. The result will be the identification of a human gene, which can then be sequenced! Note, prior sequencing of the whole human genome need play no part in this process, and can not help divide up the human genome into genes. And except for genes which are physically unique to our species, of which there is no reason to think there are any, knowing the whole sequence of the human genome is unnecessary and insufficient for the identification of any genes. It certainly cannot tell us how many genes there are! Nevertheless, Collin's and Galas's statement unequivocally commits the project to providing the whole sequence.

In an article based on an interview with Director Collins, *Science* reporter Leslie Roberts wrote

> Despite the slow progress, there is little sentiment for abandoning the goal of all-out sequencing.... But some thought is begin given to a short cut called one-pass sequencing. The original plan calls for sequencing the whole genome several times to ensure an error rate of 0.001 %. "Suppose we try one pass coverage with 1 % error rate but it only costs one tenth as much?" Asks Collins. The idea,then, would be to return to the really *interesting* regions and sequence them again." (Roberts 1993, emphasis added.)

The question raised by this claim is what the interesting regions are, how they are identified, and what can we do once we have identified them. But the answers to **none** of these questions will emerge from a complete sequence of the human genome. And that is what is wrong with Watson's claim quoted above as well. The interesting regions are the ones whose gene-products are implicated in the production of proteins in the ribosomes, the regions of DNA which produce messenger RNA for enzymes and other proteins, the regions which produce enzymes that control the gene's expression of other enzyme- and protein-producing parts of the DNA, or which control the controllers, etc. How are these genes to be identified? Not from "the bottom up", because we do not know *ab initio* about which DNA sequences do any of these things; rather, we must work from gene-products back to DNA sequences.

It is true that once we know where a functional gene's sequence lies on the chromosome and can isolate it, the sequence can tell us a great deal about the gene-product. This is because the genetic code has been broken and we know which amino acid molecule—the building block for proteins—is coded by which sequence of three DNA bases—the so-called "codon." Instead of analyzing proteins directly, the gene sequence can tell us more about the protein it codes for, and tell us faster, because we have technical means of breaking down the DNA to read off its sequence, and we do not have equally powerful techniques for breaking down the protein and reading off its sequence of amino acids. It is the advent of these means for sequencing DNA which made nucleic acids the locus for biotechnological research to design new pharmaceuticals, and whetted the molecular geneticist's appetites for the HGP.

To establish the existence of a gene functionally requires identifying its product—the phenotype which it codes for and which assorts in a family of organisms in accordance with well-known regularities of population genetics. Suppose the phenotype is an abnormality, as it often is in current research, which results from a biochemical defect in the gene-product. In this case, we may be able to make very great therapeutic advances without knowing much about the full DNA sequence, where it is, how long it is, how often it is repeated, etc. All we need to do is isolate the messenger DNA for the particular gene product, usually expressed most heavily in normal organs and tissues whose defective function we seek to understand. Thus, the brain will be richer in gene products which effect neural processes than the liver; and the richest harvest of mRNAs from the liver will be for gene products involved in storage of glycogen, and filtering of hemoglobin. Having identified high concentrations of the messenger RNA distinctive to the tissue, without proceeding back to the gene, we can employ reverse transcriptase to build complementary DNA (cDNA) clones, and polymerase chain reactions to amplify them. Once inserted in the right vectors, these synthetic genes can produce enough product to provide drugs which will treat hereditary disorders.

It has not escaped the attention of researchers that being able to produce cDNAs from messenger RNAs is a far more attractive route to understanding gene expression and gene regulation than sequencing the whole genome. Indeed this realization is at the basis of a potentially lucrative research program in pharmacology. After all, by hybridizing radioactively labelling cDNAs with the genome, molecular geneticists can zero in on the 5 to 10 % of the DNA that codes for gene produces—i.e. the genes—without wasting any time sequencing junk. Accordingly, few researchers are asking for government subsidies to produce cDNAs; instead they are attempting to patent them.

Of course it is true that once we have identified a gene through its function—the phenotype, we can begin to try to localize the gene to a chromosome. What is needed is to identify a detectable abnormality in the chromosome which co-varies systematically with the phenotype. Once we have done this we can zero in on the locus on the chromosome and sequence the DNA to find out exactly what the genetic cause is. For this reason it is important to produce physical maps of the genome at a fairly high degree of resolution. However, such a physical map is very far from the full sequence. It is composed of tens of thousands of sequence tagging sites—a few thousand base pairs long not repeated elsewhere in the genome, of which 90 to 95 % will be unrelated to any functional domain of the DNA. Constructing such a map is an integral part of the HGP. Indeed, many scientists and commentators will say it is the most important part of the project. But even a physical map of land-marks is without interest in the absence of pedegree studies that can reveal when it is worth analyzing chromosomes for distinctive markers that will physically localize genes to DNA sequences. To be useful physical maps and DNA sequences need to be preceded by genetic research that can narrow down the the focus of seqeuncing from the whole genome to the functional units.

Those who identify physical mapping as the central goal of the HGP implicitly demote sequencing the whole human genome to a derivative status. Far from being derivative, it should be no part of the project's expected goals at all.

Perhaps getting the government to support sequencing the entire human genome is part of a strategy for providing the community of molecular biologists with opportunities that they would not otherwise have, and which they cannot even identify or guess at.

To see why this possibility is worth exploring, consider some other large scientific programs. First, recall the Manhattan Project, an undertaking of breath-taking size whose magnitude has been obscured by inflation. The two billion 1942-45 dollars spent in the project to develop atomic weapons probably equal two hundred billion dollars today, and you couldn't get the result for that amount anyway. However, have you ever asked yourself what the motivation of the theoretical physicists was? Surely they realized that if the US, Canadian and UK governments could be convinced to support research aimed at building a war-ending weapon, the spin-off for experimental and theoretical research of the sort which really interests physicists could be phenomenal. Resources devoted to fundamental physics would as a result certainly be many orders of magnitude greater than they could expect in even a prosperous peace-time economy. It is worth exploring whether for some of the more influential of these scientists the real objective was increased understanding of fundamental physical processes. Many participants rated the chances of producing a successful bomb rather low at first, but recognized that the project would give them far more money to explore far more physics than they had ever anticipated. Who can blame them? It was rational to encourage the government to believe that a weapon was feasible, and there was no one to gainsay how they spent the money, not even Leslie Groves. When they succeeded the outlook for further support of fundamental research, with a national defence rationale, became even brighter, and spun off into support of all kinds of things.

J. Robert Oppenheimer cam close to admitting the motivation of the Manhattan project physicists after the war. He said:

> When you come right down to it the reason we did this thing is because it was an organic necessity. You can't stop such a thing. If you are a scientist you believe that it is a good to find out how the world works; that it is a good to find out what the realities are...

More recently the molecular biology community has come to the same realization: by harnessing the desire to understand the human immune system to public anxiety about the threatened spread of AIDS, immunology has acquired vastly more resources than it might otherwise have expected to support its aim of understanding the immune system. The character of the immune system is one of the most vexing of biologically mysteries; the immune system also seems basic both to our understanding of genetics, and neurophysiology. But its complexity made the likelihood of breakthroughs in theoretical illumination improbable. The opportunity presented by the threat of AIDS to assert research priority changed the likelihoods. It is now no longer clear that the AIDS epidemic will breakout among heterosexuals who avoid intravenous drug use. But there remains an influential portion of the population who continue to advocate a distribution of research support to the study of HIV and AIDS disproportionate to its incidence in the US population. By making common cause with this group, and providing scientific and medical grounds that substantiate their warnings about the risks to the general population, the immunology community has assured itself of the resources to support a large number of scientists' attempts to make progress in basic understanding of all aspects of the immune system.

Claims about the value of sequencing the entire human genome are mysterious enough to make one suspect that the molecular geneticists have learned well the lesson of the Manhattan Project and the AIDS-interest groups. Passing acquaintance with molecular genetics shows how useless knowing the whole sequence is by itself. Even when we have acquired the technology needed to make knowledge of the sequence possible, knowing the sequence will not add much to our therapeutic powers.

But, the goal of sequencing the entire human genome is one that can be more easily understood, will provide vast resources for more significant research, and can be urged as a visible national and international goal.

By comparison to the Manhattan Project, the HGP is small beer. At a dollar a base pair, it will come in at 3 billion. At four dollars a base pair it will still be cheaper than the Superconducting Super Collider would have been, and an order of magnitude cheaper than just building the space station will be, not to mention keeping it occupied. Under the aspect of Eternity the HGP is not really "big science". However, its institutional impact will be like that of "big science."

Big science differs from what will inevitably be called small science not because of the size of the total budget, but because of the organization of effort, the assignment of problems, and methods for dealing with them. Typically, in "small science" the individual scientist is the initiator of his or her own research program, its component problems, and the methods for dealing with them. The interest or significance of the problem, the adequacy of the scientists resources for dealing with it, and the likelihood of success is often measured by peer-review for granting agencies which provide the funds for research, of course. But the initiative in undertaking research remains with the individual scientist or a small team. The direction of scientific authority is from the bottom up. Bottom up science had several important features: first, it harnesses the individual scientist's interest in the problem, and as a result produces far more effort for the same investment than other ways of assigning problems; second, it exploits the fact that scientific knowledge is both vast and decentralized. A scientific command economy can not absorb and deploy the information scientists produce as efficiently as a decentralized one in which individuals have strong incentives to seek out relevant information; third bottom-up research reduces the bureaucratization of science: minimizes feather-bedding, cuts of projects which have outlived their scientific value, and reduces the transaction costs of research. But a program which assigns long stretches of DNA to scientists, or their technicians, for sequencing must in the nature of the case be a top-down enterprise. So far from exploiting the advantages of decentralized research, the HGP's coordination problem can only be solved by centralization. The quality of its product—reliable sequences—is likely to suffer, as the cost of its administration inevitably grows beyond any reasonable return on investment.

The question must therefore be asked, why has the molecular genetics community come so completely together in support of the Human Genome Project. As advertised it does not make scientific sense, and as organized it fails to exploit the incentives that maximize the pay off to research expenditure. I believe that the answers to this question can be found by applying some simple economic theory of information. But this is an enterprise for another paper (Rosenberg 1996).

References

Collins, F, and Galas, D. (1993), "A new five year plan for the US human genome project", *Science,* 262: 43-46.

Roberts, L. (1993), "Taking Stock of the Genome Project", *Science,* 262: 20-22.

Rosenberg, A. (1996), "Research Tactics and Science Politics: How we Got the Human Genome Project", *Social Philosophy and Policy*, forthcoming.

Watson, J. (1993), "Looking Forward", *Gene,* 135: 309-315.

Part XI

PROBABILITY AND THE ART OF JUDGMENT

Science, Probability, and the Proposition[1]

Bas C. van Fraassen

Princeton University

Traditionally, philosophy of science has focused on the product of science: the scientific hypothesis, principle, law, or more grandiosely, the theory. Using logician's license I'll think of hypotheses and theories as 'little' and 'big' (or 'weak' and 'strong') *propositions*. The tradition spoke of the product as (scientific) knowledge; the more recent phrase "current scientific opinion" carries the same connotation of uniqueness. For this to make sense, something is required: a proposition must be capable of being true or false, capable of being fully believed or disbelieved (and if you like, known).

Probabilism requires us to look at every aspect of science in a new way. In his radical brand of probabilism, Richard Jeffrey told us to reconceptualize knowledge as 'probable knowledge' and propositions as 'probasitions'—and never to resolve doubt but simply to quantify it, keeping all possibilities in play. To refuse full belief to any but tautologies is to follow the call of probabilism *au bout*. Nothing I will say is meant to eliminate this conception. It may be related to the ideal of the Zen mind, which is not in the grip of any picture however bewitching, tolerant of every doubt and possibility, strong and free enough to need no resolution. But I do not think that it is forced on us by the nature of probability, and I want to show how probabilism and traditional epistemic views can to some extent be reconciled.

There are difficulties: full belief seems to require maximal subjective probability, but also be at odds with it; the probability of a proposition seems to be the probability that it is true, yet not admit retention of the true/false dichotomy. I will propose a single unified account which takes conditional personal probability as basic. Nevertheless it remains accurate to say that the probabilities allotted by science are only a grading of the possibilities left open by my beliefs.

1. The 'Body of Science' and Maximal Probability

The ideal of unified science implies that the point of engaging in science is to construct a single (though at every humanly reachable stage incomplete) picture of what things are like. This suggests that the product of science is a set of propositions.[2] Their intersection is the proposition which captures exactly that single picture of the world which science provides. Clearly this 'body of science' can leave open many alternatives. The alternatives left open are then also represented by (sets of) propositions, namely ones that imply the whole body of science. But these alternatives do not all have the same status, though they are all "possible for all that science tells us". Some seem more or less likely than others: enter probability, as a grading of the possibilities left open by the body of accepted scientific truth.

PSA 1994, Volume 2, pp. 339-348

Probability is a continuous additive function (a measure) ranging over the interval [0,1], with the empty proposition Λ (self– contradiction) receiving 0 and the universal proposition U (tautology) receiving 1. Hence probability respects the ordering by logical implication (If $A \subseteq B$ then $P(A) \leq P(B)$). But we must be careful in any extrapolation to theories which deal with continua. For it follows from the above that at most countably many disjoint propositions can receive finite positive probability.

The so–called lottery paradox shows that we cannot equate what science tells us with what it assigns probability greater than or equal to p, if $p < 1$. For example, suppose $p = 0.99$ and that the scientific account of a certain chance process (e. g. a lottery) says that it has 1000 equiprobable outcomes. Then the probability of the kth outcome not happening equals 0.999. But of course this scientific account does not imply for each $k = 1,..,1000$, that the kth outcome will not happen.

The thesis that probabilities grade exactly the alternatives left open by science guarantees that all propositions entailed by science have maximal probability. So should we then simply set $p = 1$, that is, identify what science tells us with the propositions which it makes maximally likely? The answer is No, exactly because in science we deal with continuous quantities. The maximally likely propositions will not form a single picture—they will just give us a family of rival maximally likely pictures. Consider some such quantity as the decay time of a radium atom lying in interval [a,b]. If the probability is absolutely continuous with respect to Lebesgue measure then it equals zero that the time $t = x$, for $a \leq x \leq b$. Hence the probability that t lies in the set $[a,b] - \{x\}$ equals 1, for each such number x. Yet no real number belongs to all these sets—their intersection is empty. Probability measures of this sort (deriving from continuous probability densities) are ubiquitous in science. We are faced here with a transfinite version of the lottery paradox (compare Maher 1990).

2. Should We Reconceptualize the Idea of Proposition?

As we have just seen, in effect, the ordering $P(A) \leq P(B)$ extends the partial ordering of logical implication (if $A \subseteq B$ then $P(A) \leq P(B)$), but unfortunately $P(A) = P(B)$ is possible even when $A \neq B$. Indeed, this is inevitable if there are more than countably many disjoint propositions. As a corollary, the intersection of all propositions of maximal probability may itself even be empty.

Kolmogoroff himself reacted to this problem by suggesting that we focus on probability algebras: algebras of propositions reduced by the relation of equivalence modulo differences of measure zero. That is, we begin with the usual picture of propositions (identified through subsets of the sample space, or sets of possible worlds if you like). Then we call such propositions A and B equivalent (relative to the assignment of probabilities P) exactly if $P(A + B) = 0$. Finally, we create the new conception of proposition by identifying all elements equivalent in this sense. (See also Birkhoff (1967), XI, 5 and Kappos (1969), II, 4 and III, 3).

The difficulty with this approach is that a probability algebra does not have the structure usually demanded of an algebra of propositions. For the latter, the notion of truth is relevant, so it should be possible to map the algebra homomorphically into {0,1}. As example take the unit interval with Lebesgue measure P, reduced by the above equivalence relation. This is a probability (sigma–)algebra. Let T be the class of elements designated as true, i.e. mapped into 1, and let A with measure x be in T. Then A is the join of two disjoint elements of measure x/2 each. Since the mapping is a homomorphism, one of these is in T. We conclude that T contains a countable downward chain A_1, A_2,... with the measures converging to zero. Therefore its meet is the zero element of the algebra. The meet should be in T because it is the countable meet of a family of "true" propositions; but it can't be in T, since the zero element is mapped into 0.

Thus the "transfinite inconsistency" of the old sort of propositions of probability 1 engenders the countable inconsistency of the new type of proposition once we try to deal non–trivially with continua of possibilities. Inconsistencies at the countable level is certainly worse!

One reaction is to say: don't just reconceptualize—reconceptualize radically! Easier said than done in this case. The obvious alternative to trying for a single picture of what the world is like—a picture to call my own—is to juggle with several. But in the probability algebra we just constructed there isn't even one truthfilter with non–zero intersection. So where are the several alternatives to juggle? This question betrays my unredeemed insight, typical of the pre–radicalized. Suppose we require of single pictures of the world that they first of all not be complete, and second not necessarily consistently completable. This is reminiscent of, for example, some ideas of Bohr and perhaps Feyerabend. In its very extravant radicality lies its appeal. But here I shall try to see if a more conservative and (toward the old–fashioned) more conciliatory approach will work.

3. Irreducible Conditional Probability

Before Kolmogoroff swept the field, probability was generally regarded as irreducibly conditional. The difficulties with probability zero noted above were among the solid evidence that it was so. One common sort of example Borel's: consider the location of some point on earth identified by physical description, such as the center of mass of a certain person or vehicle. Under conditions of minimal knowledge, we must give equal probability to all equal areas; and therefore zero that it lies on the Equator. But given that it lies on the Equator, surely we must then give equal probability 1/2 that it lies in the Western Hemisphere?

The usual calculation of conditional probability, which would set $P(B|A)$ equal to $P(B \cap C|A)$ divided by $P(C|A \cap C)$, clearly cannot be carried out. The suggestion that conditional probability is irreducible means that two–place probability $P(\ |\ )$—probability of one thing given (on supposition of) another—is autonomous and one–place ("absolute") probability should be defined as $P(\ ) = P(\ |\ U)$, probability conditional on the tautology. There is a good deal of literature on this (see Appendix). Despite many individual differences, general agreement concerning two–place probability extends to:

I. If P is a 2–place probability function then $P(-|A)$ is ("normally") a (1–place) probability function with $P(A|A) = 1$, and else a 'don't care'.

II. These derivative 1–place probability functions [described in I.] are related at least by the Multiplication Axiom:

$$P(B \cap C|A) = P(B|A)P(C|A \cap C)$$

where A,B,C,... are assumed to be in the domain and co–domain of the function. The 'don't cares' include at least the case of antecedent $A = \Lambda$. I shall represent such a 'don't care' with the constant function $P(\ |A) = 1$. Given such a 2–place probability measure P, I shall call A *normal* (for P) if $P(\ |A)$ is a (1–place) probability measure, and otherwise *abnormal*.

EXAMPLE.Let U be the set of natural numbers {0,1,2, ...}. For index n = 0, 1, 2, ... let p_n be the probability measure defined on all subsets of U by the condition that it assigns 0.1 to {x} if x is in the set {10n, ..., 10n+9}, and 0 otherwise. Define:

$P(A|B) = p_n(A \cap B)/p_n(B)$ for the first index n such that

$p_n(B) > 0$, if there is any such index; = 1 otherwise.

It is easy to verify that the above principles are satisfied, and equally that we cannot find any single one–place probability measure that would do the same job.

Here are some initial consequences of the definition. The variables range of course over propositions (members of family F in space S=<U,F>):

$P(X|A) = P(X \cap A|A)$; If A is normal, so are its supersets; If A is abnormal, so are its subsets; B is abnormal iff $P(-B|B) = 1$ (and equally iff $P(B|A) = 0$ for all normal A).

Let us call the case in which only Λ is abnormal the "Very Fine" case; there are in fact Very Fine 2–place probability measures on continuously varying fields of possibility, as we would hope.

4. The Infinitely Striated Scientific World–Picture

Philosophy of science has concentrated on the product of science, the scientific theory. It does not follow that we can equate what science says—at any given historical moment—about what the world is with a single theory. There may be a single theory which has hegemony, but received scientific opinion includes a great deal more. Even putting all accepted scientific beliefs together we have too shallow a model of science–in–actu. For the scientific community is in general not at all unsure about what adjustments would be in order if any particular bit of that received opinion turned out to be wrong. Perhaps that is part of what it means to be guided by paradigms. Only for the jettisoning of very deep paradigms, system principles, is the whole scientific world thrown for a loop. Simple examples of that sort will show that not all scientific beliefs are equal—if A must be given up, which entails the fall of either B or C, there may be an immediate spontaneous response that of course it is B that goes while C should be maintained. There may be some temptation to say that C is a law and B a mere fact, for example, but that may not be backed up with any substantive notion of law.

What we need to do then is to characterize the system of accepted scientific beliefs in their hierarchical structure. This we can do while maintaining that this system can be modeled (in an idealized way of course) by an irreducible conditional probability measure. This modeling is of the state of science at one specific historic moment, and all notions to be introduced will accordingly be historically relative. What I shall present is the idea of what is held (at that time) a priori—i. e. not revisable without deep–going conceptual change—and then the idea of what is believed (at that time). Those distinctions will rest on divisions among the propositions of maximal 'absolute' probability, display a hierarchy, and allow for infinitely descending chains of retrenchement when experimental evidence goes against the received opinions.

5. The Idea of the (Relative) *A Priori*

At any stage of science there will be propositions which are not epistemically distinguishable from the tautology U. They are exactly what is certain on any supposition whatever, no matter how contrary or far–fetched. Let us call these *a priori* at that stage:

A is *a priori* for P iff $P(A|X) = 1$ for all X,

iff U–A is abnormal for P.

The strongest unconditional probability equivalence relation between A and B is that their symmetric difference (A+B) has measure zero. We can generalize this similarly. As our strictest epistemic equivalence relation between two propositions we have a priori equivalence (their symmetric difference has probability 0 on all normal suppositions). Using '+' to mark exclusive disjunction: $A + B = (A - B) \cup (B - A)$, we can write:

A<P>B iff A+B is abnormal.[3]

The abnormal propositions are the ones *a priori* equivalent to the empty set (the self–contradiction) and the a prioris are the ones *a priori* equivalent to the tautology. Note now that A<P>B iff $P(A|A+B) = 1$ and $P(B|A+B) = 1$, since additivity would not allow that if A+B were normal. We can divide this equivalence relation into its two conjuncts:

DEFINITION: A P> B iff $P(A|A+B) = 1$

What we have here is a new non–trivial relationships between propositions. De Finetti suggested relations of local comparison of this type.[4]

Here are a few facts about these notions that come in handy as we try to use them:

P> is transitive, and if A logically implies B then B P> A. If A+B is normal, then A P> B means that A is comparatively superior to B, in the sense that A is certainly true and B certainly false, on the supposition that one but not both are the case. But if A+B is abnormal then the relationship A P> B amounts to A <P> B. The right reading for " P> " is therefore "is superior to or a priori equivalent to". To be brief, however, I'll just say "A is superior to B" for "A P> B", and ask you to keep the qualifications in mind.

6. The Propositions in the 'Body of Science'

The propositions which are a priori, in the above (very non– absolute sense) at a given stage of science are those whose contraries are all abnormal. There is a weaker condition a proposition K can satisfy: namely that any normal proposition which implies K is superior to any that are contrary to K. Consider the following conditions and definitions:

(A1) Normality:	K is normal
(A2) Superiority:	If A is a non–empty subset A of K while B and K are disjoint, then A P> B
(A3) Contingency:	the complement U–K of K is normal

We can restate the "Superiority" condition informally as follows:

> Superiority: the alternatives K leaves open are all superior to any alternative that K excludes.

We can deduce from these conditions something reminiscent of Carnap's "regularity" (or Shimony's "strict coherence"):

(A4) Finesse:	all non–empty subsets of K are normal.

What we now have available as candidate for the 'body of science' is the family of propositions which are logically implied by a certain privileged family, which I will characterize as follows:

DEFINITION: K is a core proposition (for P) iff K satisfies (A1)–(A3).

Note that the a priori propositions satisfy (A1) and (A2), though definitely not (A3), but rather its opposite. However, all the a prioris are among the propositions implied by these cores. In fact:

If K is a core proposition then $P(K|U) = 1$; if K is a core proposition then A P> K iff K implies A; if K is a core proposition and A is a priori then K is a subset of A.

To characterize the full body of science we need take into account the extreme possibility of there being no core propositions. In that case we still want the a prioris to be part of what science says. (This corresponds to what I have called the "Zen minds": states of opinion in which nothing is fully believed if it is subjectively possible to withhold belief.)

DEFINITION: A belongs to the body of science (at a stage characterized by P) iff

(i) A P> K for some core proposition K; or
(ii) there is no core proposition, and A is a priori for P.

The following conditions are equivalent:

(a) A belongs to the body of science (characterized by P)
(b) Some proposition J which is either a priori or a core proposition is such that A P> J
(c) A is implied either by an a priori or by a core proposition (for P)

Intuitively we could also render these notions, a bit less rigorously, as follows: A core proposition is a proposition K such that: (a) K and its complement are both normal; (b) K does not leave open any abnormal alternatives; (c) any alternatives left open by K are superior to any alternatives K excludes. We can add: the body of science consists of exactly those propositions which are implied by core propositions (or are a priori). As before, a proposition is here called an alternative left open by K exactly if it is non–empty and implies K.

7. Below the Tip of the Iceberg

What is the advantage of thinking of the body of science in this way? Its members are all propositions which have absolute probability 1 at that stage (i. e. conditional on the tautology), but the converse will not hold in general. We should now hope to add: this body of science, though possibly infinite and not finitely axiomatizable, is guaranteed to be consistent, and moreover, its members belong to a hierarchical structure which could guide retrenchment if any of its members have to be given up.

Not every 2–place probability function may in fact give such a nice result if we take it to encapsulate scientific opinion. As usual, formalization will allow the entry of monsters and miscreants among the described flora and fauna. What matters, however, is that we have available the resources for characterizing scientific opionion in such a favorable way, that we are not forced by paradoxes either to give up our way of describing science, or to declare science to be such as to fit our Procrustean mold.

By the definition I gave, the propositions in the body of science are clustered: each belongs to a family {A: A P> K} for some core proposition K (if there are any at all), which sums up that cluster exactly: K is the intersection of {A: A P> K}, and {A: A P> K} = {A: K implies A}. We can now prove that these clusters form a chain, linearly ordered by set inclusion (implication):

> If K, K' are belief cores, then either K is a subset of K' or K' is a subset of K.

This result is crucial for both the consistency and the hierarchical structure of that body of propositions.

Writing K* for the intersection of all the belief cores, we conclude that if A is in the body of science then K* implies A. But is K* itself a core proposition? Does it have 100% probability? Is it even non–empty? This is the problem of transfinite consistency of full belief in our new setting. What we can prove is that the intersection of a non–empty countable family of belief cores is a core proposition.

The significance of this result may be challenged by noting that the intersection of countably many sets of measure 1 also has measure 1. So how have we made progress with the transfinite lottery paradox? In four ways. The first is that in the representation of scientific opinion we may have a "small" family of belief cores even if probability is continuous and there are uncountably many propositions with probability 1. The second is that no matter how large a chain is, its intersection is one of its members if it has a first (= "smallest") element. The third is that the following is a condition typically met in spaces on which probabilities are defined even in the most scientifically sophisticated applications:

> (*) Any chain of propositions, linearly ordered by set inclusion, has a countable subchain with the same intersection.

Of course, if (*) holds and there is at least one core proposition, then (by the above noted result) the intersection of all core propositions is also a core proposition. Fourthly, we will (see below) be able to describe an especially nice class of models ("lexicographic probability"). For these we can prove that the intersection of the core propositions, if any, is always also a core proposition . There are no countability restrictions there.

8. To What Extent Does Scientific Belief Guide Scientific Opinion?

There are models in which there are no core propositions at all. For example, if we take Lebesgue measure m on the unit interval, and trivially extend it to a two–place function by P(A|B)=m(AB)/m(B) if defined and P(A|B) = 1 if not (though A,B in domain of m). Then every unit set {x} is in the domain and is abnormal. Therefore there is no set all of whose subsets are normal, and hence no core propositions. The absence of core propositions in our present example derives from its triviality, and not from the continuity. All maximal probability propositions are here on a par with the tautology; this does not seem to me a good candidate for representing scientific opinion. At the other extreme from this example, there is the Very Fine case of a probability function P for which every non–empty set is normal.

DEFINITION P is core covered if the union of the core propositions equals U.

In that case, P is Very Fine. For let A be any non–empty proposition; there will be some core proposition K such that KA is not empty, hence normal, thus making A normal.

The example in section 3 furnishes us with a relatively simple example of this sort. Recall that P is there constructed from the series $p_0,p_1,...,p_n,...$ where the whole probability mass of p_n is concentrated (and evenly distributed) on the natural numbers {10n,...,10n+9}. In this example, the core propositions are exactly the sets

$$K_0=\{0,...,9\},K_1=\{0,...,19\},K_2=\{0,...,29\},...K_i=\{0,...,10i+9\}$$

These core propositions clearly cover U; P is belief covered and Very Fine. Indeed, the core propositions are well–ordered.

Define the belief remnants

$$R_0 = K_0$$
$$R_{j+1} = K_{j+1} - K_j \ (j=0,1,2,...)$$

Clearly $p_i = P(R_i)$; for example, $p_1 = P(\{10,...,19\})$ probabilities conditional on belief remnants (beliefs remaining upon retrenchment to a weaker core) determine all probabilities in this case:

$$P(-|A) = P(-|A \cap R_i) \text{ for the first i such that } P(A|R_i)>0$$

This says quite clearly that (in this case) belief guides opinion, for probabilities conditional on belief remnants are, so to speak, all the conditional probabilities there are.

The body of science, at any given stage, should in my opinion be viewed as having this sort of structure (even if such a probability function is too complete, precise, and idealized a model to be very realistic). That is, we should be able to see how, within science (and possibly relative to additional background beliefs characterizing a given scientific community) the representable possibilities left open are graded with respect to probabilities, and how essentially the same sort of structure emerges under suppositions which may or may not be contrary to the propositions currently unconditionally asserted (let alone those currently having maximal probability).

9. A Large Class of Models

I will define a class of models such that P satisfies principles I–II iff P can be represented by one of these models, in the way to be explained. A model begins with a sample space S=<U,F>, where U is a non–empty set (the universe of possibilities) and F a sigma–field of sets on U (the propositions). We define the subfields:

$$\text{if A is in F then } FA = \{E \cap A: E \text{ in } F\};$$

thus FA is a field on A. For each such field designate as PA the set of probability measures defined on FA. (When A is empty, FA = {A} and PA is empty.) The restriction of a member p of PA to a subfield FB, with B a subset of A, will be designated p|FB. Finally let PS be the union of all the sets PA, A in F.

A model M will consist of a sample space S as above, and a function π defined on a subset of F, with range in PS. That is, π associates some probability measure on some subfield with certain propositions. (These will be the normal propositions.) I will abbreviate "$\pi(A)$" to "πA". The function π is subject to the following conditions:

(M1) $\pi A(A)$ is defined and positive.
(M2) If $\pi B(A)$ is defined and positive, then πA is defined
(M3) If $\pi B(A)$ is defined and positive, then $\pi A|F(A \cap B)$ is proportional to $\pi B|F(A \cap B)$.

This does not entail that if $\pi B(A \cap B) > 0$ then $\pi A(A \cap B) > 0$, because the proportionality constant can be 0 (in which case πA gives 0 to all members of $F(A \cap B)$). It is easy to see what the constant of proportionality has to be:

If $\pi B(A)$ is defined and positive, then
$\pi A|F(A \cap B) : \pi B|F(A \cap B) = \pi A(A \cap B) : \pi B(A \cap B)$

Finally we define what it means for one of these functions to represent a two–place function:

DEFINITION: Model $M = \langle S,\pi \rangle$ with $S=\langle U,F \rangle$ represents binary function P iff the domain of P is F and for all A, B in F, $P(A|B) = \pi B(A \cap B)/\pi B(B)$ if defined, and = 1 otherwise.

It is easy to prove that:

If P is represented by a model, then P is a two–place probability measure.
If P is a two–place probability measure satisfying the principles I–II, then P is represented by a model.

Having established this representation result, we now look for easily constructed models, for illustration, refutation of conjectures, and exploration of examples.

DEFINITION: Model $M = \langle S,\pi \rangle$ with $S=\langle U,F \rangle$ is lexicographic iff there is a sequence (well–ordered class) SEQ of 1–place probability measures defined on the whole of F, such that $\pi B(A) = q(A \cap B)/q(B)$ for the first member q of the sequence SEQ such that $q(B) > 0$; πB is undefined when there is no such q.

(The term "lexicographic" is used similarly in decision theory literature; see Blume et al., 1989, 1991.) The members of SEQ correspond to the probabilities conditional on belief remnants (see discussion above). We will say that πA comes before πB in SEQ exactly when the first q in SEQ such that $q(A)>0$ comes before the first q in SEQ such that $q(B)>0$. It is easily checked that $M = \langle S,\pi \rangle$ is a model. Specifically, if A is a subset of B then πB will not come after πA, since whatever measure assigns a positive value to A will then assign one to B. Neither can πA come after πB if $\pi B(A) > 0$; in that case $\pi A = \pi B$. Consequently condition (M3) is easily verified: the proportionality constant = 1.

It is now very easy to make up examples of 2–place probability measures. Just take two or three or indeed any number, finite or infinite, of ordinary probability measures and well–order them. We can readily construct lexicographic models to show that in general not all propositions with probability 1 are members of the body of science (i. e. implied by any core proposition). A special example, whose existence depends on the axiom of choice is this: let SEQ contain all one–place probability measures defined on given domain F. In that case, the only abnormal proposition is the empty set (the self–contradiction). Also the only a priori is the tautology. Short of this, we could of course have a sequence which does not contain literally all the definable probability measures, but contains all those which give 1 to a given set A. In that case, all propositions other than Λthat imply A are normal. Let us call P Very Fine on A in such a case. (The case of P Very Fine on U was already called "Very Fine" above.) Note that one of the defining conditions of a core proposition K was that P had to be Very Fine on K.

In a lexicographic model, the intersection of all core propositions, if any, is always a core proposition too. Since this does not depend on cardinality or the character of the sample space, the result adds significantly to the previous theorems.

APPENDIX. Previous Literature

The basic theory of two–place probability functions is a common part of a number of theories. Such probability functions have been called Popper functions because Popper's axioms originally presented in his The Logic of Scientific Discovery were adopted by other writers (see Harper (1976), Field (1977), van Fraassen (1979, 1981)). Carnap used essentially the same axioms for his "c–functions". Reichenbach's probability was also irreducibly two–place. I have mentioned De Finetti's paper (1936) which introduced the idea of local comparisons (like my "superior"; Vickers' "thinner"); see also section 4.18 in his Theory of Probability, vol. 1. The most extensive work on two–place probability theory is by Renyi. The theory of two–place probability here presented is essentially as explored in my (1979), but with considerable improvement in the characterization of the described classes of models. Finally, my own work on irreducible conditional probability was from the beginning very indebted to the ideas of Isaac Levi (see e. g. Levi (1980), Ch. 10), even if I assimilated those ideas sometimes in my own idiosyncratic way.

Notes

[1]All technical details for this paper can be found in my "Fine– grained opinion, conditional probability, and the logic of full belief", in the *Journal of Philosophical Logic* (1995). The present adaptation of those results is offered on behalf of the contention that general epistemology and scientific methodology are each other writ small and writ large respectively (not necessarily in that order).

[2]By propositions I mean the semantic content of statements; the same proposition can be expressed by many statements. I am not addressing how opinion is stored or communicated.

[3]From this point on I shall drop the ubiquitous "for P" unless confusion threatens, and just write "a priori", "abnormal", etc. leaving the context to specify the relevant 2–place probability measure.

[4]De Finetti (1936); this idea is developed considerably further, with special reference to zero relative frequency, in Vickers (1988), sections 3.6 and 5.4. The relation here defined is slightly different from the so–named one in my (1979) for convenience in some of the proofs.

References

Birkhoff, G. (1967), *Lattice Theory*, 3rd ed. Providence: AMS.

Blume, L., Brandenburger, A., and Deckel. E. (1991a), "Lexicographic probabilities and choice under uncertainty", *Econometrica* 59: 61–79.

Blume, L. (1991b), "Lexicographic probabilities and equilibrium refinements", *Econometrica* 59: 81–98.

De Finetti, B. (1936), "Les probabilités nulles", *Bulletin des sciences mathématiques*: 275–288.

_ _ _ _ _ _ _. (1972), *Theory of Probability* (2 vols.). New York: John Wiley.

Field, H. (1972), "Logic, meaning and conceptual role", *Journal of Philosophy* 74: 374–409.

Hajek, A. (1992), "The conditional construal of conditional probability". Ph.D. Diss. Princeton University.

Harper, W.L. (1976), "Rational belief change, Popper functions, and counter–factuals" in C. Hooker and W. Harper (eds.) *Foundations of Probability Theory*, vol. 1: 73–112.

Kappos, D.A. (1969), *Probability Algebras and Stochastic Spaces*. New York.

Levi, I. (1980), *The Enterprise of Knowledge*. Cambridge: MIT Press.

Maher, P. (1990), "Acceptance without Belief" *PSA 1990*, volume 1, 381–392.

McGee, V. (1994), "Learning the impossible", in (Skyrms, 1994).

Popper, K. (1959), *The Logic of Scientific Discovery*. New York: Basic Books.

Renyi, A. (1959), "On a new axiomatic theory of probability", *Acta Mathematica Hungarica* 6: 285–333.

_ _ _ _ _. (1970a), *Foundations of Probability*. San Francisco: Holden–Day, 1970.

_ _ _ _ _. (1970b), *Probability Theory*. Amsterdam: North–Holland.

Skirms, B. (1983), "Three ways to give a probability function a memory", pp. 157–161 in J. Earman (ed.) *Testing Scientific Theories* (Minnesota Studies in the Philosophy of Science, vol X). Minneapolis: University of Minnesota Press.

Skyrms, B. and Eels, E. (1995), *Probabilities and Conditionals: Believ Revision and Rational Decision*. New York: Cambridge University Press, 1994.

Vickers, John M. (1988), *Chance and Structure*. Oxford: Oxford University Press.

van Fraassen, B.C. (1979), "Foundations of probability: a modal frequency interpretation", in G. Toraldo di Francia (ed.) *Problems in the Foundations of Physics* (1979), pp. 344–387.

_ _ _ _ _ _ _ _ _ _ _. (1981a), "Probabilistic semantics objectified: I. Postulates and logics" *Journal of Philosophical Logic* 10: 371–394.

_ _ _ _ _ _ _ _ _ _ _. (1981b), "Probabilistic semantics objectified: II. Implications in probabilistic model sets" *Journal of Philosophical Logic* 10: 495–510.

_ _ _ _ _ _ _ _ _ _ _. (1995), "Fine-grained opinion, probability, and the logic of belief", *Journal of Philosophical Logic*, 24 (1995), pp. 349-377.

Convergence in Radical Probabilism[1]

Brian Skyrms

University of California, Irvine

> The obvious move is to deny that the notion of knowledge has the importance generally attributed to it, and to try to make the concept of belief do the work that philosophers have assigned to the grander concept. I shall argue that this is the right move.
> - Richard Jeffrey
> "Probable Knowledge"

1. Introduction

Richard Jeffrey advocates fallibilism in the form of radical probabilism. Degrees of belief are the objects of prime interest to epistemology and it is rarely plausible that they should take the extreme form of certainty. In particular the creation of certainties by the process of belief change by conditionalization is not necessary:

> ... for a certain strict point of view, it is rarely or never that there is a proposition for which the direct effect of an observation will be to change the observer's degree of belief in that proposition to 1 ... (Jeffrey 1968)

Jeffrey offers his well-known model of belief change by probability kinematics as a plausible model where strict conditionalization does not occur, without any claims that it is the only such model.

In his rich and provocative essay on Bayesian methodology, John Earman issues a challenge to this radical probabilist epistemology:

> ...a Bayesianism that appeals to both Dutch Book and strict conditionalization is on a collision course with itself. The use of strict conditionalization leads to situations where Pr(A)=1 although $\not\models$A. As a result, something almost as bad as a Dutch book befalls the conditionalizer; namely she is committed to betting on the contingent proposition A at maximal odds, which means that in no possible outcome can she have a positive gain and in some possible outcome she has a loss (a violation of what is called *strict coherence*). It is too facile to say in response that this is a good reason for abandoning strict conditionalization in favor of Jeffrey conditionalization or some other rule for belief change; for all the results about merger of opinion and convergence to certainty so highly touted in the Bayesian literature depend on strict conditionalization ...(Earman 1992, 41).

I do not take Earman to be claiming that there it is impossible to have convergence theorems for radical probabilism, but instead I read him as issuing an invitation to investigate the question. This paper is a first step in this direction. At the onset, I would

---

PSA 1994, Volume 2, pp. 349-353

like to make it clear that Bayesian convergence theorems could not conceivably give a full solution to Hume's problem of induction. Mathematical facts about measure and integral could hardly assure you that given the evidence of the past your bread will nourish you tomorrow -a point on which Hume is absolutely correct. The significance of these theorems for the philosophy of induction is that they show that some extreme forms of skepticism which are *prima facie* possible are, in fact, inconsistent.

2. Convergence in Radical Probabilism

Contemplate, at the onset, the prospect of an infinite sequence of black box learning situations. In each episode you go into the black box with a probability of proposition A and come out with a revised probability of proposition A. Here we make no assumptions about what goes on in the black box. We do not assume that you conditionalize on some evidential proposition delivered to you in the box. We do not assume anything else about the structure of your learning experience either. Now we can look for conditions which will get almost sure convergence. Let us look for a martingale.

Consider a probability space - here your degree-of-belief space, and let $x_1, x_2, \ldots$ be a sequence of random variables on that space and $F_1, F_2, \ldots$ be a sequence of sub-sigma fields. The sequence of random variables is a *martingale relative to the sequence of sigma-fields* if:

(i) The sequence of sigma-fields is non-decreasing
(ii) x_n is measurable F_n
(iii) $E[|x_n|]$ is finite
(iv) with probability 1: $E[X_{n+1} \| F_n] = x_n$

The sequence of random variables is a *martingale* if it is a martingale relative to some sequence of sigma fields.

You are interested in whether you can have confidence that your sequence of revised probabilities will converge, so let us take the random variable x_n to be the revised probability of proposition A after coming out of the nth black box. Since this is a probability, condition (iii) is automatically satisfied. We do not have any evidence statements given in our model to generate sigma-fields, so we might as well consider the sigma-fields generated by our random variables: $F_n = \sigma[x_1, \ldots, x_n]$. With these sigma fields, (i) and (ii) are automatically satisfied and we are left as the requirement for a martingale:

$$\text{(iv')}\ E[x_{n+1} \| x_1, \ldots, x_n] = x_n$$

If (iv') is not satisfied, you may very well think that your beliefs are likely to oscillate forever - for instance with revised probability of A being high after even black boxes and low after odd black boxes. But if (iv') is satisfied and if your degrees of belief are countably additive, then by the martingale convergence theorem you believe with probability one that your sequence of revised probabilities of A will converge.

Condition (iv') is a sufficient condition for almost sure convergence of opinion in a black-box learning situation, but does it have any special status for a radical probabilist?

3. Coherence in Radical Probabilism.

In this section we see the Martingale condition (iv') is a necessary condition for dynamic coherence of degrees of belief. We will assume sigma-coherence here, in order to ensure sigma additivity. That is to say a bettor can make a countable number of bets in his attempt to dutch book you, and you are sigma coherent if no dutch book can be made.

As a preliminary, let me recall a dynamic coherence theorem of Goldstein (1983) and van Fraassen (1984). We consider only one black box learning situation. Let p be your initial probability at time t_0 as you contemplate going into the black box and x_1 as be the random variable representing your revised probability of proposition A when you come out of the black box at time t_1.

A bettor gets to bet with you now (at t_0), provided you consider each bet favorable by the lights of your current probability, p, and gets to bet with you after the learning experience (at t_1) provided you consider those favorable by the lights of the revised probability, x_1. You are dynamically coherent if the bettor can not assure that you suffer a sure loss, i.e. a net loss at every possible future outcome. Goldstein and van Fraassen show that:

Dynamic coherence requires that:
(C1) $\quad p(A) = E[x_1].$

That is to say that dynamic coherence requires that your beliefs today are equal to your present expectations of your beliefs tomorrow.

Now, let us move to the case of two black boxes. You now contemplate going through 2 black box learning situations, coming out at time t_1 with a revised probability of A, x_1, and coming out at time t_2 with a further revised probability of A, x_2. Also at t_1 you will have a revised expectation of x_2, which we will call y_1. We assume that y_1 is measurable with respect to the sigma-field generated by x_1 and integrable. From your current standpoint at t_0, y_1 is also a random variable.

(C2a) Coherence requires that y_1 is a version of the conditional expectation: $E[x_2 \| x_1]$.

Let G be a set in the σ-field generated by x_1. At t_1, a contract which pays off x_2 at t_2 has a fair price of y_1 to the agent. At t_0, a contract (CON1) with a fiducial agent to buy or sell such a contract at t_1 at its t_1 fair price, conditional on G being the case at t_1, has a fair price of:

$$\int_G y_1 \, dp \qquad \text{(CON1)}$$

At t_0, a contract, (CON2), conditional on G which pays off x_2 at t_2, has a fair price of:

$$\int_G x_2 \, dp \qquad \text{(CON2)}$$

Since these contracts have the same consequences, coherence requires that they be have equal value.

(C2b) Coherence requires that y1 = x1 almost everywhere.

If the agent were always coherent at t_1, then $y_1=x_1$ by the Goldstein-van Fraassen argument. If the agent is incoherent at t_1 for a set, S, of positive measure in p, then the agent can be dutch-booked at t_0: bet at t_0 against S; if S is not true at t_1 collect; if S is true at t_1 pay off the original bet and proceed with the dutch book at stakes large enough to assure a net profit.

(C2) Coherence requires that (for some version) E[x2 || x1] = x1.

From C2a and C2b, x_1 is a version of $E[x_2 \| x_1]$.

The foregoing reasoning generalizes. You now contemplate an infinite sequence of black box learning experiences together with the associated sequences of revised probabilities of A, x_1, x_2, x_3, ... Then the coherence argument for conditional expectation [as under C2a] gets us:

(C3a) Coherence requires that y_{n+1} is a version of the conditional expectation: $E[x_{n+2} \| x_1, ..., x_{n+1}]$.

and the coherence argument for future coherence [as under C2b] gets us:

(C3b) Coherence requires that $y_{n+1} = x_{n+1}$ almost everywhere.

Putting these together we have:

(C3) Coherence requires the martingale condition, (iv').

4. Another Martingale?

Let I_A be the indicator function for A, $F_n = \sigma[x_1, ..., x_n]$ as before and F_∞ be the sigma field generated by the union of the F_ns. The random variables $E[I_A || F_n]$ form a martingale relative to the sigma fields F_n. Because of the uniform integrability properties of conditional expectations we can not only say that this martingale converges with probability one, but we can also say something about the random variable to which it converges:

$$E[I_A || F_n] \rightarrow E(I_A || F_\infty) \text{ (with probability = 1)}$$

We might gloss this by saying that with this martingale we have convergence to a maximally informed opinion. (Compare Earman 1992 Ch. 6)

Furthermore, we can say this without invoking any dynamic coherence arguments (although we presuppose static sigma-coherence). The reason is that our conclusion does not say anything about the temporal process of belief change, since there is nothing to link the conditional expectations, $E[I_A || F_n]$, to subsequent belief states.

Suppose, however, that we now assume dynamic coherence. Let $E_n(I_A)$ be the expectation of the indicator, I_A, that you have at t_n according to your probabilities at t_n. By a coherence argument for conditional expectation like that given in section 3:

(C4) $$E_n(I_A) = E[I_A || F_n]$$

and, by definition:

$$x_n = E_n(I_A)$$

Under the assumption of dynamic coherence, the martingale of this section is the same martingale as that of section 2:

$$\langle x_n, F_n \rangle = \langle E[I_A || F_n], F_n \rangle$$

So we have:

$$x_n \rightarrow E(I_A || F) = p(I_A || F_\infty) \text{ (with probability 1)}$$

5. Probability Kinematics

What is the relation of probability kinematics to the martingale property? First, let us notice that the convergence results which we discussed for a single proposition, A, apply more widely. Consider a finite number of propositions, $A_1, ... A_n$. Their probabilities are given by a vector, **x**, in $[0,1]^n$. The foregoing martingale convergence story continues to hold for the vector valued random variables, $\mathbf{x_1}, \mathbf{x_2}, ...$ [see Neveu (1975) for vector valued martingales.]

Probability kinematics can be thought of as a technique for making the black box translucent. For example, suppose the black box learning situations consist of repeatedly looking at a jellybean by candlelight. R is the proposition that it is Red; C is the proposition that it is cinnamon flavored. $\mathbf{x_1}, \mathbf{x_2} ...$ are the probability vectors for these propositions at subsequent times, with the first coordinate being color and the second flavor: e.g. $\mathbf{x_2[1]}$ is the probability at time 2 the it is Red.

Suppose that you are certain that belief change will be by probability kinematics on {R, -R}; that probabilities conditional on R and on -R will remain unchanged. You do not automatically satisfy the martingale condition. You might believe that your probability for R will be .99 at even numbered times and .01 at odd numbered times. In such a case you would expect your beliefs to oscillate forever, and you would be susceptible to a dynamic dutch book.

But if your beliefs do have the martingale property as well, then with probability one the vector valued Martingale, $\mathbf{x_1}, \mathbf{x_2}, ...$ converges to a vector valued random variable $\mathbf{x}_{\infty}$. With probability one, the random variable $\mathbf{x}_{\infty}$ must take values which preserve the original probabilities of flavor conditional on R and -R; that is to say the limiting beliefs come from the initial ones by probability kinematics on this partition.

6. Conclusion

A coherent radical probabilist is as sure that her opinions will converge as a more conventional Bayesian. Probability kinematics can be thought of as a technique for reducing the dimensionality of the learning vector - as a way that the radical probabilist can, where appropriate, be a little less radical. The philosophical significance of these results is that they show certain extreme forms of inductive skepticism to be incoherent.

Notes

[1]This essay amplifies some remarks in Skyrms (1987), (1990). I would like to thank Bruce Bennett, for discussion.

[2]The question of sigma additivity for degrees of belief has generated a substantial literature. I discuss the question in *The Dynamics of Rational Deliberation* (1990) and in "Strict Coherence, Sigma Coherence and the Metaphysics of Quantity"(1995). Here I only want to point out that in requiring sigma additivity the martingale convergence theorems for radical probabilism are no different from those for strict conditionalization.

[3]This is something that has been proved. Its interpretation has generated a lively debate about the relation of rationality to dynamic coherence. We will not discuss these questions here. In particular, no aspersions are being cast on the character of those unfortunates who, like Ulysses, may be rendered dynamically incoherent through no fault of their own.

References

Billingsley, P. (1979), *Probability and Measure*. New York: John Wiley.

Earman, J. (1992), *Bayes or Bust* Cambridge: MIT Press.

van Fraassen, B. (1984), "Belief and the Will" *Journal of Philosophy* 81: 235-256.

Goldstein, M. (1983), "The Prevision of a Prevision" *Journal of the American Statistical Association* 78: 817-819.

Jeffrey, R. (1968), "Probable Knowledge" in I. Lakatos (ed) *The Problem of Inductive Logic*. Amsterdam and New York: Elsevier Science Publishers.

______. (1984), *The Logic of Decision* 2nd. ed. Chicago: University of Chicago Press.

______. (1992), *Probability and the Art of Judgement*. Cambridge: Cambridge University Press.

Neveu, J. (1975), *Discrete Parameter Martingales*. tr. T.P. Speed. North Holland: Amsterdam.

Skyrms, B. (1987), "On the principle of total evidence with and without observation sentences" in *Logic, Philosophy of Science and Epistemology:Proceedings of the 11th International Wittgenstein Symposium*. Vienna: Holder-Pichler-Tempsky 187-195.

Skyrms, B. (1990), *The Dynamics of Rational Deliberation*. Cambridge, Mass.: Harvard University Press.

_______. (1995), "Strict Coherence, Sigma Coherence and the Metaphysics of Quantity" *Philosophical Studies*, 77: 39-55.

Part XII

UNITY AND DISUNITY IN PHYSICS AND BIOLOGY

The Metaphysics of the Disunified World[1]

Nancy Cartwright

London School of Economics

Pluralism is usually opposed to realism. That's why realists tend to affirm reductionism, even if only the lapsed reductionism of supervenience. It is no accident that postmoderns talk about the different worlds we live in. The realist is bent upon one world with one history, and that is the history for the sciences to tell about it, albeit with different degrees of precision, for different purposes and different points of view. The opposition between realism and pluralism is multiplied when the domains of different theories float about as in the balloon image of the relation of the sciences (Figure 1)[1] and when no combination of fields can together supply a set of descriptions in terms of which at least one baseline history can be told. But the opposition is not necessary. A devotion to realism, to the faith that there is one history to be told and differences in the telling come only from a stress on different aspects, need not turn one from pluralism. The contrary view arises, I think, from too narrow a conception of the metaphysical alternatives. What I want to do here is to broaden that conception, to propose a plan for how to build the metaphysics of the disunified world.

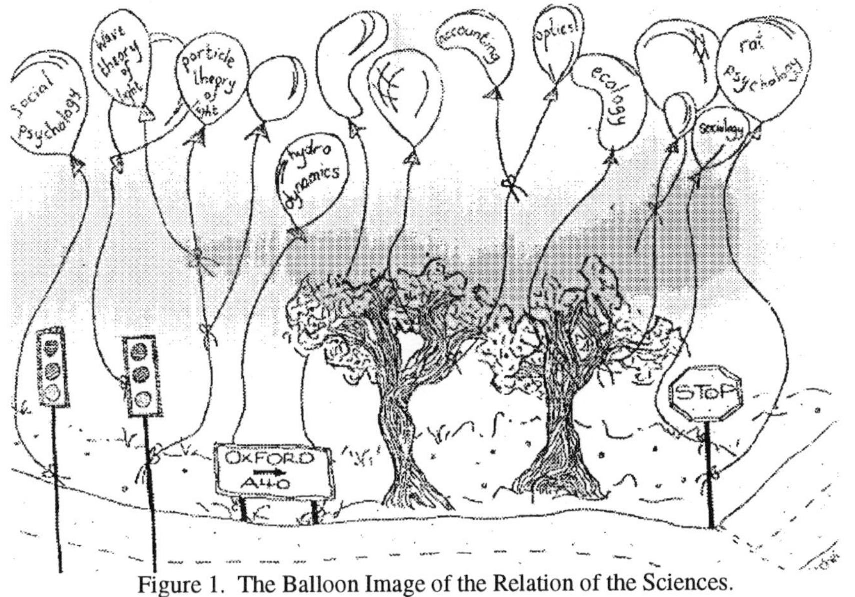

Figure 1. The Balloon Image of the Relation of the Sciences.

PSA 1994, Volume 2, pp. 357-364

My assigned subject for this symposium is physics, so I shall confine my considerations to the joint issues of realism and pluralism in physics. I begin with a claim that I have long defended: the laws of physics are true only in models. Realists very reasonably do not like this. The veryprecise fit between theoretical prediction and experimental results that occurs in the best cases argues too strongly against it. Social constructionism is often turn to the antirealist cause here: This very precise fit is almost universally confined to the laboratory; the theories we fashion are good only for the objects we make. Nevertheless by any ordinary standards it seems right to say that the theory is true of those objects whose behaviour it so precisely describes[2]. But this can be accommodated and in a way that incorporates the social constructionist challenge. "Theory is true only in models" is shorthand: The theory is true only in those situations that resemble its models. Laboratory experiments and the objects of scientific technology are chief among these, and for good reasons. We build our devices to fit our well-understood models, for then we will know what to expect of the devices.

I can illustrate with the simplest most familiar case of Newton's law, **F=ma**. There is a tendency to read this as a universal truth of all objects of a specified kind. Any object with inertial mass **m** will undergo an acceleration equal to **1/m** times the force exerted on it. I think we have learned no such thing, nor do our successes with applying mechanics argue for it. To predict what will happen in a mechanical system we must piece together a good (or good enough) description of it from our stock of standard models. These models are crucial to the content of the theory. Hempel and Nagel saw them as crucial too, but for them it was a matter of meaning."Force" is a theoretical term only partially interpreted by its role in a system of laws. The rules that tell us how to assign force-functions in standard models serve to provide it additional meaning by connecting it with terms that are antecedently understood. Questions of meaning and content aside, the point remains: "Force" is connected with real systems only via a set of models that assign force-functions to specific kinds ofsituations. Let us look at some of these standard models (Figure 2—5):[3] Simple harmonic motion, damped harmonic motion, elliptical motion, motion in a uniform magnetic field. The first line of the figure in each case gives the abstract "theoretical" description: say, motion under a force **-kx**. But when is a motion "under a force of size **-kx**"? That is the point of the model. We have pictured here one standard case, and there are clearly a number of others. As Kuhn pointed out, learning the family resemblances that make all the cases "**-kx**" cases is a good part of what learning physics amounts to. I claim that what physics teaches is just the kind of fact pictured in these figures: When you have a situation that (sufficiently) resembles this, you get a motion like that; in situations like this, a motion like that; and so forth.

But isn't that just what the semantic view of theories says? Theories just are collections of models. I think not. One for a trivial reason. This view tends to obscure the condi-

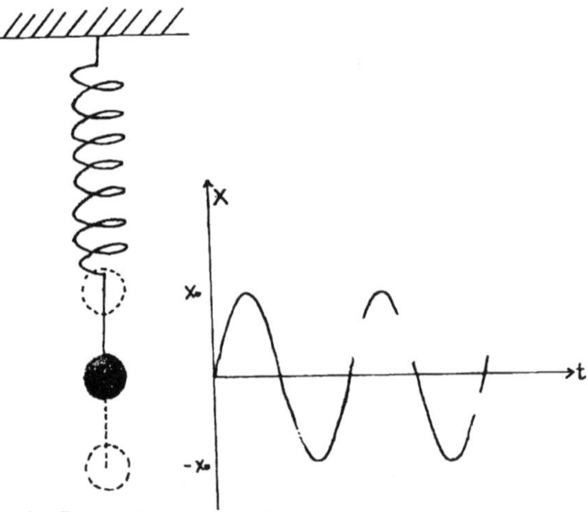

Figure 2. Simple Harmonic Motion: The motion of a body under the influence of a restoring force proportional to the displacement $F(x) = - kx$

tional claim relevant for both testing and application. It is not enough for theory adequacy that there be situations that "resemble" this with motions like that. It must be true that if a situation resembles this then the motion will be like that. The second reason is more to the point today. Think how the set of models that constitute a theory is to be characterized. Not, we know, as models of a set of axioms in some formal language. Nevertheless the models are usually thought to be sets of fictional objects characterized in terms of theoretical properties appearing in the laws—in our case **F**, **m**, **a**—exhibiting, or approximately exhibiting, the relations prescribed in the law: **F** equals **m** times **a**. The models of Figure 2—5 are characterized in a different way—they are springs, or pendula or dipole oscillators— i.e. oscillating charge distributions in an atom in an external field. Ronald Giere, like me, wants to focus on these kinds of models; not ones assigned abstract properties like **F** but rather ones that provide concrete functional forms (like **-kx**) for the abstract term "force". But I don't think he draws what appears to me as an immediate conclusion: If that is what the theory is, the theory is very limited in its domain. Any situation that does not resemble a model of the theory will not be governed by its laws.

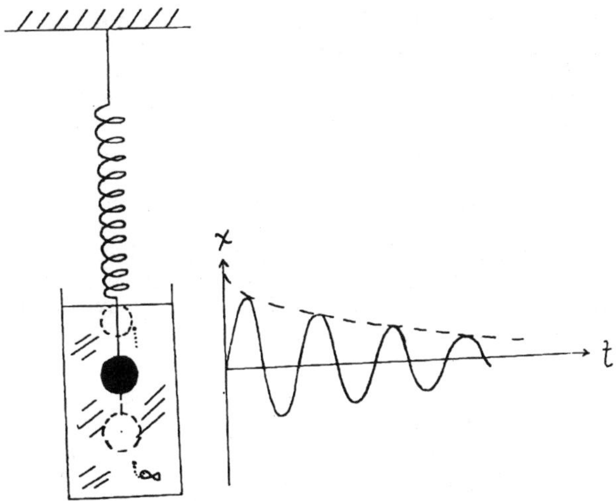

Figure 3. Damped Harmonic Motion: A simple harmonic motion with an additional force directly proportional to the velocity $F(x) = - -kx - \; bu$

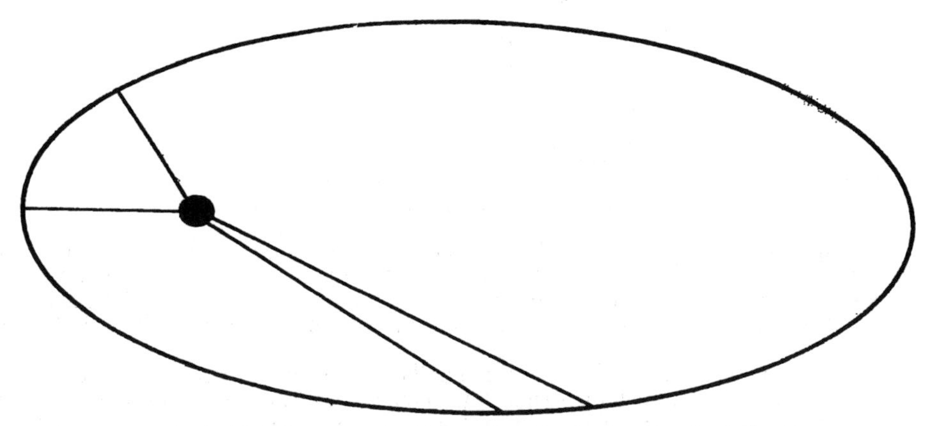

Figure 4. Elliptical motion: The motion of a body under the influence of a central force inversely proportional to the square of the distance

Consider for example a falling object. Not a nice compact one like a pound coin, but something more vulnerable to non-gravitational influence. Otto Neurath has a nice example. My doctrine about the case is much like his.

> In some cases a physicist is a worse prophet than a (behaviourist psychologist), as when he is supposed to specify where in St Stephen's Square a thousand dollar bill swept away by the wind will land, whereas a (behaviourist) can specify the result of a conditioning experiment rather accurately (Neurath 1987).

Mechanics provides no model for this situation. We have only a partial model that describes the thousand dollar bill as an unsupported object in the vicinity of the earth and thereby introduces the force exerted on it due to gravity. Is that the total force? Those who believe in the unlimited dominion of mechanics will say no. There is in principle (in God's completed theory?) a model in mechanics for the action of the wind, albeit probably a very complicated one that we maynever succeed in constructing. This belief is essential for the universal applicability of mechanics. If there is no model for the thousand dollar bill in mechanics, then what happens to the note is not determined by its laws. Some falling objects, indeed a very great number, will be outside the domain of mechanics or only partially affected by it.

What then fixes the motion of the bill if mechanics is not enough? I suppose it is too disturbing to suggest nothing. The effect of the action of the wind follows no systematic pattern. But we do not need to maintain that no laws obtain where mechanics runs out. Fluid dynamics may have loose overlaps and intertwinings with mechanics. But it is in no way a subdiscipline of basic physics; it is a discipline on its own. Its laws can direct the thousand dollar bill in addition to those of Newton.

Here begins the promised reconciliation of realism and pluralism. Fluid dynamics can be both genuinely different from and genuinely irreducible to Newtonian mechanics. Yet both can be true at once because—to put it crudely—both are true only in systems sufficiently like their models, and their models are very different. Mechanics studies hard objects, compact or rigid; fluids are floppy, extended, permeable. They do not easily fit any of the standard models that fix the extension of "force".

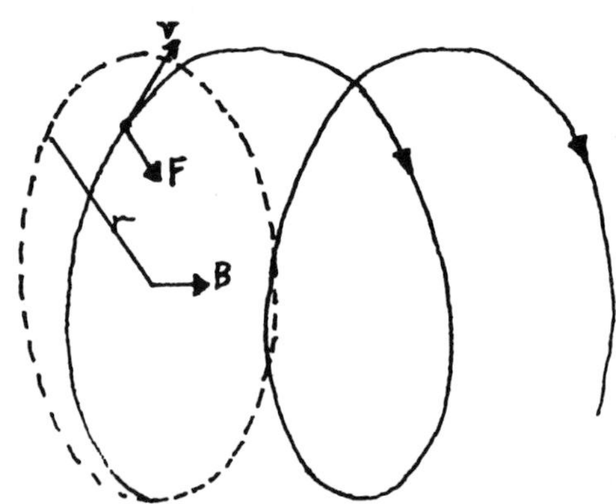

Figure 5. The motion of a charged particle of velocity **v** in a uniform magnetic Field. The force exerted on the particle is $\mathbf{F} = q\mathbf{v}\times \mathbf{B}$.

But if we are to maintain that different theories can each be true in its own domain and yet in no way reducible to an experiment on each other, what prevents inconsistencies when objects fall in the domain of both? For a general discussion, besides Dupre (1993) is Suppes (1984). I recommend Humphreys (1994) and Mitchell (1992).

Specifically about the case of the thousand dollar bill I want to argue that Newton's law **F=ma** is, like all laws a ceteris paribus law. It tells us how the acceleration of an object changes so long as nothing interferes, where "interferes" has a quite specific interpretation. F=ma is true so long as no influences on the acceleration occur that can not be modelled as a force. I have written about this in somewhat more detail in Cartwright (1994).

Here I would like in the last section to look more generally at the case of two theories and how they overlap—quantum mechanics and classical mechanics. This is a good case

Superconducting strip line and coaxial cables.

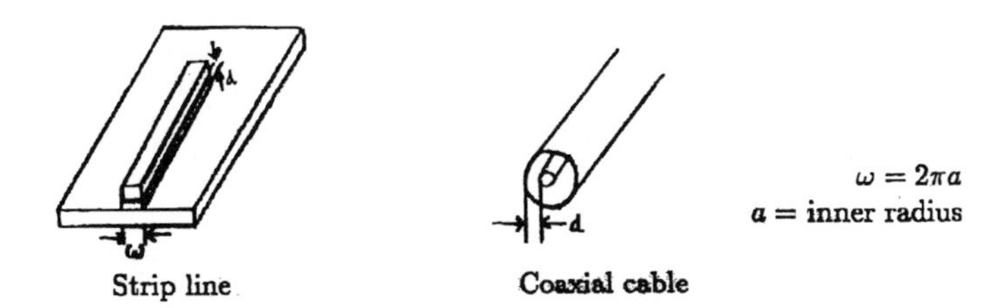

Corresponding lumped parameter equivalent circuit.

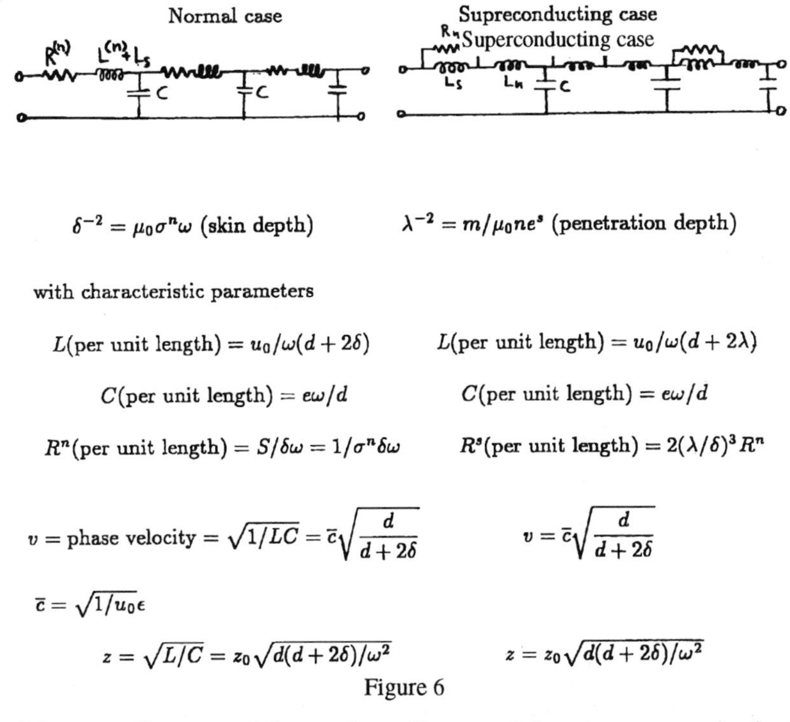

Figure 6

because it is generally assumed that we have discovered that quantum mechanics is true of some cases we had hoped to treat using classical mechanics and hence classical mechanics is false. I think just the contrary. All evidence points to the conclusion that I really like—that Nature is not reductive and single-minded. She has a rich, and diverse, tolerant imagination and is happily running both classical and quantum mechanics side-by-side[4].

At the end of a measurement we are told usually that the apparatus and system are in a composite quantum state that is a superposition across eigenstates of the apparatus pointer observable. But the pointer, we know, points in a definite direction. It has, to macroscopic accuracies, a definite position. So how do we get from here to a problem? Basically by assuming that all true descriptions are renderable as quantum descriptions. The pointer has a position. We used to have a classical physics that treated positions: Systems with position were assigned classical states and the behaviour of these states was encoded in classical mechanics. If we are going henceforth to use only quantum mechanics all these descriptions must go, and we will have to find some analogue in quantum mechanics for the pointer position that is so well treated by classical mechanics. The best candidate seems to be an eigenstate of an operator we dub "the pointer observable". But this quantum state is incompatible with the Schrödinger-evolved state. Hence the measurement problem.

My proposed strategy, consistent with the kind of theoretical pluralism I have been advocating here, is not to succumb to the quantum takeover. The world is rich in properties—they are all equal citizens. We long ago learned that there are properties like positions and momenta which are well represented by classical mechanics. The discovery that there are also features that are well represented by quantum states and well treated by quantum theory does not in itself give us reason to throw out those properties that have been long established. So my claim is this: There are both quantum and classical states and the same system can have both without contradiction. It is important here that I say classical states, not quantum analogues of classical states. There is no contradiction built in because we have no theory (nor even a good programme for such a theory) of the relation between quantum and classical characteristics. As with all cases of genuine theoretical pluralism, what we have to do is look for what connections there are and where they are. The job we have to undertake is not that of solving but rather of hunting the quantum measurement problem.

I say there is no theory of the relation between quantum and classical states. What then of the generalised Born interpretation?

Born Interpretation:

Every linear Hermitian operator $\hat{\mathbf{A}}=\Sigma \mathbf{e_i}|\Phi_\mathbf{i}\rangle\langle\Phi_\mathbf{i}|$ corresponds to an observable A, such that for systems in quantum state ψ:

$$\mathbf{Prob(A = e_i) = |\langle\psi|\Phi_i\rangle^2}$$

I don't understand this so-called interpretation. We use in it the mysterious expression "observable" but what we find represented by quantum operators is far from observable in any reasonable sense of the term. It might mean properties that a quantum system may possess, but if so it misses out a lot. Some quantum systems are for instance coloured. Nor can we fall back on what for most theories would be the right sense—these operators represent "the causally efficacious" properties or those "governed by law"—since in quantum mechanics this privilege falls to the quantum state. Worse, it does not in the end get us what we need for, as it is usually understood, systems which exhibit one of these allowed values e_i are not in nice classical states that behave in nice classical ways. They are rather still in quantum states (here $\mathbf{\Phi_i}$), and to keep their behaviour in line with classical predictions where we know them to be accurate, they have to spend all their time surreptitiously being measured and decohering. I propose we give up on this formula. We neither use it nor need it.

I turn first to the claim that we do not use it. How then do we relate quantum and classical properties? It seems nature has no general formula, or at least we haven't found it. The association is "piecemeal" and proceeds in thousands of different ways in thousands of different problems. Figuring out these connections is a good deal of what physics is about, though we often fail to notice this fact in our fascination with the abstract mathematical structure of quantum theory and quantum field theory. Consider superconductivity. This is a quantum phenomenon. We really do need quantum mechanics to understand it. Yet superconducting devices are firmly embedded in classical circuits studied by classical electronics. This is one of the things that most puzzled me in the lab studying SQUID's. You'd wire the device up, put it in the fridge to get it down below critical temperature, and then turn on the switch. Very often you simply wouldn't get the characteristic I-V curve which is the first test that the device is operating as a SQUID. What has gone wrong? To figure it out the experimenter would begin to draw classical circuit diagrams. Without going all the way to SQUID's, we can see in figure 6 an example for the simplest kind of superconducting configuration that can be found in any standard treatment of superconducting electronics.

"What allows you to draw classical circuit diagrams for these quantum devices", I would ask. The reply: "There are well known theorems that show that any complicated circuit is equivalent to certain simple circuits". But that missed my point. What allows us to associate classical circuits with quantum devices?

No matter what theory you use—London, Ginsberg Landau (Gorkov), BCS—all have as a central assumption the association of a familiar quantum quantity

$$\mathbf{Js = (e^*h / m^*i)(\psi^* \nabla \psi - \psi \nabla \psi^*) - (e^* / m^*) |\psi|^2 A}$$

with a classical current that flows around the circuit. I say it is familiar because this is just what, in the Born interpretation would be described as a probability current, taking $|\psi|^2$ as a probability and using the conventional replacement for situations where magnetic fields play a role

$$\nabla \to \nabla \pm (ie^* / \hbar)\, \mathbf{A}.$$

Yet we have all learned that we mustn't interpret $\mathbf{e}\,|\psi|^2$ as a charge density as Schrödinger wished to do. One of the reasons is that it cannot usually be expressed in the co-ordinates of physical space but needs rather some higher dimensional co-ordinate space. But in this case it can be. And we have learned from the success of the theory that this way of calculating the electrical current is a good one.

Does this not give us back the Born interpretation? No. On the Born interpretation what we have here is a probability and a probability in need of an elaborate story to prove that: (i) provides a mechanism that keeps reducing the paired electrons of the superconductor so they have a position and (ii) in some way or other ensures that the mean value (or something like it that evolves properly enough in time) is the one that almost always occurs. We have no such story and we need no such story. This formula is not an instance of a general probabilistic interpretation of quantum mechanics but rather an empirically well-confirmed context-local rule for how a quantum state ψ is associated with a classical current in a superconductor. So here we see that even in a case that looks very much like an application of the Born interpretation, it is not really the Born Interpretation that we are using.

My second point is not just that we don't use the Born interpretation, but also that we don't need it. How then do we interpret quantum mechanics? Notice first that the discussion of the measurement problem usually presupposes a strongly realist view about the quantum state function. People like me who are prepared to use different incompatible state assignments in models treating different aspects of one and the same system are hardly troubled by the contradictions that are supposed to arise in special contexts of measurement. But it is puzzling why quantum realists should be calling for interpretation. For those who take the quantum state function seriously as providing a true and physically significant description, the quantum state should need no interpretation. There is no reason to suppose that those features of reality that are responsible for determining the behaviour of its microstructure must be tied neatly to our "antecedent" concepts or to what we can tell by looking. Of course a fundamental property or state must be tied causally to anything it explains. But laying out those ties need look nothing like an interpretation.

What I want to stress here is that quantum realists should take the quantum state seriously as a genuine feature of reality and not treat it as an instrumentalist would, as a convenient way of summarising information about other kinds of properties. Nor should they insist that other descriptions cannot be assigned besides quantum descriptions. For that is to suppose not only that the theory is true but that it provides a complete description of everything of interest in reality. And that is not realism, but imperialism.

Conclusion: First the sermon. Resist the quantum takeover. All evidence is that quantum states and classical states can live peacefully in the world together. Indeed resist all takeovers. Second is the metaphysics: You don't have to be a social constructionist or a relativist to resist takeovers. Once you are willing to take seriously that for the most part there are no universal formulas for how the features studied by different disciplines relate, even a realist can live in a mottled dappled world.

Notes

[1]This paper is part of the "Research Project in Modelling in Physics and Economics" at the Centre for the Philosophy of Natural and Social Sciences, London School of Economics and Political Science.

[2]By Rachel Hacking; taken from N. Cartwright, J.Cat, K. Fleck, T.Uebel, Otto Neurath: Philosophy between science and Politics Cambridge University Press

[3]For most cases this is not my own view since I do not believe the theory does describe what happens. It serves rather as one tool among many to produce a model. The model describes what happens, more or less well, and it is not a model of the theory in the logician's sense of "model" nor even approximately like one.

[4]By G. Zouros, Department of Philosophy, Logic and Scientific Method, London School of Economics.

[5]The point of view towards quantum mechanics described here is argued in more detail in Cartwright (forthcoming) "Where in the World is the Quantum Measurement Problem".

References

Cartwright, N. (1994), "Fundamentalism vs. the Patchwork of Laws", *Proceedings of the Aristotelian Society.*

Cartwright, N. (forthcoming) "Where in the World is the Quantum Measurement Problem", *Physik, Philosophie und die Einheit der Wissenschaft, Philosophia Naturalis.*

Dupre, J. (1993), *Disunity in Science.* Cambridge: Harvard University Press.

Humphreys, P. (forthcoming), M.S. 7/22/94, Philosophy Department, University of Virginia.

Mitchell, S.D: (1992), "On Pluralism and Integration in Evolutionary Explanations" *American Zoologist*, 32: 135-144.

Neurath, O. (1987), "United Science and Psychology", in B.F. McGuiness, ed., *Unified Science.* Dordrecht: Reidel, p. 13.

Suppes, P. (1984), *Probabilistic Metaphysics.* Oxford: Blackwell

Unified Theories and Disparate Things[1]

Margaret Morrison

University of Toronto

1. Introduction

In both philosophical writing on science and scientific practice itself there has been a long standing interest in theories and explanatory frameworks that unify various phenomena. In the history of physics the most successful theories are often those that supposedly show how diverse effects can be understood as aspects of a single underlying principle or cause. For example, Maxwell's electrodynamics unified electromagnetism and optics by providing a theoretical demonstration that light and electromagnetic waves have the same velocity and are manifestations of the same kind of process. More recently in the 1970's Glashow, Weinberg and Salam produced a unified description of both electromagnetic and the weak interactions. This electroweak theory successfully describes electromagnetic interactions as well as data from a variety of electroweak processes including scattering and number of different particle collisions.

Implicit in many of the philosophical accounts of unification is a long standing assumption that the world is a unified whole capable of being described in a systematic way. In some cases this view is associated with a form of ontological reductionism where different phenomena are shown to belong to the same natural kind, or with a reduction of the laws governing two distinct theoretical domains to a single more general set. Although the assumption regarding a unified world need not have a metaphysical component (Kant, for example, thought it to be a regulative ideal necessary for scientific research) there is no doubt that unified theories were, and still are, seen by many as more likely to be true than their rivals. Indeed good deal of work in confirmation theory has focused on trying to forge a connection between unification and truth, where the unified theory is not just accepted simply because it has better predictive power but because it accurately describes how the world really is.

It is also important to note however that one need not be an advocate of unity among the sciences to uphold the connection between unified theories and truth. In thinking that each science was governed by its own particular idea, William Whewell argued for a disunified picture of the sciences while claiming that within each distinct domain we should strive for consilient theories since they carry with them the stamp of truth.

Even in cases where one doesn't share the metaphysical picture of a unified world, and where unification is not seen as evidence for a theory's truth, the desire for systematization can be a powerful one. Twentieth century philosophy of science had its

---

PSA 1994, Volume 2, pp. 365-373

beginnings in the search for a unified language and method that would provide a kind of algorithm for the way that science and philosophy ought to be done. The *Encyclopedia of the Unified Sciences* was an attempt to characterize not only the way that philosophers thought about science but also the way that philosophy of science thought about itself.

More recently disunity both among different sciences and within particular sciences has become a prominent theme in philosophical writing. Emphasis on the diversity of models within particular theories and the failure of reductionist strategies at the level of ontology and methodology (theory and experiment) has given rise to a kind of scepticism about unity at any level. (See for instance, the work of Cartwright (1994) and Dupre (1993).) Nevertheless, to the extent that theory unification plays a prominent role in the natural sciences, particularly physics, philosophy of science needs to provide some understanding of that practice and the extent to which it embodies/presupposes a traditional metaphysical ideal of a unified world. This situation leaves us with two differently motivated but related questions. First, if as recent philosophical literature suggests, the picture science presents is really one of fundamental disorder in nature how are we to understand the practice of theory unification; and second, does the success of modern science in producing unified theories lend credence to the metaphysical picture of nature as unified?

As a way of trying to understand this dilemma I want to focus on the unification provided by the electroweak theory. This case is interesting because it involves a unity at the level of theoretical structure while at the same time retaining a measure of disunity with respect to the theory's substantive aspects; namely the particles that carry the forces. In other words this case doesn't provide the kind of ontological unity necessary to motivate the metaphysical picture of a unified nature. As a result we end up with some rather different conclusions not only about the nature of the unifying process but also about the role that unity plays in philosophical arguments concerning theory assessment. Let me begin by briefly describing the history leading up to the development of the electroweak theory to give some sense of how the unification was actually achieved.

2. Unity and Symmetry

The first quantum field theory of weak interactions was formulated by Fermi in 1934. This account was modelled on electrodynamics since beta decay (a weak force phenomenon) was considered analogous to the emission of a photon from an electromagnetic transition in an excited atom; and, like photon emission, it took place at a single space-time point. The difference however, was that the role of the emitted photon was played by an electron-antineutrino pair rather than by the quantum of a new weakly interacting field. The photon emitted in a radiative transition is the quantum of the electromagnetic force field; however, it was difficult to envision how the corresponding $e^-\nu_e$ pair could be the weak force quantum, especially since the effective mass of the pair varied from process to process. But, because of the remarkable success of quantum electrodynamics it was natural to base other theories of interactions as closely as possible on the QED model. In that sense Fermi was not explicitly trying to unify electrodynamics with the weak force, he was merely following a basic principle of theory construction: use successful theories as models for new ones. Nevertheless, we can see his work as representing the beginnings of the unifying process in much the same way that Faraday's analogies were an important stepping stone for Maxwell.

Through the work of others the original Fermi theory soon evolved into a more abstract version based on the idea of interacting currents. Again, following the electrodynamic analogy these currents were modelled on the vector currents of quantum electrodynamics. The currents replaced the fields that Fermi originally used to represent particles. The weak interaction could then be described by coupling the currents together through a Hamiltonian $H=\frac{G}{\sqrt{2}}J_\mu J'_\mu$. G is the Fermi coupling constant with a value of roughly 10^{-5} and was assumed to be a weak charge analogous to the electric charge e; it governed the intrinsic strength of the interaction and hence the rate for beta decay. The process was known as a current-current interaction.

One way the analogy between electromagnetism and the weak force was strengthened was through the postulation of a weak analogue of the photon, implying again that the weak force should be represented as mediated by particle exchange rather than contact interaction between two currents. Although this postulated particle, identified as the W boson, could be considered the weak analogue of the photon, it was there that the analogy with QED ended. There were significant differences between the photon and the W particle, differences that would seem to rule out any kind of unification between the weak force and electrodyanimcs. One dissimilarity was that the photon is electrically neutral while weak processes like beta decay involved the exchange of electric charge between the currents J_μ and J'_μ. This required the W to exist in at least two charged states W^{+-}. The second and most striking difference was that the W had to be massive in order to account for the extremely short range of the weak force; the photon on the other hand is massless.

It was not until the work of Schwinger in 1957 that any significant connection was made between the weak and electromagnetic forces. Schwinger's approach was to begin with some basic principles of symmetry and field theory, and go on to develop a framework for fundamental interactions derived from that fixed structure. The power of gauge theory and symmetries was well known from its success in QED. Here it was possible to show that from the conservation of electric charge, one could on the basis of Noether's theorem assume the existence of a symmetry, and the requirement that it be local forces one to introduce a gauge field which turns out to be just the electromagnetic field. So, from the fact that the Lagrangian must be locally gauge invariant it is possible to predict the existence of the electromagnetic field since the symmetry can be preserved only by introducing this new gauge field. The symmetry group governing the phase transformations of electrodynamics is referred to as the U(1) group. What is significant about these symmetry groups is that they are more than simply mathematizations of certain kinds of transformations. In electrodynamics local symmetry requirements are capable of determining the structure of the gauge field which in turn dictates, almost uniquely, the form of the interaction; that is, the precise form of the forces on the charged particle and the way in which the electric charge current density serves as the source for the gauge field.

Although Schwinger's use of gauge symmetry enabled him to construct analogical arguments and postulate the existence of a particle field that was the physical analogue of an imaginary mathematical symmetry space; a different kind of symmetry was required if electrodynamics and the weak interaction were to be unified. The principle difficulty was again the differences between the masses of the charged bosons (large masses were required because of the short range of the weak force) and the massless photon. If there are only leptons coupled to vector bosons the theory has no symmetries; hence, a symmetry principle needs to be found in order to relate the forms of weak and electromagnetic couplings.

Because of the mass problem it was thought that perhaps only partial symmetries - invariance of only part of the Lagrangian under a group of infinitesimal transformations - could relate the massive decay intermediaries to the massless photon. The model developed by Glashow in 1961 was based on the SU(2)xU(1) symmetry group and required the introduction of an additional neutral boson Z_s which couples to its own neutral lepton current J^s_μ. By properly choosing the mass terms to be inserted into the Lagrangian, Glashow was able to show that the singlet neutral boson from U(1) and the neutral member of the SU(2) triplet would mix in such a way as to produce a massive particle B (now identified as Z^0) and a massless particle that was identified with the photon. But, in order to retain Lagrangian invariance gauge theory requires the introduction of only massless particles. As a result the boson masses had to be added to the theory by hand, making the models phenomenologically accurate but destroying the gauge invariance of the Lagrangian and thereby ruling out the possibility of renormalization. Although gauge theory provided a powerful tool for generating an electroweak model, unlike electrodynamics, one could not reconcile the *physical* demands of the weak force for the existence of massive particles with the structural demands of gauge invariance. Both needed to be accommodated if there was to be a unified theory, yet they were mutually incompatible.

Hopes of achieving a true synthesis of weak and electromagnetic interactions came a few years later in 1967 with a paper by Steven Weinberg. Weinberg's idea was that one could understand the mass problem and the coupling differences of the different interactions by supposing that the symmetries relating the two interactions were exact symmetries of the Lagrangian that were somehow broken by the vacuum. These ideas originated in the early 1960s and were motivated by work done in solid state physics on superconductivity. But, if the electroweak and the electromagnetic theory were truly unified and mediated by the same kind of gauge particles then how could such a difference in the masses of the bosons and the photons exist? In order for the electroweak theory to work it had to be possible for the gauge particles to acquire a mass in a way that would preserve gauge invariance. The answer to these questions was provided by the mechanism of spontaneous symmetry breaking.

Since 1964 had been known that when a local symmetry is spontaneously broken the vector particles acquire a mass through a phenomenon known as the Higgs mechanism.[2] This principle of spontaneous symmetry breaking implies that the actual symmetry of a system can be less than the symmetry of its underlying physical laws; in other words, the Hamiltonian and commutation relations of a quantum theory would possess an exact symmetry while physically the system (in this case the particle physics vacuum) would be non-symmetrical. In order for the idea to have any merit one must assume that the vacuum is a degenerate state (i.e. it is not unique) such that for each unsymmetrical vacuum state there are others of the same minimal energy that are related to the first by various symmetry transformations that preserve the invariance of physical laws.[3] The phenomena observed within the framework of this unsymmetrical vacuum state will exhibit the broken symmetry even in the way that the physical laws appear to operate. Although there is no evidence that the vacuum state for the electroweak theory is degenerate it can be made so by the introduction of the Higgs mechanism which is an additional field with a definite but arbitrary orientation in the isospin vector space.[4] (Isospin is the conserved quantity associated with the SU(2) symmetry group.) The orientation breaks the symmetry of the vacuum.

The Higgs field (or its associated particle the Higgs boson) is really a complex SU(2) doublet $\binom{\phi^+}{\phi^-}$ consisting of four real fields which are needed to transform the massless gauge fields into massive ones. A massless gauge boson like the photon has two orthogonal spin components transverse to the direction of motion while massive gauge bosons have three including a longitudinal component in the direction of motion. In the electroweak theory the W^{+-} and the Z^0, which are the carriers of the weak force, absorb three of the four Higgs fields, thereby forming their longitudinal spin components and acquiring a mass. The remaining neutral Higgs field is not affected and should therefore be observable as a particle in its own right. The Higgs field breaks the symmetry of the vacuum by having a preferred direction in space, but the symmetry of the Lagrangian remains invariant. So, the electroweak gauge theory predicts the existence of four gauge quanta, a neutral photon-like object, sometimes referred to as the X^0 and associated with the U(1) symmetry as well as a weak isospin triplet W^{+-} and W^0 associated with the SU(2) symmetry. As a result of the Higgs symmetry breaking mechanisms the W^{+-} particles acquire a mass and the X^0 and W^0 are mixed so that the neutral particles one sees in nature are really two different linear combinations of these two. One of these neutral particles, the Z^0, has a mass while the other, the photon, is massless. Since the masses of the W^{+-} and the Z^0 are governed by the structure of the Higgs field they do not affect the basic gauge invariance of the theory. The so-called "weakness" of the weak interaction which is mediated by the W^{+-} and the Z^0 is understood as a consequence of the masses of these particles.

In summary then the Higgs phenomenon plays two related roles in the theory. It explains the discrepancy between the photon and the intermediate vector boson masses - the photon remains massless because it corresponds to the unbroken symmetry subgroup U(1) associated with the conservation of charge, while the bosons have masses because they correspond to SU(2) symmetries that are broken. Secondly, the avoidance of an explicit mass term in the Lagrangian allows for the possibility of renormalizability. With this mechanism in place the weak and electromagnetic interactions could be unified under a larger gauge symmetry group that resulted from the product of the SU(2) group that governed the weak interactions and the U(1) group of electrodynamics.[5]

From this very brief picture one can get at least a sketch of the role played by the formal, structural constraints provided by gauge theory and symmetry in the development of the electroweak theory. Now I want to turn to a more specific account of the *kind* of unity that emerged in this context.

3. Particles and Structures

At the beginning I claimed that the unification achieved in this case was structural rather than substantial; as a result it doesn't fit with the philosophical ideal of reducing elements of the weak and electromagnetic force to the same basic entity or natural kind. This is not to say that the electroweak theory is not a remarkable achievement; but, what I want to suggest is that it may indeed be the case that the mechanisms involved in producing unified theories typically say more about the kinds of mathematical structures at the theoreticians disposal than about the phenomena we are out to explain. In the case of electrodynamics the generality provided by the Lagrangian formalism allowed Maxwell to unify electromagnetism and optics without providing any specific details about how the electromagnetic waves were produced or how they were propagated through space. The SU(2)xU(1) gauge theory furnishes a similar kind of structure; it specifies the form of the interactions between the weak and electromagnetic forces but provides no causal account as to *why* the fields must be unified. In Maxwell's early work a mechanical model of the aether was introduced as a way of understanding how electromagnetic waves might be produced and propagated. But, he was always quick to distinguish between models that described possibilities and the more basic theoretical structure. In many ways the Higgs field, a necessary constituent of the unification, resembles the aether; not as an absolute coordinate system but as a basis of potential energy and as a necessary mechanism for the unification. Although the primary unifying component in electromagnetism was played by the displacement current, displacement was understood, qualitatively, as a displacement of electricity across the aether.

In the electroweak case one can accommodate the different kinds of particles with incompatible properties (e.g. massless and massive bosons), by introducing the idea of broken symmetry. In that sense the unity is achieved at the price of introducing an element of disunity resulting from the addition of new components to the pre-existing theories of weak and electromagnetic interactions. That is to say we can't, using gauge theory alone, generate a unified theory in the way that one can with electrodynamics. Moreover, there is a strong sense in which the SU(2)xU(1) gauge theory allows only for the *subsumption* of the weak and electromagnetic forces under a larger framework rather than the kind of unity provided by electromagnetism, even in its early formulation by Maxwell.

Here I have in mind the fact that in the SU(2)xU(1) model both the electromagnetic and weak forces remain essentially distinct; the unity that is supposedly achieved results from the unique way in which these forces interact. Hence, with respect to the unifying process the core of the theory is really the representation of the interaction or mixing of the various fields. Because the fields remain distinct the theory retains two distinct coupling constants, q associated with the U(1) electromagnetic field and g with the SU(2) gauge field. In order for the theory to make specific predictions for the masses of the W^{+-} and Z^0 particles one needs to know the value for the Higgs ground state $|\phi_o|$. Unfortunately this cannot be directly calculated since its value depends explicitly on the parameters of the Higgs potential and little is known about the properties of the field. In order to rectify the problem the coupling constants are combined into a single parameter known as the Weinberg angle θ_w. The angle is defined from the normalized forms of A^{em} and Z^o which are respectively:

$$A_\mu^{em} = (gA_\mu - qW_\mu^3)/\sqrt{g^2+q^2}$$

$$Z_\mu^o = qA_\mu - gW_\mu^3/\sqrt{g^2+q^2}$$

The mixing of the A gauge field of U(1) and the new neutral gauge field W^3 is interpreted as a rotation through θ_w i.e.,

$$\sin\theta_w = q/\sqrt{g^2+q^2} \qquad \cos\theta_w = q/\sqrt{g^2+q^2}.$$

By relating the weak coupling constant g to the Fermi coupling constant G one obviates the need for the quantity $|\phi_Q|$ (the value of the Higgs ground state). The masses can now be defined in the following way:

$$M_W^2 = \frac{g^2}{2G} = \frac{e^2}{2G}\sin^2\theta_w = \frac{(37.4GeV)^2}{\sin^2\theta_w}$$

$$M_Z^2 = \frac{M_W^2}{\cos^2\theta_w}$$

In order to obtain a value for θ_w one needs to know the relative sign and values of g and q; the problem however is that they are not directly measurable. Instead one must measure the interaction rates for the W^{+-} and Z^0 exchange processes and then extract values for g, q and θ_w. What θ_w does is fix the ratio of U(1) and SU(2) couplings. In order for the theory to be unified θ_w must be the same for all processes. But, despite this rather restrictive condition the theory itself doesn't provide direct values for the Weinberg angle and as a result does not furnish a full account of how the fields are mixed (i.e.the degree of mixing is not determined by the theory). More importantly, the mixing is not the result of constraints imposed by gauge theory itself; rather it ultimately depends on the assumption that leptons can be classified as weak isospin doublets governed by the SU(2) symmetry group. This requires the introduction of the new neutral gauge field W^3 in order to complete the group generators, i.e. a field corresponding to the isospin operator τ. This is the field that combines with the neutral photon like X^0 to produce the Z^0 necessary for the unity.

We can see then that the use of symmetries to classify various kinds of particles and their interaction fields is much more than simply a phenomenological classification constructed as a convenient way of representing groups of particles; instead it allows for a kind of particle dynamics to emerge, that is to say, the symmetry group provides the foundation for the locally gauge-invariant quantum field theory. Hence, given the assumption about isospin the formal restrictions of symmetry groups and gauge theory can be deployed in order to produce a formal model showing how these gauge fields could be unified.

The crucial feature that facilitates this interaction is the non-abelian structure of the group rather than something derivable from phenomenological aspects of the theory itself. This can be seen by looking at the interaction between the W^{+-} and Z^0 fields. The diagram below depicts the scattering of a neutrino and an anti-neutrino from Z_o exchange as described in the G-W-S model.

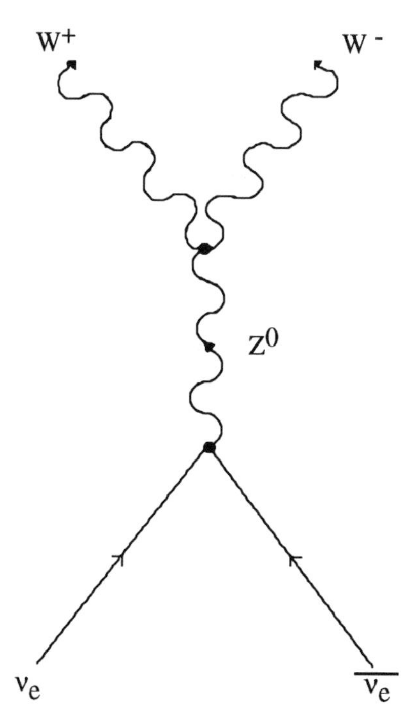

New contribution to the scattering of a neutrino and an antineutrino from Z^0 exchange in the Glashow-Weinberg-Salam unified theory. This term generates new higher-order terms which cancel the "non-renormalizable" infinities.

In any gauge theory the conserved quantity serves as the source of the gauge field in the same way that electric charge serves as the source of the electromagnetic field. In abelian gauge theories like electromagnetism the field itself is not charged but in non-abelian theories the field is charged with the same conserved quantity that generates the field. In other words the non-abelian gauge field generates itself; and as a result these fields interact with each other unlike electrodynamics. The form of the interactions (also determined by the structural constraints of the symmetry group) leads to cancellations between different contributions to high energy amplitudes. Thus, both the unity and renormalizability of the electroweak theory emerged as a result of the very powerful structural features imposed by the mathematical framework of the non-Abelian gauge group. Although the Higgs mechanism allows for the possibility of producing a unified theory the actual unity is the result of the constraints of the isospin SU(2) group and the non-abelian structure of the field.

4. The Nature of Unification

Going back to the original question, that is, how are we to understand the supposed dichotomy presented by the appearance of both unity and disunity in science, there seems to be nothing about this case that can be used to support an inference from theory unification to a metaphysical or reductivist conclusion about the underlying unity of nature. The particles which act as the sources of the fields and of course the forces themselves remain distinct, the electroweak theory or model provides a unified formal *structure* that enables us to describe how these separate entities can interact and combine. This idea of a unifying formal structure is crucial for understanding the nature of the unity produced in mathematical physics.

But, even in cases like Maxwell's electrodynamics, where there appears to be a rather straightforward reduction of electromagnetic and optical phenomena, I want to claim that the most significant component in the unifying process is not a common explanatory mechanism involving a type of reductivist claim but the presence of a mathematical structure like the Lagrangian formalism that is powerful enough to accommodate diverse phenomena within a common framework. These kinds of structures are able to serve as unifying frameworks because they embody the greatest possible generality. The important point here is that the basic structure of mathematical physics has, built into it, a methodology that facilitates the formulation of a broad class of diverse phenomena. This can be seen from the fundamental role of gauge fields in mediating physical interactions and how this role arises in a rather remarkable way from Noether's theorem and the requirement that every continuous symmetry be local. Gauge theory serves as a unifying tool by specifying the form for all the strong, weak and electromagnetic fields. In that sense it functions in a global way to restrict the class of acceptable theories, but also in a local way to determine specific kinds of interactions, producing unified theories as well as a unified method. At this point one might object that if unity is just a result of mathematics then shouldn't we have more success in producing unified theories. My claim is simply that when we unify theories there is no accompanying reason to think that we have succeeded in uncovering a fundamental unity in nature. *When* theories are unified it can sometimes by traced to the power of the mathematical structures used to represent the phenomena rather than a well worked out explanatory theory about how the phenomena/processes relate to each other. In these cases unity and explanation can have very little to do with each other. The mechanisms that allow you to unify are not necessarily the mechanisms that enable you to explain. The Higgs mechanism facilitates the unification but doesn't explain the mixing of the fields; the Weinberg angle represents the mixing yet no value is provided from within the theory that determines the degree to which the fields are mixed or that they should be so.

This way of thinking about the issue of unification suggests what I take to be a fundamental distinction implicit in the practice of theorizing; a distinction between a metaphysical unity in nature and unified theories. My point is that unifying theories involves a specific methodology that need not commit one to a corresponding unity throughout nature or science itself. Consequently we can make sense of the practice of unifying theories while embracing the powerful arguments for disunity in nature. The apparent incompatibility results from philosophical arguments that appeal to unified theories in physics to motivate a metaphysical picture about the unity of nature. This metaphysics is then used to argue for the epistemological priority of unified theories without much accompanying detail describing how the unity was actually achieved. By looking closely at the way in which theories become unified we see the significant role played by mathematics and the fundamental assumptions like Hamilton's principle or the principle of least action. Moreover, it also becomes clear that unification neither presupposes as an initial premise nor implies as a conclusion, ontological reduction. Not only is it possible to have different kinds of unity, Maxwell's theory is not unified in the same way that the electroweak theory is; as the electroweak case shows there can exist a unified structure coincident with a disunified ontology. Given the many faces of unity it becomes increasingly difficult to see how a general notion like theory unification can be used to support the kind of unified metaphysics of nature that the disunity arguments are designed to undermine. Consequently, both unity and disunity can coexist, not only within science but within the same theory.[6]

Notes

[1]I would like to thank Paul Forster for valuable comments. Support of research by the SSHRC is gratefully acknowledged.

[2]This phenomenon was an interesting counterexample to a theorem published by Goldstone, Salam and Weinberg in 1962 which showed that broken symmetries must al-

ways be accompanied by massless bosons known as the Goldstone bosons. See Goldstone, et. al. (1962). The Higgs mechanism was due to the work of Peter Higgs (1964).

[3]See Mills (1989). The most famous example of the the phenomenon is the ferromagnet which when brought to its state of lowest energy (cooled to absolute zero) must exhibit a magnetized state with a definite orientation, even though any orientation is allowed. The latter represents perfect symmetry while a definite orientation breaks the symmetry. This ground state of the ferromagnet is the analog of the vacuum state for our universe. It is perhaps important to point out that the vacuum state referred to in a quantum mechanical theory is not what one normally thinks of when we see the term "vacuum". Instead of a state of nothingness or emptiness the particle physics vacuum is the level at which physics actually takes place.

[4]For a clear account see Collins, et. al. (1989), esp. section 3.2, pp. 70-74.

[5]In order to satisfy the symmetry demands associated with the SU(2) group and in order to have a unified theory (i.e., have the proper coupling strengths for a conserved electric current and two charged W fields) the existence of a new gauge field was required; a field that Weinberg associated with a neutral current interaction similar to the one proposed by Glashow a few years earlier. evidence for neutral currents was found in 1973.

[6]In presenting the ideas involved in the physics of electoweak interactions I was aided by some especially good texts on the subject, particularly Aitchison and Hey (1989), Moriyasu (1983) and Collins, et. al. (1989).

References

Aitchinson, I.J.R. and Hey, A.J. (1989), *Gauge Theories in Particle Physics.* Bristol: Adam Hilger.

Cartwright, N. (1994), "The Patchwork of Laws" *Proceedings of the Aristotlean Society.*

Collins, P.D., Martin, A.D. and Squires, E.J. (1989), *Particle Physics and Cosmology.* New York: John Wiley.

Dupre, J. (1993), *The Disorder of Things.* Cambridge, MA: Harvard Press.

Glashow, S. (1961), "Partial Symmetries of Weak Interactions", *Nuclear Physics*: 22, 579-88.

Goldstone, J., Salam, A. and Weinberg, S. (1962), "Broken Symmetries", *Physical Review*: 127, 965-70.

Higgs, P.W. (1964a), "Broken Symmetries, Massless Particles and Gauge Fields", *Physics Letters*: 12, 132-33.

_ _ _ _ _ _ _. (1964b), "Broken Symmetries and the Masses of Gauge Bosons", *Physical Review Letters*: 13, 508-9.

Mills, R. (1989), "Gauge Fields", *American Journal of Physics*: 57, 493-507.

Moriyasu, K (1983), *An Elementary Primer for Gauge Theory.* Singapore: World Scientific

Weinberg, S. (1967), "A Model of Leptons" *Physical Review Letters*: 19, 1264-66.

Against Scientific Imperialism

John Dupré

Stanford University

Most discussion of the unity of science has concerned what might be called vertical relations between theories: the reducibility of biology to chemistry, or chemistry to physics, and so on. In this paper I shall be concerned rather with horizontal relations, that is to say, with theories of different kinds that deal with objects at the same structural level. Whereas the former, vertical, conception of unity through reduction has come under a good deal of criticism recently (see, e.g., Dupré 1993), horizontal unity has generally been conceded to be an important goal. The most pressing questions about horizontal unification arise in the study of human behavior. Numerous sciences including psychology, economics, anthropology, sociology, and parts of biology, attempt to provide explanations of human behavior. It is possible that some of these sciences may be able to coexist peacefully or even cooperatively. However things do not always go so smoothly, and at least two approaches to human behavior, those deriving from economics and evolutionary biology, often involve clearly imperialist tendencies. Devotees of these approaches are inclined to claim that they are in possession not just of one useful perspective on human behavior, but of the key that will open doors to the understanding of ever wider areas of human behavior. In this paper I shall consider some areas in which economic and evolutionary imperialists are currently staking claims. It is of particular interest to look at situations where the two imperialist programs are staking the same claim, but limitations of space force me to focus here mainly on economics, and my remarks on evolutionary imperialism will be cursory. As well as some specific insights into the particular strategies of these scientific programs, I hope that my discussion will throw some more general light on the limits of such general theoretical strategies and, thereby, I shall suggest some motivations for adhering to a horizontal pluralism of sciences that matches the vertical pluralism advocated by anti-reductionists.

Some philosophers, notably Michael Friedman (1974) and Philip Kitcher (1981), have argued that the unification of ever more phenomena under one theoretical scheme lies at the heart of scientific explanation, suggesting, if not quite entailing, that the horizontal expansion of theories is an unqualified scientific good. On the other hand it is sometimes suggested that broad generalizations are of little use in understanding human culture. For example Michael Oakeshott has written: "[K]nowledge of [a tradition of behavior] is unavoidably knowledge of its detail: to know only the gist is to know nothing. What has to be learned is not an abstract idea, or a set of tricks, not even a ritual, but a concrete coherent manner of living in all its intricateness" (1962, 129; Quoted in Shapin 1994, xix.) This perspective, I take it, is broadly shared by historians and cultural anthropologists; the theoretical conflict between the latter and their more evolutionarily in-

---

PSA 1994, Volume 2, pp. 374-381

clined colleagues is perhaps the clearest contemporary schism pitting local against global approaches to human behavior. Though I would not go so far as to say that to know the gist is to know nothing, I do believe that the local specificity of human culture is such as to limit greatly the possible illumination that can be gleaned from theories claiming to apply across the whole range of human cultural diversity. And this, if correct, reveals serious limitations to the general goal of horizontal scientific unification.

1. Imperialist Theories in Action

I begin with a very topical issue, the epidemiology of the AIDS epidemic. The attempt to treat this issue from the perspective of economics has recently been advocated in a book by the prominent judge, and proponent of an economic approach to human behavior, Richard Posner, and the economist Tomas Philipson. They suggest that traditional epidemiological approaches to the subject have been grossly misleading because they have generally ignored the behavioral changes brought on in response to the epidemic. I cannot comment on whether this criticism is justified, but to whatever extent it is, it would seem a serious omission. Philipson and Posner propose to fill this lacuna with economics. They proceed on "the assumption that the market for risky sexual 'trades'...is...much like other markets that economists study" (1994, 5) Scare quotes round the word "trades" draw attention to the fact that the discussion is not limited to prostitution, but is used in the "standard economic sense of an activity perceived as mutually beneficial to the persons engaged in it." The risk of infection by the HIV virus faced by traders in the risky sex market can be treated as analytically similar to the risk of default faced by lenders in a credit market. (Though their analysis is restricted to the sexual transfer of the HIV virus, they suggest that the market in used hypodermic syringes could be treated analogously.)

One should surely note at the outset that this starting point introduces, to put it mildly, some analogies. I suppose that a trip to the local singles bar has something in common with a trip to the supermarket: one may go to either place with the hope of bringing back something that one wants, and the most active singles bars are even occasionally referred to as "meat markets." But the analogy is very limited. The "goods" on display at a singles bar do not come with price tags, and those customers who leave at 2:00 a.m without the desired product generally do not do so because they have surveyed all the price tags (or even shadow price tags) and found that the prices are all too steep. And needless to say, many "risky sexual trades" arise in situations even less market-like than this. Of course the economist will reply that I have simply ignored the relevant definition of a trade just cited, that of any activity perceived as mutually beneficial by two consenting parties. To this one might respond that the picture of careful rational deliberation of costs and benefits (suitably discounted by estimated probabilities) seems more inappropriate to the contract for risky sex hastily drawn up at a singles bar even than to more traditional routes to sexual intimacy. The more fundamental question, to which I shall return, is whether such an abstract account of human interaction is of much use outside its core application, in this case the buying and selling of commercial goods. It is this skeptical question that casts general doubt on the desirability of this imperialistic approach to human behavior.

Philipson and Posner arrive at some surprising conclusions from their economic perspective. Most striking is the following. Policy responses to the HIV epidemic have generally advocated and subsidized widely available voluntary testing. The assumption, presumably, is that someone aware that they are HIV infected is less likely to endanger others by engaging in behavior liable to spread the disease. Philipson and Posner argue that this may well be counterproductive and increase the spread of the infection. A trader contemplating risky sex will estimate the benefits of the activity and subtract the costs of contracting a very unpleasant and ultimately fatal disease, discounted by the probability of contracting the disease. The latter will depend on the prevalence of infected persons in some relevant class and the likelihood of contracting the disease even from an infected person, both of which are quite low in most circumstances. But a person who has been able to determine, by means of a reliable test, that he or she is already infected will have no chance at all of contracting the disease (just as the only people whom it is absolutely impossible to kill are the already dead). Thus for such people the HIV-related costs of a sexual transaction are zero, and they will be much more likely to engage in risky sex, thereby spreading the infection. Philipson and Posner do acknowledge that there may be some altruists in the population, people for whom infecting a sexual partner with a fatal disease would involve some disutility. Since the proportion of altruists is unknown, and due to further complexities, the actual effects of widely available voluntary testing remains an empirical issue. Nonetheless, it is clear throughout the book that Philipson and Posner are strongly inclined to believe that the effect will be deleterious. (Even altruism can have perverse effects. Since altruists, who would prefer not to kill their sexual partners, will generally be less active in the risky sex market, the market will have a higher proportion of egoists and therefore be all the more dangerous.) Unsurprisingly, this fits into a pattern of skepticism about government interventions of various kinds, a pattern characteristic of devotees of the generally beneficial consequences of unfettered markets.

I do not know of any comparably detailed studies from the point of view of evolutionary biology except for those that focus on the evolution of the virus itself. It is plausible, however, that speculative evolutionary biology could be deployed here in support of the economistic perspective. To begin with, evolutionary biology will certainly treat sex as a major behavioral imperative, while notoriously viewing altruism as a problematic and limited hypothetical motive. Thus biology could readily be deployed in support of Philipson and Posner's evaluation of the relative significance of these motivational factors. Much more speculatively, it is widely held that a function of the often surprising mate selection criteria encountered in nature is the selection of mates with relatively low parasite loads (Hamilton and Zuk 1982). But if there is evolutionary pressure to find ways of selecting relatively parasite-free partners, there will be equally strong selective pressure to conceal the parasites that one has. Thus if, as evolutionary imperialists frequently appear to do, we see human deliberation as a Darwinian enabling mechanism, the behavior of Philipson's and Posner's egoistic HIV spreaders represents the implementation of a deep biological imperative. (It should not be objected to any of this that the sexual behavior in question is not primarily reproductive, since contemporary biology generally does not connect behavioral dispositions with explicitly held final goals. On the other hand if, as some sociobiologists seem to think, homosexuality is an evolved behavior with a unique and distinctive function, then the preceding suggestions may be irrelevant to this important case.)

Although economism and evolutionary speculation often support one another naturally, evolution explaining particular behavioral preferences, and economics exploring the consequences of choices in accordance with those preferences, relations are not always so smooth. My second example is of a phenomenon that is surely a great embarrassment to human sociobiologists, the spectacular decline in fertility in recent decades in the world's wealthiest countries. Although heroic attempts might be made to argue that somehow or other, contrary to all appearances, people are continuing to maximize reproductive success, this would have all the plausibility of the thesis that we live in the best of all possible worlds. Evolutionary approaches to this question must at least back away from direct explanation of behavior towards more causally distant psychological mechanisms. Of course, the claim that people have some serious interest in sex, an interest with an evolutionary basis in the connection between sex and reproduction is hardly controversial. But it is evident that modern Western humans have managed to decouple the interest in sex from its consequences in reproduction, something facilitated by widely available and effective methods of contraception. Evidently decisions about reproduction are now typically made in some much broader context of individual or even social goals, and evolutionary biology appears to have ceased to have much impact on for human fertility.

Economics may therefore seem much better placed to address this phenomenon. The locus classicus for such an attempt is Gary Becker's *Treatise on the Family* (1981;

revised ed., 1991). Becker's narrative begins with an account of the marriage market within which men and women attempt to acquire partners with whom they can create utility-maximizing families. Such partnerships having been formed, the members must then determine how to allocate their resources to achieve the highest accessible level of utility. Among the major items that they wish to produce and—in a chillingly Swiftian phrase—to consume, are children. Already we see, in contradistinction to a naive evolutionary perspective, that raising children is just one among many possible tastes, so that we should have no a priori expectations about natural fertility rates. Becker then makes a further distinction between two possible sources of family utility, quantity of children and quality of children. These interact in obvious ways: high quality children are costly, involving expenditures on such things as health and education, and thus a demand for superior children reduces the demand for numbers of children. Various explanations are offered for the changes in preference between quality and quantity of children with economic development. Whereas subsistence agriculture creates a demand for lots of children as a source of cheap labor, developed economies provide a range of economic opportunities that increase the returns on investment in the production of high-grade offspring. And, remarkably enough, there is a correlation between the level of education of mothers and of their children, though Becker cautions (1991,153) that this may not be a direct causal connection, but rather a consequence of the lower demand for quantity of children among more educated women, and the inverse relation between the demand for quantity and demand for quality.

I do not want to deny that the economic, and even the evolutionary, speculations just reviewed may have some grain of truth in them, and might provide a legitimate basis for empirical investigations of various kinds. And certainly economists and biologists engaged in the kinds of speculation I have just described will generally be ready to admit that various other factors are also relevant to the phenomena under consideration. So it may be wondered what my objection is. I now turn to some more critical reflections on this kind of scientific work.

2. Problems with Imperialist Science

I just remarked that there is nothing obviously inappropriate in using economic styles of thought as a source of hypotheses about various areas of human behavior. And indeed both Becker and Philipson and Posner do occasionally relate their discussions to empirical data. However, typical imperialists do not merely establish embassies in foreign countries and offer advice to indigenous populations. And similarly, economic imperialists do not merely export a few tentative hypotheses into the fields they invade, but introduce an entire methodology and one, I suggest, that is in many cases almost entirely inappropriate. Here I have in mind two things. First, a set of core assumptions about how to conceive of the phenomenon under investigation, in this case human behavior. And second, a methodology in the strict sense of a style of scientific argument. I begin with the first of these.

Economics, notoriously, conceives of human behavior as the exercise of "rational" choice. A person faced with a decision is conceived as estimating which action will generate the largest expected excess of benefits over costs to the agent. Thus in the case of the person contemplating risky sex, the benefits are the expected pleasure to be derived from the sexual contact, and the costs are the estimated risks of acquiring a fatal illness. Against the objection that human motivation is a bit more complex than this, it may be replied that this economistic perspective is at worst benignly vacuous. If it is true that people are motivated by some concern for the well-being of others, or some wish to behave in ways customary among their social group, or according to their conception of morality, duty, etc., then behavior satisfying these various criteria will simply be seen as providing some contribution to the utility of the agent. "Utility" here need not be taken as referring to any real measurable quantity, but only as a fictional device for describing a consistent set of preferences. (The normative evisceration of utility, through marginalism, ordinalism, and finally revealed preference theory, is a dominant theme of the last hundred years of economic thought (see Gagnier 1993).) Both the economic works I have been discussing exemplify such a strategy. Thus Becker suggests that parents have a utility function in which utility from their own consumption is traded off against the utility of their children. Posner and Philipson conceive of altruists as people who derive disutility from communicating a fatal disease to another person. And so on.

I want to suggest that this may in the end be vacuous, but it is hardly benign. Here I touch on a wide range of philosophical work that has criticized the rational choice foundations of economic thinking, and I can only summarize (see, e.g. Sen 1979; Anderson 1993). The most obvious point is that to treat altruism, morality, or accepted social norms simply as tastes that some people happen to have—I like candy and fast cars, you like morality and oysters—is grossly to misplace the importance of norms of behavior in peoples' lives. A second point is that whereas in principle the rational choice perspective may be capable of encompassing any mix of self-interested and non-self-interested concerns, in practice it almost invariably reflects the assumption that the former are far more significant. The most prominent contemporary defender of the project of analyzing ethics in terms of economically conceived rational choice, David Gauthier, for example, writes: "It is neither unrealistic nor pessimistic to suppose that beyond the ties of blood and friendship ... human beings exhibit little positive fellow feeling" (1986, p.101). A third point is perhaps the most important for my present concerns. The economistic perspective on human behavior is in an important sense scientistic. By this I mean here that it conceives itself as an objective and disinterested reflection on the facts of human behavior. But human behavior is not an immutable set of phenomena awaiting the correct scientific analysis, but is rather subject to constant historical evolution. And theorizing about human behavior is always to some extent an intervention in this evolution. Striking empirical confirmation of this claim in the present context is provided by recent research by the economist Robert Frank and his associates (Frank, Gilovich and Regan 1993). Frank administered tests of the disposition to cooperate to students before and after completing introductory courses in microeconomics and in astronomy, and found that the economics students were strikingly less cooperative at the end of the course. (The astronomy students were marginally more cooperative.) In confirmation of this result he also discovered that economic professors made fewer contributions to charity than professors in other fields. I share the conviction of Adam Smith (1776, 15), confirmed by Frank's first result, that on the whole people do not select their occupations because of their different dispositions, but acquire different capacities and dispositions as a result of their occupations. An unusually highly refined awareness of self-interest may be harmless or even appropriate for analyzing the futures market in pork-bellies, but it does not seem to me an asset for analyzing familial relations or the spread of AIDS.

My second more traditionally methodological point is also something I take to be a central aspect of scientism. "Serious" economic approaches to behavioral questions do not merely suggest ways in which economic factors might impinge on matters of human concern: it is a professional responsibility to dress up these suggestions in some quasi-mathematical guise. Becker's *Treatise on the Family* is an outstanding example of this problem. (Since Becker is a Nobel laureate it is of course no surprise that he adheres to the professional demands of his discipline.) The book addresses matters of obvious importance—the selection of marriage partners, decisions about child-bearing and rearing, and so on—and on occasion has illuminating insights and even empirical data that bear on these topics. On the other hand, the work as a whole is rendered largely unreadable by a continuous and obfuscating veneer of mathematics. I say "obfuscating" because the mathematical modelling at almost every point requires a level of abstraction that removes the discussion from any serious connection with the phenomena. Thus, for example, the first chapter on marriage markets, which addresses the economics of monogamy versus polygamy, assumes for purposes of model construction, that all men and all women are identical. The object of the exercise is to determine how many wives will maximize a husband's income, which is total family income minus the income of his wives. Becker is at pains to emphasize (e.g. 1991, 96) that men are not assumed to value wives for their own sakes, but only for their contributions to family productivity. While this does help the analogy between marriage and the market in, say, cars (or better, oil, since for analytic simplicity the number of spouses is allowed to vary continuously), it also makes it most unlikely that any conclusions will have much relevance to human mating patterns. As the chapter progresses, it is true, the men are allowed to differ in quality (superior men have characteristics that positively effect the marginal productivity of their identical wives), and in the following chapter, on assortative mating, high-quality and low-quality women are also introduced. Again though, differences in quality are only variations in some set of properties that contributes to efficient family production.

This, I am inclined to claim, is all fairly self-evident nonsense on its face—these abstractions would seem harmlessly ridiculous in a prose discussion of the nature of the family. The problem, however, is that its face is not easily seen. As I mentioned, the book is largely unreadable. It is, however, skimmable—informal discussion leads me to believe that even economists usually skim this kind of work—and conclusions can be seen to emerge. There is some danger that such conclusions will be given some weight as appearing from the serious scientific work (see all that mathematics) of a world-renowned scientist. One might even be tempted just to read the quite clear and intelligible summaries and conclusions at the end of each chapter. If one were to do so, one might read, for example, that "one of the more surprising conclusions of our analysis is that progressive taxes and expenditures may well widen the inequality in the long-run equilibrium disposition of disposable income" (1991, 231) Although many will be happy just to welcome this conclusion, those less enthusiastic about it might go back and see where it came from. In the section on Government Redistribution of Income (1991, 218) we may read, before diving into the alphabet soup, Becker's model for a progressive taxation system. This amounts to a flat rate tax on income, combined with a lump sum redistribution for everyone. Although this does provide an asymptotic approach towards the flat tax rate with increasing income, and thus might strictly be counted as progressive, it is hardly the kind of thing serious proponents of progressive taxation have in mind. This strikes me as rather weakly supporting the surprising conclusion in the summary. Although this is a particularly egregious example, it serves to me to illustrate clearly enough the rhetorical dangers of the formalized abstractions that fill the pages of Becker's book.

I have not tried to give detailed critiques of the examples discussed above, although I am currently engaged in a study of economics that includes critical study of several areas of economic thinking. Indeed, I am inclined to wonder whether any more than an intelligible exposition of the ideas in question, unobscured by jargon or irrelevant formalism, is required to display the implausibility of many of these account. With more space I would also like to compare the above examples with some examples of evolutionary imperialism, which I have also criticized elsewhere. One point I would like to mention here is that, in contrast with the potential vacuity of economic theory—whatever people do must reflect what they most want—evolutionary biology is hampered by a central concept with rather more content. Although evolutionary biologists have notoriously been accused of making up any old story that will link some observed behavior to reproductive success, the need for such a story is a non-trivial requirement, and stories can be investigated for plausibility. One cannot simply say that these particular animals prefer service to their kind or a glorious death to reproductive success. Thus, as indicated in the case of fertility, reproductive optimality must be sought in many cases some causal distance behind overt behavioral performance.

3. Conclusions

Preliminary and partial though my treatment has been of the foregoing examples, they do provide some grounding for my general thesis. Contrary to what may be suggested by a large body of scientific work and, to some extent, by unificatory theories of scientific explanation, imperialist science is something to be approached with considerable skepticism, at least in the human sciences. As scientific methodologies move further away from their central areas of application their abstractions become ever grosser, and their relevance to the phenomena become ever more distant. A moderate response to this observation might perhaps be to advocate a pluralistic tolerance of scientific imperialism. While acknowledging the complexity of phenomena, and especially human phenomena, should we not welcome complementary approaches from as many different directions as possible? While there is surely something to this thought, I think we should remain skeptical. For one thing, scientific accounts are seldom offered as one tiny piece of a big puzzle: such a modest picture is unlikely to attract graduate students, research grants, Nobel prizes, or invitations to appear on Night Line. For another, the modest picture offers little justification for the displays of sophisticated technique and argument that provide the admired paradigms of application of these approaches, and especially the economic approach. In a manner far removed from tolerant pluralism, therefore, enthusiasts for the economic, or the evolutionary, approach to human behavior are inclined to claim that the disposition to truck, barter, and trade, in the one case, or the fact that we evolved by natural selection, in the other, are *the* fundamental keys to understanding human behavior. And thus a few speculative suggestions are presented as the Rosetta stone of human understanding.

Advocates of the semantic view of theories have emphasized that much of science is more realistically described as consisting in sets of models than in universal laws. It seems to me that this is indeed a more realistic account of the way science is practiced in biology and economics. One important point about this general conception is that it rests uneasily with a commitment to expansionist science. Whereas it is natural to think of the power and interest of a law of nature being a function of the variety of cases to which it applies, it is much less clear that breadth of application is a virtue for models. Models are, after all, constructed to reflect as accurately as is practicable, particular kinds of situations. The further they are transported from their paradigm applications the less realistic they will become, and the more they will need to be modified to account for differences between their original home and their new areas of application. As new environments introduce different causal factors, alien models from distant domains will be increasingly partial in their relevance. This seems to me exactly the way to see the partiality and even irrelevance of the applications of economic and evolutionary models discussed in earlier parts of this paper.

The home turf of economics is the market. And while there may perhaps, in a suitably extended or analogical senses be said to be markets in children, risky sex, marriage partners, etc., paradigm markets are in oil, wheat, pork belly futures, or houses: that is, relatively interchangeable commodities that people acquire by paying money. As we move into these merely analogical or even metaphorical markets, the attempt to apply market models involves more and more abstraction from the diverse range of factors that actually affect behavior in these areas. To mention only one striking point pertinent to marriage "markets", the conception of romantic love which, for all its ideological problems, surely plays some role in matrimonial decisions in Western societies, is precisely an extreme commitment to the non-substitutability of one item for another.

I believe that the inadequacies of applications of such models so far from their natural home would seem obvious in most cases if there were not some strong motive inclining scientists to be sympathetic with the projects they represent. And indeed the standard response to such skepticism is to admit that the treatments are as yet too simplified to be altogether realistic, but that they constitute the first step towards some very important goal. What goal? The goal of applying the preferred imperialist strategy of explanation to the phenomena in question. Since I am suggesting that this is not a goal we should have any interest in pursuing, I urge that these simplistic and unconvincing explanatory endeavors should be taken at face value. Moreover, as is very clearly illustrated by incursions of economics into various domains, alien intellectual strategies may import inappropriate and even dangerous assumptions into the colonized domains. Certainly we may sensibly want to acquire a range of modelling strategies that are ready to hand when the phenomena call for them. But Procrustean fitting of phenomena into an antecedently preferred type of model is another matter.

I shall conclude with one final remark about the relevance of these suggestions to biology. I have concentrated on explanations of human behavior, in part because the intuitions here about the inadequacy of certain proferred explanations are sharpest. But I believe that concerns about scientific imperialism have much wider relevance to the practice of biology. It is true that evolution by natural selection is a process of sufficient generality and significance to have some bearing on a very wide range of biological phenomena. But what bearing, and the detailed nature of the process, seem to me to be as variable as the phenomena of human behavior. Thus the widely held belief that some mathematical models from population genetics provide us with the fundamental mechanisms of natural selection, the attempts by philosophers to provide universal, axiomatized accounts of the theory of evolution by natural selection, and even the attempt to provide a homogeneous and uniform account of biological classification across the whole biological domain, seem to me as misguidedly imperialistic as the projects I have been criticizing in the human sciences.

References

Anderson, E. (1993), *Value in Ethics and Economics.* Cambridge: Harvard University Press.

Becker, G.S. (1981; enlarged ed. 1991), *A Treatise on the Family.* Cambridge: Harvard University Press.

Dupré, J. (1993), *The Disorder of Things: Metaphysical Foundations of the Disunity of Science.* Cambridge: Harvard University Press.

Frank, R.H., Gilovich, T. and Regan, D.T. (1993), "Does Studying Economics Inhibit Cooperation?", *Journal of Economic Perspectives* 7: 159-171.

Friedman, M. (1974), "Explanation and Scientific Understanding", *Journal of Philosophy* 71: 5-19.

Gagnier, R. (1993), "On the Insatiability of Human Wants: Economic and Aesthetic Man", *Victorian Studies* 36: 125-154.

Gauthier, D. (1986), *Morals by Agreement.* Oxford: Oxford University Press.

Hamilton, W.D. and Zuk, M. (1982), "Heritable True Fitness and Bright Birds: A Role for Parasites?", *Science* 218: 384-387.

Kitcher, P. (1981), "Explanatory Unification", *Philosophy of Science* 48: 507-531.

Oakeshott, M. (1962), "Political Education", in *Rationalism in Politics and Other Essays.* New York: Basic Books, pp. 111-136.

Philipson, T.J. and Posner R.A. (1993), *Private Choices and Public Health: The AIDS Epidemic in Economic Perspective.* Cambridge: Harvard University Press.

Sen, A.K. (1979), "Rational Fools: A Critique of the Behavioural Foundations of Economic Theory", in F. Hahn and M. Hollis, (eds.), *Philosophy and Economic Theory.* Oxford: Oxford University Press, pp. 86-109.

Shapin, S. (1994), *A Social History of Truth.* Chicago: Chicago University Press.

Smith, A. (1776), *The Wealth of Nations.* Edited by E. Cannan, New York: The Modern Library (1937).

Pluralism, Normative Naturalism, and Biological Taxonomy[1]

Marc Ereshefsky

University of Calgary

1. Introduction

The discipline of biological taxonomy is rife with philosophical controversies. One of them is particularly relevant to the topic of this symposium, namely the question of taxonomic unity. Should biologists aim for a single correct classification of the world's organisms or should they allow a plurality of equally correct classifications?

For those with little or no background in evolutionary biology, the suggestion of taxonomic pluralism might seem odd. Don't introductory biology texts as well as television nature shows suggest that there is a single correct way to sort the world's organisms? They do, but that advertised agreement masks a number of controversies that have raged in biology since Darwin's time. Consider the question of how to sort organisms into species. Currently there are no less than seven prominent definitions of the species category (Ereshefsky 1992a). Those varying species definitions, in turn, give rise to disjoint classifications. This does not occur in a few isolated cases but in numerous empirical situations (Ereshefsky 1992b).

Monists and pluralists treat the diversity of species definitions in the literature differently. Monists consider the species problem an unfinished debate in which the improper definitions need to be weeded from the proper one. Pluralists, on the other hand, contend that there is no single correct definition of species. For pluralists, various species definitions provide equally correct classifications of different aspects of the organic world.

For my part, I tend to side with the pluralists. But instead of providing a thorough argument for taxonomic pluralism (for that, see Ereshefsky 1992b), I want to take up a pressing problem for pluralism. Hull (1987, 1989) provides the best characterization of this problem, and others (for example, Ghiselin 1987) have raised it as well. Their objection goes something like this: Any group of objects can be sorted into numerous classifications. Yet not every suggested classification can be adequately investigated. Society has only limited resources, and we would like those resources targeted for the most promising empirical classifications. If a pluralist provides no way of discerning among proposed projects, then our scientific resources will be spread too thinly among a number of projects. As a result, no particular classification will be adequately investigated. Thus, pluralists need to provide criteria for determining which classifications should be pursued. Otherwise, as Hull and others suggest, taxonomic pluralism boils down to a position of "anything goes".

PSA 1994, Volume 2, pp. 382-389

In this paper I offer a reply to the anything goes objection. That reply not only provides justification for taxonomic pluralism but also sheds light on why pluralism occurs in biology. The reply I offer touches on methodological issues and in doing so employs the naturalized approach to methodology suggested by Laudan (1984, 1987, 1990) and Rosenberg (1984, 1990). Consequently, an indirect result of this paper is a case study showing the usefulness of normative naturalism.

2. A Demarcation Criterion?

One way to answer the anything goes objection is to invoke a demarcation criterion. When faced with the question of whether a taxonomic project should be pursued, we should ask whether it is scientific. Those taxonomic projects that are scientific should be pursued; those that are not scientific should be abandoned, or at least given a low priority.

Employing a demarcation criterion for science, however, is not the best way to answer the anything goes objection. First, the demarcation problem itself is fraught with difficulties. As Laudan (1983) and others have observed, philosophers and scientists have failed to come up with any criterion that distinguishes all science from all non-science. Second, even if an adequate demarcation criterion were found, the anything goes problem would not be resolved. The history of science consists of previously proposed taxonomic approaches that are rejected by contemporary scientists. Such taxonomic approaches may pass a demarcation criterion, but that in itself does not imply that they should be pursued. Similarly, scientists argue over which current taxonomic projects should be pursued while allowing that competing taxonomic projects are equally scientific. So even if we had an adequate demarcation criterion, we would need further criteria to decide whether a taxonomic project should be pursued.

3. Normative Naturalism

We need not be saddled with the difficulties of the demarcation problem in answering the anything goes objection. A more promising approach is found using Laudan (1984, 1987, 1990) and Rosenberg's (1985, 1990) normative naturalism. According to Laudan (1984, 1987), disciplines contain three major components: general aims, methodological rules, and projects of inquiry. General aims are the overriding axiological considerations of a discipline. Rosenberg (1990) and Leplin (1990), for example, suggest that the general aim of all scientific disciplines is the pursuit of knowledge. Methodological rules, on the other hand, help us pick out which of a discipline's proposed projects should be pursued. According to normative naturalism, we should prefer those methodological rules that best gauge a project's ability to achieve the aims of its discipline. For example, if the general aim of a discipline is empirical knowledge and empirical vulnerability is a good indicator of which projects provide empirical knowledge, then empirical vulnerability should be adopted as one of that discipline's methodological rules.

A question arises: how do we know which methodological rules best gauge a project's ability to achieve a discipline's aims? According to normative naturalism there are several ways. We can turn to the history of science and see which methodological rules have best promoted those aims in the past. Alternatively, we can use empirical information from science itself in picking methodological rules; for example, information from evolutionary theory bears on the use of parsimony in inferring phylogenetic relations (Sober 1988). A third approach chooses methodological rules via a conceptual analysis of which rules *would* best promote the aims of a discipline. Normative naturalism employs all three approaches and in doing so provides a naturalistic approach to methodology: it uses *both* conceptual and empirical resources in choosing methodological rules.

Thus far we have seen how normative naturalism selects methodological rules. What remains to be seen is how naturalists determine a discipline's general aims. In the simplest form, it is just a matter of reading them off the discipline itself. Take a survey of the leading texts and articles of a discipline and see what their authors advocate as the aims of that discipline. Again a worry may arise: do the workers of any discipline agree on their discipline's aims? Both Rosenberg (1990) and Leplin (1990) believe that such agreement does exist –the aim of each scientific discipline is the acquisition of empirical knowledge.

I am not ready to assume that all disciplines have the same general aim, let alone assume that such agreement exists within any particular discipline. First we need to survey scientists and see what they take to be the general aims of their respective disciplines. The results of such a survey are presented in the next section of this paper.[2]

Enough of normative naturalism has been introduced so that it can be applied to the anything goes objection. We need to survey the aims of biological taxonomy and then determine which methodological rules best promote those aims. With such rules in hand, a pluralist can choose among taxonomic projects and be a discerning puralist.

4. The Aims and Methodological Rules of Biological Taxonomy

In order to gain an understanding of what biological taxonomists take to be the general aims and methodological principles of their discipline, I surveyed a number of seminal texts and journal articles in that field. That survey included texts from each of the four general schools of biological taxonomy: evolutionary taxonomy, phenetics, process cladism, and pattern cladism. (The detailed results of this survey can be found in Ereshefsky 1995.)

Explicit statements of the general aim of biological taxonomy were not hard to find. Indeed, they are easily found in the beginning chapters of the seminal texts in that field. Surprisingly, leading workers in all four schools agree on the general aim of their discipline. As they see it, the overall aim of biological taxonomy is to provide empirically accurate classifications that allow biologists to make inferences. Examples of such inferences are inferring the evolutionary history of a taxon, inferring the close relatives of taxon, and inferring what traits the other members of a taxon typically have. The primary function of such inferences is to aid in the tasks of prediction or explanation.[3]

Though biological taxonomists agree on the general aim of their discipline, they disagree on which methodological rules best promote that aim. That disagreement is interesting in itself, but is even more interesting in that it is partially responsible for the plurality of classifications found in biology. Consider an example from the debate over the correct definition of species. Definitions based on the process of interbreeding pick out groups of organisms that can interbreed and produce fertile offspring. A genealogically based definition called the "Evolutionary Species Concept" highlights groups of organisms that have their "own evolutionary tendencies and historical fate" (Simpson 1961). Unique tendencies and fates are caused by several processes, including interbreeding, selection, and genetic homeostasis. Proponents of the interbreeding approach argue that their approach is preferable because it is simpler (see Ghiselin 1987). The interbreeding approach posits one process to explain the unity of species while the Evolutionary Species Concept posits several. Proponents of the Evolutionary Species Concept, on the other hand, argue that their approach is preferable because it is more general (see Simpson 1961). The Evolutionary Species Concept applies to both sexual and asexual organisms, whereas the interbreeding approach applies to only sexual organisms. The result is two different classifications of the organic world. This is just one of many cases in biological taxonomy where methodological pluralism gives rise to taxonomic pluralism.[4]

5. Primary and Secondary Rules

With the aim of biological taxonomy in hand, we can turn to the question of which methodological rules best promote that aim. As we have seen, normative naturalism offers several ways to pursue that question: consult the history of science, turn to empirical theories, or use conceptual analysis. In this paper I employ the latter two approaches. Nevertheless, I think that the historical route is a fruitful one and substantiates the analysis I present here (see Ereshefsky 1995).

Biologists and philosophers suggest numerous methodological rules for judging general approaches to biological classification. I divide those suggested methodological rules into two classes: primary rules and secondary rules. Primary rules best gauge whether a taxonomic approach can provide empirically accurate classifications that allow biologists to make inferences. Hence primary rules serve as minimal, though not infallible, standards for judging a taxonomic approach. Secondary rules, on the other hand, affect a taxonomic approach's value, but are less important in judging whether that approach will satisfy its discipline's aim.

Before stating which rules are primary ones, I should clearly set out the components of a taxonomic approach. A taxonomic approach produces a classification using two types of principles: sorting principles and motivating principles. Sorting principles sort the constituents of a theory into taxonomic units. Motivating principles justify the use of sorting principles. As an example, consider the taxonomic approach in biology called the "Biological Species Concept". Its sorting principles assert: sort organisms that can interbreed and produce fertile offspring into the same species; sort organisms that reproduce sexually but cannot interbreed into different species; and so on. The motivating principle of that approach assumes that interbreeding causes groups of organisms with that process to form stable evolutionary units.

Returning to methodological rules, four rules best gauge a taxonomic approach's ability to satisfy the aim of biological classification. Thus they serve as primary rules for judging taxonomic approaches. Those rules are empirical sensitivity, internal coherence, coherence with theories in other fields, and coherence with the theory for which the taxonomy is being developed. Why these four rules and not others? I consider each rule in turn.

First, every biological taxonomist I surveyed writes that the primary aim of their discipline is to provide *empirically accurate* classifications. A minimal way of judging whether a taxonomic approach can satisfy that aim is to see if its sorting and motivating principles are empirically testable. For example, if the sorting principles of a taxonomic approach sort organisms into species according to their niches, then there better be some way of measuring niches in the empirical world. The same applies to motivating principles. A number of species definitions are motivated by the assumption that interbreeding causes certain clusters of organisms to remain relatively stable. If there is no possible way to test this assumption, then such definitions are based on an empirically vacuous motivating principle.

Second, if classifications are to fulfill the aim of providing a basis for various types of inference, they need to be relatively unambiguous. Suppose we want to infer the phylogenetic history of a taxon so that we can understand the current physiology of its organisms. A taxonomic approach infected with ambiguity may produce classifications that place the group in different taxonomic units. Those taxonomic units, in turn, may have distinct phylogenies. Consequently, we will not be able to explain the current physiology of the organisms in question because we will have multiple and inconsistent explanations. Thus in order to preserve the taxonomic aim of providing classifications that are useful for prediction and explanation, taxonomic approaches need to be internally consistent.

Third, motivating and sorting principles, like all scientific hypotheses, are accepted given certain background assumptions. For example, sorting principles that rely on recombinant DNA techniques for constructing phylogenetic taxonomies depend on tenets in physics and chemistry (Panchen 1992, 207). The plausibility of the Biological Species Concept's motivating principle that interbreeding causes evolutionary unity relies on tenets in genetics (Ehrlich and Raven 1969, 64; Templeton 1989, 166-168). We would like the background assumptions that bolster sorting and motivating principles to cohere with what is known elsewhere. When a taxonomic approach conflicts with well established theories in other disciplines we should be wary. Conservatism tells us to side with the cluster of theories that has the best empirical track record. Of course this is not a foolproof method. A taxonomic approach may make an assumption that conflicts with a well accepted tenet elsewhere, yet that approach may prove to be more empirically fruitful in the end. Nevertheless, intertheoretic consistency provides a way to identify suggested taxonomic approaches that have a low probably of empirical success given everything else known at the time. One cannot ask more of methodological standard than that.

Fourth, the motivating principles of a taxonomic approach should cohere with the current theory governing the entities being classified. The intention of this standard is to guard against a taxonomic approach and a well established theory in the same field being inconsistent. The history of biology is strewn with taxonomic approaches containing motivating principles that conflict with current evolutionary theory. As a result, we do not fund or teach such approaches, other than as history of science. Just as we are skeptical of outdated taxonomic approaches, we should be skeptical of currently proposed biological classifications that conflict with evolutionary theory.

Having suggested the above primary rules for judging taxonomic approaches, a question arises: must a taxonomic approach satisfy each of these to be considered worthy of pursuit? Certainly a taxonomic approach that satisfies all four is worthy of pursuit, and an approach that satisfies none should be pursued only as a last measure. The more of these rules an approach satisfies, the more worthy it is of investigation. I am hesitant to draw a more precise boundary. Some may be unhappy with the vagueness of this proposal. But the existence of vagueness around a putative distinction does not show that the distinction is not viable. Consider analogous cases. Bald and not bald, rich and not rich, even nitrogen and oxygen are vague distinctions (see Sober 1980 on the latter distinction). Yet because there are clear cases on either side of these distinctions, we accept them as workable. Similarly the distinction between taxonomic approaches that are worthy of pursuit and those that are not is workable if there are clear cases on either side. Elsewhere, I have argued that such clear cases can be found in biological taxonomy (Ereshefsky 1992b and Ereshefsky 1995).

The above rules do not exhaust the methodological rules discussed in the biological and philosophical literature. I have not, for example, considered such rules as simplicity, generality, and stability. Such rules are secondary in judging whether a taxonomic approach can satisfy the aim of biological classification. There are pragmatic reasons for preferring simple, general, and stable classifications. But these qualities are less vital than the primary rules in judging whether a taxonomic approach can provide empirically accurate classifications.

Consider the virtue of simplicity. Philosophers and biologists are well acquainted with Ockam's razor, the principle of parsimony, and the principle of common cause. Having simpler classifications certainly makes our job easier. Yet we cannot assume in an *a priori* manner that any particular process or pattern in nature is simple. That is an empirical question. And simplicity and empirical accuracy often part company, as is well illustrated in Sober's (1988) study of the use of parsimony in biological taxonomy. Consequently, the simplicity of a classification or a taxonomic approach is not an indication of its empirical accuracy.

A similar point applies to the virtue of generality. Generality is quite useful for organizing our knowledge of the world. The more general a taxonomic approach, the less taxonomic approaches biologists need to know. However, whether biological taxonomy will ultimately contain a single general approach depends on cooperation from the organic world. And the organic world could stymie that ambition. Indeed, Dupré (1993) and Kitcher (1984), and Ereshefsky (1992b) have argued that it already has.

With simplicity and generality, we like our classifications to be relatively stable. That is, we would like to avoid frequent taxonomic revision because that requires workers to constantly relearn classifications. Again the possibility of a stable classification will turn on cooperation from the empirical world. In biology we find that new discoveries of organisms often cause workers to revise previous classifications (taxa are split, taxa are lumped, and taxa placed in different higher taxa). The members of a taxon also change, causing traits that might be typical in one generation to be atypical in another. So unlike chemistry, taxonomic revision is the norm in biological classification. Stability is certainly a desirable feature of classifications. But stability cannot be taken as an indication that a classification is empirically correct, especially if there are reasons for believing that the organic world often renders such classifications unstable.

6. Results

The above dichotomy of primary and secondary rules has four implications for the topics of methodological unity and taxonomic pluralism. I end this paper by listing those results.

First, the primary rules provide a way for a taxonomic pluralist to be a discerning pluralist. They allow a pluralist to say which taxonomic approaches should and should not be pursued and thus answer the anything goes objection. Of course the argument I have offered is merely one of possibility –I have only argued that it can be done. It would be nice to see if these rules can distinguish among taxonomic approaches in actual science. I have tried to do that elsewhere by considering competing species definitions and general schools of biological taxonomy (Ereshefsky 1992b, 1995). Here are the results from one of those studies. Two general approaches to species, what I call 'the interbreeding approach' and 'the phylogenetic approach', each satisfy the four primary rules cited above. Four other approaches to species, those based on phenetics, pattern cladism, idealistic morphology, and creationism, fail to satisfy all of those rules. This study (as spelled out in Ereshefsky 1992b, 1995) shows that the set of four primary rules does discern among proposed taxonomic approaches and provides a basis for preferring certain approaches over others.[5]

Second, the primary rules not only allow one to be a discerning pluralist, they also underwrite the plausibility of taxonomic pluralism. If multiple projects score equally high on the primary rules, then all of those projects have an equal chance of satisfying the aim of biological taxonomy. In such a situation we ought to adopt taxonomic pluralism. For in such a situation there is no way to discern among taxonomic approaches. Notice that the question of whether taxonomic pluralism translates into metaphysical pluralism is a separate issue. Perhaps the world really is carved in multiple ways, corresponding to each of those approaches. On the other hand, perhaps in the end only one of those approaches will be shown empirically accurate. Nothing I have said forecloses the possibility of metaphysical monism. Either way, given a situation where several approaches score equally high, we should adopt a pluralist stance and pursue more than one approach.

Third, the division of primary and secondary rules reveals why some workers within a single discipline are motivated to advocate different but equally legitimate taxonomic approaches. Biologists are motivated to posit different taxonomic approaches because of the differential emphasis they place on secondary rules; yet a number of those approaches are equally legitimate because they satisfy the primary rules. For example, interbreeding and genealogical accounts of species pass the four primary rules. But as we saw earlier, preference for an interbreeding account is influenced by a desire for simplicity, whereas a preference for more genealogical accounts (for example, the evolutionary species concept) stems from a preference for generality. Similarly, I would argue that while the general schools of evolutionary taxonomy and process cladism pass the four primary rules, a differential preference for those schools in part stems from a varying emphasis placed on the secondary rules of simplicity and generality (see note 3).

Fourth, the discussion of taxonomic pluralism in this paper provides a lesson for the issue of methodological unity in science. Often writers treat the prospect of methodological unity as an all or nothing affair: either science has a single method or it does not. The case of biological taxonomy shows that such univocal answers do not do justice to the methodological practices found in science. The biologists surveyed here agree on the general aim of taxonomy, but they disagree on which standards select taxonomic approaches that best satisfy that aim. In biological taxonomy one finds both methodological unity and methodological disunity.

Consequently, if one wants to determine whether methodological unity exists in science, or provide normative arguments concerning methodology, one should first address such issues on a discipline by discipline basis. For even within a single discipline scientists may agree on some methodologies and disagree on others. And normative arguments, such as the one offered here, may advocate a mixture of methodological unity and disunity within a single discipline. Some may not like this local approach to the philosophy of scientific methodology. Nevertheless, I think it provides a more accurate and fruitful account of scientific methodology than more global approaches.

Notes

[1]Thanks to David Baumslag, John Dupre´, David Hull, Jim Lennox, Elliott Sober, and Brad Wilson for commenting on earlier drafts of this paper. The National Science Foundation provided financial support for writing this paper (NSF Grant SBR-9310624), and the Center for Philosophy of Science at the University of Pittsburgh provided stimulating and conducive surroundings.

[2]Though my approach towards determining the aims of a discipline will be purely descriptive, Laudan (1984, 1990) provides apparatus for evaluating aims themselves (for example, he recommends rejecting unrealizable aims).

[3]This variety of types of inferences does not draw a divide among various schools. Just as process cladists and evolutionary taxonomists want to construct hypotheses concerning phylogeny, processes cladists and phenetists allow that their hypotheses may be seen as phylogenetic ones. See Nelson and Platnick (1981, 199) and Sokal (1985, 746). On the other hand, both evolutionary taxonomists and process cladists observe that one type of hypothesis classifications offer concerns the traits found among the organisms of a taxon. See Mayr (1969, 7) and Eldredge and Cracraft (1980, 7).

[4]Briefly, here are three other cases (Ereshefsky 1995 offers a more thorough account). (i). Evolutionary taxonomists think that classifications should be as general as possible and thus encompass both common ancestry and evolutionary divergence. Cladists believe that classifications should be constructed according to a single uniform parameter –common ancestry. Their varying preferences for generality and uniformity cause cladists and evolutionary taxonomists to construct different classifications. (ii). Phenetists believe that classifications should be constructed according to theory-neutral principles. Evolutionary taxonomists and process cladists argue that classifications should be constructed according to theory-dependent principles. Their methodological disagreement causes them to construct different classifications. (iii). Proponents of the Linnaean system of classification put a premium on stable classifications. Advocates of non-Linnaean systems prefer the virtues of generality and simplicity over stability. Their varying methodological preferences causes them to produce different representations of the organic world.

[5]In Ereshefsky (1995) I argue that the set of primary rules discerns among general schools of biological taxonomy, recommending the pursuit of evolutionary taxonomy and process cladism but not the pursuit of phenetics or pattern cladism.

References

Dupre´, J. (1993), *The Disorder of Things: Metaphysical Foundations of the Disunity of Science*. Cambridge: Harvard University Press.

Ehrlich, P. and Raven, P. (1969), "Differentiation of Populations", *Science* 165: 1228-1232. Reprinted in Ereshefsky (1992b): 57-68.

Eldredge, N. and Cracraft, J. (1980), *Phylogenetic Patterns and the Evolutionary Process: Method and Theory in Comparative Biology*. New York: Columbia University Press.

Ereshefsky, M. (ed.),(1992a), *The Units of Evolution: Essays on the Nature of Species* Cambridge: MIT Press.

_________. (1992b), "Eliminative Pluralism", *Philosophy of Science* 59:671-690.

_________. (1995), *Representing Nature: Biology and the Philosophy of Classification.* Manuscript.

Ghiselin, M. (1987), "Species Concepts, Individuality, and Objectivity", *Biology and Philosophy* 2: 127-143.

Hull, D. (1987), "Genealogical Actors in Ecological Roles", *Biology and Philosophy* 2:168-183.

_____. (1989), "A Function for Actual Examples in Philosophy of Science", in M. Ruse (ed.), *What the Philosophy of Biology Is*. Dordrecht: Kluwer Academic Publishers, pps 309-321.

Kitcher, P. (1984), "Species", *Philosophy of Science* 51: 308-333.

Laudan, L. (1983), "The Demise of the Demarcation Problem", in R. S. Cohen and L. Laudan (eds.), *Physics, Philosophy and Psychoanalysis: Essays in Honor of Adolf Grunbaum*. Dordrecht: D. Reidel Publishing Company, pp.111-127.

______. (1984), *Science and Values*. Berkeley: University of California Press.

______. (1987), "Progress or Rationality?: The Prospects for Normative Naturalism", *American Philosophical Quarterly* 24: 19-31.

______. (1990), "Normative Naturalism", *Philosophy of Science* 57: 44-59.

Leplin, J. (1990), "Renormalizing Epistemology", *Philosophy of Science* 57: 20-33.

Mayr, E. (1969), *Principles of Systematic Zoology*. New York: McGraw-Hill.

Nelson, G. and Platnick, N. (1981), *Systematics and Biogeography*. New York: Columbia University Press.

Panchen, A. (1992), *Classification, Evolution and the Nature of Biology*. Cambridge: Cambridge University Press.

Rosenberg, A. (1985), "Methodology, Theory and the Philosophy of Science", *Pacific Philosophical Quarterly* 66: 377-393.

________. (1990), "Normative Naturalism and The Role of Philosophy", *Philosophy of Science* 57: 34-43.

Simpson, G. (1961), *The Principles of Animal Taxonomy*. New York: Columbia University Press.

Sober, E. (1980), " Evolution, Population Thinking, and Essentialism", *Philosophy of Science* 47: 350-383.

______. (1988), *Reconstructing the Past*. Cambridge: MIT Press.

Sokal, R. (1985), "The Continuing Search for Order", *American Naturalist* 126: 729-749.

Templeton, A. (1989), "The Meaning of Species and Speciation: A Genetic Perspective." In Otte and Endler (eds.), *Speciation and its Consequencses*. Sunderland: Sinauer Association, pp.3-27. Reprinted in Ereshefsky (1992a), pp. 159-186.

Part XIII

DISCOURSE, PRACTICE, CONTEXT: FROM HPS TO INTERDISCIPLINARY SCIENCE STUDIES

Discourse, Practice, Context: From HPS to Interdisciplinary Science Studies

Alison Wylie

University of Western Ontario

One of the most widely debated and influential implications of the "demise" of positivism was the realization, now a commonplace, that philosophy of science must be firmly grounded in an understanding of the history of science, and/or of contemporary scientific practice. While the nature of this alliance is still a matter of uneasy negotiation, the principle that philosophical analysis must engage "real" science has transformed philosophical practice in innumerable ways. For one thing, it has led to a systematic questioning, indeed, in the view of many, the dismantling, of "unity" theses and the presumption that the sciences embody a common rational core that philosophers can reasonably expect to "reconstruct." As HPS practitioners have scrutinized particular sciences, their diversity has come more clearly into focus and this has generated, in turn, vigorous programs of research that take an increasingly wide range of "special" sciences—including various life sciences, earth sciences, and social sciences—as a legitimate primary focus of concern. Increasingly these are recognized to be philosophically interesting in their own right, not just a resource for testing (a source of counterexamples), or an export destination for models of "real" science. This has put considerable strain on traditional approaches to HPS (see Baigrie, this volume), frequently foregrounding the particularities of these sciences and the (intellectual) contexts in which they have flourished, and forcing a consideration of increasingly complex explanatory models; one response has been the growing interest in strategies for "naturalizing" philosophical studies of science.

In the same period, sociologists of science have called into question the efficacy of philosophical analysis in much more general terms, intent on finally and decisively displacing any lingering philosophical convictions about the uniqueness, unity, and rationality of science. As these challenges have evolved, they have generated a quite heterogenous family of programs of science studies research, not all of which are as categorically opposed to philosophical approaches as the original Strong Program or its most direct descendants (see, for example, contributors to Pickering 1992, and Pickering's introduction to this collection). For all their diversity, however, they share an insistence on the need to understand the sciences *in context*, meaning not just intellectual context, but pragmatic, sociological, historical, and political-economic contexts. The proponents of cultural studies of science further insist that the sciences be understood as essentially cultural, discursive enterprises (see Smocovitis and Rouse, this volume).

While (some) philosophers have vehemently opposed all forms of sociological challenge, and (some) sociologists retain a rigorously anti–philosophical stance, there has been considerable movement on all sides toward more a constructive exchange on mat-

PSA 1994, Volume 2, pp. 393-395

ters of common interest (for philosophical responses, compare the exchange between contributors to Brown 1984, with the responses to Roth and Barrett 1990 and the approach taken by, for example, Henderson1990, Longino 1990, and Rouse 1987). Where philosophy of science is concerned, there is a very real sense in which the sociological demand for contextualization simply extends the earlier, internal demand that philosophical analyses of science be grounded in the detailed analysis of actual scientific practice, and complements the more recent interest in naturalizing philosophical studies of science (Manicas and Rosenberg 1985, 1988, Solomon, forthcoming). Similarly, a good many sociologists of science have backed away from the more extreme constructivism some had espoused, and from the sociological essentialism with which it is often associated. What emerges is an increasingly clear appreciation by all parties to these debates that each of the existing science studies disciplines is inherently limited, taken on its own. Indeed, given the complex and multi-dimensional nature of scientific enterprises—a feature of science that is inescapable when you attend to its details—it is simply implausible that the sciences could be effectively understood in strictly philosophical, or sociological, or historical terms. As Pickering puts the point, "my suspicion is that scientific practice has its own unity and integrity that cuts very deeply across disciplinary boundaries....[it] is situated and evolves right on the boundary, at the point of intersection, of the material, social, conceptual (and so on) worlds" (1990, 710).

At this juncture, then, philosophers, historians, and sociologists confront a common challenge; it is to recast our problems and categories of analysis so that we can comprehend more adequately the full range of factors that constitute and shape science. This will require the development of genuinely interdisciplinary programs of science studies research that draw on but are not constrained by the resources of each of the disciplines that have traditionally taken an interest in science as a subject of inquiry. And it may require substantial change in the institutions that support and structure science studies research.

Given these considerations, it seems especially fruitful to focus attention on recent developments at the interface between various disciplinary science studies fields. To this end, the symposium presented here brings together two philosophers who explore the implications of sociological and historical contextualization for philosophical studies of science (Baigrie and Rouse), with a sociologist (Pickering) and an historian (Smocovitis) whose work raises philosophical questions about the sciences and about science studies. Each argues for ways of reconceptualizing our subject domains, our purposes, and our conventional strategies of inquiry that promise much richer understanding of the sciences, but necessarily challenge discipline–specific traditions of science studies quite profoundly. If there is a common theme to be discerned in these discussions it is that, in the spirit of Rouse's recommendations (this volume), science studies should be understood to be an essentially open ended and dynamic enterprise, like the sciences they study.

References

Brown, J.R. (ed.) (1984) *Scientific Rationality: The Sociological Turn*. Dordrecht: Reidel.

Henderson, D.K. (1990), "On the Sociology of Science and the Continuing Importance of Epistemologically Couched Accounts", *Social Studies of Science* 20: 113–148.

Longino, H. (1990), *Science as Social Knowledge: Values and Objectivity in Scientific Inquiry*. Princeton: Princeton University Press.

Manicas, P.C., and A. Rosenberg (1985), "Naturalism, Epistemological Individualism and 'The Strong Programme' in the Sociology of Knowledge", *Journal for the Theory of Social Behaviour* 15.1: 76–101.

Manicas, P.C., and A. Rosenberg (1988), "The Sociology of Scientific Knowledge: Can We Ever Get it Straight?" *Journal for the Theory of Social Behaviour* 18.1: 51–75.

Pickering, A. (ed.) (1992) *Science as Practice and Culture.* Chicago: University of Chicago Press.

_ _ _ _ _ _ _. (1990), "Knowledge, Practice and Mere Construction," *Social Studies of Science* 20.4: 682–729.

Roth, P. and R. Barrett (1990) "Deconstructing Quarks," *Social Studies of Science* 20: 579–632, 633–746.

Rouse, J. (1987), *Knowledge and Power: Toward a Political Philosophy of Science.* Ithaca: Cornell University Press.

Soloman, M. (forthcoming), "Legend, Naturalism and Scientific Progress," *Studies in History and Philosophy of Science.*

Engaging Science Through Cultural Studies

Joseph Rouse

Wesleyan University

In this paper I sketch the project undertaken in my forthcoming book, *Engaging Science* (Rouse, 1995). This sketch inevitably sacrifices detail and argument, but I hope there is a commensurate gain from giving a sense of how the various aspects of the project hang together. The project itself has two parts: first, a criticism of what I call the "legitimation project" in philosophy and sociology of science; second, my treatment of some of the philosophical issues raised by an alternative approach to interdisciplinary science studies that I call cultural studies of science. I discuss the legitimation project only briefly, however, to set the stage for a discussion of the constructive alternative.

The legitimation project is characterized by the belief that the epistemic standing and the cultural authority of the sciences are in need of a general justification, and that what can appropriately provide such justification (or show its impossibility) is to ascertain the general aim of the sciences as such, or the general nature of science as a practice or achievement. Note that the legitimation project encompasses those who criticize the authoritativeness of the sciences as well as those who endorse it. The most prominent ways of addressing the legitimation project have been to display either the rationality of scientific methods, the contingent referential success of scientific theories, or the social construction of scientific knowledge. Contributors to the legitimation project include scientific realists, empiricists from the Vienna Circle to van Fraassen, post–positivist historicists from Lakatos to Laudan and Shapere, Feyerabend, and the Edinburgh, Bath, and York programs for the sociology of scientific knowledge.

My criticisms of the legitimation project have four significant targets, which I take to be fairly widely shared commitments among its quite diverse participants:

1) first and foremost, I object to the project of wholesale legitimation or critique of the rationality, referential success, or social production of scientific knowledge or scientific methods;

2) second, I reject the closely connected idea that a single aim best explains or makes sense of scientific practices and achievements (this criticism is directed against not only realist or instrumentalist accounts, but also the insistence that only "social factors" or "rational considerations" do or should count);

3) third, I deny that the proper object of philosophical interpretation or sociological explanation is the "content" of scientific knowledge, or the "internal histo-

PSA 1994, Volume 2, pp. 396-401

ry" of the sciences; this idea is more prominent within philosophical defenses of the rationality or truth of science, but the Strong Programme in the sociology of scientific knowledge and its successors also take the "content" of knowledge as their point of departure, as what is crucially in need of a distinctively sociological explanation;

4) finally, I object to the conception of scientific communities as embodying a consensus on basic beliefs, methods, and values.

I shall discuss three aspects of my proposed alternative to these four commitments. First, I emphasize understanding the sciences as ongoing and dynamic practices; second, I present a deflationary and non–representationalist approach to understanding scientific knowledge; and third, I foreground questions about the significance of scientific practices, statements, and the objects they engage, and how that significance changes within ongoing practices.

Scientific practices obviously include experimental and instrumental practices that make things newly or more reliably manifest and available for interaction or manipulation, and the practices of theorizing, modelling, and calculating that offer alternative ways of understanding and interrelating such phenomena. Yet I also want to conceive scientific practices more expansively, as encompassing the institutional, communicative, pedagogical, economic, industrial, political, and other practices that interact with, enable, constrain, enforce, utilize, and otherwise influence or even constitute the more narrowly "scientific" practices that preoccupy most philosophers of science. We cannot fully understand the significance of scientific practices without considering them in their full concreteness. Moreover, it is important to recognize that these aspects of scientific practices affect what scientists do and say, and how others respond, and that that influence cannot be dismissed as irrational or irrelevant without *a priori* commitments concerning the aims of science.

More must also be said about the concept of a 'practice'. I understand practices as patterns of situated activity. Part of the point of this formulation is to include the material setting of activities within the conception of a practice. I thereby reject both realist commitments to the philosophical primacy of "the way the world is" apart from us, and anti–realist commitments to the primacy of human subjectivity, whether in the form of observational or cognitive capacities, or of social interests or interactions. Practices respond over time to the affordances and recalcitrance of their surroundings, while those surroundings are meaningfully configured by the practices through which they become manifest.

More importantly, however, practices on my account are dynamic and temporally extended, since their patterns only exist through continuing reenactment. Their coherence and continuity depend both upon coordination among multiple participants and things, and upon the maintenance of that coordination over time. Since scientific practitioners are geographically dispersed, responsive to local opportunities and constraints, imperfectly communicative, discontinuously policed, and differently located within fields of overlapping scientific practices, there is room for considerable slippage in the ongoing reproduction of the "same" practices. Furthermore, practices are intrinsically open to continuation or extension in multiple ways, because the reenactment of patterns in the practice cannot be determined by rules. Scientific practices typically encompass considerable interpretive differences (both explicit and unarticulated), even synchronically. As a result, scientific practices have a complex temporality. As Hans–Jörg Rheinberger aptly summarized the temporal slippage in the ongoing reproduction of scientific practices, "the recent is the result of something which did not happen, [while] the past is the trace of something which will not have occurred" (Rheinberger 1994, 67).

Scientific practices therefore embody a continual tension between intelligibility and incoherence. Dispersion and openness to multiple interpretation continually threaten their coherence, but since any specific research only becomes intelligible and significant as a contribution to a project shared with others, there is also a relentless pressure to adjust one's work to fit in with what others are doing. This ongoing tension is manifest in what I call the narrative reconstruction of science. The term 'narrative' is used here not to refer to a literary form, but to capture a way of comprehending the temporality of one's own actions in their very enactment. Scientists make sense of what they are doing as a response to the situation presented by past research, and an anticipation of future developments. That is, they continually enact a narrative in the midst of which their present activities (and those of others) would be intelligibly situated. This narrative comprehension must be continually reconstructed, to accommodate the recalcitrance of other people and things, and to appropriate the new possibilities thus made available. The sense and significance of what scientists do is thus continually reconfigured by the subsequent course of research. Understanding scientific practice as narrative reconstruction shows how it becomes coherent and significant without having to rely upon problematic notions of scientific communities, consensus, or background content. Scientists share not background beliefs, but a situation, which they may understand in partially divergent ways.

Two philosophical models have especially influenced my conception of practices as dynamic. Donald Davidson's interpretive semantics (1984, 1986) encourages accounting for linguistic practices, including the linguistic aspects of scientific practices, without reifying conventional meanings, reference, or even languages. Thomas Wartenburg's (1990) broadly Foucauldian account of power as situated and dynamic suggests how to account for scientific knowledge, given my primary emphasis upon scientific practices. Wartenburg argued that power is mediated by "*social* alignments": one agent's actions effectively exercise power over another only to the extent that other agents' actions are appropriately aligned with the actions of the dominant agent. Power relations are dynamic, since they depend upon sustaining these alignments over time, in response to subordinate agents' efforts to resist or bypass them. Power is thus not something possessed or exercised by an agent, or even a relation between two agents, but is instead dispersed throughout a field. Knowing, I suggest, is similarly mediated by and dispersed across "epistemic alignments"; just as actions are only effective when appropriately aligned, skills, models, concepts, and statements only become informative about their objects when other people and things interact in constructive alignment with them. The analogy requires revision of Wartenburg's discussion of power, because he mistakenly restricts the mediation of power to social alignments of human agents. But once the greater heterogeneity of power alignments is acknowledged, we can see that analogous "alignments" situate and mediate the practices of assessing, attributing, relying upon, or contesting knowledge.

Taking seriously the dynamics of scientific practices thereby encourages a deflationary, or non–reifying account of scientific knowledge. A deflationary account of knowledge is directly opposed to those epistemological views that take knowledge to constitute a theoretically coherent kind. A conception of scientific knowledge as a coherent kind has been implicitly presumed by most participants in the legitimation project; it only makes sense to claim that scientific knowledge as a whole is approximately true, rationally arrived at, socially constructed or interest–relative if there is such a (kind of) thing. But deflationary accounts also have no truck with skepticism. Skepticism depends upon the identification of knowledge as a theoretically coherent kind; only then can the skeptic claim that that kind is empty (Williams 1991). The deflationist, by contrast, recognizes a wide range of examples of knowledge, but denies that they collectively constitute a coherent kind. Deflationary accounts should also be distinguished from epistemological eliminativism. Eliminativists argue that ordinary talk about 'knowledge' and 'justification' should be replaced by some more informative vocabulary, with which epistemological categories are incommensurable (e.g., Churchland's (1989) appeal to neurophysiology, or Fuller's (1989) social eliminativism). Deflationists, by contrast, take the ordinary uses of the term 'know', and the associated practices of justification, reliance, and criticism, to be valuable and usually unproblematic, while denying that they can be explicated as instances of a well–formed kind. The contrast to eliminativism is especially interesting, because deflationary accounts permit more heterogeneity in what is potentially relevant to ordinary ascriptions of knowledge in particular contexts than is permissable in eliminativists' proposed replacement theories.

My account of the dynamics of "epistemic alignments" is not itself another general account of knowledge that would conflict with a deflationary understanding, because it does not characterize knowledge as a whole, or as a theoretically coherent kind. The concept of an epistemic alignment is too open–ended to serve in this way as an epistemological theory. There is no reason to believe that present practices have exhausted (or present theories have exhaustively described) the sorts of elements that might contribute to epistemic alignments, or the ways in which they might effectively align. Nor do they constrain what someday might count as informative alignments. One of the historically important features of the sciences has been their role in changing what can count as knowledge. What justifies such changes is not an analysis of how they more adequately exemplify what genuine knowledge really is (such analyses, when offered, are better understood as merely codifying the conceptual changes). Their "justification" has instead been their realization of more informative ways of interconnecting what people do in their environment; but the purposes for which they count as "informative" are intelligible in turn only by maintaining appropriate configurations of practices.

One of the striking consequences of this deflationary account of knowledge is its undoing of any general category of representation. The seemingly natural idea that knowledge is representational accounts for much of the intuitive appeal of the legitimation project. This idea motivates the question of how representations could ever be appropriately connected to objects represented. Whether representations are located in people's heads, sentences, skills and practices, or forms of life, the question takes the same general form. Similarly, objects may be construed as things in themselves, or as things perceptually, practically, or conceptually manifest, without escaping the representationalist problematic. One reason Davidsonian approaches to semantics are useful is that they attend to linguistic practice as ongoing interpretation, rather than in terms of static representational structures of meaning, reference, or language. They also more readily accommodate the importance of theoretical modelling, and the interplay between modelling and scientists' interactions with their surroundings in the laboratory or the field.

My final theme is that the study of scientific practices foregrounds questions of significance, in much the same way that concern about the legitimation of scientific knowledge puts questions of truth and justification in the forefront. The significance of scientific practices is an issue at every level of scientific research. It encompasses broad, programmatic issues (which projects are worth engaging, what equipment and skills are important to acquire, what prior results must be taken into account), as well as the most mundane aspects of laboratory work (which procedural variations make a difference, which experimental runs are "good" ones). Questions of significance govern the codification of achievements (which results are worth publishing, how these results should be framed in an article), and the subsequent redirection of research (which recent developments in this field are important, and how they shape the prospects for further work). Foregrounding significance reminds us that most empirical truths are scientifically irrelevant or uninteresting; recognizing the difference between significant and insignificant projects or achievements is crucial for understanding scientific practice. Discussing significance also shows how the critical assessment of scientific work is multi–dimensional, extending well beyond the justification of claims to truth or empirical adequacy.

'Significance' is a complex notion, however. In its narrowest applications, e.g., statistical significance, it is susceptible to fairly well–defined assessment. Yet one may still ask of a claim that is clearly significant in such a narrow sense whether and how the claim is important. What is at issue in making that claim, and what is at stake in resolving the issue? Push the question far enough, and questions about significance devolve into questions about the intelligibility of a claim or the practices surrounding it. Ludwik Fleck's ([1935] 1979) classic study of the Wassermann reaction can be understood in this way: Fleck was asking how a condition of blood made manifest by the regulated performance of the Wassermann reaction came to be about syphilis. Similar questions might be asked about how events detected at a particle accelerator facility come to count as informative about the origins of the universe, or how Montagnier's and Gallo's laboratory manipulations of retroviruses came to be "about" an emerging epidemiology of acquired immune deficiency. A growing body of work in science studies takes up such questions of intelligibility and significance. Friedman's (1989) account of the construction of a modern meteorology, Haraway's (1989) studies of primatology, Smocovitis' (1992) interpretation of the neo–Darwinian synthesis, Biagioli's (1993) reading of Galileo's courtly self–fashioning, or Rheinberger's (1992, 1994) discussions of how research programs on cancer cell growth came to be about mechanisms of protein synthesis in healthy cells come to my mind, and you can likely add others.

Such interpretive programs that focus upon the emerging, sometimes contested, significance of scientific research exemplify what I mean by "cultural studies of science." Cultural studies of science thus do not reduce science to culture, as if these were discrete and separable in the first place, nor do they programmatically challenge the cultural authority accrued by the natural sciences. Cultural studies instead focus critically upon how and why science matters, to whom, and how people's possibilities for meaningful action and understanding are reconfigured in part through the development of scientific practices. This emphasis upon reshaping people's situation, or what Wartenburg calls their "action–environment," is characteristic of cultural studies. Accounting for the intertwining of knowledge and power is thus central to cultural studies, both because scientific practices significantly transform what people can do and how they can understand themselves, and because scientific practices are responsive to conflicts and resonances within larger patterns of cultural practice. And here, the analogy between Wartenburg's conception of power, and my dynamic and deflationary approach to understanding knowledge, is especially important. Neither power nor knowledge is a thing agents or knowers possess or exercise. Power and knowledge are instead dynamic structural features of agents' and knowers' situations: action and inquiry are conditioned by a field of power relations and prior knowledge, which they also partially transform.

A cultural studies perspective that foregrounds the knowledge/power nexus reminds us how narrowly philosophy of science has construed its disciplinary focus. Despite widespread renunciation of the demarcation project, philosophical attention has been almost exclusively directed to elite, academic sciences, whose historical construction as disciplines has been closely tied to ideals of a pure science unsullied by practical, material, or political concerns. Within such sciences, philosophical concerns have been even more specifically focused upon prestigious, theoretically ambitious sub–fields or theories such as quantum mechanics, general relativity, evolutionary biology, or molecular genetics, which have promised to secure the unity and autonomy of scientific work. The histories of nuclear weaponry, eugenics and genetic determinism, and the tangled cultural politics of evolution remind us that even in these philosophically intriguing fields, what is at stake extends far beyond the issues that have primarily engaged philosophers of science. Yet a more adequately inclusive philosophical perspective on scientific practices and scientific knowledge should also acknowledge more centrally the sciences' links to practices of medicine, agriculture, sex, industry, or war. The point is not to shift attention away from scientific knowledge to other topics, but to recognize how the development of scientific knowledge is more interesting, complicated, and consequential than we philosophers have frequently allowed ourselves to acknowledge.

This emphasis upon the significance of scientific practices has one further consequence for science studies, by redirecting questions about reflexivity. Philosophers have long recognized that reflexivity can pose logical conundrums: is the verificationist theory of meaning meaningful by verificationist standards? does realism depend upon a question–beggingly abductive defense of abduction? Steve Woolgar (1988), Malcolm Ashmore (1989), and others, have also urged attention to rhetorical reflexivity: does the sociology of scientific knowledge rhetorically depend upon an ironic contrast to internalist philosophy of science, or upon naive reading of its own deconstructions of the supposed naivete of scientific representations? Cultural studies encourages an ultimately political twist to such reflexive questioning. What is the significance of philosophical, historical, or sociological studies of science? How and to whom do our inquiries matter, and how do our practices position others, and respond to them? Or in Donna Haraway's provocative formulation, "With whose blood is our vision crafted?" (1991, 192). These questions need more central and explicit attention throughout the science studies fields.

References

Ashmore, M. (1989), *The Reflexive Thesis: Wrighting Sociology of Scientific Knowledge*. Chicago: University of Chicago Press.

Biagioli, M. (1993), *Galileo, Courtier.* Chicago: University of Chicago Press.

Churchland, P. (1989), *A Neurocomputational Perspective: The Nature of Mind and the Structure of Science*. Cambridge: MIT Press.

Davidson, D. (1984), *Inquiries into Truth and Interpretation*. Oxford: Oxford University Press.

________. (1986), "A Nice Derangement of Epitaphs," in E. LePore, (ed.), *Truth and Interpretation*. Oxford: Basil Blackwell.

Fleck, L. ([1935] 1979), *Genesis and Development of a Scientific Fact.* Reprint. Translated by F. Bradley and T. Trenn. Originally published as *Entstehung und Entwicklung einer wissenschaftliche Tatsache* (Basel: Benno Schwabe & Co.). Chicago: University of Chicago Press.

Friedman, R.M. (1989), *Appropriating the Weather: Vilhelm Bjerknes and the Construction of a Modern Meteorology*. Ithaca: Cornell University Press.

Fuller, S. (1989), *Philosophy of Science and its Discontents*. Boulder: Westview Press.

Haraway, D. (1989), *Primate Visions: Gender, Race and Nature in the World of Modern Science*. New York: Routledge.

________. (1991), *Simians, Cyborgs and Women*. New York: Routledge.

Rheinberger, H.–J. (1992), "Experiment, Difference, Writing," *Studies in the History and Philosophy of Science* 23: 305–31, 389–422.

___________. (1994), "Experimental Systems: Historiality, Narration, and Deconstruction," *Science in Context* 7: 65–82.

Rouse, J. (1995), *Engaging Scientce: How to Understand its Practices Philosophically.* Ithaca: Cornell University Press.

Smocovitis, V. (1992), "Unifying Biology: The Evolutionary Synthesis and Evolutionary Biology," *Journal of the History of Biology* 26: 1–65.

Wartenburg, T. (1990), *The Forms of Power: From Domination to Transformation*. Philadelphia: Temple University Press.

Williams, M. (1991), *Unnatural Doubts*. Oxford: Basil Blackwell.

Woolgar, S. (1988), Science: *The Very Idea*. London: Tavistock.

Contextualizing Science: From Science Studies to Cultural Studies[1]

Vassiliki Betty Smocovitis

University of Florida

1. Introduction

For once I find myself in the unusual position of disagreeing with Joe Rouse for I do not think that science studies can or should be simply "modeled" after cultural studies as he has suggested.[2] Instead I will argue for a stronger relationship between science studies and cultural studies that follows historically, if not logically from the progression from HPS to science studies and thence to the cultural study of scientific knowledge. The end-point of the cultural study of scientific knowledge, at least as I will locate it in this paper and elsewhere, for it depends on how one locates the meaning of culture and its study, is a return to the perspective of the scientist having made roughly a 359 degree angle of departure; that one degree more or less gives the critical distance to "defamiliarize the familiar" perspective of the scientist and to "contextualize" scientific practice.

"Discourse, Practice, Context: From HPS to Interdisciplinary Science Studies": Summary of Discussions to Date

The transition from HPS to science studies and thence to cultural studies was the subject of discussion at the spring 1994 University of Florida workshop titled *The New Contextualism: Science as Discourse and Culture*. The seeds of the workshop had been sown earlier at the *Narrative Patterns of Scientific Disciplines* conference in Tel Aviv and Jerusalem in 1992 where Joe Rouse and I had the chance to confer on science, narratives, and disciplines within our own narrower domain of science studies, as well as with the wider domain of other participants from both the sciences and humanities.[3] Earlier still in 1990 many of us had assembled at a Stanford conference organized by David Stump and Peter Galison with the title *Disunity and Contextualism* to discuss the philosophy of science studies. When Alison Wylie invited us to participate in the planning for the present PSA symposium, we decided to pool our resources and come together at the University of Florida in March 1994 as part of a pre-PSA symposium discussion. Thus, as Alison Wylie has already indicated, the present panel walked through some of these issues last spring.

The program organization for the Florida workshop followed the transition from HPS to science studies and thence to cultural studies. The subtitle of the workshop *Science as Discourse and Culture* was a direct response to Andrew Pickering's recently edited book titled *Science as Practice and Culture* (Pickering 1992) with the substitution of the word discourse for practice. The heading or lead title, *The New Contextualism* was meant to reflect the view of science as a "contextual" practice,

PSA 1994, Volume 2, pp. 402-412

and the "new" in the title was meant to draw a distinction between newer views of contextualism that are distinct from the more conventional views of context as mere synonym or substitute for "external". The goal of the workshop in Florida had been to discuss to what extent science could be viewed as discursive or non-discursive practice, how to move away from the sterile distinction between external and internal understandings of scientific knowledge, and what exactly "contextual" approaches to science meant for each of our respective disciplines.

The first session drew together philosophers David Stump, Brian Baigrie, and Alison Wylie with Andrew Pickering, who served as an able representative of the sociology of science. All participants in that session, titled *From History and Philosophy of Science to Science Studies*, took for granted the union between the H (history) and P (philosophy), and began their discussion by assessing previous attempts to incorporate the newer S (sociology) especially with respect to philosophical procedures. The transition that was implicit in the organization of this session therefore took participants from HPS to science studies.

The remaining sessions took participants logically from HPSS (also termed science studies) to the cultural study of scientific knowledge. Participants in the first of these sessions included Joseph Rouse and Elazar Barkan who were assigned the task of discussing what such a transition meant and how it would be achieved. This was followed by the third session which gave concrete examples of what discursive analysis of science looks like in the work cultural and gender historians. The final session brought together intellectual and cultural historian Harry Paul with graduate students at the University of Florida all of who had examined current literature in science studies and cultural studies and who served as critics/commentators to the entire workshop.

Although the first session generated significant agreement between members, each successive session magnified our differences. As these differences grew, communication across our respective disciplines appeared to diminish. By the end of the workshop, it was clear that not all of our goals could be met, in that forum at least. Little consensus was reached about what we meant by contextualism, and attempts to define terms such as discourse, and practice served only as an opening to further discussions. Despite these disappointments, three important things came out of that conference, especially for the historians and philosophers of science present. The first came as a result of what was *not* discussed or given only passing notice. These included some of the more conventional topics within science studies, i.e., problems with the "social construction of scientific knowledge", concomitant problems of relativism, and discussion of scientific realism. This was also one of the first meetings in science studies to problematize outright the use of "practice" and the application of practice-oriented philosophy of science; and in keeping with the absence of discussions on relativism/realism, nearly all participants within history and philosophy of science agreed to move away from the "constraint-talk" that had previously stultified science studies discussions.

The second important thing to emerge from the conference was the introduction and subsequent discussion of some key terms, including contextualism, discourse, culture and practice, which also made their way through varied audiences at the 1995 New Orleans joint meetings of History of Science Society, Philosophy of Science Association, and the Society for Social Studies of Science. Because too, the Florida workshop had included cultural historians, discussions there also took place over the knowledge/ power nexus, and power relations as a whole. Additionally, the role of the "other" within such power relations was problematized, varying forms of cultural imperialism were addressed with the aim of informing science studies, and the roles that aesthetics, emotionality, and agency play in the scientific enterprise were all discussed.

Nearly all of the participants agreed, moreover, that a return to the technical details of science was a necessary requirement for future endeavors that any of us was to make in science studies. Nearly all agreed, additionally, that existing approaches that removed the scientific perspective were unsettling and unsatisfying; and nearly all urged a move away from the unquestioned belief in the unity of scientific knowledge, and toward a multicultural, contextual theory of knowledge. In keeping with this move, discussions in the workshop blurred epistemic, political and existential dimensions of knowledge. By the end of the workshop this blurring had become so evident, that Frederick Gregory, President-Elect of the History of Science Society, commented on the profoundly intricate nature of the contextualist project that we were there to discuss.

2. Contextualizing Science: From Science Studies to Cultural Studies

In the way of introducing the second part of this paper that argues that the move towards cultural studies is a historical, if not a logical progression, I wish to return to the year 1985, the year that saw the appearance of an especially influential form of contextual historiography of science. Up to that point, what had existed as contextualist historiography would have also fallen under the category of "externalist" history. Such externalist histories had become increasingly popular with historians of science, who, in professionalizing their discipline drew farther away from the more traditional internalist histories of scientists-turned historians. No longer the mere mnemonic devices, illegitimate children or historical "handmaidens" to the scientific disciplines, professionalized historians of science increasingly distanced themselves from their scientific objects of study. By 1987 historians of science had distanced themselves so much from scientists that they frequently disregarded more traditional histories: the occasion of the 300th anniversary of the publication of Newton's *Principia*, which should have been reason for pause and reflection, if not celebration, went by largely unnoticed by the leading American journal of the history of science, *Isis*. By the late 1980s the movement for independence had been so successful, that the subtitle for *Isis* reading "An international review for the history of science and its cultural influences," weighed so much in favor of the latter half of the phrase, that it began to work to the detriment of traditional histories, and to the perspectives of scientists.

3. Contextualist Historiography in the Wake of *Leviathan*

The watershed year—or rather the apostrophe mark— for contextualist historiography was 1985, when Steven Shapin's and Simon Schaffer's *Leviathan and the Air-Pump: Hobbes, Boyle, and the Experimental Life* appeared. Informed by the sociology of knowledge (in Shapin's paraphrased terms "getting on with the job of doing the sociology of knowledge rather than just debating it"), Shapin and Schaffer demonstrated in a historically convincing manner how matters of scientific facts were constructed by the complex interplay of material, literary, and social technology within local contexts of activity in Restoration England. They summarized their argument in a critical statement in their introduction: "We argue that the problem of generating and protecting knowledge is a problem in politics and, conversely, that the problem of political order always involves solutions to the problem of knowledge"(Shapin and Schaffer 1985, 21). (Readers who miss or disagree with this argument may effectively count themselves as HP's without the S.) So compelling was the historical discussion and the argument for the emergence of modern experimental science within the sociopolitical context of Restoration England, that even historians of science who had long resisted the sociological framework introduced by Thomas Kuhn in *The Structure of Scientific Revolutions* admitted—if somewhat reluctantly—to a view of science as historically rooted and culturally embedded practice. The dichotomy between "internal" and "external" determinants of scientific practice, had been demonstrably collapsed.

At the same time that it demonstrated that the distinction between internal and external could be removed, *Leviathan and the Air-Pump* also served to blur the perspective of the historian, sociologist, and philosopher. The result was what its proponents termed "science studies", a transdisciplinary configuration in which history, philosophy and sociology of science became "inextricably linked". Amplifying *Leviathan's* impact further for historians, was not only the concomitant increase in sociological literature available, but the much wider historical movement towards social histories of the structured collective that grew out of the anti-elitist politics of the 1960s. No longer would historians contemplate the political and intellectual worlds of elite "great men", but they would instead look to the everyday life of peasants, workers, the "rank and file" to explore how their community structures functioned.

But while social historians could bask in the light of the structured collective, and while some historians of science adapted easily to the social history of science (along with weaker contextualism), others recognized the difficulties inherent with stronger contextualist historiography. Emerging, in part, from an allegiance to the sociology of knowledge (and to the sociological "Strong Programme"), the analytic framework operating in *Leviathan and the Air-Pump* supported a crude form of Marxist constructivism that effectively served to *reduce* scientific knowledge to sociology. Thus, at the same time that it admitted social and sociological components into scientific practice, it did so at the expense of the intellectual and philosophical features.

Equally problematic in its historiography, was the silencing of the voices of the historical actors. This was an especially unacceptable problem that grew out of Shapin and Schaffer's sociological approach to the writing of history that effectively approached the study of science from an outsider's or in their terms, the "stranger's" perspective. But while they could claim to use the tools of sociologists or anthropologists to give such stranger's or outsider's accounts of the science of Hobbes and Boyle, they also remained firmly *inside* the scientific and positivistic *sociology* of science. Thus, while they could argue persuasively for the social construction of scientific knowledge, they were unwilling to apply the same sociology of knowledge to their own practices as historians/analysts. Shapin and Schaffer's argument, and other such attempts to argue for the social construction of scientific knowledge, therefore bore a serious contradiction: *while they argued against simple-minded scientific empiricism, they argued for similar historical empiricism;* and at the same time that they acted to "de-privilege" the knowledge-making claims and positions of scientists, they also served to privilege their own knowledge-making claims and positions as historians/analysts of science. To summarize, *Leviathan and the Air-Pump* was effective in convincing its readers to diminish the distinction between internal and external components of science, in so doing opening the door to sociological and anthropological approaches, but ineffective as far as problematizing historiography as *the writing of history.*

4. Science as Discourse and Culture: Power/Knowledge in the Cultural History/Study of Scientific Knowledge, The Anthropology of Knowledge

Although *Leviathan and the Air-Pump* generated controversy to the point of acrimony (as did the introduction of other sociological accounts of science; see Woolgar (1988) for a synopsis of this literature), the book convinced younger historical scholars of the worthiness of sociological and anthropological approaches. As workers increasingly entertained transdisciplinary reconfigurations like "science studies," they added to the proliferation of approaches that traveled under the banner of "contextual". But rather than draw on the strictly sociological views of knowledge that had been introduced, newer contextual approaches began to lean in the direction of cultural theory and explored seriously the tools of the anthropologist. As these anthropological approaches turned to ethnographic studies, science itself, became "a culture". Because such anthropological analyses examined closely the discursive, or language-based features of cultures, as well as the rites and practices that emerged from and sustained these cultures, they also introduced discussion of discourse and practice at the same time that they discussed culture and context (Traweek 1988; Abir-Am 1992).

Possibly, the most idiosyncratic of these approaches has come from Bruno Latour. In a series of widely read and influential books, Latour has argued for an anthropological approach to understanding science as a culture (Latour 1976 and 1979; 1987). This involves "following scientists" around the laboratory and tracing out the process by which facts are made in a laboratory setting. How the individuals arrange themselves within laboratory collectives, how they generate scientific "facts" within the social setting of the scientific community through the use of inscriptional and then persuasive devices involving the marshaling of resources, enrolling of allies, and finally through subsequent "trials of strength" between rival fact-producing cultures, has been mapped systematically by Latour. Latour's work has received much attention and criticism by a range of scholars within science studies. Among the most unpalatable features of his social framework is his casual overuse of militaristic metaphors, his profoundly ahistorical orientation, his eager dismissal of cognitive content, and his rather dim view of human motivators and activities. All these criticisms stem from his naive acceptance of the colonialist ethnography that he eagerly adopts. That the power relations of ethnographer to ethnographic object have been problematized, and that ethnographers have struggled with "empathy" issues to understand the perspective of the "native" (here scientist) within a staggering diversity of post-colonial ethnographies that permit the voice of the native to speak, seems to have completely escaped Latour (despite the fact that critics like Donna Haraway have repeatedly pointed this out).

More recently, Mario Biagioli (1993), Paula Findlen (1990), Steve Shapin (1994) and especially Jay Tribby (1991; 1994) have actively reworked contextualist historiography of science by exploring the emergence of science within court culture. Although Biagioli's theoretical grounding for his contextual theory of knowledge is the most lucid and complete application of cultural theory to the history of science to date, his emphasis on Galileo and the system of patronage within court culture still suffers from some of the same problems in *Leviathan and the Air-pump* (though for different reasons). Not so much because of its theoretical scaffolding, but because of its actual writing, Biagioli's history serves to reduce science to court culture. One reason for this is due to Biagioli's choice of synchronic historical analysis for his diachronic theory of knowledge (the latter is part of the "new historicism" of some schools of literary history). To deal with the historicity of scientific knowledge—as he so wishes— Biagioli would have to explore the narrativity of scientific knowledge to rework the grand narrative of the history of science that constructs, locates, and determines the character of Galileo. Without this consideration, Galileo becomes hardly more than a courtly parvenu: his passionate aestheticism is forgotten, and the language of his physics is silenced.

The importance of narratives, and the fundamental narrativity of all knowledge underscores the work of Donna Haraway (1989). For Haraway all of knowledge is narrative, or story-constituted. Drawing creatively on some of the most recent post-colonial ethnography, Haraway's historical practice seeks to disrupt or diffuse existing power structures inherent in all social systems through which race, class and gender become structurated. In keeping with post-colonial ethnography, "objectivity" becomes a function of the observer's critical positionality (their vantage point or point of view). Positioning herself as feminist critic, Haraway appropriates critical tools that enable the reworking of the narratives of science that serve to unmask, expose, and disrupt notions of race, class, and gender embedded within the scientific system of power relations. Critical knowledge, in her view, becomes a *tool for social action.* The problem with this approach comes from what appears an ideological epistemology: is all knowledge *merely* a tool for social action that seeks to break deterministic structures? This is clearly not *always* a tenable, nor I confess, a much desirable option.

Successful applications of contextualism have also made their way to the philosophy of science through the work of philosophers of science like David Stump, Peter Galison, and other members of this panel (Pickering 1992; Pickering forthcoming).[4] As part of the move away from theory-dominated and representational accounts of science, the focus instead is on the practice of science to understand what role instruments, models, experiments and other such interventionist procedures play in science. While the contextualism adopted holds that knowledge is localized practice, it fails to confront the textuality or discursivity of knowledge. Although their retreat from theory and representational practices permits the growing "practice industry" to avoid charges of destructive relativism in favor of instrumentalism/realism and pragmatic theories of knowledge (and suitable variations on these themes), their philosophy of science has *only* limited validity with respect to sciences whose procedures effectively diminish theory, representational, or narrative practices—sciences, for example, like experimental physics. What sort of "contextualist" account could they then give of historical sciences like archaeology, cosmology, geology, and evolutionary biology whose textuality and narrativity is the most transparent feature of the science and which have limited use of material or observational evidence? Equally problematic with this practice-oriented philosophy is an obsession with the underlying question of "how science (actually) works"; that science has a historicity that may defy attempts to define, essentialize, or typologize "it", that it may, like a "form of life", defy attempts to freeze it (synchronically) for analysis, and that equal consideration should be given the questions like "how did science come to be?" have not received proper discussion. That science consists of more than just material practices, that it functions as a belief-system whose narratives lend coherence to the community (or any of the myriad terms that have been invented like life-world, *Weltanschauung*, forms of life, thought-collective, paradigm, and discursive *mentalité,* etc.) seem to have gained little serious discussion (despite the gallons of ink that have been spilled on such subjects); worse still, that science emerges from, and is inextricably linked to humanistic practices that serve existential and aesthetic needs and that it may be modeled after aesthetics in the way of being an expression of humanistic desires, seems to have been forgotten completely. To sum: the problem with much of the practice-oriented contextual philosophy is an over-emphasis on the material culture of the science and the materiality of knowledge to the exclusion of the narrative worlds, discursive mentalities or—in whatever word we choose here—something approximating the *perspective* of the scientists.

Here I wish to return to those forms of contextualism that draw heavily on post-colonial ethnography, the anthropology of knowledge, and the new intellectual/cultural history; it is on their theoretical scaffolding that the transition from science studies to cultural studies may be supported. This transition hinges on the form of contextualism that is adopted, for the meaning of *this* term is clearly context-bound.

5. What is contextualism? Defining contextualism

The two questions that appear to occur with the greatest frequency in circles engaging such a transition (certainly evident at the University of Florida workshop) are 1. what is contextualism? and 2. what is culture? Growing out of these two questions is also the question of what exactly one means by cultural studies of scientific knowledge. In one recent article titled "What are cultural studies of scientific knowledge?", Joseph Rouse (1993) did an excellent job of telling readers what cultural studies *are not.* While this position is consistent with the aims of contextualism (see discussion below), it does not help inform a wide audience. In this next section, I would like to attempt to transmit some of the meanings of these relevant terms in response to the questions posed. Since philosophers like terms like rigorous, robust, and strong, let us make the distinction between weaker and stronger versions of the contextualist project (weaker versions won't interest us here, but strong versions may help to transmit more recent uses of the term).

Strong contextualism is very strong: the notion that one can define "context" i.e., to limit or restrict the meaning of the term; or even the notion that one would attempt to essentialize, delimit and typologize *the* context (emphasis here on the definite article) without the concomitant consideration of the shifting critical position or standpoint of the observer, is antithetical to the strong contextualist project. Those of us still needing some kind of "fix" or some provisional working meaning of the term (despite this admonition) may note that the term "culture"—another equally nebulous term—nearly always has *something* to do with "context"[5]; but the conjunction of the two terms in the oft-used phrase "cultural context" would be redundant to adherents of strong contextualism, for there is no meaning outside of context, and culture represents the processes by which meaning is attached.

Another way to understand the stronger version of contextualist movements is to recognize their strong commitment to the view that knowledge is grounded not in foundational, first, or axiomatic principles, but is instead best seen as a cultural artifact (for some it is a product) emerging from more localized and specific contexts of cultural activity. Knowledge is thus "culturally embedded" and may be seen as an artifact of the culture—a cultural construction—though not necessarily holding any artifice or falseness in its meaning. Rather than upholding the view that knowledge is universal and transcendent, therefore, contextualism instead emphasizes the local, situated and embodied features of knowledge.

Although the turn towards contextualism has met with opposition from traditionalists within all the relevant fields of knowledge, the opposition has been the strongest in those fields whose historical development has been to make the greatest commitment to belief in universal, transcendent knowledge. Standard scientific disciplines, the so-called "hard" sciences on the bottom (or the top, depending on one's vantage point) in the disciplinary ordering of knowledge, largely compartmentalized or sheltered from currents in the humanities, have been spared these controversies. The "softer" sciences that border the humanities like anthropology, history, and philosophy have experienced the greater turbulent activity as forms of contextualism make their way into general discussions.

The introduction of contextualist theories of knowledge has possibly met with the greatest opposition in our own HPS. That this opposition has been especially severe is no surprise given the fact that it is the field, which, in occupying a disciplinary location mid-way between the sciences and humanities, serves as a conduit for intellectual exchange between the so-called "two cultures". A mixing of approaches from these areas is inevitable, and though frequently generating innovative work, the same mixing results in some of the most vituperative of exchanges. The controversies surrounding the application of contextualism to science are so great—and have become so confusing to participants—that, taken as a whole, they are possibly the most divisive of issues in the history and philosophy of science.

The intensity of the opposition to contextualism emerges not only from the fact that the interdisciplinarity of the field facilitates the mixing of approaches, but also by the extraordinarily complex range of problems introduced by the application of stronger contextualism to scientific practice that relies heavily on the use of instruments, experiments, and modeling procedures, all of which seem to resist simple discursive analysis. Given these complications, some of which have been discussed by McGuire and Melia (1989), as well as the range of choices in what can effectively count as science, and to whom, the application of the contextualist project—and what it means for the sciences— requires constant close critical examination. To sum: contextualism holds a variety of meanings, not all of which are compatible with each other (Chatman 1990 includes discussion of some of the contextualist forms in the humanities).

6. Situating Text in Context: The Return of Intellectual History

Historiographic concerns aside, how exactly does one proceed to write history within such a contextualist framework? How can contextualist approaches help to inform our historical work on a practical level? And where can one look for historiographic models or exemplars that can be adapted to the history of science? Here I rely on the well-worn work of intellectual historian Keith Michael Baker (1990) and the more recent work of cultural historians like Roger Chartier (1988) and Lynn Hunt (1989), who remind their historical audiences that context means in or within the text. Knowledge thus becomes (con)textual, in accord with forms of conversation, or in some cases in the forms of dialogues between texts. In this view what was termed the history of ideas or intellectual history now becomes the history of discourse (see discussion below for differences). Following this, contextual historical accounts seek to situate text, within text, stressing the polysemous nature of any reading. Methodologically, the stress is on the close reading and reproduction of texts, which is another way of emphasizing the interpretive nature of historical practice and at the same time giving "voice" to the text. Combined with post-colonialist ethnographic theory, which recognizes the critical positionality of the historian and the system of power relations between historian and the historical actor, the history of discourse adapted to the history of science, can be an effective way of returning the perspective of the historical actor. Here it should be noted that such histories (like ethnographies) that silence the perspective of the historical actor are not only historiographically, but also morally, politically, and epistemically bankrupt. Where does the voice of the narrator come through in such a project? The answer: in the text proper; rather than being a stranger's account, this approach comes instead from the insider (an enculturated member, for all are "inside" some cultural framework), who adopts critical tools (mostly linguistic) that disrupt conventions, rituals and practices so that a "defamiliarization" takes place. The hopeful outcome is the narrator who can situate their own being or voice within the historical narrative, effectively *writing themselves into the story*. For this reason, some post-colonial ethnographers intentionally play with reflexive modes of inquiry (see Resaldo 1989 for an example of reflexivity in ethnographic practice, and for other sources into post-colonial ethnographies).

An additional feature highlighted in historiographic models that play on narrativity and post-colonial ethnography is an emphasis on the script-like nature of the narrative pattern. Whether the script be for the unfolding of a mega-event like the French Revolution, or for a micro-event like the unfolding of a life, the narrative serves to play itself out through this script, or "runs" itself in the historical actors and their historical account. (Baker 1990). Similarly, knowledge of science emerges from the writing of grand historical narratives that function like scripts that run themselves from scientific micro-events to mega-events and which ultimately lend coherence to the scientific project (see Smocovitis 1992 for an example of this).

Rather than continue with abstruse and arcane history and theory, I would instead like to demonstrate how such contextual historiography can inform the history of science with a concrete example from my field of the history of biology. Within the history of "evolutionary studies", one central concern has been the rise of Darwinism and Darwin's "evolutionary theory" in the nineteenth century. Historians of ideas have conventionally viewed Darwin as a revolutionary thinker who introduced a dynamic view of organic change. Questions in Darwin studies have traditionally taken the following direction: was Darwin a product of his age? was evolutionary theory in the "air"? especially given the simultaneous co-discovery by Alfred Russel Wallace? What was it in Darwin's theory that was so revolutionary or original if others were independently deriving similar theories of organic change? A contextualist here would rework narratives conventionally disengaged from the narrative of evolution like the wider narrative of the history of the "West" and the narrower personal narrative of the figure of Darwin, in a way to bring as many such narratives together. If one assumes that such engagements between narratives always exist, rather than assuming that they are disengaged (so that one then must demonstrate engagements) then it is possible to reframe the questions posed. In more familiar terms, contextualizing involves bringing narratives that had been previously disengaged, together in an overlapping mode within a rewoven grander narrative. The problem in this contextually polysemous scheme, is not to account for "connections" or "causal influences" but to account for the dislocations or breaks between the narratives. A contextualist thus begins his or her historical work assuming that such "connections" exist within a larger discursive formation, and may begin to reweave another story, possibly with a view of explaining the breaks or dislocations within such a discursive formation.

Returning to the concrete historical example from evolutionary studies, the question becomes not was Darwin a "product of his age?" but instead, "what made us think that he was disengaged from his age?"; so too in this contextualist history, Darwin is hardly an "original" thinker for there are few "originary" points in the history of discourse, but is instead himself a part of, or a "node" within a discursive network or formation that actively constructed *him*; in this view Darwin was not revolutionary but conservative, and all such scientific "revolutions" become conservative moments of ordering the world. That species "transmute" and "transform" had been part of pre-*Origin* scientific discourse. Darwin himself introduced his own "descent with modification" that became "evolution", and which made possible a remarkably orderly view of organic change, given the alternatives. Within this history, if Darwin had not re-ordered the world, someone else would have; for the script for evolution was part of the longer and grander script of the "Enlightened West". In this sense, Darwin's historical "other" was his co-discoverer, Alfred Russel Wallace.

The success of contextualist historiography in the example noted above clearly depends on the existence of narratives that can be rethought, revised, and then rewritten. Thus, this form of contextualism accompanies a historical discipline that has reached some level of maturity (in a sense, the texts and narratives must have accumulated); but similar contextualist methods can be used for less mature disciplines or historical subjects. To sum: this version of contextualism upholds the belief that knowledge is contextual (in and within text); it emphasizes the close reading of texts with attention to precise use of language; it stresses both the polysemy in interpretive readings, and the interwoven nature of narratives. The goal of this contextualist project is to narrate an account that allows the voices and perspectives of the historical actors to speak along with other historical voices, and the narrator(s) all of whom have written themselves into the story. In the best of possible histories, the result is a polyphony of historical perspectives.

7. Closing Thoughts

The contextualist project described above assumes the discursivity and textuality of scientific knowledge. For philosophers of science, this is not an unproblematic position. How the narrative reworking takes place to accommodate material evidence in historical disciplines like archaeology, cosmology, geology and evolutionary biology should be explored through further inquiry (Wylie, forthcoming). If we view scientific narratives as being of "mythopoetic origins", rewoven by historians to accommodate material evidence within a set of unyielding Western values (the Greek word here is *axioma*) such as the value of life, then we have returned to the classic narratives of the history of science in the "west", a position not so very different from the perspective of the scientist.

Last, philosophers of science may quite rightly pick up a call to explore the relationship of discursive and non-discursive elements in the philosophy science; but the call that may not be heard is not only for a philosophy of science, but for a philosophy of *history*. Until the two are adequately addressed, historians, philosophers and sociologists may just as well view themselves as solitary H's, P's and S's, and their hope of transdisciplinarity diminished.

Notes

[1]I wish to thank N. Doran, M. Futch, R. Hampton, C. Koehler, G. Kroll, M. Lesney, G. Weisel and other students in the "Cultural Study/Cultural History of Scientific Knowledge" at the University of Florida. I wish also to acknowledge the support of the National Science Foundation and the Division of Sponsored Research at the University of Florida. Support for the *The New Contextualism: Science as Discourse and Culture* was provided by the Dept. of History and the Humanities Council at the University of Florida; the Philosophy and English Departments provided additional sponsorship.

[2]See Joseph Rouse, "Cultural Studies as a Model for Science Studies," paper presented to *Philosophy of Science Association*, 1994.

[3]For the volume of proceedings see Joseph Mali and Gabriel Motzkin (eds.) *Science in Context*, 7 (1994).

[4]See David Stump and Peter Galison (eds.) (forthcoming), *Disunity and Contextualism: Philosophy of Science Studies,* Stanford: Stanford University Press. The literature on practice oriented philosophy is vast and includes the work of Ian Hacking, Nancy Cartwright, and Peter Galison. For a survey of these approaches see Timothy Lenoir and Yehuda Elkana, (1988), "Practice, Context and the Dialogue Between Theory and Experiment," *Science in Context* 2 (1). For another survey of practice philosophy to history of science see Jan Golinski, (1990), "The Theory of Practice and the Practice of Theory: Sociological Approaches in the History of Science," *Isis*, 81: 492-505.

[5]In attempting to articulate the meaning of "culture" Stephen Greenblatt states that culture is "a term that is repeatedly used without meaning much of anything at all, a vague gesture toward a dimly perceived ethos." In "Culture" Frank Lentricchia and Thomas McLaughlin (eds.), *Critical Terms for Literary Study*,(Chicago: University of Chicago Press, 1990), p. 225.

References

Abir-Am. (1992), "A Historical Ethnography of A Scientific Anniversary," *Social Epistemology* 6:323-354.

Baker, K.M. (1990), *Inventing the French Revolution*. Cambridge: Cambridge University Press.

Biagioli, M. (1993), *Galileo, Courtier. The Practice of Science in the Culture of Absolutism*. Chicago: University of Chicago Press.

Chatman, S. (1990), "What Can We Learn from Contextualist Narratology?", *Poetics Today* 11: 309-328

Chartier, R. (1988). *Cultural History. Between Practices and Representations*. Ithaca: Cornell University Press.

Findlen, P. (1990), "Jokes of Nature and Jokes of Knowledge: The Playfulness of Scientific Discourse in Early Modern Europe," *Renaissance Quarterly* 43:292-331.

Haraway, D. (1989), *Primate Visions*. New York: Routledge.

Hunt, L. (ed.). (1989), *The New Cultural History*, Berkeley: University of California Press.

Latour, . and Woolgar, S. [1979] (1986), *Laboratory Life: The [Social] Construction of Scientific Facts*. 2d (revised) ed. Princeton, N.J.: Princeton University Press.

Latour, B. (1987), *Science in Action: How to Follow Scientists And Engineers through Society*. Cambridge: Harvard University Press.

McGuire,J.E. and Melia, T. (1989), "Some cautionary strictures on the writing of rhetoric of science," *Rhetorica* 7:87-99.

Pickering, A. (ed.) (1992), *Science as Practice and Culture*. Chicago: University of Chicago Press.

_ _ _ _ _ _ _. (forthcoming), *The Mangle of Practice*.

Rouse, J. (1993), "What Are Cultural Studies of Scientific Knowledge?", *Configurations* 1:1-22.

Rosaldo, R. (1989), *Culture and Truth*. Boston: Beacon Press.

Shapin, S. and Schaffer, S. (1985), *Leviathan and the Air-Pump. Hobbes, Boyle, and the Experimental Life*. Princeton: Princeton University Press,

Shapin, S. (1994), *A Social History of Truth. Civility and Science in Seveteenth-Century England*. Chicago: University of Chicago Press.

Smocovitis, V.B. (1992) "Unifying Biology: The Evolutionary Synthesis and Evolutionary Biology," *Journal of the History of Biology* 25: 1-65.

Traweek, S. (1988), *Beamtimes and Lifetimes. The World of High-Energy Physics*. Cambridge, Mass.: Harvard University Press.

Tribby, J. (1991), "Cooking with Clio and Cleo: Eloquence and Experiment in Seventeenth Century Florence," *Journal of the History of Ideas* 52:417-429.

______. (1994), "Club Medici: Natural Experiment and the Imagineering of 'Tuscany'", *Configurations* 2:215-235.

Woolgar, S. (1982), *Science: The Very Idea*. Chichester, Sussex: Ellis Horwood Ltd.

Wylie, A. (forthcoming). *No Return to Innocence: Philosophical Writings in American Archaeology*. Princeton: Princeton University Press.

After Representation: Science Studies in the Performative Idiom[1]

Andy Pickering

University of Illinois at Urbana-Champaign

> Satisfied that the sequence of men led to nothing and that the sequence of their society could lead no further, while the mere sequence of time was artificial, and the sequence of thought was chaos, he turned at last to the sequence of force; and thus it happened that, after ten years' pursuit, he found himself lying in the Gallery of Machines at the Great Exposition of 1900, his historical neck broken by the sudden irruption of forces totally new.
>
> Henry Adams, The Education of Henry Adams.

This essay is about science studies: history, philosophy and sociology of science, etc. My interest is in where the field is now and where I would like it go. Taking my cue from actor-network theory, my central theme is agency—questions of who acts? who does what to whom, how and why? And to develop this theme I contrast two different idioms for thinking about science—two different metaphysics—which I call the representational and the performative idioms.[2]

1. The Representational Idiom

The representational idiom is the traditional one in science studies, the one that long dominated history of science and that runs from logical positivism and logical empiricism to the canonical works on the sociology of scientific knowledge and to the many recent attempts to understand science (and technology) as text, including discourse analysis and reflexivity. Representationalism takes it for granted that the defining characteristic of science is its production of representations of nature, facts and theories; it studies, one can say, science-as-knowledge. And, as far as agency is concerned, the representationalist idiom takes it for granted that the world gets into knowledge only through the medium of inert statements of matters of fact. All of the agency in this idiom, then, is the agency of knowledge's human producers, the scientists. And all representationalist accounts of science can, I think, be phrased as accounts of specifically human agency. Thus, recognising the integral role of human agency in theory construction, representationalist philosophy of science fears it, and, in a courageous attempt to stop scientists just making up whatever stories they like, seeks to police it, to articulate and impose rules, standards, norms of rationality, objectivity, method on theory-choice. Early sociology of scientific knowledge, in contrast, celebrates human agency, looking to the interests of social groups as the explanation of the production and use of specific knowledge claims. And so on. Whichever way one develops the representationalist idiom, the material world remains without agen-

PSA 1994, Volume 2, pp. 413-419

cy: all of the interesting and important action is on the human side of science; all of the theory, all the analytic effort in science studies is focussed there.

I think these remarks are sufficient to make clear the sense in which a lot of work in traditional science studies has been, in fact, representationalist, and has presupposed an asymmetrical distribution of agency: all to human beings, none to nature. And now I want to enter two comments on this representationalist idiom. The first concerns the reference to interdisciplinarity in the title of this symposium. As far as I can make out, within the representationalist idiom it is very difficult to achieve any real synthesis between the science-studies disciplines (or between those disciplines and their parents). The problem is that the disciplines take up quite different perspectives on agency: philosophers reinforce their own disciplinary identity by trying to spell out superlocal characteristics of reason and so on; sociologists are likewise enamoured of local and situated interests, or whatever; and historians tend to oscillate between the two competing master-narratives. The best that one can do towards synthesis in this situation is, it would appear, to add up the rival stories, to run both at once in the approach that I call multidisciplinary eclecticism. As Ronald Giere puts it in an essay entitled 'Prospects for an Enlightened Postmodern Synthesis' in science and technology studies: 'the goal is not "unification" within a single perspective but the "integration" of several different perspectives. Rather than interdisciplinary research, one should think in terms of multidisciplinary research' (1993, 108; see also his 1994 Presidential Address to the PSA, this volume). From my point of view, this kind of eclecticism is undoubtedly a step in the right direction—in a limited sense, at least, it admits the social into the hitherto pure precincts of reason—but, as I will try to show in a moment, I think we can go much further in the direction of synthesis. Before that, however, my second comment on representationalism.

Though people have tended to adopt it unthinkingly, the representational idiom is not compulsory in science studies. We do not have to think of science as primarily a matter of facts and theories, and I, at least, have come via empirical studies of scientific practice to the conclusion that it is a somewhat perverse perspective (and also that it is an even more perverse perspective if one is interested not just in science but in technology as well). So let me now start talking about the alternative that I call the performative idiom.

2. The Performative Idiom

The basic idea of the performative idiom is that the world is full of agency. Human beings are agents, in the traditional voluntarist sense delineated within the representational idiom, and in other ways besides; but so is nature: the material world is continually acting, too. Think of the weather, bubble chambers, machine tools, TV sets, atom bombs. All of these, I want to say, are agents, continually acting and performing in ways that are not at all reducible to naked human agency. This idea seems to me rather obvious, and for the rest of this talk, rather than trying to deal with the representational contortions that can make it hard to grasp, I want to see where it can lead us.

The performative idiom invites us to think symmetrically about agency: human beings are not the only actors around; the material world acts too. And it invites the further idea that science and technology are amongst our ways of coping with this busy world—especially, in the case of the natural sciences and engineering, of coping with material agency, warding it off, capturing and seducing it, harnessing it and channeling its flow and so on, via the construction of machines and instruments. This is my basic performative image of science. I should immediately add that the performative idiom has no need to deny that scientists are in the business of producing knowledge and representations as well as machines and instruments. It suggests, though, that we should be interested in how the field of representations is threaded through the machinic field of science, in trying to understand each in relation to the other, rather than treating the representational aspects of science in isolation. I want to emphasise, therefore, that the move from the representational to the performative idiom is a rebalancing of our understanding of science. The performative idiom includes the representational one; it recognises that science does produce knowledge and representations, but it also recognises the material and social dimensions of science, and tries to get all of these strata into focus at once.

So, in the performative idiom, scientific practice, the doing of science, appears as struggles in fields of human and nonhuman agency, and the question I want to address next is: what's at stake in these struggles? I raise this question because I think the answer to it is interesting and important and goes to the heart of interpretive debates in science studies. Empirically, it seems to me, everything is at stake in these struggles; nothing necessarily endures. Every single element or stratum of scientific culture—material, conceptual, social—is revisable in practice: the material contours of machines and instruments and their performances; facts, theories and mathematical formalisms; the scale of social actors and their relations with one another; skills, disciplines, plans and intentions; norms, standards, rules; you name it. All of these evolve open-endely into the future. And to draw out the significance of this conclusion, I want to emphasise two features of cultural evolution thus understood, features which I call temporal emergence and posthumanism.

I say that the evolution of scientific culture is temporally emergent in that what culture becomes in any passage of practice cannot be foreseen or explained in advance; the future genuinely emerges in the real time of practice. Perhaps the easiest way to see this is to think about the material stratum of science. One can try to build a new machine, say, which will capture material agency and channel it in a particular direction. But the expectation has to be that one will fail. At minimum, the construction of a new machine entails a kind of open-ended tuning—repeated reconfiguration of its material specifications until some sort of desired or desirable performance emerges. No-one can know in advance just what precise tunings will be made in practice, nor what their upshot will be. This is what I mean by temporal emergence. And the same goes for all of the cultural strata of science: the material, the social, the conceptual, these are all continually tuned and retuned in the struggles in fields of agency that the performative idiom thematises.

Now for posthumanism. The point here is that the tunings of the different strata of science that I have just distinguished—the material, the social, the conceptual, and so on—do not, in general, proceed independently of one another. Practical manoeuvres in fields of agency typically couple the tunings of these heterogeneous strata together, so that, for example, the contours of new machines are often interactively stabilised, as I put it, against revised conceptual structures and transformed social actors and their relations. And that means that what human beings are—their goals and intentions, skills and disciplines, aggregation into macroactors of different scales, tied to one another in different ways—itself becomes in practice in its intertwining with the nonhuman world of material agency. Human agency, then, is not, as the representationalist idiom would have it, something reliably given in advance that can provide an enduring explanatory resource in the analyis of scientific knowledge production. (Nor is material agency reliably given in advance as the scientists and technological determinists would have us believe.) This displacement of the human from the explanatory centre of the action—a displacement, I insist, not an erasure—is what I mean by the posthumanism of the performative idiom.

So, my suggestion for science studies is that we might move away from representationalism and the analytic apparatuses that have accreted around it in favour of a performative image of science in which scientific culture is recognised as the product of temporally emergent posthuman transformations, or manglings as I call them. The rest of this essay just sketches out some aspects and corollaries of this shift.

* * *

I begin with the question of interdisciplinary synthesis. The performative idiom suggests, and probably requires, a much more thoroughgoing synthesis of the science studies disciplines than the multidisciplinary eclecticism mentioned earlier. This is because it denies the existence of the pure objects that the pure disciplines purport to study and through which they perpetuate themselves. Thus although I have been speaking about the social, the material and the conceptual as distinct strata of scientific culture, it should be obvious that I have been using these terms in a rough-and-ready, commonsense fashion with no foundational or disciplinary implications. The very point that I want to emphasise is that each of these strata is continually and constitutively intertwined with the others in practice via processes of heterogeneous interactive stabilisation. The social, then, for example, is never purely social; there is no purely social dynamics of scientific practice; and there is, therefore, no room in the world for a pure (e.g. Durkheimian) sociology of science. And the same goes for the material and the conceptual. The performative idiom thus undercuts any rationale for traditional disciplinary divisions of labour in science studies, whether competitively set against one another or eclectically summed. To put the same point constructively, the synthesis promoted by the performative idiom is an antidisciplinary one, in which history, philosophy, sociology, anthropology and whatever collapse into one another.

The question then arises of what this new performative antidisciplinary synthesis might look like; what substantively it might amount to. Here an interesting worry surfaces. John Dewey once remarked of pragmatism that it 'seems to many to be the suicide of philosophy' (1960, 68) and the performative idiom might similarly seem to be the suicide of science studies. Thus it is clear that the performative idiom undermines the traditional explanatory projects that go along with representationalism. The posthumanism of the performative idiom implies that is in no use looking for explanatory variables in the purely human realm, and temporal emergence implies that looking for enduring explanatory variables anywhere is a mistake. The old problematics thus collapse in the performative idiom along with disciplinarity, and from the traditional representationalist perspective it can therefore appear that the thematisation of agency and performativity is a dead end, that leaves us nothing to think and write about—an academic disaster of truly major proportions. In fact, however, I think that there is life after representationalism, and I therefore turn to some lines of present and future work within the performative idiom that seem to me interesting and promising.

* * *

Let me start with the discipline presently called sociology. What can people who now call themselves sociologists do after representation? Empirically, I think they can do what they should already have been doing. They can investigate the social contours of science, technology, engineering, the factory and so on. What they have to stop doing is assuming that the social that they document causes or explains the material and conceptual strata that they must also encounter. The implication of the performative idiom for sociologists is, then, that they have to develop an impure sociology that can recognise, thematise, bring into focus, the intertwining of social transformations with material and conceptual ones. This should anyway be the central problematic of science, technology and society studies (STS). If anyone has ever lived in a society that is shot through with captured and seduced material agency (without being determined by it, or vice versa) it is us. I am therefore inclined to think that the performative idiom is our best hope for getting to grips with who we are and in what kind of a world we have become it. I return to this sentiment below, but now I turn to philosophy.

In the representational idiom there exists a special set of objects and topics that sustain a purely philosophical discourse on science—reason, understood in terms of the rules or norms of scientific method, for example. Such objects lose their privilege and purity when science is understood in the performative idiom. The more closely one tries to specify what the rules are, the clearer it becomes that they are themselves at stake in scientific practice and subject to mangling and transformation in relation to 'extra-philosophical' cultural strata. So the prospects for pure, disciplinary philosophy of science look gloomy in the performative idiom. But still, there are plenty of projects that one can call philosophical in an everyday sense and that offer plenty of space for constructive thought. Let me list a few.

First, the whole business of thinking through the shift to the performative idiom—how best to conceptualise heterogeneous agency and cultural multiplicity—remains to be worked out. The present essay is thus an exercise in philosophy, as far I am concerned, and I do not suggest that the task is completed. More specifically, one can generate much food for thought by running through the old problematics of representationalism in the performative idiom. One finds they have been constructively displaced.

As an example, take the problematic of realism. Instead of attempting to decide whether scientific representations correspond to how nature nakedly is, in the performative idiom one can explore what the connections between knowledge and the world actually look like as they are made in scientific practice. And one finds that these are highly nontrivial connections, depending on the emergent construction of alignments between representational chains and uncertain captures and framings of material agency in machines and instruments. What emerges, therefore, is, in the first instance an a-correspondence realist appraisal of scientific knowledge (not an antirealist one): an appraisal that I call pragmatic realism, which recognises the constitutive and formative engagement of knowledge with the world, and vice versa, without implying any particular correspondence or lack of it between representation and represented. Actually, however, one can pursue this line of thought further, in a direction which does, in the end, serve to undercut our correspondence intuitions.

What I have in mind is this. In the performative idiom one sees that scientific knowledge attaches, visibly, not to 'the world itself,' but to specific machinic fields, distributions of specific and specifically tuned machines and instruments. This being the case, what comes clearly into view is the possibility of what Ian Hacking once called 'a new and fundamental type of incommensurability' (1992, 54) which I call performative incommensurability, an incommensurability that resides in the fact that different bodies of knowledge and representation, of facts and theories, often terminate in different machinic fields and their different performativities. Looking at the other end of the chain, the performative idiom also makes it possible to imagine an incommensurability of human powers (as conjured up, for instance, in the writings of Carlos Castaneda, eg Castaneda 1968)—the idea being that in different cultural circumstances, the agency of human minds and bodies might appear radically different from our usual characterisations of it. The critique of correspondence realism that goes along with the recognition of the possibility of such kinds of incommensurability is obvious. Here I just want to suggest that there is room for plenty of 'philosophical' reflection in these kind of spaces that the performative idiom opens up for us. And much the same could be said for other traditional problematics like rationalism and relativism. My argument would be that within the performative idiom one can grasp the sense in which scientific knowledge is objective, relative and truly historical, all at once. But I will let that go, and turn to place of history in a performative science-studies synthesis.

My description of scientific culture as temporally emergent is a forward-looking one. It says that we can never know ahead of practice what its products will be. Looking backwards in time instead, as historians like to do, the image of science is a historicist one: if there are no enduring substantive principles that explain how science gets to be what it is, all that we can do is trace out the specific developments that have led to specific end-points. The heart of a performative science studies, then, has to be history, understood as empirical research into specifics (a definition that includes ethnography, too). Historians can thus only profit from the shift from the representational to the performative idiom. All that they have to do is stop imposing the old representationalist master-narrative structures on their stories. That is, however, easier said than done. Old habits die hard. The temptation is always to drift into multidisciplinary eclecticism, swapping between the explanatory registers of realism, rationalism and sociologism to connect up events as seems easiest. I therefore want to close by discussing the historiographic approaches that seem most promising in leaving the old master narratives behind.

First, what people have started calling cultural studies of science. At this symposium, both Rouse and Smocovitis have 'cultural studies' in their titles, so I probably do not need to say too much here. I just want to say that on my definition (which, I should acknowledge, seems to differ from Rouse's) cultural studies of science is a genre that seeks self-consciously to discard traditional representationalist preconceptions of its object of study, in favour of perspicuous macro-mappings of specific alignments of heterogeneous cultural elements—instruments, machines, social groupings and relations, conceptual structures, etc—within specific sciences or between them and specific technological and social formations. Donna Haraway's 'Manifesto for Cyborgs' (1985) might also be taken as a manifesto for this approach to the history of science and, evidently, I think that it is a very promising line of historiographic development within the performative idiom. And this being the case, I want to enter a couple of caveats concerning cultural studies of science.

First, it is worth noting that the designation 'cultural studies of science' aims to cement an alliance with the wider field of cultural studies at large. In general, I am in favour of this: the bigger the synthesis the better. I worry a bit, however, about the title of Rouse's talk, which invites us to think of 'cultural studies as model for science studies.' The danger here is that, historically, cultural studies proper has inherited a representationalist image of culture. One starts by thinking about Henry IV, Part I, and ends up with an account even of science and technology as text and discourse ('discourse' being the first word in the title of this symposium). This is not the way I want cultural studies of science and technology to go. It is not that I object to the study of discourse, but I would be sad to see cultural studies of science lapse back into representationalism. It is precisely when one wants to study science (and technology and engineering), rather than culture in general, that one needs to be clear on the heterogeneity of agency right from the start.

Now for my second caveat about cultural studies, namely that, as currently practised, it is not very good on time. It is posthuman (in its performative variants) but the pull of synchronous definitions of culture blunts any awareness of temporal emergence. One deleterious effect of this is that fragments of traditional explanatory schemes can hang on like the living dead in otherwise exemplary historical accounts. I will not go into this any further here, except to invite you to beware especially of prison metaphors in the cultural-studies literature—explanations couched in terms of nonemergent limits and constraints on practice.

Instead, I want to talk about how one might add an explicit time dimension to cultural studies, about how one might combine the cultural-studies project of large-scale cultural mapping with an interest in cultural transformations over time. More specifically, I want to ask what kind of a 'big picture' of the overall history of science (and technology and society) would go with the performative idiom. It might seem that as a general perspective on practice the performative idiom has nothing special to offer us here, but in fact one can reason like this. How should we periodise the history of science? The representational idiom encourages us to do so in terms of major transformations in the realm of representation, meaning in theory. And it thus fosters a historiography organised around great men and their great ideas—Galileo, Newton, Darwin, Einstein. In the performative idiom one can reason along similar lines but to a different destination. The performative idiom asks us to pay attention to transformations in the domain of performativity, which singles out, to put it very crudely, not the Scientific Revolution but the Industrial Revolution as a key moment in the history of science, etc.

Where this line of thought leads is, I think, fairly obvious, so I shall develop it telegraphically. A performative big picture of the history of science would be one in which Karl Marx, Boris Hessen and John Desmond Bernal basically got it right. Science should not be approached as an object sui generis that from time to time interacts with some extrascientific 'context.' Instead we should look to fields of agency—in social production, consumption, reproduction and destruction; from the factory to the battlefield—as surfaces of emergence and return for science. The steam engine and thermodynamics; the electrical telegraph industry and electromagnetic theory; brewing and microbiology; etc. The only sense, I think, in which the Marxist tradition has tended to get it wrong is in thinking that the base somehow determines the superstructure; that one can, as it were, read off the form and substance of science from cannons and cotton mills and class struggle. If my earlier remarks about temporal emergence have any substance, this cannot be right. It is not Marxist theory that can tell us just how science has emerged from the factory, say, and how it has returned to the battlefield, it is historians and empirical historical research. And this brings me to my last remark.

The performative big picture of the history of science that I have in mind hardly exists at present. One can find a growing collection of bits and pieces of it in the literature, but no synthetic overviews other than classic Marxist texts that are hitched to classic non-emergent master-narratives. And I think that this is a shame. To return to a line of thought I introduced earlier, I think that it is precisely a performative historiography of science and technology that we need if we are ever to get the specifics and singularity of our own, intrinsicially technoscientific, late-20th century culture into focus and thence to think constructively about it. It would, of course, be a massive task to do the job properly—performative history is much more difficult to write than representationalist history—but it needs to be done.

And so, in the end, I have persuaded myself, at least, that the performative idiom is not the suicide of science studies. It is not a cul-de-sac for constructive thought and practice. It precipitates instead all sorts of fascinating and important lines of enquiry, from the narrowly academic to the globally political. It may be posthuman, but there is a life for science studies after representation.

Notes

[1]I am grateful to participants in a workshop on 'The New "Contextualism:" Science as Discourse and Culture,' University of Florida, Gainesville, 11-13 March 1994, for their reactions to an earlier presentation of these ideas, and to Stefan Timmermans, Geof Bowker and Bert Kögler for comments on an earlier version of this essay.

[2]The canonical introduction to actor-network theory is Latour (1987). The ideas put forward below are more fully worked out, exemplified and related to the science-studies literature in Pickering (1995).

References

Castaneda, C. (1968), The Teachings of Don Juan: A Yaqui Way of Knowledge. Harmondsworth: Penguin.

Dewey, J. (1960), "Need for a Recovery of Philosophy", in R. J. Bernstein, (ed.), On Experience, Nature, and Freedom: Representative Selections. New York: Bobbs-Merrill, pp. 19-69.

Giere, R.N. (1993), "Science and Technology Studies: Prospects for an Enlightened Postmodern Synthesis", Science, Technology, & Human Values 18: 102-12.

______. (this volume), "Viewing Science".

Hacking, I. (1992), "The Self-Vindication of the Laboratory Sciences," in A. Pickering (ed.), Science as Practice and Culture. Chicago: University of Chicago Press, pp. 29-64.

Haraway, D. (1985), "A Manifesto for Cyborgs: Science, Technology, and Socialist Feminism in the 1980s", Socialist Review 80: 65-107.

Latour, B. (1987), Science in Action: How to Follow Scientists and Engineers through Society. Cambridge, MA: Harvard University Press.

Pickering, A. (1995), The Mangle of Practice: Time, Agency, and Science. Chicago: University of Chicago Press.

HPS and the Classic Normative Mission

Brian S. Baigrie

The University of Toronto

1. Introduction

This session is about the future of philosophy of science, one of a series of negotiations occasioned by the suggestion that philosophy of science must engage, not only the history of science and/or contemporary scientific practice but also the challenge, raised by social scientists, of seeing science as essentially a cultural and dynamic activity. The session is timely because these negotiations are well underway. Many philosophers of science are already committed to an inter-disciplinary eclecticism that has generated a heterogeneous family of science studies programs and projects, all designed to situate science in its social, historical, and politico-economic contexts, but each with its own sense of what shape inter-disciplinary science studies research will take in the coming years. Philosophers who favor this new disciplinary eclecticism face many problems if they are to successfully forge a hybrid science studies that does not violate their integrity as philosophers. If the proposed transformation is to be successful, philosophers of science must isolate an intellectual space in which traditional agendas, such as the concern for the clarification of concepts, can hold court.

In this space, I cannot possibly comment on these contending varieties of inter-disciplinary science studies. I can, however, outline what I regard as a new brand of HPS, one that is deeply rooted in the history of the exact science and that takes the perspective of scientific and cultural actors at face value. The virtue of this New HPS, I will submit, is that it furnishes philosophers of science with a fresh perspective from which to carry on philosophy's classic normative mission.

2. Two Styles of HPS

While recognizing that philosophy of science includes a vast array of projects and characteristic styles of exposition, as a preliminary move I want to offer a general contrast on two general positions that we can take on the relationship between the history and the philosophy of science:

(1) we can see history *as something that is applied to the philosophy of science*. Following Karl Popper, Imre Lakatos, and Larry Laudan, we can regard the history of science as a constraint on philosophical activity and as an external court of appeal for the viability of philosophical theses. For lack of a better expression, let's call this view classical HPS. It reached its apex with Larry Laudan's conference "Testing Theories of Scientific Change," held at Virginia Polytechnic and State University in 1987.

PSA 1994, Volume 2, pp. 420-427

The regulative principle of Classical HPS is that philosophers of science ought to ground their work in an accurate representation of the practical activities of scientists, whether this consist in genuine engagement with real science or with historical narratives about the development of scientific practices and institutions. As applied to philosophical practice, this principle is registered in the insistence that there are important differences between "historical" and "philosophical" questions, "narrow" and "broad" questions, and, most fundamentally, between "historical" and "philosophical" methods and tools of analysis. Classical HPSers expend vast amounts of energy worrying about these differences, with the aim of isolating an intellectual space where traditional philosophical methods and tools of analysis still hold court.

The supposition that there are methods and problems special to philosophy is reflected in the fairly widespread conviction that philosophy of science should not be allowed to remain at the micro level, lest the broad questions that we traditionally associate with philosophical discourse be obscured by technical detail: "philosophers," David Stump submits, in his Afterward to a forthcoming volume—*The Disunity of Science*: *Boundaries, Contests, and Power*—"must not ignore science studies and simply get lost in the technical details of scientific sub-disciplines without considering broader issues." The message here seems to be that traditional philosophical methods and approaches must dictate how it is that context and, in particular, historical narrative, is to be engaged. We are to keep the broad issues in the forefront and only then examine the historical record to sustain or deny these general theses.

(2) we can see philosophy as something *that is applied to the history of science* and/or scientific practice. Here we regard philosophical agendas as constraints on historical activity; following Foucault (1970), Hacking (1983, 1995), and perhaps Lorraine Daston, the desire to get clear on philosophical concepts and broad systems of classification is the final court of appeal for the relevance and scope of historical narrative. Though ethnophilosophy might be a better term, let's call this view New HPS. The regulative principle of New HPS is that philosophical agendas are to be seen in historical relief, that concepts and systems of classification that currently authorize behavior are themselves historical and dynamical entities. New HPS has barely got off the ground, though I would submit that Hacking's conference on Historical Epistemology held in 1993 at the University of Toronto signaled the public recognition of a hybrid style of science studies that already involves many philosophers of science.

3. New HPS and the History of the Exact Sciences

These two styles of HPS have different pedigrees. Classical HPS is standardly portrayed in the literature as a fairly recent development connected with the demise of logical positivism. Nicholas Jardine (1984), however, has argued convincingly, I think, that Johannes Kepler employed a history of hypotheses to defend the legitimacy of Tycho Brahe's planetary hypothesis. Indeed, Jardine claims that the use of the historical record as a constraint on philosophical activity gave birth to what we now commonly regard as history and philosophy of science. If Jardine is right, Classical HPS was an intellectual reaction to a worry about the epistemological credentials of Tycho's planetary hypothesis. This is what one would suppose, except that most of us get the date wrong by some four hundred years. Clearly, Kepler did not give Classical HPS a form that it has sustained throughout the centuries; his writings testify that HPS is not a recent creation but that it has been recreated many times.

New HPS is a comparatively recent creation with a very different pedigree. In order to get clear on this, we need to recount some details about the rise of history of the exact sciences. By the time Kuhn's seminal work appeared in 1962, technical history of science (which I use here as short-hand for history of the exact sciences) was well-established; the *Archive for History of Exact Sciences* was established in 1960 under the editorialship of Clifford Truesdell, a mathematician at Johns Hopkins University. Until fairly recently, technical history of science only existed in any proper form in the history of astronomy; now it exists in the history of exact sciences and, to a lesser extent, in some branches of biology. The organizing principle of technical history of science is the conviction that since 1700 (and in isolated instances much before that) science has been organized for control production in a highly specific way. Two convictions are responsible for this control production, that (a) special training (or at least intensive work) is essential to science, which is amply attested to by the production of exercise books, practice primers, instrument manuals, as well as the rise of institutionalized modes-of-inculcation; and (b) instruments provide reliable and special means for doing science. What technical historians are engaged in is figuring out how these two convictions cash out in the creation of specific sets of practical activities that include an attitude towards nature, namely, ones that enable access to control, manipulation, novel device production, and prediction. Many scientists are convinced that they are gaining intimate access to reality—that there is something in scientific practice that goes beyond manipulation and device production—but technical historians of science do not have to share these beliefs and, indeed, few do. When the technical historian reaches into the inner core of scientific practice and pulls out original meaning and skill—even when the skill is reproduced from archival and other evidence—no claims need be made about "reality" in a deep sense.[1]

The requirements for technical history of science are daunting—technical scientific training (usually to the graduate level), linguistic skills, including reading knowledge of Latin, French and German, training in historical methodology. This last requirement is critical since even competent scientists with good language skills can produce flawed work because of inadequate historical methods. As a field, technical history of science is associated with a number of canonical studies that serve as stable benchmarks for historical practice—Stillman Drake's work on Galilean mechanics, Derek Whiteside on patterns of mathematical thought in the 17th century, Philip Lervig on Carnot's theory of heat, Noel Swerdlow on Renaissance astronomy; more recently, Allan Shapiro on Newton's optics, Jed Buchwald on 19th century wave optics and Maxwell's electrodynamics, Istvan Szabo and Wilbur Knorr on the origins of Euclidean geometry, and Thomas Hankins on the Lebesque measure.

Some of the major players are housed in scientific departments (Swerdlow in Astronomy, Stigler in Statistics, Edwards and Hankins, Feigenbaum, and Berggren in Mathematics). Others are housed in a handful of institutions—in North America, Toronto, Minnesota, The Dibner, Harvard and perhaps Wisconsin; in Europe, Aarhus, Utrecht, Hamburg, Frankfurt, and Copenhagen. It's worth noticing that over the last twenty years a number of history of science departments have been absorbed into history departments—Johns Hopkins, Princeton and Montreal are prominent examples that come to mind. One of the advantages of independent institutions is that they provide a home for specialists who would otherwise be isolated in science departments or who are too technically-minded for history departments. On the other hand, this institutional separation tends to distance history of science from general history, such that historians of science are often seen by historians as not being real historians.

By the time philosophers of science warned up to Kuhn's *Structure* in 1970 or so, institutions had already been created which were geared towards forging closer links between history and philosophy of science. The institutional negotiations that led to the creation of these institutions cries out for careful study, since they proved to be critical to the creation of New HPS. It may very well have been Kuhn's book that persuaded philosophers of science that they ought to take the history of science more seriously, but those few philosophers (and, in some cases, classicists) who were shunted to institutions dedicated to the history of the exact science have discovered that technical history of science has a value in its own right that gives philosophers a fresh perspective for addressing traditional normative agendas.

What's more, technical history itself has undergone an appreciable broadening of its scope, in large part because institutions dedicated to technical history have opened their doors to philosophers, sociologists, anthropologists and others who are interested in technical story-telling. In its first incarnation, it was burdened by an excessively narrow take on the factors that are proper to science and those that are not. Its pioneers championed an unwarranted distinction between factors "internal" and "external" to scientific practice—the adage "physics of the past" seems an apt description for the first wave which was hedged on this distinction. A second generation, however, recognized that technical history was a very particular way of constructing historical narrative and that, if managed properly, its underlying principles could address historical variables that members of the first generation would have castigated as "external" to science.

What's more, New HPSers drew on the work of Foucault (1970) to discipline historical story-telling in order to make it responsive to our present circumstances and conditions. A New HPSer would be interested in Descartes' scattered remarks about the possibility that God might deceive if it could be shown that they are relevant to our present concerns, say our views on plagiarism. Kepler's optical researches—which gave modern physiology a blueprint for conceiving the human body in mechanical terms as a "system of corpuscles"—would be relevant for precisely the same reason. By the same token, however, New HPSers would not be at all interested in Newton's remarks on the luminiferous ether or in Gassendi's conception of causation unless it could be shown that they speak to our present conditions and circumstances.

For New HPSers, then, there is no domain of philosophy of science outside of the historical domain. None of the dichotomies that are constitutive of Classical HPS are countenanced. There are no "broad" issues and "narrow" issues; no "internal" and "external." There are nuances and differences in emphasis that distinguish HPS from technical history of science but these differences by and large are inappreciable to those who do not engage in technical history of science. With the exception of this principle of relevance, New HPSers see no interesting differences between technical history of science and philosophy of science.

For philosophers of science working in Philosophy Departments, the opposite is necessarily true. There is the need to function as a general philosopher with one hand firmly on the "broad issues," offering the standard courses in epistemology, logic, metaphysics, the history of philosophy (and the other sorts of courses that philosophers of science are obliged to teach). Since the other hand is firmly on one's practices as a philosopher of science, this creates a pressing need to "rethink philosophy of science" in a way that rationalizes it with these other constraints on practice. The practice must still be philosophy, or at least perceived by moral philosophers, Kantians, and logicians to still be philosophy. One can engage technical history in a manner of speaking, but only at a safe distance. The situation is necessarily different with HPSers. HPS is shaped and defined by technical history. The need to rationalize it with general philosophy and to engage issues in a general way is eliminated. There is of a consequence no need whatsoever to rethink one's work. The history is no longer external to the philosophy but is what one does as a philosopher. Of course, one is compelled to work in a narrowly historical way but that is part and parcel of the reason for migration to institutions for history and philosophy of science.

3. Contrasts

New HPS is not utterly removed from traditional philosophy of science—its legacy is apparent in its interest in the classification and clarification of concepts, though these concepts are now taken in a circumspect manner as historical creations. HPSers tend to produce novella-length studies, in contrast to technical history of science which tends to run into the hundreds and even thousands of pages. Focusing on an isolated concept will do that to the length of a paper, even one that is embedded in technical history of science.

New HPS, however, is quite distinct from technical history of science in that HPSers tend to focus on concepts that *authorize* our present behavior. Where a technical historian may spend years reconstructing a skill that came into existence and then vanished after a decade, the New HPSer tends to be interested in concepts that confer authority—i.e., concepts that have normative force and which, therefore, can tell us a great deal about ourselves. HPS, then, is not just technical history (i.e., it is not history of past science), but, to Foucault claims, the history of science insofar as it is still present.

It is instructive that proponents of these two styles of HPS have reacted very differently to the rise of the sociology of scientific knowledge (SSK). Those who insist that there are historical and philosophical domains, also tend to take the view that there are social and philosophical domains (sometimes called "the rational" and "the social"). A sociological project, on this view, is a different kind of project than a philosophical or an historical one. What's more, sociological explanations are castigated as violations of the line between "internal" and "external" history that is invoked as a general strategy for assimilating technical history of science to philosophical projects. The reaction by Classical HPSers to the proliferation of sociological studies of science has been harsh and, not surprisingly, the startling success of SSK has occasioned yet another crisis and many new critical volumes geared towards seeking a new reconciliation. By now the pattern of denial, anger, and acceptance is familiar.

The reactions of New HPSers have been very different. Conceiving philosophy as something that is applied to hand-crafted studies of scientific practice, New HPSers have welcomed those sociological and anthropological works that go at things at the micro level. *Laboratory Life* (Bruno Latour and Steve Woolgar, 1979) and (with the exception of a few pages and the beginning and at the end) Pickering's *Constructing Quarks* (1984) have been well-received, for the most part. Though Pickering cautions that SSK takes science to be "social all the way to its technical core" (1992, p. 1), New HPSers have no trouble taking both as collaborative works—respectively, as anthropology and sociology as applied to the history of science. Other works do not measure up, not because they are seen to be sociological or anthropological, but because they are fueled by an attached interest that overrides any real concern for detailed analysis. Works by Barnes (1977), Bloor (1976), and Shapin and Schaffer (1985) have been less well received for this reason; they are viewed by New HPSers as exercises in history of science applied to the sociology of knowledge (an exercise that is reminiscent of Classical HPS, except that history is now yoked to an attached sociological agenda). For New HPSers it is the attached agenda that is cause for concern, not the fact that the micro analysis focuses on sociological, anthropological, economic, and other contextual variables. HPSers are equally wary of attached philosophical agendas, and are wary of the work of Fuller and Goldman for precisely the same reasons.

4. Dealing With The Broad Questions

One of the reasons why many philosophers of science insist that philosophers of science need to look at things in their generality is that this seems to afford a platform for addressing normative issues. The surest way of responding to philosophy's "classic normative mission" is to ensure that philosophers do not take the perspective of actors at face value and "simply get lost in the technical details of scientific sub-cultures."

My own position as a practitioner of New HPS is that the best way to come to grips with these "broader issues" is to look at how they are realized in very localized contexts. This is not merely a theoretical preference but a practical response on the part of New HPSers to the appreciable shift in the kinds of normative issues raised by philosophers and the new kinds of normative issues raised by feminists, political theorists, and philosophers working with sciences that have traditionally received little attention. Many of these contextually-nuanced normative worries only make sense if we take the perspective of the actors in question. An example is anatomical illustration. What constitutes a gendered anatomical representation? Is the discovery that anatomical representations are grounded in a set of nineteenth century pictorial conventions that classified women and blacks in the same way normatively relevant? Well, yes, I expect that it is if, as a feminist or as a black activist, you are eager to advance a series of political reforms that impact on all cultural minorities and if, as a feminist academic, you have been treated by your male colleagues as a privileged white academic and, therefore, not deserving of initiatives in the name of equity.

I suspect that proponents of Classical HPS will strongly resist my contention that the local context is the best place to raise normative issues. David Stump gives voice to a powerful organizational principle of Classical HPS when he asserts that "the best philosophy of science has always engaged broad philosophical issues by being immersed in the technical aspects of cutting edge science, just as the best history of science has always kept large issues in the forefront while documenting and analyzing the situated context in the most minute detail." This contention is arguably false on both counts. If historians of the exact science are our benchmark, the "best history of science" has been the canonical work that I have cited—work that carefully avoids loose generalization and is highly sensitive to the attachment of interests that threaten to skew the narrative in favor of some global conceptions of science. If history of the exact sciences is one's measure, Kuhn (1978) on black body radiation is "the best history of science," and not Kuhn on normal science. By the same token, Hacking's *Representing and Intervening* (1983), highly esteemed by Classical HPSers, does its best to focus on a handful of inter-related concepts—manipulation, control, and novel device production that are central to the history of the exact sciences. Hacking's interest in these ends was shaped by his proximity to science and to technical history of science, not by a concern for generalization. He gives us a new take on science and a new way of looking at the concept of reality in science by bracketing many concepts that philosophers have long regarded as their staples, and by refusing to talk about science, except as it is practiced in laboratories. Yes, I suppose that the so-called "broad issues" sneak back onto center stage from time to time but the virtue of the work is to be found in its narrowness and detail, not in its generality.

Hacking's very latest work takes this historical project a step further. For some time, he has been working on the history of psychology in an effort to say something about the creation of human kinds—fugues, split personalities, syndromes, and other psychological classifications. The work is pioneering because it is written in the manner of technical history of science—it is built from the ground up from sources that philosophers who specialize in philosophy of mind have not bothered to examine. This work, which will soon be published under the title *Rewriting the Soul: Multiple Personality and the Sciences of Memory* (Princeton, 1995), is an exemplar of what I call "philosophy as applied to the history of science" or ethnophilosophy. The historical narrative focuses tightly on the creation of a few concepts; his historical practice is disciplined by his interest in these concepts.

These concepts for Hacking are historical and dynamical entities, but the ramifications of this kind of work are exciting—it opens up the black box on psychological classifications. Since the concepts that Hacking scrutinizes authorize the way that we sort out people, his work tells us a great deal about the creation of our identity, at least insofar as we are subject to these classifications. What's more, his work on human kinds furnishes us with a new way of raising normative issues. These issues are now part of the story: the interest in what he calls "human kinds" is part and parcel of the narrative; it is not imposed on it.

Hacking is not the only philosopher of science who approaches normative questions in this way. Nor is it only philosophers of science who raise normative issues in this manner. Feminist studies of the creation of the dual concepts of race and gender are by-products of detailed historical research. The normative concern is the story, the central claim being that you cannot understand race and gender as inter-connected systems of social classification (and stigmatization) unless you are fully apprised of the history. Here the philosophy and the history are not distinct entities; there are no philosophical questions to be asked over and above the history. There are no supervenient "broad questions" but there are plenty of positive results that makers of political and scientific policy can reference in their deliberations. We have no use for social epistemologists holding court over the history, asking "what can we now do with this history to make it a force for social change?" The history has normative force because it tells us about the creation of our value systems and how they impact on us.

5. Objections

One objection to the hand-crafted science studies that I am here advocating is that it will prevent us from subjecting science to public scrutiny. Social epistemologists and those interested in science policy, for example, could object that the kind of micro analysis that I am encouraging encourages us to frame the philosophical questions in a way that makes scientific and cultural communities seem more autonomous from the rest of society than they really are. Further to this, those who are convinced that scientists often engage in a great deal of rhetorical activity will object that this approach requires that we take the point of view of social actors at face value. Micro analysis will compel that scholar who knows little or nothing about, say, nineteenth century physics, to evaluate scientific activities with the scientist's own criteria; the further we get into these cultural communities the further removed we will be from a point of view that allows us to subject the products of these communities to public scrutiny.

This issue crystallizes in a very neat way what is at issue in the very idea of an interdisciplinary science studies. Philosophers have traditionally been highly suspicious of special claims to expertise—epistemologists, for example, have worked hard to set themselves up as gatekeepers to Solomon's House; their descendants, self-styled 'social epistemologists,' have taken this project a step further (some would say to its logical conclusion) by insisting that expert opinion is merely the willingness of an uneducated public to accept the technical and highly diffuse jargon of scientists at face value. For those who are housed in Philosophy Departments, gatekeeping is a strategy for sticking close to the action and, therefore, one can readily understand why Classical HPSers are eager to retain their traditional right to look at science in all its generality.

My own view, in contrast, is that the increasing specialization, not only of scientists, but also of scholars in the humanities and social sciences, is a reflection of our growing acceptance that knowledge is the possession of distinct cultures—that the knowledge possessed by women and aboriginal cultures, for example, is different in context but not in kind than that possessed by the scientific culture of particle physicists. Culture, as Max Weber (1949, p. 76) liked to say, is a value concept—it is always 'culture from a particular point of view.' Since we can only speak meaningfully of the culture of science from the perspectives of its practitioners, I question whether we can meaningfully embrace the vision of science as comprising many heterogeneous elements and communities and still cling to the globalist supposition that there is a privileged position for evaluating science.

The recognition of the difference that culture makes demands a less skeptical attitude on the part of science studies practitioners. We must rethink the "classical normative mission" in a way which is consistent with thinking in the small and taking at face value the claims of specialized communities and, in particular, science studies researchers who are engaged in different projects. We need to think of one another's projects as resources and not, in the manner of classical HPSers, as claims to expertise that need to satisfy global criteria. There is room for some good old fashioned philosophical debate, of course, to the extent that scholars mutually participate in the same projects, but philosophers would be surprised, I suspect, just how little debate there is among science studies researchers who deeply engage the perspectives of scientific actors.

Notes

[1]I'm drawing heavily on the work of Jed Z. Buchwald (1994) for my characterization of the history of the exact sciences.

References

Barnes, B. (1977), *Interests and the Growth of Knowledge*. London: Routledge & Kegan Paul.

Bloor, D. (1976), *Knowledge and Social Imagery*. London: Routledge & Kegan Paul.

Buchwald, J. Z. (1994), *The Creation of Scientific Effects: Heinrich Hertz and Electric Waves*. Chicago: The University of Chicago Press.

Foucault, M. (1970), *The Order of Things: An Archeology of the Human Sciences*. New York: Pantheon.

Hacking, I. (1983), *Representing and Intervening: Introductory Topics in the Philosophy of Natural Science*. Cambridge: Cambridge University Press.

_ _ _ _ _ _. (1995),*Rewriting the Soul: Multiple Personality and the Sciences of Memory*. Princeton: Princeton University Press.

Jardine, N. (1984), *The Birth of the History and Philosophy of Science: Kepler's Defence of Tycho Against Ursus*. Cambridge: Cambridge University Press.

Kuhn, T.S. (1962), *The Structure of Scientific Revolutions*. Chicago: The University of Chicago Press. Enlarged 1970.

_ _ _ _ _ _. (1978), *Black-Body and Quantum Discontinuity, 1894-1912*. Oxford: Clarendon Press.

Latour, B. and S. Woolgar (1979), *Laboratory Life: The Construction of Scientific Facts*. Princeton: Princeton University Press. Enlarged 1989.

Pickering, A. (1984), *Constructing Quarks: A Sociological History of Particle Physics*. Edinburgh: Edinburgh University Press.

_ _ _ _ _ _ _ _(ed.). (1992), *Science as Culture and Practice*. Chicago: The University of Chicago Press.

Shapin, S. and S. Schaffer (1985), *Leviathan and the Air-Pump: Hobbes, Boyle, and the Experimental Life*. Princeton: Princeton University Press.

Stump, D. and P. Galison (eds.) (forthcoming), *The Disunity of Science: Boundaries, Contests, and Power*. Stanford: Stanford University Press.

Weber, M. (1949),"'Objectivity' in Social Science and Science Policy." In E. A. Shils and H. A. Finch (eds.), *The Methodology of the Social Sciences*. New York: The Free Press.

Part XIV

THE TECHNOLOGICAL INFRASTRUCTURE OF SCIENCE

Science, Technology and Experiments; the Natural Versus the Artificial[1]

Peter Kroes

University of Technology, Eindhoven

1. Introduction

Against the traditional 'discovery–view' of experiments, Hacking has maintained that in experimental practice natural phenomena are created, not discovered. By intervening in the world with the help of technology, we create and at the same time come to know phenomena. This claim, together with the one that scientific entities are tools for intervening in the world, undermines the classic distinction between the natural and the artificial, more particularly, between science and technology: phenomena become artifacts just as technological products and scientific entities become tools for doing. Hacking's view raises the question whether it can still be said that science studies natural phenomena, and if so, in what sense. Are we not forced to give up the distinction between the natural and the artificial, between science and technology, altogether? Recently, for instance (Lelas 1993) has argued that science is a form of technology.

I shall argue 1) that experimentalists do indeed create phenomena, but in a specific sense which does not undermine the distinction between the natural and the artificial, 2) that scientific entities are *used as* tools instead of *being* tools, and 3) that Hacking's view on experiments may be reconciled with the traditional view, on condition that the concept of nature be reinterpreted. I shall suggest a reinterpretation in terms of constraints imposed on action.

The paper starts with a brief discussion of the distinction between the natural and the artificial (sect. 2), followed by a description of the traditional view of the natural and artificial in experiments (sect. 3). Then I will criticize Hacking's claims that phenomena are created and that scientific entities are tools (sect. 4). The paper ends with a proposal for interpreting nature as constraints imposed on action (sect. 5).

2. The natural versus the artificial

A general dividing line between the natural and the artificial is difficult to draw.[2] Within the present context it will be sufficient to indicate some of the most salient differences between natural objects/processes as generally conceived within the physical sciences, and artificial objects/processes[3] produced by technology.[4]

The modern physical sciences lack a clear conception of nature and natural objects. The still widespread idea that nature is composed of objects with certain intrinsic properties and interactions between those objects is hardly compatible with mod-

PSA 1994, Volume 2, pp. 431-440

ern physical theories. But whatever may be the precise character of the (ultimate) constituents of the world, it is assumed that, contrary to artificial entities, natural entities and their behavior are not man–made. According to modern physical theories it makes, moreover, no sense to attribute some goal or function to natural objects (at least, these notions do not figure in physical theorizing).

Artificial objects, on the contrary, are man–made; they are the outcome of *intentional* human action.[5] I shall concentrate here on technological artifacts.[6] Technological artifacts, such as a bicycle, a pencil, a radio or a TV–set, perform a practical *function* on the basis of a *human design*. In technology, a design is taken to be a scheme or plan that shows how a particular function may be realized. Technological artifacts have a dual nature. On the one hand, they are physical objects which obey the laws of nature; as physical objects their behavior can be explained in a non–teleological way. On the other hand, they are the physical embodiment of a design that has a teleological character; the whole construction is intended to perform a practical function. This function is an integral part of a technological artefact and without taking it into account, a technological artifact can not be properly understood.

Thus, the distinction between the natural and the artificial is primarily a genetic one.[7] Parallel to it runs the difference between discovery and invention/creation: natural objects (relations) are said to be discovered, artificial objects to be invented/created. The common view holds that science discovers what is already present and that technology invents new things.[8]

3 The traditional view of the natural and the artificial in experiments

Traditional philosophy of science has been preoccupied with the representation (conceptualization) of reality on the basis of data, particularly with he relation between theory and facts (Hacking 1983, 149 ff). Theory, not experimentation and the use of technology, has been the focus of most work in the philosophy of science. More recently, with the growing interest in the experimental aspects of science, particularly of physics (Hacking 1983; Franklin 1986; Gallison 1987; Le Grand 1990), the role of technology in science has become a topic of discussion, since in most experiments extensive use is made of technology.[9]

In the traditional view of experiments, technology is only a means to generate new data: once the new data are produced, technology has played its part and the real scientific work, theorizing, may begin. Technology may contribute to the generation of new data in two different ways:

1) it may help to overcome imperfections and limitations in human perception by providing measuring equipment, that is, it may extend and refine our sensory apparatus (Ackermann 1985, 127), or

2) it may provide equipment for studying the behavior of physical systems under very special, artificial conditions which do not occur spontaneously in nature.

According to this view, science is an activity that is primarily concerned with the understanding of nature. The technological/artificial means and processes by which data about nature are obtained play no part in that understanding (Lelas 1993, 423–424; Tiles 1992, 99). Of course, the use of technology in experiments is not unproblematic in the sense that the technological equipment simply delivers the facts or tells us what nature looks like. Many experiments fail due to malfunctioning or to incorrect handling of equipment and the performance of experiments usually requires a lot of technological skills. Moreover, like science, technology is dominated by theory and therefore the evaluation and interpretation of the results of experiments may involve the use of a lot of theory. The creation of experimental evidence (facts, data) in experimental practice is thus not a straightforward affair. But when properly performed and interpreted, experiments will deliver reliable facts with the help of technology. These facts constitute the evidence for developing and evaluating theories about the physical world.

This traditional view is based on a strict separation of the *natural* and the *artificial* in experimenting. The equipment through which nature is observed and the conditions under which it is studied are artificial, whereas the objects and/or processes studied behave naturally in spite of their artificial environment, and thus show their natural properties. Though not man–made, they show themselves through man–made equipment and under man–made conditions. Whereas all technological objects involved in an experiment perform a particular *function* on the basis of a *design*, the notions of functionality and design do not apply to the objects/processes studied in the experiment. While a microscope is designed so as to perform a particular function, it makes no sense to say that an electron is based on a design or has an intrinsic functionality.

Given this traditional conception of experimenting, the scientist remains essentially a passive spectator of nature who with the aid of technology gains access to parts of nature that would otherwise remain hidden because of human shortcomings or of contingent boundary conditions prevailing in our universe. The task of technology is to remove any obstacle between the observer and nature which is waiting there to be discovered.

This distinction between the natural and artificial at the *object level* is reflected at the *level of data*. It is quite common among experimentalists to speak of *artifacts* of the measurement equipment or of the experimental setup. They thereby refer to results that are generated by the artificial surrounding or artificial means of observation of the natural phenomenon under study (Franklin 1986, 3). Data are called 'artifacts', as opposed to genuine data, when they carry no information about the object of study, but only tell us something about the equipment used in the experiment.

Many measuring instruments produce artifacts; for instance the early telescopes produced colored fringes due to chromatic aberration. The specific conditions under which an object is observed too may produce artifacts; take for instance a stick that is held partly under water. The stick looks broken, but this effect is caused by the conditions under which the stick is observed; this property of the stick is an artefact. Although the artefact is real and not an illusion in the observation context, is does not say anything about the object itself.

It is, of course, of prime importance in experiments to discriminate between artifacts and genuine results that contain real information about the natural system that is being studied. The results of an experiment are always the outcome of natural objects interacting with an artificial environment, and therefore it is always necessary to filter out the component in the results that tells us something about nature. Although in practice this may be extremely difficult, and may involve long and intricate chains of reasoning, the traditional view maintains that it is always possible in experimental results to eliminate all that is due to the use of technology.[10] There exists, in other words, an epistemology of experiment, that is, "a set of strategies that are used to provide rational belief in an experimental result. These strategies distinguish between a valid observation or measurement and an artifact created by the apparatus" (Franklin 1986, 192).

This traditional view of experiments and of the role of technology in science has become under fire from different directions. The most far reaching criticism comes from (social) constructivists quarters, where nature is interpreted as a (social) construction which is the outcome of a scientific practice, not its object. The outcome of an experiment is taken to be a social construction; it is the result of negotiation processes between all actors involved. In these it is not possible to appeal to nature as an independent arbiter. The outcome of an experiment is ultimately determined by the interests of the actors involved. Nature itself becomes a social construction and thus an artefact.

This position appears untenable for at least the following two reasons. In the first place, it implies that there is in principle no difference at all in the way discussions about the acceptability of respectively physical laws and state laws are conducted, nor in the way these discussions come to an end (that is, how consensus comes about).

Secondly, if scientific knowledge, particularly the outcomes of experiments, are social constructions conditioned by power structures and interests of actors, how is it possible to explain the successful operation of technological artifacts designed on the basis of that knowledge? The answer, that the successful operation of technological artifacts is itself a social construction, is in my opinion not very convincing.[11]

In the following I will discuss Hacking's criticism against the traditional view of experiments, which is of a more moderate nature.

4. Hacking's view of experiments

In his famous book *Representing and intervening* Hacking claims that phenomena are created. He rejects the idea that experimental scientists simply discover phenomena in the world. "To experiment" in his own words "is to create, produce, refine and stabilize phenomena" (Hacking 1983, 230), a phenomenon being "something public, regular, possibly law–like, but perhaps exceptional" (Hacking 1983, 222). Discussing the example of the Hall effect, he states that this effect was not found by Hall simply because it did not exist before Hall succeeded in producing this effect in the laboratory. It was literally created by him,[12] because this effect does not exist without the appropriate experimental setup. If science should have taken another historical path, the Hall effect might never have been created (Hacking 1989, 21).

The idea that phenomena are created does not imply, according to Hacking, some sort of subjectivism or relativism in the sense that all is possible. The experimentalist cannot create phenomena at will. In his interaction with the world, he is subjected to all kinds of constraints: relativism is barred by the fact that the world seldom does what the experimentalist wants (Hacking 1989, 22).

Hacking uses the creation of phenomena in experiments to defend a 'hard–headed' scientific realism about unobservable or theoretical entities. In his opinion it is not because we can perform successful experiments on them that such entities are real. They become real as soon as they can be *manipulated* to produce new phenomena (Hacking 1983, 262 & 274):

> Experimental work provides the strongest evidence for scientific realism. This is not because we test hypotheses about entities. It is because entities that in principle cannot be 'observed' are regularly manipulated to produce a new phenomena and to investigate other aspects of nature. They are tools, instruments not for thinking but for doing. [...] Hence, engineering, not theorizing, is the best proof of scientific realism about entities.

According to this line of thought, the best evidence for, for instance, the existence of electrons is the common television set using a cathode ray tube (CRT). In a CRT electrons are produced by an electron gun, accelerated and deflected so as to hit appropriate spots on the TV–screen, where they cause a phenomenon known as electroluminescence: the electrons hit a substance that starts to produce light of a certain wavelength. Here, indeed, electrons have become an element of engineering and from an engineering point of view they are as real as the directly observable deflection coils in a CRT.

Hacking's ideas on experiments throw a new light on the role of technology in science. Two differences with the traditional view emerge:

1) with the help of technology the experimentalist does not just disclose or discover phenomena but he creates them; and

2) engineering and technology, rather than theory, determine what is real; thus technology is not a mere instrument for science that leaves no trace at all.

We will discuss these two points more closely and examine their consequences for the distinction between the natural and the artificial.

5. Creation versus discovery

From Hacking's claim that phenomena are created –a claim which is meant to be taken literally– the obvious conclusion may be drawn that, just like the objects of technology, phenomena belong to the domain of the artificial; they are the product of intentional human activity. The expression 'natural phenomena' would be a *contradictio in terminis*. If phenomena are artifacts, then science apparently investigates an artificial world, created or invented by experimentalists. Contrary to the traditional view, it would, therefore, no longer make sense to distinguish between the natural and the artificial in experiments.

I shall argue that Hacking's view of creating phenomena is much closer to the traditional view than the above suggests. To see this we have to take a closer look at Hacking's use of the expression 'to create phenomena'. This expression can be interpreted in a weak and a strong sense. In the weak sense it means that the experimentalist creates the proper conditions for a phenomenon to take place, but does not create its specific characteristics. In the strong sense he not only causes the occurrence of the phenomenon, but also creates the specific features of the phenomenon itself.

In my opinion, there can be no doubt that Hacking uses the expression 'creating phenomena' in the weak sense. In the first place, to claim that phenomena are created in the strong sense would either lead to "some sort of ultimate idealism in which *we* make the phenomena",[13] whereas Hacking defends scientific realism, or to relativism, which he rules out on the ground that the world imposes constraints on our interaction with it.[14] Secondly, Hacking states that science may develop along different historical paths, in each of which different phenomena might be created because other experimental techniques and equipment would be used or be available. Thus, it is possible to imagine that the Hall effect would never have been created, since it can only occur in some type of apparatus. The occurrence of this phenomenon is caused by the experimentalist who builds and operates the necessary apparatus. Creating phenomena, therefore, means that the experimentalist creates the right boundary conditions for the phenomenon to occur. Finally, the Hall effect can not be created in the strong sense, because Hacking states that it cannot be ruled out that the *same* effect occurs spontaneously in nature, i.e., that it is created by nature itself (1983, 226): "If anywhere in nature there is such an arrangement, with no intervening causes, then the Hall effect occurs."

If we accept the weak interpretation of Hacking's expression 'creating phenomena', then we may conclude that the Hall effect itself, the character of the regularity, is not created by man and therefore is not an artefact. Consider another example: the phenomenon that all objects fall with the same speed in vacuum. Clearly, Hacking is right in claiming that this phenomenon was created; it did not exist before man was able to create a vacuum. Nevertheless we are dealing here with a *natural phenomenon in the sense that this phenomenon expresses a constraint on the free fall of bodies which is not itself created by the experimentalist*. This constraint is dictated by the real world in which we live. That is the reason why it is called a *natural* phenomenon.[15] Hacking's use of the term 'creating' is misleading, because it suggests that phenomena are created in the same way a sculptor creates a statue.

If indeed Hacking intends to claim that phenomena are created in the weak sense, than the distinction between the natural and the artificial can be upheld, and then Hacking' view is much closer to the traditional view of experiments (and on the role of technology therein). At first sight, there seems to be a strong tension between the traditional view that phenomena are discovered and Hacking's claim (1983, 225) that phenomena are created and are not "part of God's handiwork, waiting to be discovered". However, we have to realize that the traditional view that phenomena are discovered does not exclude that it may take a lot of work and ingenuity to get an experiment going, that is, to let phenomena occur. The experimentalist indeed creates phenomena in the sense that he causes phenomena to occur by producing the proper boundary conditions. To claim that phenomena are discovered does not imply that the phenomena occur spontaneously. There can be no doubt that in complex experiments the occurrence of phenomena is caused by the experimentalist.

Neither does the claim that phenomena are discovered imply "that the phenomena have always been there, waiting to be discovered" (Hacking 1983, 226). This claim may also be interpreted as saying that a particular feature of *our world* is disclosed or revealed. Here the expression 'our world' is crucial: the phenomenon is a specific feature of our world with its specific experimental techniques and equipment, not of all possible worlds. In other words, the phenomenon does not exist apart from the appropriate apparatus and therefore it can be said to be created by us in our world. Nevertheless, the phenomenon is discovered in the sense that an objective feature of our world, and of all worlds in which the appropriate boundary conditions are realized, is brought to light.

Thus, Hacking's idea that phenomena are created may be interpreted along lines that bring his view close to the traditional view on experiments. The distinction between the natural and the artificial, which is the core of the traditional view, appears to be compatible with the claim that phenomena are created in the weak sense. However, if we accept that phenomena are created in that sense, the idea of a pre–existing nature has to be abandoned. Moreover, our view of the role of technology in science has to be modified. Technology, indeed, creates phenomena, but by creating phenomena, it discloses objective features of our universe.

The discussion of the question, what kind of conception of nature might be compatible with Hacking's idea of creating phenomena, will be postponed until after the examination of Hacking's claim that scientific entities are tools for doing.

6. Scientific entities as tools

It is interesting to note that a hard–headed *realist* like Hacking characterizes scientific entities as *tools*, that is, as *instruments* not for thinking but for doing. Here, realism and instrumentalism come close together: objects are real because they turn out to be effective instruments! But Hacking is not defending some kind of Machian instrumentalism which is based on economy of thought (Hacking 1983, 263):

> Electrons are no longer ways of organizing our thoughts or saving the phenomena that have been observed. They are ways of creating phenomena in some other domain of nature. Electrons are tools.

For Hacking scientific entities are tools for doing, for intervening in the world. Such a characterization of scientific entities is remarkable, to say the least; it brings science very close to technology, since an important aspect of technology is the design and production of tools. But technological tools are artifacts based on a human design. Does the same apply to scientific entities, when conceived as tools? Are they artifacts that may be characterized by a human design and a functionality? A positive answer would, of course, completely undermine the distinction between the natural and the artificial. Again, I shall argue that it is not necessary to give up the distinction between the natural and the artificial provided that we modify Hacking's characterization of scientific entities in an important way.

We will first address the question whether scientific entities, conceived as tools, are necessarily based on a human design. Consider again electrons. On Hacking's construal, electrons are real because we know how to exploit their causal properties in building equipment that performs its function well; they are effective tools. May we conclude from this that they are also based on a human design? That conclusion does not follow; using an object as a tool, does not mean it is man–made. To clarify this, consider a stone being used as a primitive hammer. Its use as a hammer is based on a specific physical property of the stone, namely its inertia. This property makes it possible to turn the object into an object with a specific functionality, without altering the object itself. Thus the object itself is not artificial, yet it may be used as a hammer.

The crucial point here is the recognition of the dual nature of any technological object: it is a physical object that is the carrier of a (socially constructed) functionality. In some cases the functionality may be carried by natural objects, in others the physical carrier of the functionality must be specifically constructed by man. A stone may be used as a simple hammer on the basis of its inertial mass; for a pair of scissors a specific physical object has to be constructed. To use electrons as tools, therefore, does not imply that electrons are the embodiment of a human design.

What about the functionality of scientific entities? If they are tools, they ought to possess a functionality. Even when the underlying physical object is not based on a human design, tools posses a function; with the help of tools we can achieve certain ends. Without that function, the object is surely not a tool. Therefore, to say that scientific entities are tools, as Hacking does, implies ascribing an (intrinsic?) functionality to those entities. As objects with a functionality, they are not natural objects. Again, the distinction between the natural and the artificial is endangered.

To get out of this predicament, I think we have to adapt Hacking's account. The fact that we become to believe in the reality of scientific entities because they can be *used as* tools, does not imply that they *are* tools, as Hacking claims. I guess that when Hacking characterizes scientific objects as *being* tools, he has in mind natural objects that can function *as* tools on the basis of their properties, or "causal powers" as he puts it; these causal properties are exploited in engineering (Hacking 1983, 274):

> The best kinds of evidence for the reality of a postulated or inferred entity is that we can begin to measure it or otherwise understand its causal powers. The best evidence, in turn, that we have this kind of understanding is that we can set out, from scratch, to build machines that will work fairly reliably, taking advantage of this or that causal nexus.

Consider again an electron in a CRT. As a scientific entity it has certain properties, for instance charge; to say that it has charge is to say that it will show certain types of causal behavior. That causal behavior or causal nexus may be used by engineers to let the electron perform a certain function in producing another phenomenon. In other words, the electron can be used as a tool in a CRT.

In the above way, we can avoid ascribing (intrinsic) functionalities to scientific entities; from the point of view of their causal properties or powers, scientific entities remain natural objects. Through their use as tools, they acquire a functionality; qua scientific entities, however, that functionality is incidental and therefore not the subject matter of scientific inquiry. It is hard to reconcile Hacking's claim that scientific entities are tools with the fact that functions play no role in the vocabulary used in science for describing the physical world. Talk about functions is, of course, part and parcel of the vocabulary of the experimentalist, but *only in so far as he is describing the equipment employed in an experiment, not its object of study*.

Summing up, neither Hacking's claim that phenomena are created, nor the claim that scientific entities are used as tools, implies in my opinion that the distinction between the natural and the artificial must be abandoned. Even when science is taken to be a form of practice in which intervention in the world through experiments plays a crucial role, science and technology remain two different kinds of activities, dealing with different kinds of entities.

7. Discussion: nature as constraints in action

In the foregoing, I have argued that Hacking's criticism against the traditional view of experiments does not render the distinction between the natural and the artificial obsolete. A reconsideration of the concept of nature, however, seems necessary. I will put forward a tentative suggestion for interpreting nature from the perspective of science as a form of experimental practice. Hacking himself gives an interesting clue.He clearly recognizes the danger of a relativistic interpretation of his claim that phenomena are created. To avoid the conclusion that they are created at will, he points out that experimentalists experience all kinds of constraints when intervening in the world. I will take the notion of constraint as the starting point for suggesting a reinterpretation of nature.

Science in the form of theory or representation is usually a form of ontology; it tells what really exists (Lelas 1993, 425). Correspondingly, nature is described as consisting of some sort of entities whose behavior is governed by natural laws. If we consider science as a form of practice or action, another conception of nature, in terms of restrictions on our actions, seems more appropriate. We cannot transform or intervene in our environment in any way we like. We experience all kinds of constraints. Nature might, therefore, be conceived as the totality of constraints imposed on our action.

This characterization of nature is, however, clearly inadequate. Various types of constraints are operative in our interaction with the world. Constraints may find their origin in the individual involved in an action, or may be biological or cultural in origin. Others are due to our limited technological capabilities. These are not the object of study of the physical sciences; they are not considered to be *natural* constraints.

What kind of constraints, then, are natural constraints? This is a difficult question. At first sight, one might be tempted to answer that nature as the object of science consists of those constraints that are valid in our interaction with the material world independently of any specific context (decontextualized constraints), that is, natural constraints are universal constraints. Such constraints are usually called natural laws. But this answer will not do; it is much too restrictive. Take the law of free fall, Ohm's law or the Hall effect; they impose restrictions on the way we may interact with our physical environment (we cannot prepare a system such that objects in vacuum will not fall at the same speed etc.[16]). They are, however, only valid in highly specific, *idealized* contexts (which make those constraints amenable to mathematical treatment).[17] With Hacking I agree that these constraints are created to the extent that they appear only within those contexts; these constraints do not exist apart from these contexts, but are nevertheless natural constraints.

Natural constraints might also be characterized as constraints that cannot be overcome, no matter how we intervene in our physical environment; they transcend human power. For instance, the law of conservation of energy forbids the creation of energy from nothing. This proposal sounds promising, but also raises problems. Only constraints that cannot *in principle* be overcome qualify as natural constraints, not those that in a given historical situation *de facto* cannot be overcome. This brings us to the problem of distinguishing between *technological* and *natural* constraints.

Technological constraints have a contingent character; they change over time. Let me illustrate this point with the example of the traditional light microscope. The first-microscopes had only a limited resolution power. That was not due to physical constraints, but due to technological imperfections. There was still scope for considerable technical improvement by using better lenses etc. Nowadays, however, the resolution power of these microscopes has reached a certain limit: *given their design and the behavior of light*, an improvement of resolution power is no longer possible. With regard to this type of microscope we may say that technology has run up against a natural constraint. Note that the design of the microscope plays a crucial role: by changing the design of the light microscope (and by exploiting other properties of light), the resolution power of light microscopes may still be improved. Apparently, light has certain properties which makes it in principle impossible to improve on the resolution power of this type of microscope and that is the reason why we call them natural properties.

Other examples may be added, for instance the efficiency of steam engines. By removing technological constraints, their efficiency may be improved, but not beyond a certain physical limit described by the second law of thermodynamics. Such examples make clear that technological constraints depend upon human capacities (skills and knowledge) to intervene in the environment. But there is a class of constraints which are not conditioned by human capacities and that is precisely the reason why we call them 'natural' or 'physical' constraints.

Notes

[1]I thank Guy Debrock, Andries Sarlemijn, Marc de Vries and Menno Hulswit for their valuable comments on an earlier version of this paper.

[2]It changes in the course of the history of science and it depends upon the available technology and our understanding of that technology; see Tiles (1993).

[3]In the following we will restrict ourselves primarily to objects.

[4]For a more extensive discussion of the distinction between the natural and the artificial, see Fehér (1993).

[5]It is doubtful whether the reverse is true; not every object or state of affairs that is the outcome of intentional human action has to be an artifact. Breeding animals may be a counter example.

[6]Not all artifacts are technological artifacts (e.g., a painting or sculpture).

[7]Note that the above distinction between the natural and the artificial presupposes that in some respect man is not part of nature.

[8]This schematic characterization of the difference between the natural and the artificial is not without problems. In biology, the difference between the natural and the artificial is rather intricate, as recent discussions about the patentability of the Harvard mouse demonstrate. Furthermore, in biology the notion of functionality is also applied to natural objects (the function of the eye or stomach). Finally, from an evolutionary point of view it may be very difficult to draw in general a clear cut borderline between the natural and the artificial. We will leave these problems aside; for our purposes, the above characterization is sufficient.

[9]Not all experiments involve technology; for instance, the real performance of Galilei's alleged experiment of the tower of Pisa would not require any specific technological equipment.

[10]The traditional view maintains that "anything artificial can be extracted, and its traces erased so that the natural shines out in its full splendour to the glassy essence of scientific apparatuses" (Lelas 1993, 432).

[11]This rejection of constructivism does not imply that I think that science is free of any constructivist elements. On the contrary, the work of Poincaré, Duhem and the logical positivists (in particular Reichenbach), have shown that there is much room for conventions (that is, social constructions) in science, because there is no unique correspondence between sets of data and theories (known as the 'underdetermination of theory by facts').

[12]See Hacking (1989, 21), where he says that the creation of phenomena has to be taken literally.

[13]See Hacking (1983, 220). If we assume that creating is a stronger notion than making, it seems to me that Hacking contradicts himself; on the same page (p. 220) he says that on the one hand scientists create phenomena, on the other that we do not make the phenomena.

[14]See Hacking (1989, p. 22); the following remark by Hacking, however, suggests a possibly relativistic position (1983, 228): "But the phenomena of physics–the Faraday effect, the Hall effect, the Josephson effect – are the keys that unlock the universe. People made the keys–*and perhaps the locks in which they turn*" (the italics are ours).

[15]See also Galilei's definition of *naturally* accelerated motion (Galilei 1974, 153); note that Galilei admits that this kind of motion does not occur in nature (Galilei 1974, 223)!

[16]Here, of course, we have to add the *ceteris paribus* clause.

[17]Of course, given those contexts, the constraints are universally valid. But that is not the point here; the constraints, like the laws of nature, are considered to be universally valid in any context, but because of all kinds of interfering processes, they do not show up in pure form or not at all. Cfr. Nancy Cartwright's idea that the laws of physics lie (Cartwright, 1983).

References

Ackermann, R.J. (1985), *Data, instruments and theory.* Princeton: Princeton University Press.

Cartwright, N. (1983), *How the laws of physics lie.* Oxford: Clarendon Press.

Fehér, M. (1993), "The natural and the artificial", *Periodica Polytechnica; humanities and social sciences* (Technical Univ. of Budapest, Budapest) 1: 67–76.

Franklin, A. (1986), *The neglect of experiment.* Cambridge: Cambridge University Press.

Galilei (1974), *Two new sciences.* transl. S. Drake, Madison: University of Wisconsin Press.

Gallison, P. (1987), *How experiments end.* Chicago: University of Chicago Press.

le Grand, F.E. (ed.) (1990), *Experimental inquiries.* Dordrecht: Kluwer.

Hacking, I. (1983), *Representing and intervening.* Cambridge: Cambridge University Press.

_ _ _ _ _ _. (1989), "Filosofen van het experiment", *Kennis en Methode* XIII: 11–27.
Lelas, S. (1993), "Science as technology", *Brit. J. Phil. Sci.* 44: 423–442.

Tiles, J.E. (1992), "Experimental evidence vs. experimental practice?", *Brit. J. Phil. Sc.* 43: 99–109.

_ _ _ _ _ . (1993), "Experiment as intervention", *Brit. J. Phil. Sci.* 44: 463–475.

Meaning in a Material Medium

Davis Baird

University of South Carolina

1. Michael Faraday's First Electric Motor

On September 3 and 4, 1821 Michael Faraday, age 30, performed a series of experiments which ultimately produced what were called "electromagnetic rotations." Faraday showed how an appropriately organized combination of electric and magnetic elements would produce rotary motion. He invented the first electric motor.

Faraday's work resulted in several "products." He published several papers describing his discovery (Faraday 1821; 1821-2; 1822c). He wrote letters to many scientific colleagues (Faraday 1812-48, pp. 122-39). He built, or had built, several copies of an apparatus which, requiring no experimental knowledge or dexterity on the part of its user, would display the notable rotations (Faraday 1822a; 1822b). He shipped these to his scientific colleagues (Faraday 1812-48, pp. 128-9). It is this material product which I would like to focus on.

For the presentation of this talk in New Orleans, I intended to have my own version of Faraday's first electric motor. Alas, while I did build—with considerable help from my colleague Richard Ray of the USC School of Engineering—a version of Faraday's motor, I had considerable difficulty shipping it to New Orleans. Mercury is a hazardous substance and, in the 20th Century, it is difficult to ship for this reason. In a very important sense, my main point must be made by demonstration in the material medium. The fact that I failed to get my apparatus to New Orleans undermined the possibility of making this point. In the spirit of irony, I can say that the degree to which I suceed making my point in this literary mode, without the apparatus, is a measure of the degree to which I fail to make my point.

A literary description: A permanent magnet is cemented vertically in the center of a mercury bath. A wire, with one end immersed a little into the mercury, is suspended over the magnet in such a way as to allow for free motion around the magnet. The suspension of the wire is such that contact can be made with it and one pole of a battery. The other pole of the battery is connected to the magnet which carries the current to the mercury bath, and thence to the other end of the wire, completing the circuit. The apparatus produces a very striking phenomenon: When an electric current is run through the wire, via the magnet and the mercury bath, the wire spins around the magnet.

PSA 1994, Volume 2, pp. 441-451

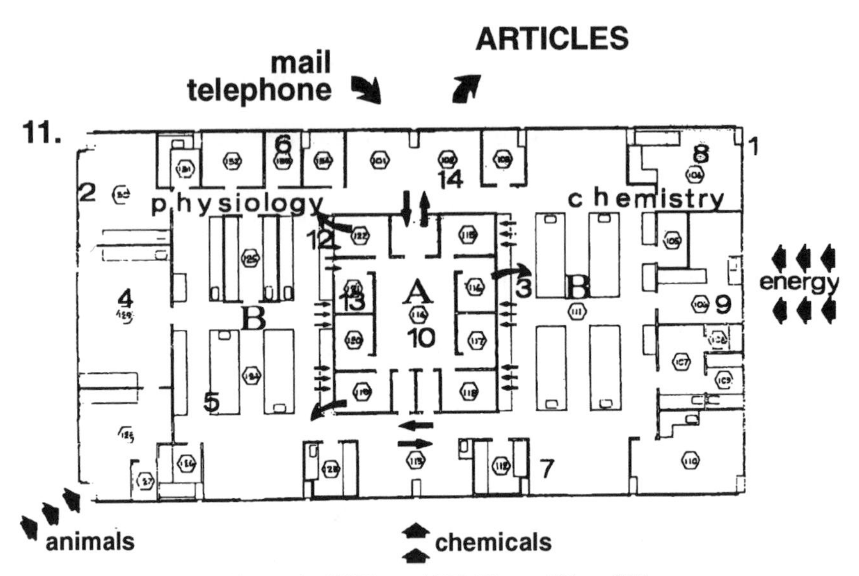

Figure 1. Williams 1978, Figure 491, p. 334

The observed behavior of Faraday's apparatus requires no interpretation. While there was considerable disagreement over the explanation for this phenomenon, no one contested what the apparatus did: It exhibited (still does) rotary motion as a consequence of a suitable combination of electric and magnetic elements.

Instruments such as this, usually called demonstration devices, are extremely important. They create a phenomenon, frequently for the first time, in a field of inquiry where there is much theoretical confusion. They provide a public and stable empirical anchor—no one could disagree that rotations could be produced—in a sea of theoretical confusion—everyone disagreed about the explanation for the rotations. This point of instrumental stability provides an excellent point of departure for fruitful theoretical work—to explain a phenomenon everyone agrees exists—and fruitful empirical work—to produce other similar and more pronounced phenomena (Baird and Nordmann 1994; Gooding 1990; Schaffer 1993). Faraday's apparatus also encouraged those of a more speculative cast to consider both the technological possibilities—of producing an electromagnetic motor capable of useful work—and the metaphysical possibilities—that all forces were convertible (Williams 1964, 157).

Faraday's material product, what might be called a "pocket edition" of his newly created phenomenon, communicated something better than his literary products. It is even possible to imagine that this material product communicated something which was not communicated at all in the literary products. At the very least, the material product encapsulated all of Faraday's considerable manipulative skill—his "fingertip knowledge"—in such a way that someone without the requisite skill could still experience first-hand the new phenomenon. I am not saying here that Faraday's literary products did not communicate something better than his material product. I am saying that the two kinds of products communicate differently, and thus allow different contents to be communicated.

2. Instrument Epistemology

My concern with meaning in a material medium is rooted in concerns about the nature of scientific knowledge. How can instruments—material products—contain and convey scientific knowledge? Some people might be inclined to dismiss the possibility that scientific instruments could contain and convey scientific knowledge. Knowledge requires semantic content. Semantic content must be propositional in nature. Propositions, except insofar as they might be "encoded" (e.g., in software), are not material in nature. So, instruments cannot contain and convey scientific knowledge. Part of the point of my paper is to undermine the first premise: meaningful knowledge, without semantic content, can be conveyed, in particular in the material medium.

I begin with Faraday's rotation apparatus because I think it provides an immediately persuasive example of my thesis. I do not believe Faraday's apparatus "encodes" certain propositions. I do believe Faraday's device contains scientific knowledge.

I call the view of scientific knowledge which I advocate "instrument epistemology." Stated directly, it is that there are two different modes for the expression of scientific knowledge, a literary mode and a material mode. I believe that much of the recent work in science studies on experiment implicitly calls for instrument epistemology (Ackermann 1985; Baird 1993; Baird and Faust 1990; Baird and Nordmann 1994; Franklin 1986; 1990; Galison 1985; 1987; Galison and Assmus 1988; Gooding 1990; Gooding et. al. 1988; Hacking 1983; Helden and Hankins 1993; Ihde 1991; Latour 1987; Lenoir 1988; Pickering 1984; Rouse 1987; Vincenti 1990). Peter Galison's paper on the "central metaphor" (1988) urges that, not only is there a theoretical tradition in science, but, in addition, there are instrumental and experimental traditions. And still, despite all that we have learned about experiment, we remain fixed with the same basic picture of scientific knowledge: Scientific knowledge is expressed in a literary mode; epistemologically speaking, the material end of science plays only a supporting role. Cannot—should not—the experimental and instrumental traditions have epistemological lives of their own too?

3. Text Bias

Before I consider alternative, material, ways to express meaning, I present some of the ways scholars who are well informed about the ways of empirical science, have been drawn into what I call "text bias." My hope is to avoid any such reading of what I have to say about meaning in a material mode.

Bruno Latour and Steve Woolgar's book, *Laboratory Life* (1979), can serve as a first example. This book reports on the authors' "anthropological expedition" to a scientific research laboratory, the Salk Institute in La Jolla, California. Latour and Woolgar focus

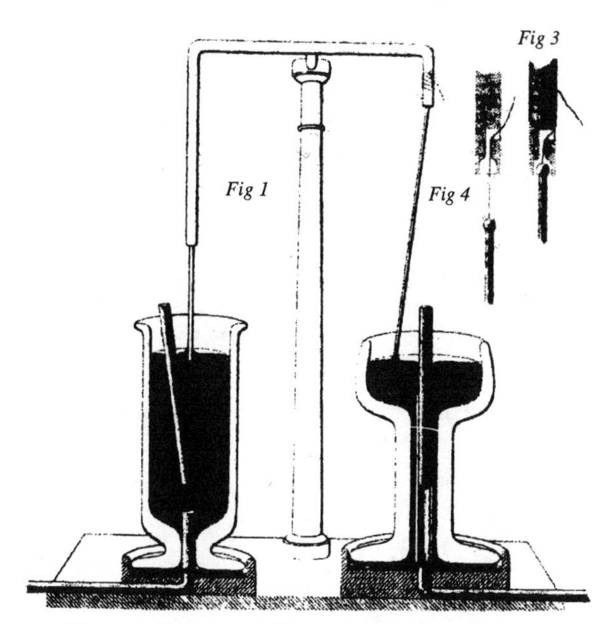

Figure 2. Latour and Woolgar 1977, Figure 2.1, p. 46

on the construction of a particular fact, the structure of the substance, "TRF." It might seem that such a study would acknowledge the importance of a material, non-literary, product—TRF itself. Yet this is not how Latour and Woolgar see things. The authors adopt a self-conscious position about the importance of "the word." They approach their study of the laboratory with the basic concept of "literary inscription." They call on the authority of the scientists themselves: "The production of papers is acknowledged by participants as the main objective of their activity" (p. 71). They provide a floorplan of the laboratory showing its function in terms of inputs and outputs: Animals, chemicals, mail, telephone information and energy goes in; articles go out.

Latour and Woolgar describe instruments as "inscription devices:"

> By contrast with the expense and bulk of this apparatus, the end product is no more than a curve, a diagram, or a table of figures written on a frail sheet of paper. ... While participants in the office space struggle with the *writing* of new drafts, the laboratory around them is itself a hive of *writing* activity. Sections of muscle, light beams, even shreds of blotting paper activate various recording equipment. *And the scientists themselves base their own writing on the written output of the recording equipment.* (pp. 50-1; emphasis added).

The picture Latour and Woolgar present of science is thoroughly literary. "Nature," with the help of inscription devices (i.e., instruments), produces literary outputs for scientists; scientists use these outputs, plus other literary resources (mail, telephone, preprints etc.) to produce their own literary outputs. For Latour and Woolgar, the material product of the work they investigate—the substance TRF—is merely an instrumental good: "TRF became just one more of the many tools utilized as part of long research programmes" (p. 148).

There is much of interest in Latour and Woolgar's work, and in the more fully developed view of science found in Latour's subsequent, *Science in Action* (1987). While the rhetoric with which they introduce their "literary" framework for analysis seems new, even "post-modern," it is very old. Once again scholars—word smiths—have reduced science to the mode in which they are most familiar, words.

A more recent example, David Gooding's *Experiment and the Making of Meaning* (1990), also is instructive. A considerable portion of the book focuses on Michael Faraday's experimental production of electromagnetic rotations. As Faraday came to this work, theory, experimental practice and available instrumentation were in undeveloped and confused states. Scientists both did not know what phenomena could be made, nor how to speak about them. Gooding tells a story of mutually reflective refinement: scientists got better at making new phenomena as they got better at speaking about them, the convergence of practice and talk.

It would seem that Gooding sees the making of phenomena as one of the epistemological goals of science. He writes, "Where a process is convergent the outcome is a discovery *or* an invention. Convergent experimentation brings an empirical phenomenon, a device *or* a law, into the public domain" (p. 168; emphasis added). This is very close to the picture of instrument epistemology sketched above: experiment produces both literary products (laws) and material products (inventions).

This is not Gooding's view of things, however. His focus on words is evident in the first sentences of the book:

> It is inevitable that language has, as Ian Hacking put it, mattered to philosophy. It is not inevitable that practices—especially extra-linguistic practices—have mattered so little. Philosophy has not yet addressed an issue that is central to any theory of the language of observation and therefore, to any theory of science: how do observers ascend from the world to talk, thought and argument about the world (p. 3).

Scientists semantically ascend from the world to talk about the world, from instruments to words, from the material realm to the literary realm. It is notable that Gooding self-consciously retains W.V.O. Quine's metaphor of "ascent." For Gooding a primary project for experimental science is semantic ascent; I would prefer to call this literary descent.

It is instructive to see how Gooding sees Faraday's literary and material products. In comparing Faraday's published accounts of his experiments with his laboratory records, Gooding writes:

> Comparison to the laboratory record suggests that his published account packaged phenomena as evidentially relevant to theoretical issues in a manner analogous to the packaging of skilled work that shaped those phenomena into the demonstration device: the literary account places phenomena in an objective relationship to theories just as the material embodiment of the skills places phenomena in an objective relation to human experience (p. 177).

With the semantic ascent which Faraday's experimental work allowed, the objective relations of logic could be brought to bear: Faraday's experimental results "spoke to" theoretical issues. Analogously, for Gooding, Faraday's apparatus speaks to, "human experience." The very choice of concept here renders ineffable the meaning carried by the apparatus; "human experience" is too broad.

On the contrary, I would say that the apparatus had a good bit "to say." The apparatus "spoke" objectively about the possibilities for producing rotary motion from electromagnetism; these possibilities could be developed through material manipulations, starting with the apparatus as a material given. These possibilities for material refinement are the analogs to the live theoretical issues to which Faraday's experimental results spoke.

4. Metaphor

Now I turn to ways meaning can be carried in a material medium. I begin with one widely acknowledged as a way meaning can come in a material medium, metaphor. Instead of expressing Kepler's three laws in words, one can build elaborate mechanical instantiations of these laws. Mechanically elaborate models of the solar system, called orreries, simulate the motions of the planets (King 1978). Derek de Solla Price has argued that, far from being pedagogic devices, orreries make the more abstract point that the complicated phenomena of the heavens can and should be understood mechanically; they, perhaps more than any theoretical advance, are responsible for ushering in the mechanical philosophy of science of the 17th Century (1964; 1984).

Timothy Lenoir (1993) has argued that the telegraph provided an essential metaphorical resource in Hermann Helmholtz's experimental elaboration of Thomas Young's three-receptor theory of color vision:

> From as early as 1850 he drew analogies between the electrical telegraph and the process of perception. The telegraph began to serve as a generalized model for representing the process of sensation and perception. In light of this telegraph analogy Helmholtz, so I hypothesize, imagined the virtual image cast on the retina as dissolved into a set of electrical impulses, data to be represented by symbols as an "image" in the brain through a perceptual analog of Morse code (p. 186).

Beyond the fact that metaphor is a basically literary notion of meaning, it would be misleading to see metaphor as the sole means by which meaning can be carried in a material medium. There are other ways for the material medium to carry meaning. What is worse, there is a widespread, if vague, suspicion of metaphoric meaning. This is of particular concern if we are to speak of scientific knowledge in terms of material meanings.

These issues are subtle. Norton Wise (1988; see also Smith and Wise 1989) has studied the meaning of instrumentation, and technological systems more generally. Wise argues, for example, that the steam engine played a crucial role in fixing William Thomson's ideas on energy. The material medium of the engine carried a set of ideas which both explained its physical operation and its societal function. While Wise clearly acknowledges the ability of the material medium to carry meaning, still, as far as scientific knowledge is concerned, the material medium functions instrumentally. It provides the medium for mediating and integrating societal values into scientific knowledge:

> Although the all-powerful engine symbolized value and progress in industrial society quite generally, it actually instantiated relations between political economy and natural philosophy only in a narrow region of common reference. The work of an engine, therefore, could not dictate how one ought to proceed in generalizing either political economy or dynamics. Its great value lay in its specificity, in its role as epitome or exemplar within whatever larger theory one might construct in the one sphere or the other. As a general symbol it motivated such constructions; as functioning system in everyday practice it structured and constrained their form, imposing the condition that an adequate theory would preserve the concept of work. *From motivation and structured constraints one cannot deduce explanations. Nevertheless they are highly productive elements in the generation of knowledge* (1988, 88, emphasis added).

The metaphoric meanings that might be carried in the material medium can be essentially productive of knowledge, but they themselves are not suitable for carrying knowledge.

Metaphor is important. Arguably, in terms of impact on history, metaphor is the most important way instruments can carry meaning. But, if instruments are to have epistemological lives, there needs to be other, more direct, ways for instruments to carry meaning. I now discuss two.

5. Representation

Instruments can carry meaning representatively. Consider material models. Models are a useful kind of instrument, for they help us learn about nature when theory is stumped. Models directly represent nature in much the same way that theories do.

There are many different kinds of model. Architectural models typically are static three-dimensional representations of how spaces in a design relate to each other. Other material models are built to simulate dynamically particular aspects of bits of the world. Professor Bijker's garage-size model of Rotterdam harbor simulates the flow of salt water in the harbor and its estuaries (Latour 1987, 230-2). Here a strictly theoretical approach would be too cumbersome. Still other material models are scaled-down versions of what engineers, and/or scientists hope ultimately to build full size; the small size allows for careful experimentation, varying the physical characteristics systematically to determine optimal forms for the full-size version. The air-propeller models of W. F. Durand and E. P. Leslie discussed by Walter Vincenti (1979) are of this sort.

John Smeaton's model waterwheel provides yet another kind of example which is particularly instructive (1759). Smeaton's model waterwheel is a dynamical model. But, unlike orreries, its principle of motion is the same as for full-size waterwheels; running water turns the wheel. Smeaton's model waterwheel is not, however, a scaled-down version of some particular waterwheel he hoped to build. His model serves the more abstract purpose of allowing him to better understand how waterwheels in general extract power from water in motion. I do not have the space to go into detail here, but I urge one central point about Smeaton's model: In quite specific ways it functioned just as theory functions. This was important because the theory available at the time was incapable of producing useful or correct conclusions about the behavior of waterwheels. Smeaton's was an instrument for circumventing (inadequate) theory.

In 1704, Antoine Parent presented a theoretical analysis of waterwheel operation that became the standard (Reynolds 1983, 206-10). I bypass the details, but note that through an early application of differential calculus, he determined those conditions under which, in the terms of his theoretical framework, the operation of a waterwheel would be most efficient. Parent's work suffered from several errors. There were conceptual errors concerning the proper measure of the work. Several of the assumptions on which he based his calculations were in error. Most importantly, he treated all waterwheels—overshot and undershot—the same. This was partly a consequence of the mechanical philosophy of the time.

Smeaton could adjust or vary several parameters of his model waterwheel. By means of a stop he could adjust the size of the sluice opening. He could vary the height of the head of water used in a run. He could vary the load which the wheel lifted. He could run tests on both undershot and overshot wheels. He conducted trials of one minute each. Trials were organized into sets. In any given set of trials, he would vary the load—from 4 pounds to 9 pounds—and keep the other parameters of the experiment constant. In this way he found the load which would allow for the maximum effect. Parent used the differential calculus to find the point of maximum efficiency; Smeaton used what Walter Vincenti has dubbed "the method of parameter variation" (1979, 714) to find this maximum. The theoretical parameters Parent maximized over, function the same way as the physical parameters Smeaton varied in his model.

Smeaton's model was a better source for determining waterwheel efficiency than Parent's theory for two reasons. In the first place, the model provided a better representation than the theory. In the second place, it was physically straightforward to vary the point at which the water meets the wheel. The common understanding of the mechanical philosophy and confusion with the concepts of work and power made this operation conceptually difficult.

Theory and model operated representationally in similar ways. Parent's theory had "built in" assumptions about efficiency and work. With Smeaton's model they were literally "built in." Thus the material medium can carry meaning representationally, much as the literary medium does. Sometimes such representational meaning is intentionally encoded theoretical meaning, as in contemporary "smart instrumentation," and sometimes it is simply built in as the maker's understanding of things, as in Smeaton's model.

6. "Making-Meaning" Meaning

I now turn to a third way in which instruments can carry meaning. Consider Faraday's rotations apparatus. Simply in demonstrating a material reality it carries meaning. Before Faraday built the apparatus there was all kinds of speculation about what might be possible with electric and magnetic elements. Creating something real stands apart from speculating about what might happen, even if the explanation for this new bit of reality is not to hand. Faraday's apparatus carried a very significant message about where, among many possibilities, a bit of reality lies. For a contemporary example with a different fate, consider cold fusion.

It is not appropriate to say that Faraday's apparatus "simply demonstrated the existence of a new phenomenon." There is tremendous portent in Faraday's apparatus—and cold fusion. From the physical/material set-up of Faraday's apparatus, one can imagine and build other apparatuses. Theoreticians use logic and mathematics to manipulate their word-based meanings, to explore implications and possibilities. "Instrumenticians" use their visual and material/physical imagination to direct physical operations to explore the material/physical possibilities which a given material/physical reality suggests. An engineer can see many realities and possibilities in a material artifact. Here is meaning.

Consider two other examples from the development of the cyclotron (Baird and Faust 1990). A cyclotron accelerates a beam of sub-atomic particles; it would be of little use if the beam were not focused. That is, it is necessary for the particles to "stay on track." After building the first successful four-inch cyclotron, M. S. Livingston, a student of E.O.

Lawrence, had difficulties in keeping the beam focused in a scaled up ten-inch instrument. Livingston's first guess was that this was due to irregularities in the magnetic field. He tried to true the faces of the magnet by re-machining them; this did not help. He then tried adding iron shims; this worked. While this procedure worked, Livingston subsequently found out that it was not irregularities in the magnetic field that his shims corrected; rather these shims created a magnetic field which systematically decreased in intensity as a function of the radius. Such a decrease in intensity, as it turns out, helps focus the beam.

The point of the example is this. Livingston did not have the theoretical knowledge that a systematic decrease in magnetic beam intensity would focus the beam. He did have the ability to produce this effect through trial and error shimming. Livingston built focusing into the material medium, without a theory to explain how or why his shims worked.

At some point in the development of the 27-inch cyclotron, R. R. Wilson devised what came to be known as the Wilson seal. A metal rod is surrounded by a rubber gasket cut with an inside diameter considerably smaller than that of the rod; the gasket would bend out to one side or the other. Surrounding metal flanges insured that it bent toward the high-pressure side of the barrier, and this forced the gasket against the rod. This produced a good seal even when the rod was rotated or moved back and forth.

There is no theory for this kind of accomplishment, although with some work, a verbal explanation might be developed. Verbal explanations are not the point. The point is to accomplish something in the material medium directly.

We can think of meaning is in terms of information, and we can think of information in terms of restricting possibilities: information reduces the number of remaining viable possibilities in some situation. An instrument, such as Faraday's, reduces possibilities in two ways. In the first place, it fixes one way in which rotations can occur; this way is now special, importantly different from all the other material/physical possibilities which might have been speculated about. In the second place, it "points" to a set of other physical/material possibilities as possible extensions and/or refinements. I see this "pointing" as analogous to the function of logic with theory. Using logic, other propositions, beyond those explicitly stated in a theory, become special by being implied, inductively supported, contradicted, etc. So it is with material "pointing." Here it is the "visual-physical/material logic" that allows a person to see, draw and ultimately to build, new material possibilities "implied" by the given material reality (Ferguson 1993).

7. Theses on Material Meaning

1. Literary meaning is hard for the scholar to get away from. Scholars usually express themselves in words. As a consequence there is a strong temptation to see all expression in this way.

2. We should not simply slap a notion of literary meaning on the material medium. This way lies the temptation of slipping back into thinking of the literary medium as the only source of meaning.

3. Metaphor is one way for there to be meanings in the material medium; but metaphor is held under suspicion as far as expressing knowledge is concerned. Most people who think about such topics acknowledge the ability of metaphor to be expressive in the material medium. Clearly metaphor is a very powerful expressive force.

4. Instruments can represent the world. Models perform this function and in some instances they do a better job of representation than any available theory does.

5. Establishing in a material medium that something, once thought only possible, is real, contains meaning. Faraday's apparatus and Wilson's seal contain meaning.

6. *Beyond establishing a bit of reality, the material medium points to the likelihood of other material realities.* Using what we can call "visual-material/physical logic," one can "infer" other arrangements in the material medium which may accomplish desired results.

7. *There need not be a univocal literary expression with is synonymous with—or worse, which expresses—a meaning expressed in the material medium.* While we might be inclined to say that Faraday's rotation device "shows that" it is possible to create rotary motion for a suitable combination of electric and magnetic elements, such a literary expression is not synonymous with the meaning of the rotation device. In the first place such a literary expression, of necessity carries a load of conceptual baggage which the material medium does not have. In the second place such a literary expression does not allow the same "visual-material/physical inferences" to be drawn.

8. *We can think of the "establishing a material/physical reality" kind of meaning in terms of information.* Before Faraday built his apparatus there was a very wide range of thought-of and un-thought-of material/physical arrangements which might have produced a phenomenon, and the particular phenomenon of rotations. After Faraday built his apparatus, this range was substantially altered: one way does the job, others "implied" by Faraday's way may do so as well. His apparatus conveyed information and, in this sense, meaning.

References

Ackermann, R. (1985), *Data, Instruments, and Theory,* Princeton: Princeton University Press.

Baird, D. (1993), "Analytical Chemistry and the 'Big' Scientific Instrumentation Revolution", *Annals of Science*, 50: 267-290.

Baird, D. and Faust, T. (1990), "Scientific Instruments, Scientific Progress and the Cyclotron", *British Journal for the Philosophy of Science*, 41: 147-75.

Baird, D. and Nordmann, A. (1994), "Facts-well-Put", *British Journal for the Philosophy of Science*, 45: 37-79.

Faraday, M. (1812-48), *The Selected Correspondence of Michael Faraday, Volume 1, 1812-1848,* L. P. Williams (ed.), Cambridge: Cambridge University Press. Published in 1971.

_______. (1821), "On some new Electromagnetical Motions, and the on the Theory of Magnetism",*Quarterly Journal of Science,* 12: 74-96.

_______. (1821-2), "Historical Sketch of Electro-magnetism", *Annals of Philosophy*, 18: 195-200, 274-90, 19:107-21.

_______. (1822a), "Electro-magnetic Rotations Apparatus", *Quarterly Journal of Science,* 12: 186.

_______. (1822b), "Description of an Electro-magnetical Apparatus for the exhibition of rotatory motion", *Quarterly Journal of Science*, 12: 285-5.

_______. (1822c), "Note on new electro-magnetical motions", *Quarterly Journal of Science*, 12: 416-21.

Ferguson, E. (1993), *Engineering and the Mind's Eye,* Cambridge, Massachusetts: M.I.T. Press.

Franklin, A. (1986), *The Neglect of Experiment.* Cambridge: Cambridge University Press.

_______. (1990), *Experiment: Right or Wrong,* Cambridge: Cambridge University Press.

Galison, P. (1985), "Bubble Chambers and the Experimental Workplace", In P. Achinstein and O. Hannaway (eds.),*Observation, Experiment and Hypothesis in Modern Physical Science,* Cambridge, Massachusetts: M.I.T. Press, pp. 309-73.

_______. (1987), *How Experiments End,* Chicago: University of Chicago Press.

_______. (1988), "History, Philosophy, and the Central Metaphor", In Lenoir (ed.), pp. 197-212.

Galison, P. and Assmus, E. (1988), "Arificial Clouds, Real Particles", In Gooding et. al. (eds.), pp. 225-274.

Gooding, D., Pinch, T. and Schaffer, S. (eds.) (1988), *The Uses of Experiment,* Cambridge: Cambridge University Press.

_______. (1990), *Experiment and the Making of Meaning,* Dordrecht: Kluwer Academic Publishers.

Hacking, I. (1983) *Representing and Intervening,* Cambridge: Cambridge University Press.

Helden, A. V. and Hankins, T. (eds.) (1993), "Instruments",*Osiris, Second Series*, 9.

Ihde, D. (1991), *Instrumental Realism,* Bloomington: Indiana University Press.

King, H. (1978) *Geared to the Stars,* Toronto: University of Toronto Press.

Latour, B. (1987) *Science in Action,* Cambridge: Harvard University Press.

Latour, B. and Woogar, S. (1979), *Laboratory Life,* Beverly Hills: Sage Press.

Lenoir, T. (ed.) (1988), "Practice, Context, and the Dialogue Between Theory and Experiment", *Science in Context,* 2 (1).

______. (1993), "Helmholtz and the Materialities of Communication", in Helden and Hankins (eds.), pp. 183-207.

Pickering, A. (1984), *Constructing Quarks,* Edinburgh: Edinburgh University Press.

Price, D. de S. (1964), "Automata and the origins of Mechanism and Mechanistic Philosophy", *Technology and Culture,* 5: 9-23.

_________. (1984), "Notes Towards a Philosophy of the Science/Technology Interaction", In R. Lauden (ed.), *The Nature of Technological Change,* Dordrecht: D. Reidel.

Reynolds, T. (1983), *Stronger than a Hundred Men,* Baltimore: Johns Hopkins University Press.

Rouse, J. (1987), *Knowledge and Power,* Ithica: Cornell University Press.

Schaffer, S. (1993), "Machine Philosophy: Demonstration Devices in Georgian Mechanics", in Helden and Hankins (eds.), pp. 157-83.

Smeaton, J. (1759), "An Experimental Examination of the Quantity and Proportion of Mechanic Power necessary to be employed in giving Different Degrees of Velocity of Heavy Bodies from a State of Rest", *Philosophical Transactions of the Royal Society of London*, reprinted in Hutton et. al. (eds.) (1809), *The Philosophical Transactions of the Royal Society of London From Their Commencement in 1665 to the year 1800, Abridged with notes and illustrations,* London: C. and R. Baldwin, 14: 72-84.

Smith, C. and Wise, N. (1989), *Energy and Empire,* Cambridge: Cambridge University Press.

Vincenti, W. (1979), "The Air-Propeller Tests of W. F. Durand and E. P. Lesley: A Case Study in Technological Methodology", *Technology and Culture,* 20: 712-51.

Vincenti, W. (1990), *What Engineers Know and How They Know It,* Baltimore: Johns Hopkins University Press.

Williams, L. P. (1978), *Album of Science: The Nineteenth Century,* New York: Charles Scribner's Sons.

_ _ _ _ _ _ _ _ _. (1964), *Michael Faraday: A Biography,* New York: Basic Books.

Wise, N. (1988), "Mediating Machines", In Lenoir (ed.), pp. 77-113.

Commentary on the Papers of Davis Baird, Peter Kroes, and Michael Dennis

Allan Franklin

University of Colorado

One important point that has emerged from recent work on the history and philosophy of experiment is that technology plays an integral role in experiment, and therefore in science. Technology determines what experimenters can measure and how well it can be measured. For example, it was advances in technology that made possible the early searches for gravity waves in the 1970s. The importance of technology, along with several new questions that its use raises, has been made quite clear in the papers presented in this session.

Davis Baird has suggested that we need to extend our concept of meaning in science to include both the literary mode and the material mode, as expressed in instruments and experimental apparatus. Peter Kroes has extended the discussion of a traditional problem in philosophy of science, the distinction between the real and the artificial and its relation to the scientific realism, to include complex modern apparatus. Michael Dennis has suggested that because technology requires substantial funding, attempts to secure such funding may have an important, and sometimes negative, effect on experimental results.

I will begin my discussion with Davis Baird's discussion of Faraday's apparatus for demonstrating electromagnetic rotation. Unfortunately, the model itself wasn't available. Nevertheless, no one who has seen such an apparatus in operation can doubt that it tells us,quite clearly and obviously, something striking about the world. One would have a similar reaction to seeing Oersted's apparatus that showed that currents exert a force on magnets. When the compass needle deflects when the current is turned on, we have learned something. These apparatuses convey both meaning and information. Baird is correct when he notes that for far too long philosophy of science, and science studies in general, have concentrated on the literary mode of meaning. His suggestion that there is also a material mode that should be considered is long overdue. I might suggest, however, that dealing with the material mode is likely to be quite difficult. Unlike Faraday, who sent working models of his apparatus tc other scientists, we may not even be able to view a complex experimental apparatus. This will pose problems because not everything one learns from an apparatus is easily expressed in words. Pictures and diagrams can help, but they cannot do the job alone. (I am not, of course, suggesting here that what we learn from an apparatus cannot be expressed in words. I am, however, suggesting that it will require care and effort).

PSA 1994, Volume 2, pp. 452-457

There is a distinction that might prove useful in such discussions. It seems appropriate to distinguish between an apparatus in which the apparatus itself is the phenomenon under investigation, such as Faraday's apparatus, and an experimental apparatus that is used to investigate another phenomenon. This might be made clear by the following example. Consider a large vat of superheated liquid hydrogen used to investigate bubble formation caused by the passage of charged particles through the liquid. Contrast this with the same vat used as a hydrogen bubble chamber and used to investigate neutrino interactions and the weak neutral current. In the former case, as with Faraday's apparatus, the phenomenon is directly and easily observable. In the latter case, although the events themselves are readilyobservable in the bubble chamber photographs, the production of an experimental result from this data is a complex process, involving considerable background knowledge. It is important to distinguish between data and experimental results in such discussions. (For a detailed discussion of this issue see Bogen and Woodward 1988).

I also note that there are often times when the literary and material modes of meaning are complementary. An anecdote may help. When Charles Sinclair and I were asked to build the first thin–plate (1 mil aluminum) spark chamber at Cornell University, we had only an article from the *Review of Scientific Instruments.* We followed the instructions given in that paper and cooled down both the square lucite frame and the aluminum foil before gluing them together. (We had the use of a refrigerated room that was also used for storing garbage. No analogy intended). When the material warmed to room temperature, the lucite expanded more than the aluminum giving us a taut, flat plate that could be used in the construction of a spark chamber. We learned about the use and construction of such chambers by doing. Thus, we learned that the technique wouldn't work for rectangular plate because the differential expansion of sides of different lengths produced ripples in the thin aluminum plates. We also learned which gases could be used in the chamber, what constituted adequate flatness of the plates, and what voltages were required. Once the chamber was built and we observed tracks of sparks produced by charged particles passing through the chamber there was no doubt that we had a working apparatus and that we had learned something about the world. Such spark chambers were then used to investigate other aspects of the world such as the photoproduction of ρ mesons.

Pace Derrida, Baird is correct. There is more in science than just the text, and the text interacting with other texts.

The distinction between data and experimental result leads quite naturally to Peter Kroes' discussion of technology and the distinction between the natural and the artificial. Kroes contrasts the traditional view that technology or experimental apparatus reveals Nature with the criticism offered by Ian Hacking (1983) that the experimenter *creates* the phenomenon with the apparatus. This would seem to imply a form of relativism. How can what is created really preexist in the world? I believe that Kroes is correct when he attributes a weak form of "creates the phenomenon" to Hacking. The weak form of the concept is that the experimenter creates the proper conditions for the phenomenon to take place, but does not create the specific characteristics of the phenomenon. (One might also speak here of the experimenter isolating, rather than creating, the phenomenon). Kroes gives an example of this in his discussion the fact that objects fall freely at the same rate in a vacuum. The experimenter creates the vacuum in which the objects fall. In this case, however, we also have the same phenomenon illustrated naturally. Who can forget an astronaut simultaneously dropping a feather and a hammer on the moon, and observing that they fell at the same rate.[1] Thus, there is a constraint on the falling bodies that is not created by the experimenter. We may create the conditions that allow the effect to be observed, but the world creates constraints that we cannot change. Objects fall at the same rate in a vacuum, regardless of their mass, no matter what we believe. This view of "creating the phenomenon" allows Kroes to argue for a kind of scientific realism based on the use of entities, such as electrons, as tools to investigate other phenomena. This doesn't mean that the electron is only a tool for furtherinvestigation. Kroes is correct when he notes that because an entity is used as a tool, it doesn't mean that it is a tool.

I suggest, in addition, that we can have good reasons for belief in entities by experimenting on them, not just with them. Consider an experiment to measure the K^+_{e2} branching ratio , the fraction of all K^+ mesons that decay into a positron and an electron neutrino (Bowen *et al.* 1967). One needed a large supply of K^+ mesons to detect that rare decay mode (approximately one part in 100,000). The experimental apparatus detected an entity with a definite charge, a definite mass, and a definite lifetime. These three measurements were sufficient to identify the particle as a K meson, rather than some other elementary particle, and as a real entity. (Normally mass alone would be sufficient to identify an elementary particle). For those who doubt this, let us consider the question of whether or not there is a real "Bas van Fraassen." Suppose we observe an entity and measure or detect that it has a definite height, weight, hair color, gender, home address, and birthdate. Suppose, in addition, that these measurements match the information given on Bas van Fraassen's driver's license. Would we not then be justified in concluding not only that the entity exists, but that we were, in fact, observing the famous philosopher? The arguments that one gives for the reality of Bas van Fraassen are the same as those one gives for the existence of K mesons.

Throughout this discussion I have been relying on the validity and reliability of experimental results. Michael Dennis' paper attempts to cast doubt on the reliability of such results. In his discussion of the discord between Tuve's and Lawrence's results on deuteron scattering, hesuggests that Lawrence's error (and to some extent that of the Cavendish group) was caused by a lack of care due to a desire for interesting results so as to secure funding for future experiments. To be fair, Dennis attributes this view to Tuve, but because he presents no alternative explanation I assume he agrees. I am not convinced. Even if one regards securing funds as a motive of the experimenters, and it certainly was, the securing of funds does not depend solely on producing interesting and spectacular results. Surely it also depends, and even more importantly, on getting correct results. Scientists have no career interest in being wrong. No one is likely to receive further funding of their work if their results have been consistently shown to be wrong.

In the episode of Tuve and Lawrence and deuteron scattering we are faced with the use of a new apparatus to investigate a hitherto unobserved phenomenon. We can't calibrate the apparatus against other known phenomena, because such phenomena don't exist in these circumstances. Tuve attempted to use independent confirmation, the agreement between his results and those of Lawrence to support his result. This failed. Although Tuve attributes Lawrence's error to the desire for funding, I suggest another reason. These were difficult experiments using new technology and apparatuses. It isn't easy to get correct experimental results, particularly in such circumstances. In fact, it is difficult to get correct experimental results, period. The history of experimental physics is full of examples of discordant and incorrect results. Let us consider some cases from the same time period as the Tuve and Lawrence experiments, the 1920s and 1930s.

Consider the history of experiments on beta decay during the 1930s. (For details of this episodesee Franklin 1990, Chapter 1). In 1934 Fermi proposed a theory of beta decay. Although early experimental results gave qualitative support to his theory, more detailed examination of the results showed discrepancies, particularly in the number of electrons emitted at low energies. In 1935 Konopinski and Uhlenbeck proposed an alternative theory that seemed to fit the results better (Figure 1). The better theory is that which gives the better fit to a straight line. That is clearly the Konopinski–Uhlenbeck (K–U) modification. It was soon realized that energy loss by the electrons in the source was an important effect, one that could produce an incorrect result. One needed to worry about the effect of source thickness. Further experiments were done with both thick and thin sources. As the sources were made thinner,

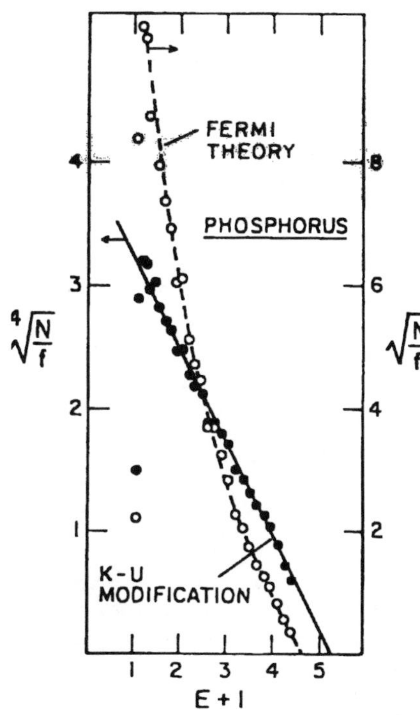

Figure 1. "The (black) points marked 'K–U' modification should fall as they do on a straight line. If the Fermi theory is followed the (white) points should follow a straight line as they clearly do not (Kurie *et al.* 1936)."

reduing energy loss in the source, the Fermi theory fit the results better than did the K–U theory (Figures 2, 3). Energy loss in the source had produced both incorrect results and an incorrect theory choice. When the experimental error was corrected the decision was reversed. As Konopinski himself remarked, "Thus, the evidence of the spectra, which had previously comprised the sole support for the K–U theory, now definitely fails to support it (Konopinski 1943, 218)."

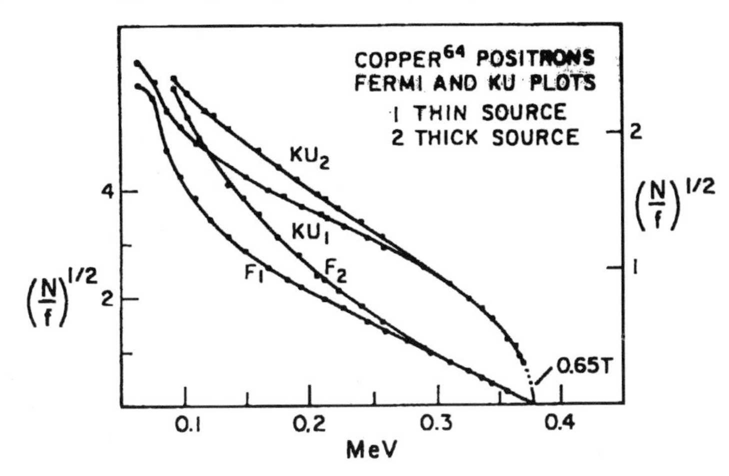

Figure 2. Fermi and K–U plots of positrons from thick and thin Cu^{64} sources. From Tyler (1939). As the source is made thinner the Fermi theory fits the data better than does the K–U modification.

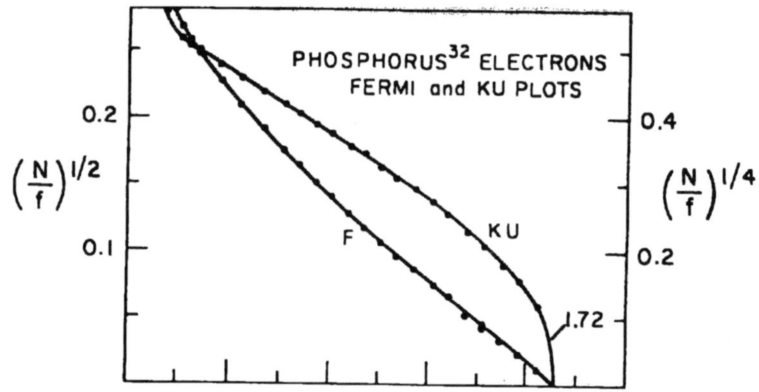

Figure 3. Fermi and K–U plots for electrons from a thin source of phosphorus. From Lawson (1939). The better theory is that which gives the better fit to a straight line, which is clearly the Fermi theory.

In another episode from the 1920s, Duane could not reproduce Compton's experimental results on the scattering of x–rays and ?–rays from electrons. (For details see Stuewer 1975). Duane did not observe the shift in the energy peak of scattered radiation that Compton had found. It was only after several years of further experiments, and even public debates between Duane and Compton, that it was realized that Duane's source was not strong enough and that his detector had insufficient resolution to see the effect. When the apparatus was improved, agreement was obtained. Other historical examples are easy to find.

One does not need to invoke the desire for future funding as an explanation of incorrect experimental results. Sometimes, particularly in the early stages of an experimental investigation, it is difficult to get correct results. Dennis is correct to note the importance of funding for large modern experiments involving complex apparatus and technology. I believe he is incorrect when he attributes incorrect results to a lack of care resulting from the desire for new and interesting results that would enhance the chances of such funding.

Note

[1]People often forget what the astronaut said at the time. It was, "I'll be damned." He was not expressing disbelief at the result, but rather illustrating the point that it is difficult to get experiments to work. When the experiment had been tried in a vacuum chamber on earth it hadn't worked. Electrical charging of the feather hindered its release so that the expected equality of fall did not occur. To solve the problem the feather was coated with metallic paint, which would prevent a charge buildup. Unfortunately there hadn't been sufficient time to try the experiment with the new feather before the moon voyage. Hence the astronaut's surprise.

References

Bogen, J. and Woodward, J. (1988), "Saving the Phenomena," *The Philosophical Review* 97: 303–352,

Bowen, D.R. *et al.* (1967), "Measurement of the K^{+}_{e2} Branching Ratio," *Physical Review* 154: 1314–1322.

Franklin, A. (1990), *Experiment, Right or Wrong*, Cambridge: Cambridge University Press.

Hacking, I. (1983), *Representing and Intervening*, Cambridge: Cambridge University Press.

Konopinski, E. (1943), "Beta Decay," *Reviews of Modern Physics*, 15: 209–245.

Stuewer, R. (1975), *The Compton Effect*, New York: Science History Publications.